Major Application Examples by Engineering Discipline

Number and Topic

Chemical Engineering

4.4–2	Temperature dynamics
5.3–5	Production planning
7.1–1	Breaking strength of thread
7.4–1	Breaking strength and alloy composition

Civil/Environmental Engineering

2.3–1	Transportation route analysis
2.5–1	Earthquake-resistant building design
3.5–1	Optimization of an irrigation channel
3.6–1	An environmental database
5.2–4	Calculation of cable tension
5.3–6	Traffic engineering
7.4–1	Breaking strength and alloy composition
8.5–3	Liquid height in a spherical tank

Electrical Engineering

2.3–2	Current and power dissipation in resistors
2.3–3	Maximum power transfer in a speaker-amplifier system
3.3–1	Design of a parallel-plate capacitor
4.2–1	Load-line analysis of electrical circuits
4.3–1	Frequency-response plot of a low-pass filter
5.2–3	An electrical-resistance network
7.5–1	Robot path control using three knot points
8.5–1	Response of an RC circuit
8.5–2	Decaying sine voltage applied to an RC circuit
8.6–2	Trapezoidal profile for a dc motor
9.2–2	Positioning a robot arm

Number and Topic

Industrial Engineering

3.7–1	A student database
6.6–1	A college enrollment model: Part I
6.6–2	A college enrollment model: Part II
7.3–1	Optimal production quantity
7.3–2	Statistical analysis and manufacturing tolerances

Mechanical/Aerospace Engineering

1.5–1	Piston motion
4.3–2	Plotting orbits
4.4–1	A cantilever beam-deflection model
4.4–3	Hydraulic resistance
5.3–3	A statically indeterminate problem
6.2–1	Height and speed of a projectile
6.4–1	Flight of an instrumented rocket
6.4–2	Time to reach a specified height
7.5–1	Robot path control using three knot points
8.1–1	Velocity from an accelerometer
8.5–3	Liquid height in a spherical tank
8.6–1	A nonlinear pendulum model
9.2–2	Positioning a robot arm

Of Interest to All Disciplines

2.4–1	Manufacturing cost analysis
2.4–2	Product costs
7.2–1	Mean and standard deviation of heights
7.2–2	Estimation of height distribution
8.2–2	Evaluation of Fresnel's cosine integral
9.3–1	Topping the Green Monster

MATLAB® for Engineering Applications

MATLAB® for Engineering Applications

William J. Palm III
University of Rhode Island

Boston Burr Ridge, IL Dubuque, IA Madison, WI New York San Francisco St. Louis
Bangkok Bogotá Caracas Lisbon London Madrid
Mexico City Milan New Delhi Seoul Singapore Sydney Taipei Toronto

WCB/McGraw-Hill

A Division of The **McGraw-Hill** *Companies*

MATLAB® FOR ENGINEERING APPLICATIONS

2 3 4 5 6 7 8 9 0 DOC/DOC 9 3 2 1 0 9

ISBN 0-07-047330-7

Vice president and editorial director: *Kevin T. Kane*
Publisher: *Thomas Casson*
Executive editor: *Eric Munson*
Developmental editor: *Holly Stark*
Marketing manager: *John T. Wannemacher*
Senior project manager: *Susan Trentacosti*
Production supervisor: *Michael R. McCormick*
Freelance design coordinator: *JoAnne Schopler*
Senior photo research coordinator: *Keri Johnson*
Photo researcher: *Elyse Rieder*
Supplement coordinator: *Carol Loreth*
Compositor: *Publication Services, Inc.*
Typeface: *10/12 New Century Schoolbook*
Printer: *R. R. Donnelley & Sons Company*

Library of Congress Cataloging-in-Publication Data

Palm, William J. (William John), 1944–
    MATLAB for engineering applications / William J. Palm III.
        p.   cm.
    Includes index.
    ISBN 0-07-047330-7
        1. MATLAB.   2. Numerical Analysis--Data processing.   I. Title.
    II. Series.
    QA297.P33   1999
    620′.00285′53--dc21   98-40456

http://www.mhhe.com/engcs/general/

The MathWorks, Inc.
24 Prime Park Way
Natick, MA 01760
Tel: 508-647-7000
Fax: 508-647-7001
WWW: http//www.mathworks.com
E-mail: info@mathworks.com

To my sisters: Linda and Chris

About the Author

WILLIAM J. PALM III is Professor of Mechanical Engineering at the University of Rhode Island. He received the Ph.D. in Mechanical Engineering and Astronautical Sciences from Northwestern University in 1971. During his 26 years as a faculty member, he has taught 19 courses and written three other textbooks, *Modeling, Analysis, and Control of Dynamic Systems* (1983) and *Control Systems Engineering* (1986), both published by John Wiley and Sons, and *Introduction to MATLAB for Engineers* (1998), published by McGraw-Hill. His research and industrial experience are in control systems, robotics, vibrations, and system modeling. He helped found the Robotics Research Center at the University of Rhode Island and was its director from 1985 to 1993. He is also one of the developers of the university's freshman engineering course, which is based on MATLAB.

Preface

Formerly used mainly by specialists in signal processing and numerical analysis, MATLAB® in recent years has achieved widespread and enthusiastic acceptance throughout the engineering community. Many engineering schools now require a course based entirely or in part on MATLAB early in the curriculum. MATLAB is programmable and has the same logical, relational, conditional, and loop structures as other programming languages, such as Fortran, C, BASIC, and Pascal. Thus it can be used to teach programming principles. In some schools a MATLAB course has replaced the traditional Fortran course and MATLAB is the principal computational tool used throughout the curriculum. In some technical specialties, such as signal processing and control systems, it is the standard software package for analysis and design.

The popularity of MATLAB is partly due to its long history, and thus it is well developed and well tested. People trust its answers. Its popularity is also due to its user interface, which provides an easy-to-use interactive environment that includes extensive numerical computation and visualization capabilities. Its compactness is a big advantage. For example, you can solve a set of many linear algebraic equations with just three lines of code, a feat that is impossible with traditional programming languages. MATLAB is also extensible; currently more than 16 "toolboxes" in various application areas can be used with MATLAB to add new commands and capabilities.

MATLAB is available for MS Windows and Macintosh personal computers and for UNIX and Open VMS systems. It is compatible across all these platforms, which enables users to share their programs, insights, and ideas.

Text Objectives and Prerequisites

This text is intended as a stand-alone introduction to MATLAB. It can be used in an introductory course, as a self-study text, or as a supplementary text. The text's material is based on the author's experience in teaching a required two-credit semester course devoted to MATLAB for engineering freshmen. In addition, the text can serve as a reference for later use. The text's many tables, and its referencing system in an appendix and at the end of each chapter, have been designed with this purpose in mind.

A secondary objective is to introduce and reinforce the use of problem-solving methodology as practiced by the engineering profession in general and as applied to the use of computers to solve problems in particular. This methodology is introduced in Chapter 1.

The reader is assumed to have some knowledge of algebra and trigonometry; knowledge of calculus is not required for the first seven chapters. Some knowledge of high school physics, primarily simple electrical circuits, and basic statics and dynamics is required to understand some of the examples.

MATLAB 5 was released in the spring of 1997. However, because MATLAB 5 requires Windows 95 or Windows NT on PC systems, MATLAB 4 will continue to be used for some time until users upgrade their computer systems to handle one of these operating systems. Thus one challenge in writing this text was to make it relevant to users of MATLAB 4 without neglecting the new features of MATLAB 5. In most cases the features unique to MATLAB 5 have been described in separate sections that are clearly identified, as are chapter problems that require MATLAB 5.

Text Organization

The text consists of nine chapters. The first chapter gives a brief overview of MATLAB features, including its windows and menu structures. It also introduces the problem-solving methodology. Chapter 2 introduces the concept of an array, which is the fundamental data element in MATLAB, and describes how to use arrays for basic mathematical operations. Arrays in MATLAB 4 are limited to two dimensions (rows and columns), but MATLAB 5 allows for multidimensional arrays.

Chapter 3 discusses the use of files, functions, and data structures. Files are used for storing work sessions, programs, and data. MATLAB has an extensive number of built-in math functions, and users can define their own functions. MATLAB 5 introduces two new data structures: the cell array and the structure array. Two sections are devoted to them in this chapter.

Chapter 4 treats two- and three-dimensional plotting. It first establishes standards for professional-looking, useful plots. In the author's experience beginning students are not aware of these standards, so they are emphasized. The chapter then covers

MATLAB commands for producing different types of plots and for controlling their appearance. Function discovery, which uses data plots to discover a mathematical description of the data, is a common application of plotting, and a separate section is devoted to this topic.

Chapter 5 covers the solution of linear algebraic equations, which arise in applications in all fields of engineering. "Hand" solution methods are reviewed first. This review has proved helpful to many students in the author's classes. This coverage also establishes the terminology and some important concepts that are required to use the computer methods properly. The chapter then shows how to use MATLAB to solve systems of linear equations that have a unique solution. The use of MATLAB with underdetermined and overdetermined systems is covered in two optional sections.

Chapter 6 treats programming with MATLAB and covers relational and logical operators, conditional statements, for and while loops, and the switch structure, which is new with MATLAB 5. A major application of the chapter's material is in simulation, to which a section is devoted.

Chapter 7 reviews basic statistics and probability and shows how to use MATLAB to generate histograms, perform calculations with the normal distribution, and create random number simulations. The chapter also covers polynomial and multiple linear regression and linear and cubic-spline interpolation. This chapter can be skipped if necessary. None of the following chapters depend on it.

Chapter 8 covers numerical methods for calculus and differential equations. Analytical methods are reviewed to provide a foundation for understanding and interpreting the numerical methods. Numerical integration and differentiation methods are treated. Ordinary differential equation solvers in the core MATLAB program are covered, as well as the linear-system solvers in the Control System toolbox. This chapter need not be covered to read Chapter 9.

Chapter 9 covers symbolic methods for manipulating algebraic expressions and for solving algebraic and transcendental equations, calculus, differential equations, and matrix algebra problems. The calculus applications include integration and differentiation, optimization, Taylor series, series evaluation, and limits. Laplace transform methods for solving differential equations are also introduced. This chapter requires the use of the Symbolic Math toolbox or the Student Edition of MATLAB.

Appendix A contains a guide to the commands and functions introduced in the text. Appendix B is a list of references. Answers to selected problems and an index appear at the end of the text.

All figures, tables, equations, and exercises have been numbered according to their chapter and section. For example, Figure 3.4–2 is the second figure in Chapter 3, section 4. This system is designed to help the reader locate these items. The end-of-chapter problems are the exception to this numbering system. They are numbered 1, 2, 3, and so on to avoid confusion with the in-chapter exercises.

The first four chapters should be covered. If time is limited, either one or both of Chapters 5 and 6 can be omitted. If students have had prior programming experience with another language, the material in Chapter 6 can be covered quickly. My colleagues and I have also experimented with covering Chapter 6 after the first three chapters were covered. This sequence worked fine.

For those desiring coverage of the topics in the first six chapters only, another text by the same author covers only these topics. Its title is *Introduction to MATLAB for Engineers* (WCB/McGraw-Hill, 1998).

Special Reference Features

The text has the following special features, which have been designed to enhance its usefulness as a reference.

- Throughout each of the last eight chapters, numerous tables summarize the commands and functions as they are introduced.
- At the end of each of the last eight chapters is a guide to tables in that chapter. These master tables will help the reader find descriptions of specific MATLAB commands.
- Appendix A is a complete summary of all the commands and functions described in the text, grouped by category, along with the number of the page on which they are introduced.
- All commands and functions covered in the text are listed alphabetically in the index.
- At the end of each chapter is a list of the key terms introduced in the chapter, with the page number referenced.
- Key terms have been placed in the margin where they are introduced.

Pedagogical Aids

The following pedagogical aids have been included:

- Each chapter begins with an overview.
- **Test Your Understanding** exercises appear throughout the chapters near the relevant text. These relatively straightforward exercises allow readers to assess their grasp of the material as soon as it is covered. In most cases the answer to the exercise is given with the exercise. Students should work these exercises as they are encountered.
- Each chapter ends with numerous problems, grouped according to the relevant section.
- Each chapter contains numerous practical examples. The major examples are numbered.

- Each chapter has a summary section that reviews the chapter's objectives.
- Answers to many end-of-chapter problems appear at the end of the text. These problems are denoted by an asterisk next to their number (for example, **[15]***).

Two features have been included to motivate the student toward MATLAB and the engineering profession:

- Most of the examples and the problems deal with engineering applications. These are drawn from a variety of engineering fields and show realistic applications of MATLAB. A guide to these applications appears on the inside front cover.
- The facing page of each chapter contains a photograph of a *recent* engineering achievement that illustrates the challenging and interesting opportunities that await engineers in the 21st century. A description of the achievement, its related engineering disciplines, and a discussion of how MATLAB can be applied in those disciplines accompanies each photo.

An Instructor's Manual is available for instructors who have adopted this text for a course. This manual contains the complete solutions to all the **Test Your Understanding** exercises and to all the chapter problems.

Acknowledgments

I want to acknowledge the following individuals for their help in this effort. Professor Leland Jackson of the University of Rhode Island cheerfully provided many useful insights into the workings of MATLAB. Professors Peter Swaszek, Harry Knickle, George Veyera, David Shao, James Miller, and Stan Barnett of the University of Rhode Island worked with me in developing a freshman course based on MATLAB. This experience greatly influenced the development of this text. The following people patiently reviewed the manuscript and suggested many helpful corrections and additions: Nancy Lamm, *Purdue University;* Estelle M. Eke, *California State University–Sacramento;* David A. Pape, *Alfred University;* Don Riley, *Walla Walla College;* Faisal Saied, *University of Illinois–Urbana-Champaign;* Mahesh C. Aggarwal, *Gannon University;* and Byron Gottfried, *University of Pittsburgh.* In addition, Naomi Bulock of The MathWorks, Inc. provided software support and a manuscript review. Eric Munson and Holly Stark of McGraw-Hill were always there for prompt help and advice. Susan Trentacosti of McGraw-Hill efficiently guided the manuscript through production. Finally, I wish to express my gratitude to my wife Mary Louise and to my children Aileene, Bill, and Andy for their understanding and support during this project.

William J. Palm III

Contents

MATLAB® for Engineering Applications

Photo courtesy of NASA Jet Propulsion Laboratory.

Engineering in the 21st Century . . .

Remote Exploration

It will be many years before humans can travel to other planets. In the meantime unmanned probes have enabled us to rapidly increase our knowledge of the universe. Their use will increase in the future as new technologies make remote exploration more reliable and more versatile. Better sensors are expected for imaging and other data collection. Improved robotic devices will make these probes more autonomous and more capable of interacting with their environment, instead of just observing it.

NASA's planetary microrover *Sojourner*, shown above, landed on Mars on July 4, 1997, and people on Earth watched it successfully explore the Martian surface to determine wheel-soil interactions, to analyze rocks and soil, and to return images of the lander for damage assessment. *Sojourner* is about the size of a microwave oven, weighs 24 pounds, and can traverse obstacles as large as 13 cm. Each of the six wheels is independently driven with a gear ratio of 2000:1 to provide good climbing ability in soft sand. A solar panel/battery system capable of 30 W powers the electric motors. Normal driving power is 10 W.

Although the onboard computer has only 576Kb of RAM and 176Kb of PROM, efficient and clever programming allows it to control many of the vehicle's functions, including 70 sensor channels for cameras, modems, motors, and experiments.

The MATLAB® Neural Network, Signal Processing, Image Processing, and various control system toolboxes are well suited to assist designers of probes and autonomous vehicles like *Sojourner.*

1

MATLAB and Problem Solving

Outline

1.1 An Overview of MATLAB

MATLAB is both a computer programming language and a software environment for using that language effectively. It is maintained and sold by The MathWorks, Inc., of Natick, Massachusetts, and is available for MS Windows and Macintosh personal computers and for UNIX and Open VMS systems. The MATLAB interactive environment enables you to manage variables, import and export data, perform calculations, generate plots, and develop and manage files for use with MATLAB. The language was developed in the 1970s for applications involving matrices, linear algebra, and numerical analysis (the name MATLAB stands for "Matrix Laboratory"). Thus the language's numerical routines have been thoroughly tested and improved through many years of use, and its capabilities have been greatly expanded during that time.

MATLAB has a number of add-on software modules, called *toolboxes*, that perform more specialized computations. Although you can purchase the toolboxes separately, you must have the core MATLAB program in order to use them. More than 16 toolboxes, dealing with applications such as image and signal processing, financial analysis, control systems design, and fuzzy logic, are currently available. An up-to-date list appears on The MathWorks Web site, which is discussed later in this chapter. The first seven

TOOLBOX

3

chapters of this text do not use material from the toolboxes; all of the examples and problems in these chapters can be done with the core MATLAB program. Section 8.7 of Chapter 8 requires the Control System toolbox, which is also available within the Student Edition. However, this section can be skipped if desired, because the succeeding material does not depend on it. Chapter 9 requires the Symbolic Math toolbox, which is also available within the Student Edition.

The MathWorks released MATLAB 5.0 in the spring of 1997. On MS Windows systems it requires Windows 95 or Windows NT to run. MATLAB 4 runs under either of these operating systems, as well as under Windows 3.1. The current release is MATLAB 5.2, which added some new differential equation solvers (covered in Section 8.5). With the exception of these solvers, all the commands covered in this text work with MATLAB 5.0, and most of them work with MATLAB 4. In those instances where the commands work only with MATLAB 5, this restriction is clearly noted. The Student Editions of MATLAB 4 and MATLAB 5 contain the core MATLAB program plus some commands from three MATLAB toolboxes: the Control Systems toolbox, the Signal Processing toolbox, and the Symbolic Math toolbox. The Student Edition is purposely limited in the size of the problems it can handle, but it is adequate for all exercises in this text.

This book does not explain how to install MATLAB. If you purchased it for your own computer, the installation instructions are in a manual that comes with the software. If you will be using MATLAB in a computer lab, it will have been installed for you.

In this chapter we introduce MATLAB through a simple session that illustrates its interactive nature. Then we explain the various windows and menus that are available and discuss the extensive MATLAB online help system, which can be accessed in several ways. Finally we present a methodology for solving engineering problems in general and one for solving computer problems in particular. These methodologies will be useful to you for solving the chapter problems.

1.2

A Sample MATLAB Session

This section explains how to start MATLAB, how to perform some calculations, how to obtain plots, how to save your results, and how to exit MATLAB.

Conventions

In this text we use `computer display font` to represent MATLAB commands, any text that you type in the computer, and any MATLAB responses that appear on the screen; for example,

Figure 1.2–1
The Command window in
MATLAB 4.

$y = 6 \star x$. Variables in normal mathematics text appear in italic; for example, $y = 6x$. We use boldface type for three purposes: to represent vectors and matrices in normal mathematics text (for example, **Ax** = **b**), to represent a key on the keyboard (for example, **Enter**), and to represent the name of screen menu or an item that appears in such a menu (for example, **File**). You should always press the **Enter,** or **Return,** key after you type a command. (We do not show this action with a separate symbol.)

Starting MATLAB

To start MATLAB on an MS Windows or Macintosh system, double-click on the MATLAB icon. On a UNIX system, type `matlab` at the operating system prompt. You will then see the Command window, which looks like Figure 1.2–1 in MATLAB 4 and like Figure 1.2–2 in MATLAB 5. This window is the main one with which you communicate with the main MATLAB program. On UNIX systems this window is the terminal window you used to start MATLAB. The MATLAB prompt (>>) indicates that the program is ready to receive instructions. To enter instructions, make sure the cursor is located just after the prompt. If it is not, use the mouse to move the cursor. The prompt in the Student Edition looks like EDU>>. We use the normal prompt symbol >> to illustrate commands in this text.

COMMAND WINDOW

PROMPT

Entering Commands and Expressions

To see how simple it is to use MATLAB, try entering a few commands on your computer. If you make a mistake while typing these commands, just press the **Enter** key until you get the prompt. In Chapter 2 you learn how to correct mistakes.

At the prompt type $8/10$ and press **Enter**. On the screen your entry and the MATLAB response look like the following three lines.

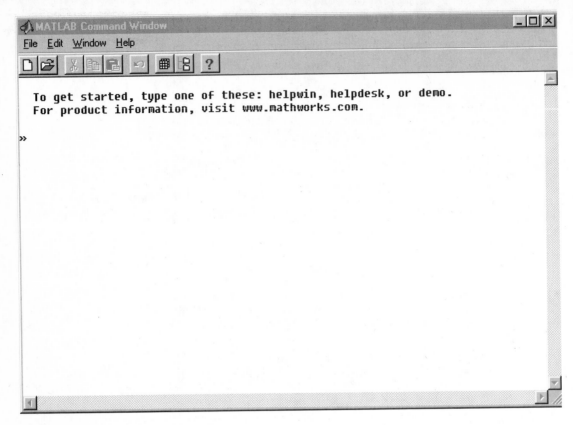

To get started, type one of these: helpwin, helpdesk, or demo.
For product information, visit www.mathworks.com.

>>

Figure 1.2–2
The Command window in MATLAB 5.

(We call this interaction between you and MATLAB an interactive session.)

```
>>8/10
ans =
    0.8000
```

MATLAB usually displays its results using four decimal places. We discuss how to change this representation in Chapter 3. Thus you can use MATLAB like a calculator. MATLAB has assigned the answer to a temporary variable called ans. You can assign the result to a variable of your own choosing, say, r, as follows:

```
>>r=8/10
r =
    0.8000
```

If you now type r at the prompt, you will see

```
>>r
r =
    0.8000
```

thus verifying that the variable r has the value 0.8. You can use this variable in further calculations. For example:

```
>>s=10*r
s =
    8
```

MATLAB has hundreds of built-in functions, which we will discuss throughout the text. For example, to compute $v = \sin s$, where s is in radians, continue the preceding session as follows:

```
>>v=sin(s)
v =
    0.9894
```

The strength of MATLAB is that it can handle many numbers in one expression. For example, to compute $z = 5 \sin u$ for $u = 0$, 0.1, 0.2, ..., 10, the session is:

```
>>u=[0:.1:10];
>>z=5*sin(u);
```

The single line z=5*sin(u) computes the formula $z = 5 \sin u$ 101 times, once for each value in the array u, to produce an array z that has 101 values. This example illustrates some of the power of MATLAB to perform many calculations with just a few commands.

The semicolon at the end of each line in the preceding session tells MATLAB not to display the results on the screen. The values are stored in the variables u and z if you need them. You can see all the u values by typing u after the prompt, or, for example, you can see the seventh value by typing u(7). You can see the z values the same way.

```
>>u(7)
ans =
    0.6000
>>z(7)
ans =
    2.8232
```

The variables u and z in the preceding session are examples of *arrays*, which are ordered collections of numbers. In this example *ordered* means that the seventh value of z corresponds to the seventh value of u by the relation $z = \sin u$. Much of the power of MATLAB results from its capability to work with arrays efficiently. We discuss arrays in more depth in Chapter 2.

Obtaining Plots

As another example of the power and usefulness of MATLAB, let us plot the function $y = \sin 2x$ for $0 \le x \le 10$. An increment of

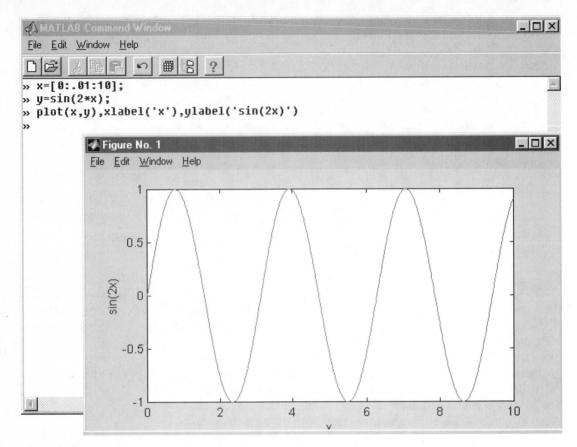

Figure 1.2–3
A graphics window showing a plot.

0.01 enables us to generate a large number of x values, thereby producing a smooth curve. The session is

```
>>x=[0:.01:10];
>>y=sin(2*x);
>>plot(x,y)
```

GRAPHICS WINDOW

The plot appears on the screen in a graphics window, named **Figure No. 1**, as shown in Figure 1.2–3, except it would not have labels. Because we should never leave a plot unlabeled, we can replace the third line in this session with the following line to produce the labeled plot shown in Figure 1.2–3.

```
>>plot(x,y),xlabel('x'),ylabel('sin(2x)')
```

When the plot command is successfully executed, a graphics window automatically appears. To print a hard copy of the plot, select **Print** from the **File** menu on the graphics window. To close the window and return to the prompt in the Command window, select **Close** on the **File** menu. We discuss the plotting commands

8

in more detail in Chapter 4. The next section discusses the use of the various windows in MATLAB.

Saving Your Work and Quitting

If you want to save the results of your calculations (for example, the names and values of any variables you created), but not your keystrokes, type `save myfile` at the prompt to save your results in the file `myfile.mat`. To continue your session at a later time, type `load myfile` at the prompt. If you are using a floppy disk in drive a:, substitute `save a:myfile` and `load a:myfile` for these commands. We discuss these operations further in Chapter 3.

To exit or quit MATLAB, type `quit` at the prompt. On MS Windows and Macintosh systems, you can also click on the **File** menu and then click on **Exit** or **Quit**.

You are likely to use three types of windows in a MATLAB session: the Command window for entering commands and displaying results, a graphics window for displaying plots, and an editor window for creating program files. In MATLAB 4 running under Windows, the editor is the Windows Notepad editor unless you change the default setting in the **Options** menu. On the Macintosh the window is that of the built-in Macintosh text editor. In MATLAB 5 the default editor is the M-file Editor/Debugger. Use of these editors is discussed in Chapter 3. Each window type has a menu bar, with one or more menus, at the top. To activate, or select, a menu, click on it. Each menu has several items. Click on an item to select it.

EDITOR WINDOW

The Command Window Menus

Most of your interaction will be in the Command window. The MATLAB 4 Command window (refer to Figure 1.2–1) has five menus: **File, Edit, Options, Windows,** and **Help.** The **File** menu in MATLAB 4 contains the following items, which perform the indicated actions when you click on them. Items followed by three dots (...) open a submenu or another window containing a dialog box. The MATLAB 5 **File** menu has one additional item (**Preferences**), which is discussed later in this section.

FILE MENU

The File Menu (MATLAB 4)

New Opens a dialog box that allows you to create a new program file, called an M-file, using a text editor.

Open M-file... Opens a dialog box that allows you to select an M-file for editing.

Open Selected Opens an M-file whose name is selected in the Command window.

Save Workspace As...   Opens a dialog box that allows you to save the names and values of the variables in a file whose name you select.

Run M-file...   Executes a MATLAB program stored in an M-file.

Look for Selected   Searches all MATLAB Help entries for the word or words selected (by dragging the mouse cursor across them) in the Command window.

Print...   Prints the text on the screen. If text has been previously selected by dragging the mouse cursor across it, this menu item changes to **Print Selected.**

Printer Setup...   Opens a dialog box that allows a specific printer to be selected and some of its functions to be modified.

Exit Matlab   Exits MATLAB.

The **Edit** menu contains the following items. The first three are active (available for selection) only if you have previously selected text by dragging the mouse cursor across it.

The Edit Menu

Cut   Removes the selected text and stores it for pasting later.

Copy   Copies the selected text for pasting later, without removing it.

Paste   Inserts any text on the clipboard at the current location of the cursor. (Pressing **Ctrl** and **v** simultaneously does the same thing.)

Clear Session   Removes all commands you typed and all MATLAB responses from the Command window. You can also type `clc` at the prompt to clear the session. However, with either method all variables retain their values. (To erase the values from memory, use the `clear` command.)

The **Cut, Copy,** and **Paste** features are part of the standard operating system environment and have limited use in MATLAB. You can use them to cut and paste only the current command. You can copy previous commands that appear on the screen by dragging the mouse cursor across them and selecting **Copy.** However, an easier way to retrieve a command is to use the up-arrow key to scroll through the previous commands and then press **Enter** when you see the command you want. We discuss this feature in more detail in Chapter 2.

The **Options** window contains six items that, except for the first (**Numeric Format**), have very specialized uses and are not used in this text. In Chapter 3 we discuss how to specify the numeric format.

The **Windows** menu has one or more items depending on what you have done thus far in your session. Click on the name of a window that appears on the menu to open it. For example, if you have created a plot and not closed its window, the plot window will appear on this menu as **Figure 1.** The Command window is always a choice on the Windows menu. However, there are other ways to move between windows (such as pressing the **Alt** and **Tab** keys simultaneously on an MS Windows system).

When you start MATLAB 4, a list of useful commands appears at the top of the Command window (see Figure 1.2–1). The `intro` command leads you through a brief introduction to MATLAB. The `demo` command executes a series of live action demonstrations of the various MATLAB features. Type `help topic` to obtain help on any topic, even `help` itself. Type `help help` to learn how to use the help system. The `whatsnew`, `info`, and `subscribe` commands give information about the company responsible for MATLAB, The MathWorks, Inc.; the MATLAB toolboxes; last minute changes to the program; and instructions for subscribing to The MathWorks e-mail information service.

The MATLAB 5 Command window (refer to Figure 1.2–2) is similar to that of MATLAB 4 but lacks the **Options** menu. Some of the items formerly on the **Options** menu are now on the **Preferences** item under the new **File** menu. MATLAB 5 has a new optional feature, the Command Toolbar, which provides shortcut "buttons" to access some of the features on the menus. Clicking on the button is equivalent to clicking on the menu and then clicking on the menu item, thus saving one click of the mouse. The first six buttons from the left correspond to **New File, Open File, Cut, Copy, Paste,** and **Undo.** Clicking on the **Undo** button cancels the effect of the preceding operation. The rightmost button on the toolbar is the **Help** button. The remaining buttons (**Workspace Browser** and **Path Browser**) enable you to examine your variables and the file paths that MATLAB is using. We discuss these concepts in Chapter 3.

MATLAB gives you several ways to obtain help online. You can click on the **Help** menu in the Command window. In MATLAB 4 the following choices appear in an MS Windows system:

The Help Menu (MATLAB 4)

Table of Contents...   Opens a window containing a list of the major feature categories. Click on any highlighted category to obtain more information.

Index...   Opens a window containing an alphabetical list of all MATLAB commands and functions. Click on the name to obtain information about the syntax.

Help Selected   Click on this item after dragging the mouse cursor over a command or function in the Command window. The syntax will be displayed.

About   Click on this item to obtain the MATLAB version number and the serial number.

On MS Windows systems the MATLAB 5 **Help** menu is organized as follows:

The Help Menu (MATLAB 5)

Help Window Opens a window containing a list of the major function categories. Double-click on any topic to see the associated functions or subtopics. Double-click on any function to see the help text for that function.

Help Tips Accesses tips for effective use of MATLAB functions.

Help Desk Accesses HTML documents containing graphics and "hot links." All MATLAB functions have an HTML document, which is a common format used for Web pages. These documents have more details and examples than the basic `help` entries. However, you must have the Netscape or Internet Explorer Web browser to access these HTML documents (but you need not have a network connection to do so, because the files are stored in the computer).

Examples and Demos Click on this item to see examples and demonstrations.

About Matlab... Click on this item to obtain the MATLAB version number and the serial number.

Subscribe(HTML) Click on this item to subscribe to The Math-Works e-mail information service.

Help is also available at the prompt. If you know the name of the command or function, for example, sin, type `help sin`. This is what you will see:

```
>>help sin
SIN Sine.
   SIN(X) is the sine of the elements of X.
```

However, if you type `help sine`, you will get the message `sine not found`. Instead, you can use the `lookfor` command. Type `lookfor sine`. The MATLAB help facility searches for the occurrence of the text `sine` in its help files. This is what you will see:

```
>>lookfor sine
ACOS      Inverse cosine.
ACOSH     Inverse hyperbolic cosine.
ASIN      Inverse sine.
ASINH     Inverse hyperbolic sine.
COS       Cosine.
COSH      Hyperbolic cosine.
SIN       Sine.
```

```
SINH      Hyperbolic sine.
TFFUNC    time and frequency domain versions of a cosine
modulated Gaussian pulse.
```

From this list you can find the correct name for the sine function.

The MATLAB help files are organized by categories, and you can obtain a list of the functions within a category by typing `help name`, where `name` is the name of the category. For example, the elementary functions such as sine, tangent, and log are in the `elfun` category. Type `help elfun` to see a listing and description of the functions. Throughout this text we point out the appropriate category name so that you can get more information if you need it.

If you have an Internet connection, you can obtain help from The MathWorks Web site at the address `http://www.mathworks.com`. You will find links to product information, user-contributed software, the newsgroup, MATLAB books, technical notes, and technical support, as well as links to specific areas for education and some applications. If you know how to transfer files from an *anonymous FTP* site, you can download files from The MathWorks site at `ftp.mathworks.com`.

Problem-Solving Methodologies

Designing new engineering devices and systems requires a variety of problem-solving skills. (This variety is what keeps engineering from becoming boring!) When solving a problem, it is important to plan your actions ahead of time. You can waste many hours by plunging into the problem without a plan of attack. Here we present a plan of attack, or *methodology*, for solving engineering problems in general. Because solving engineering problems often requires a computer solution and because the examples and exercises in this text require you to develop a computer solution (using MATLAB), we also discuss a methodology for solving computer problems in particular.

Several types of tools are available to perform engineering calculations. Each has its own advantages, and knowing how their utility compares with that of MATLAB will help you. Here we discuss the major types of computational tools.

Computational Tools

Some advanced calculators can now perform very sophisticated calculations, including polynomial root finding, matrix operations, graphing, statistics, and programming. They are the most portable of the tools. However, this advantage is lost if you need hard copy output.

Spreadsheet programs are effective with data that can be displayed in a grid of rows and columns. Popular spreadsheet programs include Excel, Quattro Pro, and Lotus 1-2-3. Originally developed for accounting applications, these programs are now widely used in engineering. As we explain in Chapter 2, MATLAB performs many of the same calculations as a spreadsheet program performs. A spreadsheet program has an advantage in applications involving a large grid of data that must be readily visible to the user (perhaps by "scrolling" the screen display). MATLAB can handle very large amounts of data, but its display capabilities are not as sophisticated as those of a spreadsheet program. Spreadsheet programs have certain types of optimization methods, which are available in MATLAB only if you have the Optimization toolbox. For some people another advantage of spreadsheet programs is that they can be operated largely by using the mouse to select menu items and to perform operations on data. MATLAB, on the other hand, requires you to type in commands for most of its operations. Some people prefer this mode of operation because they are not constrained by the structure of the menus. Another distinguishing factor is cost. The Professional Version of MATLAB (as opposed to the Student Edition) costs more than spreadsheet programs, and the toolboxes add to the cost. However, compared to spreadsheets, MATLAB has more built-in functions that are of use to various engineering specialties, so the extra cost might be justified.

Database management software packages, such as Paradox, Access, and dBase, enable you to store and easily access very large databases such as mailing lists and records. MATLAB has some of these capabilities, especially with the new features introduced in MATLAB 5, so if you don't need to use very large databases, MATLAB might be an appropriate choice.

Symbolic processing software is capable of doing algebra, calculus, and other mathematical operations symbolically, rather than numerically. For example, such software can solve the equation $x^2 + 2x + b = 0$ to obtain $x = -1 \pm \sqrt{1-b}$ without knowing the numerical value of b. Maple, Macsyma, Derive, and Mathematica are the most widely used symbolic processing software packages. A portion of the Maple "engine," which performs the symbolic operations, is included in MathCAD, another package for performing engineering calculations. The Maple engine has been licensed by The MathWorks for use in the MATLAB Symbolic Math toolbox. So, with this toolbox, you can do symbolic processing with MATLAB! (This toolbox is included in the Student Edition of MATLAB.)

Maple, Macsyma, Derive, Mathematica, and MathCAD can do numerical calculations also, and thus they compete with MATLAB. The choice of which package to use depends on several factors.

For example, the MathCAD interface depends on menu operations more than MATLAB does and uses the concept of a graphical "worksheet," which is a generalization of a spreadsheet to include equations and plots. Some users might find the MathCAD interface easier to use, whereas others might prefer the command-line interface of MATLAB, which allows more precise control of the program. Other factors in favor of MATLAB include (1) its long history (it is thoroughly tested and well entrenched in several areas of engineering, including signal processing and control systems) and (2) its numerous toolboxes.

The MATLAB Notebook enables you to establish a "live" link between MATLAB and a document in Microsoft Word, version 6.0 or higher. This link updates the numerical results, including plots, in the document as you use MATLAB to do the calculations. The Notebook is available for MS Windows and Macintosh systems and is included in the Student Edition.

Other computer languages have been, until recently, the primary tool for complicated engineering calculations. *Assembly language* is a low-level language, whose instructions are specific to the particular computer processor. Assembly language is very fast; it is used primarily for low-level hardware control, but rarely for engineering calculations because it is so tedious to write. Fortran, BASIC, C, and C++ are widely used higher-level languages in engineering applications. However, the user interface and integrated features such as plotting and equation solving give packages like MATLAB a very competitive edge over these languages in many engineering applications.

Steps in Engineering Problem Solving

Table 1.5–1 summarizes the methodology that has been tried and tested by the engineering profession for many years. These steps describe a general problem-solving procedure. Simplifying the problem sufficiently and applying the appropriate fundamental principles is called *modeling*, and the resulting mathematical description is called a *mathematical model*, or just a *model*. When the modeling is finished, we need to solve the mathematical model to obtain the required answer. If the model is highly detailed, we might need to solve it with a computer program. Most of the examples and exercises in this text require you to develop a computer solution (using MATLAB) to problems for which the model has already been developed. Thus we will not always need to use all the steps shown in Table 1.5–1. More discussion of engineering problem solving can be found in [Eide, 1998].[1]

MODEL

---

[1]References appear in Appendix B.

Table 1.5–1 Steps in engineering problem solving

1. Understand the purpose of the problem.
2. Collect the known information. Realize that some of it might be discovered later to be unnecessary.
3. Determine what information you must find.
4. Simplify the problem only enough to allow the required information to be obtained. State any assumptions you make.
5. Draw a sketch and label any necessary variables.
6. Determine which fundamental principles are applicable.
7. Think about your proposed solution approach in general and consider other approaches before proceeding with the details.
8. Label each step in the solution process.
9. If you are solving the problem with a program, hand check the results using a simple version of the problem. Checking the dimensions and units and printing the results of intermediate steps in the calculation sequence can uncover mistakes.
10. Perform a "reality check" on your answer. Does it make sense? Estimate the range of the expected result and compare it with your answer. Do not state the answer with greater precision than is justified by any of the following:
    a. The precision of the given information.
    b. The simplifying assumptions.
    c. The requirements of the problem.

    Interpret the mathematics. If the mathematics produces multiple answers, do not discard some of them without considering what they mean. The mathematics might be trying to tell you something, and you might miss an opportunity to discover more about the problem.

Example of Problem Solving

Consider the following simple example of the steps involved in problem solving. Suppose you work for a company that produces packaging. You are told that a new packaging material can protect a package when dropped, provided that the package hits the ground at less than 25 feet per second. The package's total weight is 20 pounds, and it is rectangular with dimensions of 12 by 12 by 8 inches. You must determine whether the packaging material provides enough protection when the package is carried by delivery persons.

The steps in the solution are as follows:

1. *Understand the purpose of the problem.*

   The implication here is that the packaging is intended to protect against being dropped while the delivery person is carrying it. It is not intended to protect against the package falling off a moving delivery truck. In practice, you should make sure that the person giving you this assignment is making the same assumption. Poor communication is the cause of many errors!

2. *Collect the known information.*

   The known information is the package's weight, dimensions, and maximum allowable impact speed.

3. *Determine what information you must find.*

   Although not explicitly stated, you need to determine the maximum height from which the package can be dropped without damage. You need to find a relationship between the speed of impact and the height at which the package is dropped.

4. *Simplify the problem only enough to allow the required information to be obtained. State any assumptions you make.*

   The following assumptions will simplify the problem and are consistent with the problem statement as we understand it:
   a. The package is dropped from rest with no vertical or horizontal velocity.
   b. The package does not tumble (as it might when dropped from a moving truck). The given dimensions indicate that the package is not thin and thus will not "flutter" as it falls.
   c. The effect of air drag is negligible.
   d. The greatest height the delivery person could drop the package from is 6 feet (and thus we ignore the existence of a delivery person 8 feet tall!).
   e. The acceleration g due to gravity is constant (because the distance dropped is only 6 feet).

5. *Draw a sketch and label any necessary variables.*

   Figure 1.5–1 is a sketch of the situation, showing the height h of the package, its mass m, its speed v, and the acceleration due to gravity g.

6. *Determine what fundamental principles are applicable.*

   Because this problem involves a mass in motion, Newton's laws are applicable. From physics we know that the following relations result from Newton's laws and the basic kinematics of an object falling a short distance under the influence of gravity, with no air drag or initial velocity:
   a. Height versus time to impact t_i: $h = \frac{1}{2}gt_i^2$.
   b. Impact speed v_i versus time to impact: $v_i = gt_i$.
   c. Conservation of mechanical energy: $mgh = \frac{1}{2}mv_i^2$.

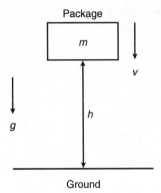

Figure 1.5–1
Sketch of the dropped-
package problem.

7. *Think about your proposed solution approach in general and consider other approaches before proceeding with the details.*

We could solve the second equation for t_i and substitute the result into the first equation to obtain the relation between h and v_i. This approach would also allow us to find the time to drop t_i. However, this method involves more work than is necessary because we need not find the value of t_i. The most efficient approach is to solve the third relation for h.

$$h = \frac{1}{2}\frac{v_i^2}{g} \tag{1.5–1}$$

Notice that the mass m cancels out of the equation. The mathematics just told us something! It told us that the mass does not affect the relation between the impact speed and the height dropped. Thus we do not need the weight of the package to solve the problem, and this information is superfluous.

8. *Label each step in the solution process.*

This problem is so simple that there are only a few steps to label:
a. Basic principle: conservation of mechanical energy

$$h = \frac{1}{2}\frac{v_i^2}{g}$$

b. Determine the value of the constant g: $g = 32.2$ ft/sec^2
c. Use the given information to perform the calculation and round off the result consistent with the precision of the given information:

$$h = \frac{1}{2}\frac{25^2}{32.2} = 9.7 \text{ feet}$$

Because this text is about MATLAB, we might as well use it to do this simple calculation. The session looks like this:

```
>>g=32.2;
>>vi=25;
>>h=vi^2/(2*g)
h =
    9.7050
```

9. *Check the dimensions and units.*

   This check proceeds as follows, using (1.5–1),

   $$[ft] = \left[\frac{1}{2}\right]\frac{[ft/sec]^2}{[ft/sec^2]} = \frac{[ft]^2}{[sec]^2}\frac{[sec]^2}{[ft]} = [ft]$$

   which is correct.

10. *Perform a reality check and precision check on the answer.*

    If the computed height were negative, we would know that we did something wrong. If it were very large, we might be suspicious. However, the computed height of 9.7 feet does not seem unreasonable.

    If we had used a more accurate value for g, say $g = 32.17$, then we would be justified in rounding the result to $h = 9.71$. However, given the need to be conservative here, we probably should round the answer *down* to the nearest foot. So we probably should report that the package will not be damaged if it is dropped from a height of less than 9 feet.

    The mathematics told us that the package mass does not affect the answer. The mathematics did not produce multiple answers here. However, many problems involve the solution of polynomials with more than one root; in such cases we must carefully examine the significance of each.

Steps for Obtaining a Computer Solution

If you use a program such as MATLAB to solve a problem, follow the steps shown in Table 1.5–2. More discussion of modeling and computer solutions can be found in [Starfield, 1990] and [Jayaraman, 1991].

MATLAB is useful for doing numerous complicated calculations and then automatically generating a plot of the results. The following example illustrates the procedure for developing and testing such a program.

Example 1.5–1   Piston motion   Figure 1.5–2a shows a piston, connecting rod, and crank for an internal combustion engine. When combustion occurs, it pushes the piston down. This

Table 1.5–2 Steps for developing a computer solution

1. State the problem concisely.
2. Specify the data to be used by the program. This is the "input."
3. Specify the information to be generated by the program. This is the "output."
4. Work through the solution steps by hand or with a calculator; use a simpler set of data if necessary.
5. Write and run the program.
6. Check the output of the program with your hand solution.
7. Run the program with your input data and perform a reality check on the output.
8. If the program will be used as a general tool in the future, test it by running it for a range of reasonable data values; perform a reality check on the results.

Figure 1.5–2
A piston, connecting rod, and crank for an internal combustion engine.

(a)   (b)

motion causes the connecting rod to turn the crank, which causes the crankshaft to rotate. We want to develop a MATLAB program to compute and plot the distance d traveled by the piston as a function of the angle A, for given values of the lengths L_1 and L_2. Such a plot would help the engineers designing the engine to select appropriate values for the lengths L_1 and L_2.

We are told that typical values for these lengths are $L_1 = 1$ foot and $L_2 = 0.5$ foot. Because the mechanism's motion is symmetrical about $A = 0$, we need consider only angles in the range $0 \leq A \leq 180°$.

Figure 1.5–2b shows the geometry of the motion. From this figure we can use trigonometry to write the following expression for d:

$$d = L_1 \cos B + L_2 \cos A \qquad (1.5\text{–}2)$$

Thus to compute d given the lengths L_1 and L_2 and the angle A, we must first determine the angle B. We can do so using the law of sines, as follows:

$$\frac{\sin A}{L_1} = \frac{\sin B}{L_2}$$

Solve this for B:

$$\sin B = \frac{L_2 \sin A}{L_1}$$

$$B = \sin^{-1}\left(\frac{L_2 \sin A}{L_1}\right) \qquad (1.5\text{–}3)$$

Equations (1.5–2) and (1.5–3) form the basis of our calculations. Develop and test a MATLAB program to plot d versus A.

Solution:

Here are the steps in the solution, following those listed in Table 1.5–2.

1. **State the problem concisely.**

   Use equations (1.5–2) and (1.5–3) to compute d; use enough values of A in the range $0 \leq A \leq 180°$ to generate an adequate (smooth) plot.

2. **Specify the input data to be used by the program.**

   The lengths L_1 and L_2 and the angle A are given.

3. **Specify the output to be generated by the program.**

   A plot of d versus A is the required output.

4. **Work through the solution steps by hand or with a calculator.**

   You could have made an error in deriving the trigonometric formulas, so you should check them for several cases. You can check for these errors by using a ruler and protractor to make a scale drawing of the triangle for several values of the angle A, measure the length d, and compare it to the calculated values. Then you can use these results to check the output of the program.

   Which values of A should you use for the checks? Since the triangle "collapses" when $A = 0$ and $A = 180°$, you should check these cases. The results are $d = L_1 - L_2$ for $A = 0$, and $d = L_1 + L_2$ for $A = 180°$. The case $A = 90°$ is also easily checked by hand, using the Pythagorean theorem; for this case $d = \sqrt{L_1^2 - L_2^2}$. You should also check one angle in the quadrant $0 < A < 90°$ and one in the quadrant $90° < A < 180°$. The following table shows the results of these calculations using the given typical values: $L_1 = 1$, $L_2 = 0.5$ ft.

A (degrees)	d (feet)
0	1.5
60	1.15
90	0.87
120	0.65
180	0.5

5. *Write and run the program.*

The following MATLAB program uses the values $L_1 = 1$, $L_2 = 0.5$ ft.

```
>>L_1 = 1;
>>L_2 = .5;
>>R=L_2/L_1;
>>A_d=[0:.5:180];
>>A_r=A_d*(pi/180);
>>B=asin(R*sin(A_r));
>>d=L_1*cos(B)+L_2*cos(A_r);
>>plot(A_d,d),xlabel('A (degrees)'), ...
ylabel('d (feet)'),grid
```

This program introduces some new features. Note the use of the underscore (_) in variable names to make the names more meaningful. The variable A_d represents the angle A in degrees. Line 4 creates an array of numbers 0, 0.5, 1, 1.5,..., 180. Line 5 converts these degree values to radians and assigns the values to the variable A_r. This conversion is necessary because MATLAB trigonometric functions use radians, not degrees. (A common oversight is to use degrees.) MATLAB provides the built-in constant pi to use for π. Line 6 uses the inverse sine function asin. The plot command requires the label and grid commands to be on the same line, separated by commas. The line-continuation operator, called an *ellipsis,* consists of three periods. This operator enables you to continue typing the line after you press **Enter.** Otherwise, if you continued typing without using the ellipsis, you would not see the entire line on the screen. Note that the prompt is not visible when you press **Enter** after the ellipsis. The grid command puts grid lines on the

Figure 1.5–3
Plot of the piston motion versus crank angle.

plot so that you can read values from the plot more easily. The resulting plot appears in Figure 1.5–3.

6. ***Check the output of the program with your hand solution.***

Read the values from the plot corresponding to the values of A given in the preceding table. They agree with each other.

7. ***Run the program and perform a "reality check" on the output.***

You might suspect an error if the plot showed abrupt changes or discontinuities. However, the plot is smooth and shows that d behaves as expected. It decreases smoothly from its maximum at $A = 0$ to its minimum at $A = 180°$.

8. ***Test the program for a range of reasonable input values.***

Test the program using various values for L_1 and L_2 and examine the resulting plots to see whether they are reasonable. Something you might try on your own is to see what happens if $L_1 \leq L_2$. Should the mechanism work the same way it does when $L_1 > L_2$? What does your intuition tell you to expect from the mechanism? What does the program predict?

___

Besides using degrees instead of radians, a common mistake in programming is forgetting to put the multiplication symbol ($*$) between two variables. This is easy to overlook because we are used to writing xy in algebra, rather than $x*y$. Forgetting to enclose function arguments in parentheses, as `sin 2`, is another common mistake, instead of typing `sin(2)`.

1.6

Summary

If you entered our sample MATLAB session on your computer, you should now be familiar with the following MATLAB basic operations:

- Starting and exiting MATLAB.
- Entering simple mathematical expressions.
- Creating and printing a simple plot.
- Saving your results to a file.
- Using the online help facility.
- Using the menu system.

You should also be familiar with the methodology used for problem solving and the specific methodology used for solving problems by computer.

The remaining chapters expand on the topics introduced here and introduce even more of the MATLAB capabilities.

Key Terms with Page References

Command window, **5**

Edit menu, **10**

Editor window, **9**

File menu, **9**

Graphics window, **7**

Help menu, **11**

Model, **15**

Online help, **11**

Prompt, **5**

Session, **6**

Toolbox, **3**

Problems

Section 1.2

1. Make sure you know how to start and quit a MATLAB session. Use MATLAB to make the following calculations, using the values $x = 10$, $y = 3$. Use a calculator to check the results.

   a. $u = x + y$ b. $v = xy$ c. $w = x/y$
   d. $z = \sin x$ e. $r = 8\sin y$ f. $s = 5\sin 2y$

2. Suppose x takes on the values $x = 1, 1.2, 1.4, \ldots, 5$. Use MATLAB to compute the array y that results from the function $y = 7\sin 4x$.

   How many elements are in the array y? Use MATLAB to determine the value of the third element in the array y.

3. Use MATLAB to obtain a labeled plot on the screen of the function $y = 10 \sin 3x - 4$ for $0 \le x \le 5$. Read a point off the plot and check the values with a calculator.

Section 1.4

4. Use the MATLAB help facilities to find information about the following topics and symbols: plot, label, cos, cosine, :, and *.

Section 1.5

5. a. With what initial speed must you throw a ball vertically for it to reach a height of 20 feet? The ball weighs 1 pound. How does your answer change if the ball weighs 2 pounds?
   b. Suppose you wanted to throw a steel bar vertically to a height of 20 feet. The bar weighs 2 pounds. How much initial speed must the bar have to reach this height? Discuss how the length of the bar affects your answer.

6. Consider the motion of the piston discussed in Example 1.5–1. The piston *stroke* is the total distance moved by the piston as the crank angle varies from 0° to 180°.
   a. How does the piston stroke depend on L_1 and L_2?
   b. Suppose $L_2 = 0.5$ foot. Use MATLAB to plot the piston motion versus crank angle for two cases: $L_1 = 0.6$ foot and $L_1 = 1.4$ feet. Compare each plot with the plot shown in Figure 1.5–3. Discuss how the shape of the plot depends on the value of L_1.

Engineering in the 21st Century . . .

Innovative Construction

We tend to remember the great civilizations of the past in part by their public works, such as the Egyptian pyramids and the medieval cathedrals of Europe, which were technically challenging to create. Perhaps it is in our nature to "push the limits," and we admire others who do so. The challenge of innovative construction continues today. As space in our cities becomes scarce, many urban planners prefer to build vertically rather than horizontally. The newest tall buildings push the limits of our abilities, not only in structural design but also in areas that we might not think of, such as elevator design and operation, aerodynamics, and construction techniques. The photo above shows the 1149-feet-high Las Vegas Stratosphere Tower, the tallest observation tower in the United States. It required innovative techniques to be assembled. The construction crane shown in use is 400 feet tall.

Designers of buildings, bridges, and other structures will use new technologies and new materials, some of which are based on nature's designs. Pound for pound, spider silk is stronger than steel, and structural engineers hope to use cables of synthetic spider silk fibers to build earthquake-resistant suspension bridges. *Smart* structures, which can detect impending failure from cracks and fatigue, are now close to reality, as are *active* structures that incorporate powered devices to counteract wind and other forces. The MATLAB Financial toolbox is useful for financial evaluation of large construction projects, and the MATLAB Partial Differential Equation toolbox can be used for structural design.

2

Basic Operations and Arrays

Outline

The brief MATLAB session in Chapter 1 used simple arithmetic to acquaint you with the MATLAB Command window, its Figure window, and a text editor window. In this chapter we begin to explore MATLAB commands in more depth. One of the strengths of MATLAB is the capability to handle collections of numbers, called *arrays,* as if they were a single variable. For example, when we add two arrays A and B by typing the single command C = A + B, MATLAB actually adds all the corresponding numbers in A and B to produce C. In most other programming languages, this operation requires more than one command. The array-handling feature means that MATLAB programs can be very short. Thus they are easy to create, read, and document.

The MATLAB array capabilities make it a natural choice for engineering problems that require a set of data to be analyzed. If you have been using a spreadsheet for data analysis, you may find that MATLAB is an easier and more powerful tool for such work.

A scalar is a single number, and we begin with scalar operations, which are operations between single numbers. Then we introduce the concept of an array, which is the basic building block in MATLAB. We explain how to create, address, and edit arrays and how to use array operations including addition,

27

subtraction, multiplication, division, and exponentiation to solve practical problems. We then introduce matrix operations, which are performed differently than array operations, and have their own applications. You probably have performed algebra with polynomials, including finding polynomial roots. We explain how to use arrays in MATLAB to do polynomial algebra and root finding.

2.1
───

Scalar Operations

SCALAR

We refer to a single number as a *scalar*, and we now introduce MATLAB operators for doing calculations with scalars. Later we show that many calculations are more conveniently performed with *arrays*, which are collections of scalars arranged in a logical structure.

MATLAB uses the standard computer programming symbols + - * / ^ for addition, subtraction, multiplication, division, and exponentiation (power), respectively. For example, typing x = 8 + 3*5 returns the answer x = 23. Typing 2^3-10 returns the answer ans = -2.

A semicolon at the end of a line suppresses printing the results to the screen. If a line does not end with a semicolon, MATLAB displays the results of the line on the screen. For example, compare the MATLAB session

```
>>x = 2+3
x =
    5
```

with typing x = 2+3;.

To see the results of this line, you must then type x and press **Enter.** You will see the following:

```
>>x =
    5
```

Even if you suppress the display with the semicolon, MATLAB still retains the variable's value.

You can put several commands on the same line if you separate them with a comma—if you want to see the results of the previous command—or with a semicolon if you want to suppress the display. For example:

```
>>x=2;y=6+x,x=y+7
y =
    8
x =
    15
```

Note that the first value of x was not displayed. Note also that the value of x changed from 2 to 15.

If you need to type a long line, you can type an *ellipsis,* that is, three periods, to delay execution. For example:

```
>>Number_Apples = 10; Number_Oranges = 25; Number_Pears = 12;
>>Fruit_Purchased = Number_Apples + Number_Oranges ...
+ Number_Pears
   Fruit_Purchased =
                  47
```

The symbol % designates a comment, which is not executed by MATLAB. Comments are not that useful for interactive sessions and are used mainly in M-files, which are covered in section 3.2. The comment symbol can go anywhere in the line. MATLAB ignores everything to the right of the % symbol. For example:

COMMENT

```
>>% This is a comment.
>> x = 2+3 % So is this.
x =
   5
```

When we do not specify a variable name for a result, MATLAB uses the symbol ans as a temporary variable containing the most recent answer. For example:

```
>>2+3
ans =
   5
```

MATLAB has several special constants. The symbol Inf stands for ∞, which in practice means a number so large that MATLAB cannot represent it. For example, typing 5 / 0 generates the answer Inf. The symbol NaN stands for "not a number." It indicates an undefined numerical result such as that obtained by typing 0/0. The symbol eps is the smallest number which, when added to 1 by the computer, creates a number greater than 1. It is used as an indicator of the accuracy of computations. The symbol pi represents the number $\pi = 3.14159\ldots$

The symbols i and j denote the imaginary unit, where $i = j = \sqrt{-1}$. They are used to create and represent complex numbers, such as x = 5 + 8i. Table 2.1–1 summarizes these special variables and constants.

Table 2.1–1 Special variables and constants

Command	Description
ans	Temporary variable containing the most recent answer.
eps	Specifies the accuracy of floating-point precision.
i,j	The imaginary unit $\sqrt{-1}$.
Inf	Infinity.
NaN	Indicates an undefined numerical result.
pi	The number π.

Table 2.1–2 Scalar arithmetic operations

Symbol	Operation	MATLAB form
^	exponentiation: a^b	a^b
*	multiplication: ab	a*b
/	right division: $a/b = \frac{a}{b}$	a/b
\	left division: $b \backslash a = \frac{a}{b}$	b\a
+	addition: $a + b$	a+b
−	subtraction: $a - b$	a-b

Order of Precedence

As we have seen, MATLAB uses the standard computer programming symbols + - * / ^ for addition, subtraction, multiplication, division, and exponentiation (power), respectively. For example, typing 3 + 5*2 returns the answer ans = 13. Typing 2^3-7 returns the answer ans = 1. The *forward slash* / represents *right division,* which is the normal division operator. Typing 15/3 returns the answer ans = 5.

MATLAB has another division operator, called *left division,* which is denoted by the *backslash* \. The left-division operator is useful for solving matrix equations, as you will see in Chapter 5. A good way to remember the difference between the right- and left-division operators is to note that the slash slants towards the denominator. For example, 7/2 = 2\7 = 3.5. Table 2.1–2 summarizes these operators.

PRECEDENCE

The mathematical operations represented by the symbols + - * / and ^ follow a set of rules called *precedence.* These rules are the same as those of major programming languages; thus they follow conventional programming standards. Mathematical expressions are evaluated starting from the left, with the exponentiation operation having the highest order of precedence, followed by multiplication and division with equal precedence, followed by addition and subtraction with equal precedence. Parentheses can be used to alter this order. Evaluation begins with the innermost pair of parentheses and proceeds outward. Table 2.1–3 summarizes these rules. For example, the following statements are true:

$$4^2 - 12 - 8/4 * 2 = 0$$

$$4^2 - 12 - 8/(4 * 2) = 3$$

$$3 * 4^2 + 5 = 53$$

$$(3 * 4)^2 + 5 = 149$$

Table 2.1-3 Order of precedence

Precedence	Operation
First	Parentheses; evaluated starting with the innermost pair.
Second	Exponentiation; evaluated from left to right.
Third	Multiplication and division with equal precedence; evaluated from left to right.
Fourth	Addition and subtraction with equal precedence; evaluated from left to right.

Test Your Understanding

T2.1-1 Use MATLAB to verify the preceding expressions.

Both scalars and arrays can have names in MATLAB. Names must begin with a letter and must contain fewer than 20 characters in MATLAB 4, fewer than 32 characters in MATLAB 5; the rest of the name can contain letters, digits, and underscore characters. Try not to use the names of special constants such as i or j. Although MATLAB allows you to assign other values to these constants, it is not good practice to do so.

MATLAB is case sensitive. MATLAB 4 enabled you to turn off this feature by typing the command `casesen off`. However, this command was removed in MATLAB 5. Thus the following names represent five different variables: `speed`, `Speed`, `SPEED`, `Speed_1`, and `Speed_2`.

MATLAB uses double-precision for its computations but prints results on the screen using the *short* format. You can change this default by using the `format` command, which is discussed in section 3.3. MATLAB uses the notation e and E to represent exponentiation to a power of 10; for example, the number 5.316×10^2 is expressed as `5.316e+2`.

Complex Number Operations

MATLAB handles complex number algebra automatically. Use the symbols i and j to denote the imaginary part, where $i = j = \sqrt{-1}$. For example, the number $c_1 = 1 - 2i$ is entered as follows: `c1 = 1-2i`.

Caution: Note that an asterisk is not needed between i or j and a number, although it is required in other cases, such as `c2 = 5 - i*c1`. This convention can cause errors if you are not careful. For example, the expressions `y = 7/2*i` and `x = 7/2i` give two different results: $y = (7/2)i = 3.5i$ and $x = 7/(2i) = -3.5i$.

Addition, subtraction, multiplication, and division of complex numbers are easily done. For example:

```
>>s = 3+7i;
>>w = 5-9i;
>>w+s
ans =
   8.0000 - 2.0000i
>>w*s
ans =
   78.0000 + 8.0000i
>>w/s
ans =
  -0.8276 - 1.0690i
```

COMPLEX CONJUGATE

Complex conjugates have the same real part but imaginary parts of opposite sign; for example, $-3 + 7i$ and $-3 - 7i$ are complex conjugates. The product of two conjugates is the sum of the squares of the real and imaginary parts; for example:

```
>>(-3 + 7i)*(-3 - 7i)
ans =
   58
```

Test Your Understanding

T2.1-2 Given $x = -5 + 9i$ and $y = 6 - 2i$, use MATLAB to show that $x + y = 1 + 7i$, $xy = -12 + 64i$, and $x/y = -1.2 + 1.1i$.

Managing Your Work Session

MATLAB retains the last value of a variable until you quit MATLAB or clear its value. Overlooking this fact is a common source of errors in MATLAB. For example, you might prefer to use the variable x in multiple calculations. If you forget to enter the correct value for x, MATLAB uses the last value and you get an incorrect result. You can use the `clear` command to remove the values of *all* variables from memory, or you can use the form `clear name1 name2` to clear the variables named `name1` and `name2`. The effect of the `clc` command is different; it clears the Command window of everything displayed on the screen, but the values of the variables remain. You can also clear the Command window by selecting **Clear Session** from the **Edit** menu. These and related commands are described in Table 2.1–4.

You can type the name of a variable and press **Enter** to see its current value. If the variable does not have a value, you will see an error message. The `who` command lists the names of all the

Table 2.1–4 Commands for managing the work session

Command	Description
casesen	casesen on turns on case sensitivity; casesen off turns it off. (MATLAB 4 only)
clc	Clears the Command window.
clear	Removes variables from memory.
exist('name')	Determines whether an existing file or variable has the name 'name'.
help name	Searches online help for the topic name.
lookfor name	Searches the help entries for the specified keyword name.
quit	Stops MATLAB.
who	Lists the variables currently in memory.
whos	Lists the current variables and sizes, and indicates whether they have imaginary parts.

variables in memory, but does not give their values. The who's command not only lists the variable names and their sizes but also indicates whether the variables have nonzero imaginary parts.

MATLAB retains your previous keystrokes in a command file. Use the **up-arrow** key (↑) to scroll back through the commands. Press the key once to see the previous entry, twice to see the entry before that, and so on. Use the **down-arrow** key (↓) to scroll forward through the commands. When you find the line you want, you can edit it using the **left-** and **right-arrow** keys (← and →), the **back space** key, and the **Delete** key. Press **Enter,** or **Return,** to execute the command. This technique is a quick way to correct your typing mistakes.

2.2

Arrays

We can represent the location of a point in three-dimensional space by three Cartesian coordinates x, y, and z. As shown in Figure 2.2–1, these three coordinates specify the *vector* **p**. (In mathematical text we often use boldface type to indicate vectors.) The set of *unit vectors* **i**, **j**, **k**, whose lengths are 1 and whose directions coincide with the x, y, and z axes, respectively, can be used to express the vector mathematically as follows: $\mathbf{p} = x\mathbf{i} + y\mathbf{j} + z\mathbf{k}$. The unit vectors enable us to associate the vector components x, y, z with the proper coordinate axes; therefore, when we write $\mathbf{p} = 5\mathbf{i} + 7\mathbf{j} + 2\mathbf{k}$, we know that the x, y, and z coordinates of the vector are 5, 7, and 2, respectively. We can also write the components in a specific order, separate them with a space, and identify the group with brackets, as follows: [5 7 2]. As long as we agree that the vector components will be written in the order x, y, z, we can use this notation instead of the unit-vector notation. In fact, MATLAB uses this style for vector notation. MATLAB allows us to separate the components with commas for improved readability if we desire so that the equivalent way of writing the preceding vector is [5, 7, 2]. This expression is a *row* vector, which is a horizontal arrangement of the elements.

We can also express the vector as a *column* vector, which has a vertical arrangement, as follows:

$$\begin{bmatrix} 5 \\ 7 \\ 2 \end{bmatrix}$$

Figure 2.2–1
Specification of a position vector using Cartesian coordinates.

Creating Vectors in MATLAB

Although a position vector cannot have more than three components, the concept of a vector can be generalized to any number of components. In MATLAB a vector is simply a list of scalars, whose order of appearance in the list may be significant, as it is when specifying *xyz* coordinates. As another example, suppose we measure the temperature of an object once every hour. We can represent the measurements as a vector, and the 10th element in the list is the temperature measured at the 10th hour.

To create a row vector in MATLAB, you simply type the elements inside a pair of square brackets, separating the elements with a space or a comma. Brackets are required for arrays in some cases, but not all. To improve readability, we will always use them. The choice between a space or comma is a matter of personal preference, although the chance of an error is less if you use a comma. (You can also use a comma followed by a space for maximum readability.) For example, the following session creates three row vectors named r, s, and t, which all have the same values in MATLAB.

```
>>r = [2,4,10]
r =
    2.0000    4.0000    10.0000
>>s = [2 4 10]
s =
    2.0000    4.0000    10.0000
>>t = [2,  4,  10]
t =
    2.0000    4.0000    10.0000
```

To create a column vector, you can separate the elements by semicolons; alternatively, you can create a row vector and then use the *transpose* notation ('), which converts a row vector into a column vector, or vice versa. For example:

```
>>g = [3;7;9]
g =
    3
    7
    9
```

```
>>g = [3,7,9]'
g =
    3
    7
    9
```

The third way to create a column vector is to type a left bracket ([) and the first element, press **Enter**, type the second element, press **Enter**, and so on until you type the last element followed by a right bracket (]) and **Enter**. On the screen this sequence looks like

```
>>g = [3
7
9]
g =
    3
    7
    9
```

Note that MATLAB displays row vectors horizontally and column vectors vertically.

You can create vectors by "appending" one vector to another. For example, to create the row vector u whose first three columns contain the values of r = [2,4,20] and whose fourth, fifth, and sixth columns contain the values of w = [9,-6,3], you type u = [r,w]. The result is the 1 × 6 vector u = [2,4,20,9,-6,3].

The colon operator (:) easily generates a large vector of regularly spaced elements. Typing

```
>>x = [m:q:n]
```

creates a vector x of values with a spacing q. The first value is m. The last value is n if m - n is an integer multiple of q. If not, the last value is less than n. For example, typing x = [0:2:8] creates the vector x = [0,2,4,6,8], whereas typing x = [0:2:7] creates the vector x = [0,2,4,6]. To create a row vector z consisting of the values from 5 to 8 in steps of 0.1, you type z = [5:0.1:8]. If the increment q is omitted, it is presumed to be 1. Thus y = [-3:2] produces the vector y = [-3,- 2,-1,0,1,2].

The increment q can be negative. In this case m should be greater than n. For example, u = [10:-2:4] produces the vector [10,8,6,4].

The linspace command also creates a linearly spaced row vector, but instead you specify the number of values rather than the increment. The syntax is linspace(x1,x2,n), where x1 and x2 are the lower and upper limits and n is the number of points. For example, linspace(5,8,31) is equivalent to [5:.1:8]. If n is omitted, the spacing is 1.

The `logspace` command creates an array of logarithmically spaced elements. Its syntax is `logspace(a,b,n)`, where n is the number of points between 10^a and 10^b. For example, `x = logspace(-1,1,4)` produces the vector `x = [0.1000, 0.4642, 2.1544, 10.000]`. If n is omitted, the number of points defaults to 50.

Two-Dimensional Arrays

ARRAY

An *array* is a collection of scalars arranged in a logical structure. An array may have a single row; if so, it is called a row vector. A column vector has a single column. An array can have multiple rows, multiple columns, or both. Such a two-dimensional array

MATRIX

is called a *matrix*. In mathematical text we often use boldface type to indicate vectors and matrices, for example, **A**. If possible, vectors are usually denoted by lowercase letters and matrices by uppercase letters.

An example of a matrix having three rows and two columns is

$$\mathbf{M} = \begin{bmatrix} 2 & 5 \\ -3 & 4 \\ -7 & 1 \end{bmatrix}$$

A matrix should not be confused with a determinant, which also has rows and columns but can be reduced to a *single* number. Two parallel lines usually denote a determinant; square brackets usually denote matrices. Determinants are discussed in Chapter 5.

ARRAY SIZE

We refer to the *size* of an array by the number of rows and the number of columns. For example, an array with 3 rows and 2 columns is said to be a 3×2 array. *The number of rows is always stated first!* A row vector has a size of $1 \times n$ where n is the number of columns. A column vector has a size of $n \times 1$ where n is the number of rows.

We sometimes represent a matrix **A** as $[a_{ij}]$ to indicate its elements a_{ij}. The subscripts i and j—called *indices*—indicate the row and column location of the element a_{ij}. *The row number must always come first!* For example, the element a_{32} is in row 3, column 2. Two matrices **A** and **B** are equal if they have the same size and if all their corresponding elements are equal; that is, $a_{ij} = b_{ij}$ for every value of i and j.

Creating Matrices

The most direct way to create a matrix is to type the matrix row by row, separating the elements in a given row with spaces or commas and separating the rows with semicolons. For example, typing

```
>>A = [2,4,10;16,3,7];
```

creates the following matrix:

$$A = \begin{bmatrix} 2 & 4 & 10 \\ 16 & 3 & 7 \end{bmatrix}$$

Remember, spaces or commas separate elements in different *columns*, whereas semicolons separate elements in different *rows*.

If the matrix has many elements, you can press **Enter** and continue typing on the next line. MATLAB knows you are finished entering the matrix when you type the closing bracket (]).

You can also create a matrix from row or column vectors. A row vector r can be appended to a matrix A if r and A have the same number of columns. The command B = [A c] appends the column vector c to the matrix A. Similarly, a column vector c can be appended to a matrix A if c and A have the same number of rows. The command B = [A;r] appends the row vector r to the matrix A. Note the difference between the results given by [a b] and [a;b] in the following session:

```
>>a = [1,3,5]
a =
   1   3   5
>>b = [7,9,11]
b =
   7   9   11
>>c = [a b];
c =
   1   3   5   7   9   11
>>D = [a;b]
D =
   1   3   5
   7   9   11
```

You need not use symbols to create a new array. For example, typing D = [[1,3,5];[7,9,11]]; produces the same result as typing D = [a;b].

Matrices and the Transpose Operation

The transpose operation interchanges the rows and columns. In mathematics text we denote this operation by the superscript T. For an $m \times n$ matrix $\mathbf{A}$ with m rows and n columns, $\mathbf{A}^T$ (read "A transpose") is an $n \times m$ matrix. For example, if

$$\mathbf{A} = \begin{bmatrix} -2 & 6 \\ -3 & 5 \end{bmatrix}$$

then

$$\mathbf{A}^T = \begin{bmatrix} -2 & -3 \\ 6 & 5 \end{bmatrix}$$

If $A^T = A$, the matrix $\mathbf{A}$ is *symmetric*. Only a square matrix can be symmetric, but not every square matrix is symmetric.

If the array contains complex elements, the transpose operator ($'$) produces the *complex conjugate transpose*; that is, the resulting elements are the complex conjugates of the original array's transposed elements. Alternatively, you can use the *dot transpose* operator (`. '`) to transpose the array without producing complex conjugate elements, for example, `A. '`. If all the elements are real, the operators $'$ and `. '` give the same result.

Array Addressing

Array indices are the row and column numbers of an element in an array and are used to keep track of the array's elements. For example, the notation `v(5)` refers to the fifth element in the vector `v`, and `A(2,3)` refers to the element in row 2, column 3 in the matrix `A`. The row number is always listed first! This notation enables you to correct entries in an array without retyping the entire array. For example, to change the element in row 1, column 3 of the matrix $\mathbf{D}$ to 6, you can type `D(1,3) = 6`.

The colon operator selects individual elements, rows, columns, or "subarrays" of arrays. Here are some examples:

- `v(:)` represents all the elements of the vector `v`.
- `v(2:5)` represents the second through fifth elements; that is `v(2),v(3),v(4),v(5)`.
- `A(:, 3)` denotes *all* the elements in the third column of `A`.
- `A(:,2:5)` denotes all the elements in the second through fifth columns of `A`.
- `A(2:3,1:3)` denotes all the elements in the second and third rows that are also in the first through third columns.

You can use array indices to extract a smaller array from another array. For example, if you create the array $\mathbf{B}$

$$\mathbf{B} = \begin{bmatrix} 2 & 4 & 10 & 13 \\ 16 & 3 & 7 & 18 \\ 8 & 4 & 9 & 25 \\ 3 & 12 & 15 & 17 \end{bmatrix} \qquad (2.2\text{--}1)$$

by typing

```
>>B = [2,4,10,13;16,3,7,18;8,4,9,25;3,12,15,17];
```

and then type

```
>>C = B(2:3,1:3);
```

you can produce the following array:

$$\mathbf{C} = \begin{bmatrix} 16 & 3 & 7 \\ 8 & 4 & 9 \end{bmatrix}$$

The *empty* array contains no elements and is expressed as [ ]. Rows and columns can be deleted by setting the selected row or column equal to the null array. This step causes the original matrix to collapse to a smaller one. For example, A(3,:) = [] deletes the third row in A, while A(:,2:4) = [] deletes the second through fourth columns in A. Finally, A([1 4],:) = [] deletes the first and fourth rows of A.

Suppose we type A = [6,9,4;1,5,7] to define the following matrix:

$$\mathbf{A} = \begin{bmatrix} 6 & 9 & 4 \\ 1 & 5 & 7 \end{bmatrix}$$

Typing A(1,5) = 3 changes the matrix to

$$\mathbf{A} = \begin{bmatrix} 6 & 9 & 4 & 0 & 3 \\ 1 & 5 & 7 & 0 & 0 \end{bmatrix}$$

Because **A** did not have five columns, its size is automatically expanded to accept the new element in column 5. MATLAB adds zeros to fill out the remaining elements.

MATLAB does not accept negative or zero indices, but you can use negative increments with the colon operator. For example, typing B = A(:,5:-1:1) reverses the order of the columns in **A** and produces

$$\mathbf{B} = \begin{bmatrix} 3 & 0 & 4 & 9 & 6 \\ 0 & 0 & 7 & 5 & 1 \end{bmatrix}$$

Suppose that C = [-4,12,3,5,8]. Then typing B(2,:) = C replaces row 2 of B with C. Thus **B** becomes

$$\mathbf{B} = \begin{bmatrix} 3 & 0 & 4 & 9 & 6 \\ -4 & 12 & 3 & 5 & 8 \end{bmatrix}$$

Suppose that D = [3,8,5;2,-6,9]. Then typing E = D([2,2,2],:) repeats row 2 of D three times to obtain

$$\mathbf{E} = \begin{bmatrix} 2 & -6 & 9 \\ 2 & -6 & 9 \\ 2 & -6 & 9 \end{bmatrix}$$

Using clear to Avoid Errors

You can use the clear command to protect yourself from accidentally reusing an array that has the wrong dimension. Even if you set new values for an array, some previous values might still remain. For example, suppose you had previously used the 2×2 array A = [2, 5; 6, 9], and you then create the 5×1 arrays x = [1:5]' and y = [2:6]'. Suppose you now redefine A so that its columns will be x and y. If you then type A(:,1) = x to create the first column, MATLAB displays an error message telling you that the number of rows in A and x must be the same. MATLAB thinks A should be a 2×2 matrix because A was previously defined to have only two rows and its values remain in memory. The `clear` command wipes A and all other variables from memory and avoids this error. To clear A only, type `clear A` before typing `A(:,1) = x`.

Some Useful Array Commands

MATLAB has many commands for working with arrays (see Table 2.2–1). Here is a summary of some of the more commonly used commands.

The `max(A)` command returns the algebraically greatest element in **A** if **A** is a vector having all real elements. It returns a row vector containing the greatest elements in each column if **A** is a matrix containing all real elements. If *any* of the elements are complex, `max(A)` returns the element that has the largest magnitude. The command `[x,k] = max(A)` is similar to `max(A)`, but it stores the maximum values in the row vector **x** and their indices in the row vector **k**.

The commands `min(A)` and `[x,k] = min(A)` are the same as `max(A)` and `[x,k] = max(A)` except that they return minimum values.

Table 2.2–1 Array commands

Command	Description
`cat(n,A,B,C, ...)`	Creates a new array by concatenating the arrays A, B, C, and so on along the dimension n (MATLAB 5 only).
`find(x)`	Computes an array containing the indices of the nonzero elements of the array **x**.
`[u,v,w] = find(A)`	Computes the arrays **u** and **v**, containing the row and column indices of the nonzero elements of the matrix *A*, and the array **w**, containing the values of the nonzero elements. The array **w** may be omitted.
`length(A)`	Computes either the number of elements of **A** if A is a vector or the largest value of *m* or *n* if **A** is an $m \times n$ matrix.
`linspace(a,b,n)`	Creates a vector of *n* regularly spaced values between *a* and *b*.
`logspace(a,b,n)`	Creates a vector of *n* logarithmically spaced values between *a* and *b*.
`max(A)`	Returns the algebraically largest element in **A** if **A** is a vector. Returns a row vector containing the largest elements in each column if **A** is a matrix. If any of the elements are complex, `max(A)` returns the elements that have the largest magnitudes.
`[x,k] = max(A)`	Similar to `max(A)` but stores the maximum values in the row vector **x** and their indices in the row vector **k**.
`min(A)`	Same as `max(A)` but returns minimum values.
`[x,k] = min(A)`	Same as `[x,k] = max(A)` but returns minimum values.
`size(A)`	Returns a row vector `[m n]` containing the sizes of the $m \times n$ array **A**.
`sort(A)`	Sorts each column of the array **A** in ascending order and returns an array the same size as **A**.
`sum(A)`	Sums the elements in each column of the array **A** and returns a row vector containing the sums.

The command `size(A)` returns a row vector [m n] containing the sizes of the $m \times n$ array **A**. The `length(A)` command computes either the number of elements of **A** if A is a vector or the largest value of m or n if **A** is an $m \times n$ matrix.

For example, if

$$\mathbf{A} = \begin{bmatrix} 6 & 2 \\ -10 & -5 \\ 3 & 0 \end{bmatrix}$$

then `max(A)` returns the vector [6,2]; `min(A)` returns the vector [-10,-5]; `size(A)` returns [3,2]; and `length(A)` returns 3. If A has one or more complex elements, `max(A)` returns the element that has the largest magnitude. For example, if

$$\mathbf{A} = \begin{bmatrix} 6 & 2 \\ -10 & -5 \\ 3 + 4i & 0 \end{bmatrix}$$

then `max(A)` returns the vector [-10,-5] and `min(A)` returns the vector [3+4i,0]. (The magnitude of $3 + 4i$ is 5.)

The `sum(A)` command sums the elements in each column of the array **A** and returns a row vector containing the sums. The `sort(A)` command sorts each column of the array **A** in ascending order and returns an array the same size as **A**.

The `find(x)` command computes an array containing the indices of the nonzero elements of the vector **x**. The command [u,v,w] = `find(A)` computes the arrays **u** and **v**, containing the row and column indices of the nonzero elements of the matrix **A**, and the array **w**, containing the values of the nonzero elements. The array **w** may be omitted. These commands are summarized in Table 2.2–1.

Magnitude, Length, and Absolute Value of a Vector

The terms *magnitude, length,* and *absolute value* are often loosely used in everyday language, but you must keep their precise meaning in mind when using MATLAB. The MATLAB `length` command gives the number of elements in the vector. The *magnitude* of a vector **x** having elements $x_1, x_2, \ldots, x_n$ is a scalar, given by $\sqrt{x_1^2 + x_2^2 + \cdots + x_n^2}$, and is the same as the vector's geometric length. The *absolute value* of a vector **x** is a vector whose elements are the absolute values of the elements of **x**. For example, if x =[2,-4,5], its length is 3; its magnitude is $\sqrt{2^2 + (-4)^2 + 5^2} = 6.7082$; and its absolute value is [2,4,5].

LENGTH

MAGNITUDE

ABSOLUTE VALUE

Test Your Understanding

T2.2–1 For the matrix **B**, find the array that results from the operation [B;B']. Use MATLAB to determine what number is in row 5, column 3 of the result.

$$\mathbf{B} = \begin{bmatrix} 2 & 4 & 10 & 13 \\ 16 & 3 & 7 & 18 \\ 8 & 4 & 9 & 25 \\ 3 & 12 & 15 & 17 \end{bmatrix}$$

T2.2–2 For the same matrix **B**, use MATLAB to (a) find the largest and smallest element in **B** and their indices and (b) sort each column in **B** to create a new matrix **C**.

Multidimensional Arrays

Before MATLAB 5, arrays were restricted to one or two dimensions; that is, they could have only rows and columns. MATLAB 5 supports multidimensional arrays. Here we present just some of the MATLAB capabilities for such arrays; to obtain more information, type help ndfun.

A three-dimensional array has the dimension $m \times n \times q$. A four-dimensional array has the dimension $m \times n \times q \times r$, and so forth. The first two dimensions are the row and column, as with a matrix. The higher dimensions are called *pages*. The elements of a matrix are specified by two indices; three indices are required to specify an element of a three-dimensional array, and so on. You can think of a three-dimensional array as layers of matrices. The first layer is page 1; the second layer is page 2, and so on. If A is a $3 \times 3 \times 2$ array, you can access the element in row 3, column 2 of page 2 by typing A(3,2,2). To access all of page 1, type A(:,:,1). To access all of page 2, type A(:,:,2).

The ndims command returns the number of dimensions. For example, for the array A just described, ndims(A) returns the value 3.

You can create a multidimensional array by first creating a two-dimensional array and then extending it. For example, suppose you want to create a three-dimensional array whose first page is

$$\begin{bmatrix} 4 & 6 & 1 \\ 5 & 8 & 0 \\ 3 & 9 & 2 \end{bmatrix}$$

and whose second page is

$$\begin{bmatrix} 6 & 2 & 9 \\ 0 & 3 & 1 \\ 4 & 7 & 5 \end{bmatrix}$$

To do so, first create page 1 as a 3×3 matrix and then add page 2, as follows:

```
>>A = [4,6,1;5,8,0;3,9,2];
>>A(:,:,2) = [6,2,9;0,3,1;4,7,5]
```

MATLAB displays the following:

```
A(:,:,1) =
    4   6   1
    5   8   0
    3   9   2
A(:,:,2) =
    6   2   9
    0   3   1
    4   7   5
```

Another way to produce such an array is with the `cat` command, which is also new to MATLAB 5. Typing `cat(n,A,B,C, ...)` creates a new array by concatenating the arrays A, B, C, and so on along the dimension n. Note that `cat(1,A,B)` is the same as `[A;B]` and that `cat(2,A,B)` is the same as `[A,B]`. For example, suppose we have the 2×2 arrays **A** and **B**:

$$\mathbf{A} = \begin{bmatrix} 8 & 2 \\ 9 & 5 \end{bmatrix} \qquad \mathbf{B} = \begin{bmatrix} 4 & 6 \\ 7 & 3 \end{bmatrix}$$

Then `C = cat(3,A,B)` produces a three-dimensional array. We can think of this array as composed of two layers; the first layer is the matrix A, and the second layer is the matrix B. The element `C(m,n,p)` is located in row m, column n, and layer p. Thus the element `C(2,1,1)` is 9, and the element `C(2,2,2)` is 3. These new commands are summarized in Table 2.2–1.

Multidimensional arrays are useful for problems that involve several parameters. For example, if we have data on the temperature distribution in a rectangular object, we could represent the temperatures as an array T with three dimensions. Each temperature would correspond to the temperature of a rectangular block within the object, and the array indices would correspond to x, y, z locations within the object. For example, `T(2,4,3)` would be the temperature in the block located in row 2, column 4, page 3 and having the coordinates x_2, y_4, z_3.

2.3

Array Operations

To increase the magnitude of a vector, multiply it by a scalar. For example, to double the magnitude of the vector `r = [3,5,2]`, multiply each component by two to obtain `[6,10,4]`. In MATLAB you type `v = 2*r`. See Figure 2.3–1 for the geometric interpretation of scalar multiplication of a vector in three-dimensional space.

Multiplying a matrix **A** by a scalar w produces a matrix whose elements are the elements of **A** multiplied by w. For example:

$$3 \begin{bmatrix} 2 & 9 \\ 5 & -7 \end{bmatrix} = \begin{bmatrix} 6 & 27 \\ 15 & -21 \end{bmatrix}$$

Figure 2.3–1
Geometric interpretation of scalar multiplication of a vector.

This multiplication is performed in MATLAB as follows:

```
>>A = [2,9;5,-7];
>>3*A
ans =
      6     27
     15    -21
```

Thus multiplication of an array by a scalar is easily defined and easily carried out. However, multiplication of two arrays is not so straightforward. In fact, MATLAB uses two definitions of multiplication: (1) array multiplication and (2) matrix multiplication. Division and exponentiation must also be carefully defined when you are dealing with operations between two arrays. MATLAB has two forms of division and exponentiation of arrays. In this section we introduce one form, called *array* operations, which are also called *element-by-element* operations. In the next section we introduce *matrix* operations. Each form has its own applications, which we illustrate by examples.

ARRAY OPERATIONS

MATRIX OPERATIONS

Array Addition and Subtraction

Vector addition can be done either graphically (by using the parallelogram law in two dimensions (see Figure 2.3–2a)), or analytically by adding the corresponding components. To add the vectors $r = [3,5,2]$ and $v = [2,-3,1]$ to create w in MATLAB, you type $w = r + v$. The result is $w = [5,2,3]$. Figure 2.3–2b illustrates vector addition in three dimensions.

When two arrays have identical size, their sum or difference has the same size and is obtained by adding or subtracting their corresponding elements. Thus $\mathbf{C} = \mathbf{A} + \mathbf{B}$ implies that $c_{ij} = a_{ij} + b_{ij}$ if the arrays are matrices. The array $\mathbf{C}$ has the same

(a)

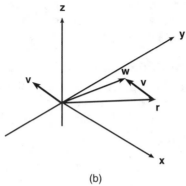

(b)

Figure 2.3–2
Vector addition. (a) The
parallelogram law. (b)
Addition of vectors in three
dimensions.

size as **A** and **B**. For example:

$$\begin{bmatrix} 6 & -2 \\ 10 & 3 \end{bmatrix} + \begin{bmatrix} 9 & 8 \\ -12 & 14 \end{bmatrix} = \begin{bmatrix} 15 & 6 \\ -2 & 17 \end{bmatrix} \qquad (2.3–1)$$

Array subtraction is performed in a similar way.

The addition shown in (2.3–1) is performed in MATLAB as follows:

```
>>A = [6,-2;10,3];
>>B = [9,8;-12,14]
>>A+B
ans =
    15    6
    -2   17
```

Array addition and subtraction are associative and commutative. For addition these properties mean that

$$(\mathbf{A} + \mathbf{B}) + \mathbf{C} = \mathbf{A} + (\mathbf{B} + \mathbf{C}) \qquad (2.3–2)$$

$$\mathbf{A} + \mathbf{B} + \mathbf{C} = \mathbf{B} + \mathbf{C} + \mathbf{A} = \mathbf{A} + \mathbf{C} + \mathbf{B} \qquad (2.3–3)$$

Table 2.3–1   Element-by-element operations

Symbol	Operation	Form	Example
+	Scalar-array addition	A + b	[6,3]+2=[8,5]
−	Scalar-array subtraction	A − b	[8,3]-5=[3,-2]
+	Array addition	A + B	[6,5]+[4,8]=[10,13]
−	Array subtraction	A − B	[6,5]-[4,8]=[2,-3]
.*	Array multiplication	A.*B	[3,5].*[4,8]=[12,40]
./	Array right division	A./B	[2,5]./[4,8]=[2/4,5/8]
.\	Array left division	A.\B	[2,5].\[4,8]=[2\4,5\8]
.^	Array exponentiation	A.^B	[3,5].^2=[3^2,5^2]
			2.^[3,5]=[2^3,2^5]
			[3,5].^[2,4]=[3^2,5^4]

Array addition and subtraction require that both arrays have the same size. The only exception to this rule in MATLAB occurs when we add or subtract a *scalar* to or from an array. In this case the scalar is added or subtracted from each element in the array. Table 2.3–1 gives examples.

Array Multiplication

The data in Table 2.3–2 illustrates the difference between the two types of multiplication that are defined in MATLAB. The table gives the speed of an aircraft on each leg of a certain trip and the time spent on each leg.

We can define a row vector s containing the speeds and a row vector t containing the times for each leg. Thus s = [200, 250, 400, 300] and t = [2, 5, 3, 4]. To find the miles traveled on each leg, we multiply the speed by the time. To do so, we *specify* the multiplication s.*t to produce the row vector whose elements are the products of the corresponding elements in s and t:

s.*t = [200(2), 250(5), 400(3), 300(4)] = [400, 1250, 1200, 1200]

With this notation the symbol .* signifies that each element in s is multiplied by the corresponding element in t and that the resulting products are used to form a row vector having the same number of elements as s and t. This vector contains the miles traveled by the aircraft on each leg of the trip.

If we had wanted to find only the total miles traveled, we could have used another definition of multiplication, denoted by s*t′. In this definition the product is the *sum* of the individual element

Table 2.3–2   Aircraft speeds and times per leg

	Leg			
	1	2	3	4
Speed (mph)	200	250	400	300
Time (hrs)	2	5	3	4

products; that is

$$\texttt{s*t'} \; = \; [200(2) + 250(5) + 400(3) + 300(4)] = 4050$$

These two examples illustrate the difference between *array* multiplication $\texttt{s.*t}$—sometimes called *element-by-element* multiplication—and *matrix* multiplication $\texttt{s*t'}$. We examine matrix multiplication in more detail in section 2.4.

MATLAB defines element-by-element multiplication only for arrays that have the same size. The definition of the product $\texttt{x.*y}$, where $\texttt{x}$ and $\texttt{y}$ each have n elements, is

$$\texttt{x.*y} \; = \; [\texttt{x(1)y(1), x(2)y(2), ... , x(n)y(n)}]$$

if $\texttt{x}$ and $\texttt{y}$ are row vectors. If $\texttt{x}$ and $\texttt{y}$ are column vectors, the result of $\texttt{x.*y}$ is a column vector. For example, if

$$\mathbf{x} = [2,\ 4,\ -5] \qquad \mathbf{y} = [-7,\ 3,\ -8]$$

then $\texttt{z = x.*y}$ gives

$$\mathbf{z} = [2(-7),\ 4(3),\ -5(-8)] = [-14,\ 12,\ 40]$$

Note that $\texttt{x'}$ is a column vector with size 3×1 and thus does not have the same size as $\texttt{y}$, whose size is 1×3. Thus the operations $\texttt{x'.*y}$ and $\texttt{y.*x'}$ are not defined in MATLAB and will generate an error message.

The generalization of array multiplication to arrays with more than one row or column is straightforward. Both arrays must have the same size. If they are matrices, they must have the same number of rows and the same number of columns. The array operations are performed between the elements in corresponding locations in the arrays. For example, the array multiplication operation $\texttt{A.*B}$ results in a matrix $\texttt{C}$ that has the same size as $\texttt{A}$ and $\texttt{B}$ and the elements $c_{ij} = a_{ij}b_{ij}$. For example, if

$$\mathbf{A} = \begin{bmatrix} 11 & 5 \\ -9 & 4 \end{bmatrix} \qquad \mathbf{B} = \begin{bmatrix} -7 & 8 \\ 6 & 2 \end{bmatrix}$$

then $\texttt{C = A.*B}$ gives this result:

$$\mathbf{C} = \begin{bmatrix} 11(-7) & 5(8) \\ -9(6) & 4(2) \end{bmatrix} = \begin{bmatrix} -77 & 40 \\ -54 & 8 \end{bmatrix}$$

With element-by-element multiplication, it is important to remember that the dot ($.$) and the asterisk ($*$) form *one* symbol ($.*$). It might have been better to have defined a single symbol for this operation, but the developers of MATLAB were limited by the selection of symbols on the keyboard.

Array Division

The definition of array division, also called element-by-element division, is similar to the definition of array multiplication except, of course, that the elements of one array are divided by the elements of the other array. Both arrays must have the same size. The symbol for array right division is ./. For example, if

$$\mathbf{x} = [8, \ 12, \ 15] \qquad \mathbf{y} = [-2, \ 6, \ 5]$$

then $z = x./y$ gives

$$\mathbf{z} = [8/(-2), \ 12/6, \ 15/5] = [-4, \ 2, \ 3]$$

Also, if

$$\mathbf{A} = \begin{bmatrix} 24 & 20 \\ -9 & 4 \end{bmatrix} \qquad \mathbf{B} = \begin{bmatrix} -4 & 5 \\ 3 & 2 \end{bmatrix}$$

then $C = A./B$ gives

$$\mathbf{C} = \begin{bmatrix} 24/(-4) & 20/5 \\ -9/3 & 4/2 \end{bmatrix} = \begin{bmatrix} -6 & 4 \\ -3 & 2 \end{bmatrix}$$

The array left-division operator (.\) is defined to perform element-by-element division using left division. Refer to Table 2.3–1 for examples. Note that A.\B is not equivalent to A./B.

Example 2.3–1   Transportation route analysis

The following table gives data for the distance traveled along five truck routes and the corresponding time required to traverse each route. Use the data to compute the average speed required to drive each route. Find the route that has the highest average speed.

	1	2	3	4	5
Distance (miles)	560	440	490	530	370
Time (hrs)	10.3	8.2	9.1	10.1	7.5

Solution:

For example, the average speed on the first route is 560/10.3 = 54.4 miles per hour. First we define the row vectors d and t from the distance and time data. Then, to find the average speed on each route using MATLAB, we use array division. The session is

```
>>d = [560, 440, 490, 530, 370]
>>t = [10.3, 8.2, 9.1, 10.1, 7.5]
>>speed = d./t
speed =
    54.3689   53.6585   53.8462   52.4752   49.3333
```

The results are in miles per hour. Note that MATLAB displays more significant figures than is justified by the three-significant-figure accuracy of the given data, so we should round the results to three significant figures before using them. Thus we should report the average speeds to be 54.4, 53.7, 53.8, 52.5, and 49.0 miles per hour, respectively.

To find the highest speed and the corresponding route, continue the session as follows:

```
>>[highest_speed, route] = max(speed)
highest_speed =
    54.3689
route =
    1
```

The first route has the highest speed.

If we did not need the speeds for every route, we could have solved this problem by combining two lines as follows: [highest_speed, route] = max(d./t). As you become more familiar with MATLAB, you will appreciate its power to solve problems with very few lines and keystrokes.

Array Exponentiation

MATLAB enables us not only to raise arrays to powers but also to raise scalars and arrays to *array* powers. To perform exponentiation on an element-by-element basis, we must use the .^ symbol. For example, if x = [3, 5, 8], then typing x.^3 produces the array $[3^3, 5^3, 8^3] = [27, 125, 512]$. If x = [0:2:6], then typing x.^2 returns the array $[0^2, 2^2, 4^2, 6^2] = [0, 4, 16, 36]$. If

$$A = \begin{bmatrix} 4 & -5 \\ 2 & 3 \end{bmatrix}$$

then B = A.^3 gives this result:

$$B = \begin{bmatrix} 4^3 & (-5)^3 \\ 2^3 & 3^3 \end{bmatrix} = \begin{bmatrix} 64 & -125 \\ 8 & 27 \end{bmatrix}$$

We can raise a scalar to an array power. For example, if p = [2, 4, 5], then typing 3.^p produces the array $[3^2, 3^4, 3^5] = [9, 81, 243]$. This example illustrates a common situation in which it helps to remember that .^ is a *single* symbol; the dot in 3.^p is not a decimal point associated with the number 3. The following operations, with the value of p given here, are equivalent and give the correct answer:

```
3.^p
3.0.^p
3..^p
(3).^p
3.^[2,4,5]
```

Example 2.3–2   Current and power dissipation in resistors

The current i passing through an electrical resistor having a voltage v across it is given by Ohm's law: $i = v/R$, where R is the resistance. The power dissipated in the resistor is given by v^2/R. The following table gives data for the resistance and voltage for five resistors. Use the data to compute (a) the current in each resistor and (b) the power dissipated in each resistor.

	1	2	3	4	5
R (ohms)	10^4	2×10^4	3.5×10^4	10^5	2×10^5
v (volts)	120	80	110	200	350

Solution:

(a) First we define two row vectors, one containing the resistance values and one containing the voltage values. To find the current $i = v/R$ using MATLAB, we use array division. The session looks like

```
>>R = [10000, 20000, 35000, 100000, 200000];
>>v = [120, 80, 110, 200, 350];
>>current = v./R
current =
    0.0120   0.0040   0.0031   0.0020   0.0018
```

The results are in amperes and should be rounded to three significant figures because the voltage data contains only three significant figures.

(b) To find the power $P = v^2/R$, use array exponentiation and array division. The session continues as follows:

```
>>power = v.^2./R
power =
    1.4400   0.3200   0.3457   0.4000   0.6125
```

These numbers are the power dissipation in each resistor in watts. Note that the statement `v.^2./R` is equivalent to `(v.^2)./R`. Although the rules of precedence are unambiguous here, we can always put parentheses around quantities if we are unsure how MATLAB will interpret our commands.

Example 2.3–3   Maximum power transfer in a speaker-amplifier system

In many engineering systems an electrical power source supplies current or voltage to a device called the "load." A common example is an amplifier-speaker system. The load is the speaker, which requires current from the amplifier to produce sound. Figure 2.3–3a shows the general representation of a source and load. The resistance R_L is that of the load. Figure 2.3–3b shows the circuit representation of the system. The source supplies a voltage v_S and a current i_S and has its own internal resistance R_S. For optimum efficiency, we want to maximize the power supplied to the speaker for given values of v_S and R_S. We can do so by properly selecting the value of the load resistance R_L.

Consider the specific case where the source resistance can be $R_S = 10, 15, 20,$ or $25\ \Omega$ and where the available load resistances are $R_L = 10, 15, 20, 25,$ and $30\ \Omega$. For a specific value of R_S, determine which value of R_L will maximize the power transfer.

(a)

(b)

Figure 2.3–3
An electrical power source and load. (a) Component diagram. (b) Equivalent circuit representation.

Solution:

To solve this problem, we first need to obtain a mathematical description, or "mathematical model," of the system. This model should describe the power supplied to the speaker in terms of v_S, R_S, and R_L. We can develop this model by applying basic circuit principles. Kirchhoff's voltage law (which is equivalent to the conservation of energy law) states that the sum of signed voltages around a loop must be zero. Thus

$$v_S - i_S R_S - i_S R_L = 0$$

We want to find v_L in terms of v_S, so we must eliminate the variable i_S. The first step is to solve this equation for i_S:

$$i_S = \frac{v_S}{R_S + R_L}$$

Then multiply both sides by R_L and use the voltage-current relation $v_L = R_L i_S$ to obtain

$$v_L = \frac{R_L}{R_S + R_L} v_S$$

The power consumed by the load is $P_L = i_S^2 R_L = v_L^2/R_L$. Using the relation between v_L and v_S we can express P_L in terms of v_S as

$$P_L = \frac{R_L}{(R_S + R_L)^2} v_S^2$$

To maximize P_L for a fixed value of v_S, we must maximize the ratio

$$r = \frac{R_L}{(R_S + R_L)^2}$$

Because we have a small number of allowable values for R_S and R_L, the most direct way to choose R_L is to compute the values of r for each combination of R_S and R_L. Because there are four possible values of R_S and five values of R_L, there are 4(5) = 20 combinations. We can use an array operation in MATLAB to compute r for each combination by defining two 5×4 matrices R_L and R_S. The five rows of R_L contain the five values of R_L, and its four columns are identical. The four columns of R_S contain the four values of R_S, and its five rows are identical. These matrices must have the same size so that we can perform element-by-element operations with them. Thus we define

$$\mathbf{R_L} = \begin{bmatrix} 10 & 10 & 10 & 10 \\ 15 & 15 & 15 & 15 \\ 20 & 20 & 20 & 20 \\ 25 & 25 & 25 & 25 \\ 30 & 30 & 30 & 30 \end{bmatrix} \qquad \mathbf{R_S} = \begin{bmatrix} 10 & 15 & 20 & 25 \\ 10 & 15 & 20 & 25 \\ 10 & 15 & 20 & 25 \\ 10 & 15 & 20 & 25 \\ 10 & 15 & 20 & 25 \end{bmatrix}$$

The MATLAB session follows.

```
>>a=[10;15;20;25;30];
>>R_L=[a,a,a,a];
>>b=[10,15,20,25];
>>R_S=[b;b;b;b;b];
>>r =R_L./((R_S+R_L).^2)
>>r =
    0.0250    0.0160    0.0111    0.0082
    0.0240    0.0167    0.0122    0.0094
    0.0222    0.0163    0.0125    0.0099
    0.0204    0.0156    0.0123    0.0100
    0.0188    0.0148    0.0120    0.0099
```

Each *column* in the matrix r corresponds to a specific value of R_S. Each *row* corresponds to a specific value of R_L. For example, the result 0.0163 in column 2, row 3 of r is the value of r for the second value of R_S ($R_S = 15$) and the third value of R_L ($R_L = 20$). We can and should check this result by hand. Using $R_S = 15$ and $R_L = 20$ in the formula, we obtain $r = 0.0163$, the same value computed by our program.

Thus for a specific value of R_S, say, $R_S = 15$, we can look down the corresponding column of r (i.e., column 2) and find the maximum value of r. The maximum value in column 2 is 0.0167, in row 2, which corresponds to the second value of R_L, namely, $R_L = 15$. Thus for $R_S = 15$, the value that maximizes r is $R_L = 15$.

We can have MATLAB do this calculation for us as follows.

```
>>[max_ratio, row] = max(r)
max_ratio =
    0.0250    0.0167    0.0125    0.0100
row =
    1    2    3    4
```

Recall that the rows correspond to $R_L = 10$, 15, 20, 25, and 30, respectively, and the columns correspond to $R_S = 10$, 15, 20, and 25. Thus the correct solution for column 1 is row 1, the solution for column 2 is row 2, and so on. This result tells us that if the given value of R_S is its first value ($R_S = 10$), then the correct choice for R_L is its first value ($R_L = 10$). Similarly, if the given value of R_S is its second value ($R_S = 15$), then the correct choice for R_L is its second value ($R_L = 15$), and so on. The following table shows the value of R_L that maximizes the power to the load for specific values of R_S:

R_S	R_L
10	10
15	15
20	20
25	25

These numerical results suggest that to maximize the power to the load we should choose $R_L = R_S$. This is, in fact, the general answer, which we can prove with calculus. As in this example, numerical results sometimes indicate a trend that suggests a more general result, which we can verify with higher-level mathematics.

Using Array Operations to Evaluate Multivariable Functions

We can generalize the trick we used in Example 2.3–3 as follows: To evaluate a function of two variables, say, $z = f(x, y)$, using array operations, for the values $x = x_1, x_2, \ldots, x_m$ and $y = y_1, y_2, \ldots, y_m$, define the $m \times n$ matrices:

$$\mathbf{x} = \begin{bmatrix} x_1 & x_1 & \cdots & x_1 \\ x_2 & x_2 & \cdots & x_2 \\ \vdots & \vdots & \vdots & \vdots \\ x_m & x_m & \cdots & x_m \end{bmatrix} \qquad \mathbf{y} = \begin{bmatrix} y_1 & y_2 & \cdots & y_n \\ y_1 & y_2 & \cdots & y_n \\ \vdots & \vdots & \vdots & \vdots \\ y_1 & y_2 & \cdots & y_n \end{bmatrix}$$

When the function $z = f(x, y)$ is evaluated in MATLAB using array operations, the resulting $m \times n$ matrix $\mathbf{z}$ has the elements $z_{ij} = f(x_i, y_j)$. We can extend this technique to functions of more than two variables by using multidimensional arrays (in MATLAB 5 only).

Test Your Understanding

T2.3–1 Given the matrices

$$\mathbf{A} = \begin{bmatrix} 21 & 27 \\ -18 & 8 \end{bmatrix} \qquad \mathbf{B} = \begin{bmatrix} -7 & -3 \\ 9 & 4 \end{bmatrix}$$

find their (a) array product, (b) array right division (**A** divided by **B**), and (c) **B** raised to the third power element by element.

Answers: (a) [-147, -81;-162, 32], (b) [-3, -9;-2, 2], and (c) [-343, -27;729, 64].

2.4

Matrix Operations

Matrix addition and subtraction are identical to array addition and subtraction. The corresponding matrix elements are summed or subtracted. However, matrix multiplication and division are not the same as array multiplication and division.

Multiplication of Vectors

Recall that vectors are simply matrices with one row or one column. Thus matrix multiplication and division procedures apply to vectors as well, and we will introduce matrix multiplication by considering the vector case first. The *vector dot product* $\mathbf{u} \cdot \mathbf{w}$ of the vectors $\mathbf{u}$ and $\mathbf{w}$ is a scalar and can be thought of as the perpendicular projection of $\mathbf{u}$ onto $\mathbf{w}$. It can be computed from $|\mathbf{u}||\mathbf{w}|\cos\theta$, where θ is the angle between the two vectors and $|\mathbf{u}|$, $|\mathbf{w}|$ are the magnitudes of the vectors. Thus if the vectors are parallel and in the same direction, $\theta = 0$ and $\mathbf{u} \cdot \mathbf{w} = |\mathbf{u}||\mathbf{w}|$. If the vectors are perpendicular, $\theta = 90°$ and thus $\mathbf{u} \cdot \mathbf{w} = 0$. Because the unit vectors $\mathbf{i}, \mathbf{j}$, and $\mathbf{k}$ have unit length:

$$\mathbf{i} \cdot \mathbf{i} = \mathbf{j} \cdot \mathbf{j} = \mathbf{k} \cdot \mathbf{k} = 1 \qquad \text{(2.4–1)}$$

Because the unit vectors are perpendicular:

$$\mathbf{i} \cdot \mathbf{j} = \mathbf{i} \cdot \mathbf{k} = \mathbf{j} \cdot \mathbf{k} = 0 \qquad \text{(2.4–2)}$$

Thus the vector dot product can be expressed in terms of unit vectors as

$$\mathbf{u} \cdot \mathbf{w} = (u_1\mathbf{i} + u_2\mathbf{j} + u_3\mathbf{k}) \cdot (w_1\mathbf{i} + w_2\mathbf{j} + w_3\mathbf{k})$$

Carrying out the multiplication algebraically and using properties (2.4–1) and (2.4–2), we obtain

$$\mathbf{u} \cdot \mathbf{w} = u_1w_1 + u_2w_2 + u_3w_3$$

The *matrix* product of a row vector **u** with a column vector **w** is defined in the same way as the vector dot product; the result is a scalar that is the sum of the products of the corresponding vector elements; that is,

$$[u_1 \ u_2 \ u_3] \begin{bmatrix} w_1 \\ w_2 \\ w_3 \end{bmatrix} = u_1 w_1 + u_2 w_2 + u_3 w_3$$

if each vector has three elements. Thus the result of multiplying a 1×3 vector times a 3×1 vector is a 1×1 array; that is, a scalar. This definition applies to vectors having any number of elements, as long as both vectors have the same number of elements. Thus

$$[u_1 \ u_2 \ u_3 \ \cdots \ u_n] \begin{bmatrix} w_1 \\ w_2 \\ w_3 \\ \cdots \\ w_n \end{bmatrix} = u_1 w_1 + u_2 w_2 + u_3 w_3 + \cdots + u_n w_n$$

if each vector has n elements. Thus the result of multiplying a $1 \times n$ vector times an $n \times 1$ vector is a 1×1 array; that is, a scalar.

Vector-Matrix Multiplication

Not all matrix products are scalars. To generalize the preceding multiplication to a column vector multiplied by a matrix, think of the matrix as being composed of row vectors. The scalar result of each row-column multiplication forms an element in the result, which is a column vector:

$$\begin{bmatrix} a_{11} & a_{12} \\ a_{21} & a_{22} \end{bmatrix} \begin{bmatrix} x_1 \\ x_2 \end{bmatrix} = \begin{bmatrix} a_{11}x_1 + a_{12}x_2 \\ a_{21}x_1 + a_{22}x_2 \end{bmatrix}$$

For example:

$$\begin{bmatrix} 2 & 7 \\ 6 & -5 \end{bmatrix} \begin{bmatrix} 3 \\ 9 \end{bmatrix} = \begin{bmatrix} 2(3) + 7(9) \\ 6(3) - 5(9) \end{bmatrix} = \begin{bmatrix} 69 \\ -27 \end{bmatrix} \qquad \textbf{(2.4–3)}$$

Thus the result of multiplying a 2×2 matrix times a 2×1 vector is a 2×1 array; that is, a column vector. Note that the definition of multiplication requires that the number of columns in the matrix be equal to the number of rows in the vector. In general, the product **Ax**, where **A** has p columns, is defined only if **x** has p rows. If **A** has m rows and **x** is a column vector, the result of **Ax** is a column vector with m rows.

Matrix-Matrix Multiplication

We can expand this definition of multiplication to include the product of two matrices **AB**. The number of columns in **A** must equal the number of rows in **B**. The row-column multiplications form column vectors, and these column vectors form the matrix result. The product **AB** has the same number of rows as **A** and the same number of columns as **B**. For example,

$$
\begin{bmatrix} 6 & -2 \\ 10 & 3 \\ 4 & 7 \end{bmatrix} \begin{bmatrix} 9 & 8 \\ -5 & 12 \end{bmatrix} = \begin{bmatrix} (6)(9) + (-2)(-5) & (6)(8) + (-2)(12) \\ (10)(9) + (3)(-5) & (10)(8) + (3)(12) \\ (4)(9) + (7)(-5) & (4)(8) + (7)(12) \end{bmatrix}
$$

$$
= \begin{bmatrix} 64 & 24 \\ 75 & 116 \\ 1 & 116 \end{bmatrix} \qquad \textbf{(2.4–4)}
$$

Use the operator * to perform matrix multiplication in MATLAB. The following MATLAB session shows how to perform the matrix multiplication shown in (2.4–4).

```
>>A = [6,-2;10,3;4,7];
>>B = [9,8;-5,12];
>>A*B;
ans =
    64    24
    75   116
     1   116
```

Array multiplication is defined for the following product:

$$
[3\ 1\ 7][4\ 6\ 5] = [12\ 6\ 35]
$$

However, this product is *not* defined for *matrix* multiplication, because the first matrix has three columns, but the second matrix does not have three rows. Thus if we were to type [3, 1, 7]*[4, 6, 5] in MATLAB, we would receive an error message.

The following product is defined in matrix multiplication and gives the result shown:

$$
\begin{bmatrix} x_1 \\ x_2 \\ x_3 \end{bmatrix} [y_1\ y_2\ y_3] = \begin{bmatrix} x_1y_1 & x_1y_2 & x_1y_3 \\ x_2y_1 & x_2y_2 & x_2y_3 \\ x_3y_1 & x_3y_2 & x_3y_3 \end{bmatrix}
$$

The following product is also defined:

$$
[10\ 6]\begin{bmatrix} 7 & 4 \\ 5 & 2 \end{bmatrix} = [10(7) + 6(5)\ \ 10(4) + 6(2)] = [100\ 52]
$$

Test Your Understanding

T2.4–1 Use MATLAB to compute the dot product of the following vectors:

$$
\mathbf{u} = 6\mathbf{i} - 8\mathbf{j} + 3\mathbf{k}
$$

$$
\mathbf{w} = 5\mathbf{i} + 3\mathbf{j} - 4\mathbf{k}
$$

Check your answer by hand. (Answer: −6)

T2.4–2 Use MATLAB to show that

$$\begin{bmatrix} 7 & 4 \\ -3 & 2 \\ 5 & 9 \end{bmatrix} \begin{bmatrix} 1 & 8 \\ 7 & 6 \end{bmatrix} = \begin{bmatrix} 35 & 80 \\ 11 & -12 \\ 68 & 94 \end{bmatrix}$$

Example 2.4–1 Manufacturing cost analysis

Table 2.4–1 shows the hourly cost of four types of manufacturing processes. It also shows the number of hours required of each process to produce three different products. Use matrices and MATLAB to solve the following. (a) Determine the cost of each process to produce one unit of product 1. (b) Determine the cost to make one unit of each product. (c) Suppose we produce 10 units of product 1, 5 units of product 2, and 7 units of product 3. Compute the total cost.

Table 2.4–1 Cost and time data for manufacturing processes

Process	Hourly cost ($)	Hours required to produce one unit		
		Product 1	Product 2	Product 3
Lathe	10	6	5	4
Grinding	12	2	3	1
Milling	14	3	2	5
Welding	9	4	0	3

Solution:

(a) The basic principle we can use here is that cost equals the hourly cost times the number of hours required. For example, the cost of using the lathe for product 1 is ($10/hr)(6 hrs) = $60, and so forth for the other three processes. If we define the row vector of hourly costs to be `hourly_costs` and define the row vector of hours required for product 1 to be `hours_1`, then we can compute the costs of each process for product 1 using *array* multiplication. In MATLAB the session is

```
>>hourly_cost = [10, 12, 14, 9];
>>hours_1 = [6, 2, 3, 4];
>>process_cost_1 = hourly_cost.*hours_1
process_cost_1 =
    60    24    42    36
```

These are the costs of each of the four processes to produce one unit of product 1.

(b) To compute the total cost of one unit of product 1, we can use the vectors `hourly_costs` and `hours_1` but apply *matrix* multiplication instead of array multiplication, because matrix multiplication sums the individual products. The matrix multiplication gives

$$[10 \ 12 \ 14 \ 9] \begin{bmatrix} 6 \\ 2 \\ 3 \\ 4 \end{bmatrix} = 10(6) + 12(2) + 14(3) + 9(4) = 162$$

We can perform similar multiplication for products 2 and 3, using the data in the table. For product 2:

$$[10 \ 12 \ 14 \ 9] \begin{bmatrix} 5 \\ 3 \\ 2 \\ 0 \end{bmatrix} = 10(5) + 12(2) + 14(3) + 9(0) = 114$$

For product 3:

$$[10 \ 12 \ 14 \ 9] \begin{bmatrix} 4 \\ 1 \\ 5 \\ 3 \end{bmatrix} = 10(4) + 12(1) + 14(5) + 9(3) = 149$$

These three operations could have been accomplished in one operation by defining a matrix whose columns are formed by the data in the last three columns of the table:

$$[10 \ 12 \ 14 \ 9] \begin{bmatrix} 6 & 5 & 4 \\ 2 & 3 & 1 \\ 3 & 2 & 5 \\ 4 & 0 & 3 \end{bmatrix} = \begin{bmatrix} 60 + 24 + 42 + 36 \\ 50 + 36 + 28 + \ 0 \\ 40 + 12 + 70 + 27 \end{bmatrix} = [162 \ 114 \ 149]$$

In MATLAB the session continues as follows. Remember that we must use the transpose operation to convert the row vectors into column vectors.

```
>>hours_2 = [5, 3, 2, 0];
>>hours_3 = [4, 1, 5, 3];
>>unit_cost = hourly_cost*[hours_1', hours_2', hours_3']
unit_cost =
    162    114    149
```

Thus the costs to produce one unit each of products 1, 2, and 3 is $162, $114, and $149, respectively.

(c) To find the total cost to produce 10, 5, and 7 units, respectively, we can use matrix multiplication:

$$[10 \ 5 \ 7] \begin{bmatrix} 162 \\ 114 \\ 149 \end{bmatrix} = 1620 + 570 + 1043 = 3233$$

In MATLAB the session continues as follows. Note the use of the transpose operator on the vector unit_cost.

```
>>units = [10, 5, 7];
>>total_cost = units*unit_cost'
total_cost =
   3233
```

The total cost is $3233.

The General Matrix Multiplication Case

We can state the general result for matrix multiplication as follows: Suppose A has dimension $m \times p$ and B has dimension $p \times q$. If C is the product AB, then C has dimension $m \times q$ and its elements are given by

$$c_{ij} = \sum_{k=1}^{p} a_{ik} b_{kj} \qquad (2.4\text{–}5)$$

for all $i = 1, 2, \ldots, m$ and $j = 1, 2, \ldots, q$. For the product to be defined, the matrices A and B must be *conformable;* that is, the number of *rows* in B must equal the number of *columns* in A. The product has the same number of rows as A and the same number of columns as B.

The algorithm defined by (2.4–5) is easy to remember. Each element in the ith row of A is multiplied by the corresponding element in the jth column of B. The sum of the products is the element c_{ij}. If we write the product AB in terms of the dimensions, as $(m \times p)(p \times q) = m \times q$, we can easily determine the dimensions of the product by "canceling" the inner dimensions (here p), which must be equal for the product to be defined.

Matrix multiplication does not have the commutative property; that is, in general, $AB \neq BA$. A simple example will demonstrate this fact:

$$AB = \begin{bmatrix} 6 & -2 \\ 10 & 3 \end{bmatrix} \begin{bmatrix} 9 & 8 \\ -12 & 14 \end{bmatrix} = \begin{bmatrix} 78 & 20 \\ 54 & 122 \end{bmatrix} \qquad (2.4\text{–}6)$$

whereas

$$BA = \begin{bmatrix} 9 & 8 \\ -12 & 14 \end{bmatrix} \begin{bmatrix} 6 & -2 \\ 10 & 3 \end{bmatrix} = \begin{bmatrix} 134 & 6 \\ 68 & 66 \end{bmatrix} \qquad (2.4\text{–}7)$$

Reversing the order of matrix multiplication is a common and easily made mistake.

The associative and distributive properties hold for matrix multiplication. The associative property states that

$$A(B + C) = AB + AC \qquad (2.4\text{–}8)$$

The distributive property states that

$$(AB)C = A(BC) \qquad (2.4\text{–}9)$$

T2.4–3 Use MATLAB to verify the results of equations (2.4–6) and (2.4–7).

Applications to Cost Analysis

Data on business operations are often recorded as tables. The data in these tables must often be analyzed in several ways. The elements in MATLAB matrices are similar to the cells in a spreadsheet, and MATLAB can perform many spreadsheet-type calculations for analyzing such tables.

Example 2.4–2 Product costs Table 2.4–2 shows the costs associated with a certain product, and Table 2.4–3 shows the production volume for the four quarters of the business year. Use MATLAB to find the quarterly costs for materials, labor, and transportation; the total material, labor, and transportation costs for the year; and the total quarterly costs.

Table 2.4–2 Product costs

Product	Unit costs ($ \times 10^3$)		
	Materials	Labor	Transportation
1	6	2	1
2	2	5	4
3	4	3	2
4	9	7	3

Table 2.4–3 Quarterly production volume

Product	Quarter 1	Quarter 2	Quarter 3	Quarter 4
1	10	12	13	15
2	8	7	6	4
3	12	10	13	9
4	6	4	11	5

Solution:

The costs are the product of the product's unit cost times the production volume. Thus we define two matrices: U contains the unit costs in Table 2.4–2 in thousands of dollars, and P contains the quarterly production data in Table 2.4–3.

```
>>U = [6, 2, 1;2, 5, 4;4, 3, 2;9, 7, 3];
>>P = [10, 12, 13, 15;8, 7, 6, 4;12, 10, 13, 9;6, 4, 11, 5];
```

Note that if we multiply the first column in U times the first column in P, we obtain the total materials cost for the first quarter. Similarly, multiplying the first column in U times the *second* column in P gives the total materials cost for the *second* quarter. Also, multiplying the second column in U times the first column in P gives the total *labor* cost for the first quarter, and so on. Extending this pattern, we can see that we must multiply the *transpose* of U times P. This multiplication gives the cost matrix C.

```
>>C = U'*P
```

The result is

$$\mathbf{C} = \begin{bmatrix} 178 & 162 & 241 & 179 \\ 138 & 117 & 172 & 112 \\ 84 & 72 & 96 & 64 \end{bmatrix}$$

Each column in **C** represents one quarter. The total first-quarter cost is the sum of the elements in the first column, the second-quarter cost is the sum of the second column, and so on. Thus because the sum command sums the columns of a matrix, the quarterly costs are obtained by typing:

```
>>Quarterly_Costs = sum(C)
```

The resulting vector, containing the quarterly costs in thousands of dollars, is [400 351 509 355]. Thus the total costs in each quarter are $400,000; $351,000; $509,000; and $355,000.

The elements in the first row of **C** are the material costs for each quarter; the elements in the second row are the labor costs, and those in the third row are the transportation costs. Thus to find the total material costs, we must sum across the first row of **C**. Similarly, the total labor and total transportation costs are the sums across the second and third rows of **C**. Because the sum command sums *columns,* we must use the transpose of **C**. Thus we type the following:

```
>>Category_Costs = sum(C')
```

The resulting vector, containing the category costs in thousands of dollars, is [760 539 316]. Thus the total material costs for the year are $760,000; the labor costs are $539,000; and the transportation costs are $316,000.

We displayed the matrix **C** only to interpret its structure. If we need not display **C**, the entire analysis would consist of only four command lines.

```
>>U = [6, 2, 1;2, 5, 4;4, 3, 2;9, 7, 3];
>>P = [10, 12, 13, 15;8, 7, 6, 4;12, 10, 13, 9;6, 4, 11, 5];
>>Quarterly_Costs = sum(U'*P)
Quarterly_Costs =
    400    351    509    355
```

```
>>Category_Costs = sum((U'*P)');
Category_Costs =
    760   539   316
```

This example illustrates the compactness of MATLAB commands.

Special Matrices

Two exceptions to the noncommutative property are the *null* matrix, denoted by **0**, and the *identity*, or *unity*, matrix, denoted **I**. The null matrix contains all zeros and is not the same as the empty matrix [ ], which has no elements. The identity matrix is a square matrix whose diagonal elements are all equal to one, with the remaining elements equal to zero. For example, the 2×2 identity matrix is

$$\mathbf{I} = \begin{bmatrix} 1 & 0 \\ 0 & 1 \end{bmatrix}$$

These matrices have the following properties:

$$\mathbf{0A} = \mathbf{A0} = \mathbf{0}$$

$$\mathbf{IA} = \mathbf{AI} = \mathbf{A}$$

MATLAB has specific commands to create several special matrices. Type help specmat to see the list of special matrix commands; also check Table 2.4–4. The identity matrix **I** can be created with the eye(n) command, where n is the desired dimension of the matrix. To create the 2×2 identity matrix, you type eye(2). Typing eye(size(A)) creates an identity matrix having the same dimension as the matrix **A**.

Sometimes we want to initialize a matrix to have all zero elements. The zeros command creates a matrix of all zeros. Typing zeros(n) creates an $n \times n$ matrix of zeros, whereas typing zeros(m,n) creates an $m \times n$ matrix of zeros. Typing zeros(size(A)) creates a matrix of all zeros having the same dimension as the matrix **A**. This type of matrix can be useful for applications in which we do not know the required dimension

Table 2.4–4 Special matrices

Command	Description
eye(n)	Creates an $n \times n$ identity matrix.
eye(size(A))	Creates an identity matrix the same size as the matrix **A**.
ones(n)	Creates an $n \times n$ matrix of ones.
ones(m,n)	Creates an $m \times n$ array of ones.
ones(size(A))	Creates an array of ones the same size as the array **A**.
zeros(n)	Creates an $n \times n$ matrix of zeros.
zeros(m,n)	Creates an $m \times n$ array of zeros.
zeros(size(A))	Creates an array of zeros the same size as the array **A**.

ahead of time. The syntax of the ones command is the same, except that it creates arrays filled with ones.

Matrix Operations **63**

Matrix Division

Matrix division is a more challenging topic than matrix multiplication. Matrix division uses both the right- and left-division operators, / and \, for various applications, a principal one being the solution of sets of linear algebraic equations. Chapter 5 covers matrix division and a related topic, the matrix inverse.

Matrix Exponentiation

Raising a matrix to a power is equivalent to repeatedly multiplying the matrix by itself, for example, $\mathbf{A}^2 = \mathbf{AA}$. This process requires the matrix to have the same number of rows as columns; that is, it must be a *square* matrix. MATLAB uses the symbol ^ for matrix exponentiation. To find $\mathbf{A}^2$, type A^2.

We can raise a scalar n to a matrix power $\mathbf{A}$, if $\mathbf{A}$ is square, by typing n^A, but the applications for such a procedure are in advanced courses. However, raising a matrix to a matrix power—that is, $\mathbf{A}^\mathbf{B}$—is not defined, even if $\mathbf{A}$ and $\mathbf{B}$ are square.

Note that if n is a scalar and if $\mathbf{B}$ and $\mathbf{C}$ are not square matrices, then the following operations are not defined and will generate an error message in MATLAB:

```
B^n
n^B
B^C
```

Special Products

Many applications in physics and engineering use the cross product and dot product—for example, calculations to compute moments and force components use these special products. If $\mathbf{A}$ and $\mathbf{B}$ are vectors with three elements, the cross-product command cross(A,B) computes the three-element vector that is the cross-product $\mathbf{A} \times \mathbf{B}$. If $\mathbf{A}$ and $\mathbf{B}$ are $3 \times n$ matrices, cross(A,B) returns a $3 \times n$ array whose columns are the cross-products of the corresponding columns in the $3 \times n$ arrays $\mathbf{A}$ and $\mathbf{B}$. For example, the moment $\mathbf{M}$ with respect to a reference point O due to the force $\mathbf{F}$ is given by $\mathbf{M} = \mathbf{r} \times \mathbf{F}$, where $\mathbf{r}$ is the position vector from the point O to the point where the force $\mathbf{F}$ is applied. To find the moment in MATLAB, you type M = cross(r,F).

The dot-product command dot(A,B) computes a row vector of length n whose elements are the dot products of the corresponding columns of the $m \times n$ arrays $\mathbf{A}$ and $\mathbf{B}$. To compute the component of the force $\mathbf{F}$ along the direction given by the vector $\mathbf{r}$, you type dot(F,r). Table 2.4–5 summarizes the dot and cross product commands.

Table 2.4–5 Special products

Command	Syntax
cross(A,B)	Computes a $3 \times n$ array whose columns are the cross products of the corresponding columns in the $3 \times n$ arrays **A** and **B**. Returns a three-element cross-product vector if **A** and **B** are three-element vectors.
dot(A,B)	Computes a row vector of length n whose elements are the dot products of the corresponding columns of the $m \times n$ arrays **A** and **B**.

2.5

Polynomials

MATLAB has some convenient vector-based tools for working with polynomials, which are used in many advanced courses and applications in engineering. Type help polyfun for more information on this category of commands. We will use the following notation to describe a polynomial:

$$f(x) = a_1 x^n + a_2 x^{n-1} + a_3 x^{n-2} + \cdots + a_{n-1} x^2 + a_n x + a_{n+1}$$

This polynomial is a function of x. Its *degree* or *order* is n, the highest power of x that appears in the polynomial. The a_i, $i = 1, 2, \ldots, n + 1$ are the polynomial's *coefficients*. We can describe a polynomial in MATLAB with a row vector whose elements are the polynomial's coefficients, *starting with the coefficient of the highest power of x*. This vector is $[a_1, a_2, a_3, \ldots, a_{n-1}, a_n, a_{n+1}]$. For example, the vector [4,-8,7,-5] represents the polynomial $4x^3 - 8x^2 + 7x - 5$.

Polynomial Algebra

To add two polynomials, add the arrays that describe their coefficients. If the polynomials are of different degrees, add zeros to the coefficient array of the lower-degree polynomial. For example, consider

$$f(x) = 9x^3 - 5x^2 + 3x + 7$$

whose coefficient array is f = [9,-5,3,7] and

$$g(x) = 6x^2 - x + 2$$

whose coefficient array is g = [6,-1,2]. The degree of $g(x)$ is one less that of $f(x)$. Therefore, to add $f(x)$ and $g(x)$, we append one zero to g to "fool" MATLAB into thinking $g(x)$ is a third-degree polynomial. That is, we type g = [0 g] to obtain [0,-6,-1,2] for g. This vector represents $g(x) = 0x^3 - 6x^2 - x + 2$. To add the polynomials, type h = f+g. The result is h = [9,1,2,9], which corresponds to $h(x) = 9x^3 + x^2 + 2x + 9$. Subtraction is done in a similar way.

To multiply a polynomial by a scalar, simply multiply the coefficient array by that scalar. For example, $5h(x)$ is represented by [45,5,10,45].

Multiplication of polynomials by hand can be tedious, and polynomial division is even more so, but these operations are easily done with MATLAB. Use the `conv` command (it stands for "convolve") to multiply polynomials and use the `deconv` command (`deconv` stands for "deconvolve") to perform synthetic division. Table 2.5–1 summarizes these commands.

The product of the polynomials $f(x)$ and $g(x)$ is

$$f(x)g(x) = (9x^3 - 5x^2 + 3x + 7)(6x^2 - x + 2)$$
$$= 54x^5 - 39x^4 + 41x^3 + 29x^2 - x + 14$$

Dividing $f(x)$ by $g(x)$ using synthetic division gives a quotient of

$$\frac{f(x)}{g(x)} = \frac{9x^3 - 5x^2 + 3x + 7}{6x^2 - x + 2} = 1.5x - 0.5833$$

with a remainder of $-0.5833x + 8.1667$. Here is the MATLAB session to perform these operations.

```
>>f = [9,-5,3,7];
>>g = [6,-1,2];
>>product = conv(f,g);
product =
    54    -39    41    29    -1    14
>>[quotient, remainder] = deconv(f,g)
quotient =
   ·1.5    -0.5833
remainder =
    0    0    -0.5833    8.1667
```

The `conv` and `deconv` commands do not require that the polynomials have the same degree, so we did not have to fool MATLAB as

Table 2.5–1   Polynomial commands

Command	Description
`conv(a,b)`	Computes the product of the two polynomials described by the coefficient arrays `a` and `b`. The two polynomials need not be the same degree. The result is the coefficient array of the product polynomial.
`[q,r] = deconv(num,den)`	Computes the result of dividing a numerator polynomial, whose coefficient array is `num`, by a denominator polynomial represented by the coefficient array `den`. The quotient polynomial is given by the coefficient array `q`, and the remainder polynomial is given by the coefficient array `r`.
`poly(r)`	Computes the coefficients of the polynomial whose roots are specified by the vector `r`. The result is a *row* vector that contains the polynomial's coefficients arranged in descending order of power.
`polyval(a,x)`	Evaluates a polynomial at specified values of its independent variable `x`, which can be a matrix or a vector. The polynomial's coefficients of descending powers are stored in the array `a`. The result is the same size as `x`.
`roots(a)`	Computes the roots of a polynomial specified by the coefficient array `a`. The result is a *column* vector that contains the polynomial's roots.

we did when adding the polynomials. Table 2.5–1 gives the general syntax for the `conv` and `deconv` commands.

The `polyval(a,x)` command evaluates a polynomial at specified values of its independent variable x, which can be a matrix or a vector. The polynomial's coefficient array is a. The result is the same size as x. For example, to evaluate the polynomial $f(x) = 9x^3 - 5x^2 + 3x + 7$ at the points $x = 0, 2, 4, \ldots, 10$, type

```
>>a = [9,-5,3,7];
>>x = [0:2:10];
>>f = polyval(a,x);
```

The resulting vector f contains six values that correspond to $f(0)$, $f(2), f(4), \ldots, f(10)$. These three commands can be combined into a single command:

```
>>f = polyval([9,-5,3,7],[0:2:10]);
```

Personal preference determines whether to combine terms in this way; some people think that the single, combined command is less readable than three separate commands.

In the next chapter you will see that the `polyval` command is very useful for plotting polynomials.

Polynomial Roots

The *roots* of the polynomial $f(x)$ are the values of x such that $f(x) = 0$. A polynomial of degree n has n roots. The roots can be real or complex. If the polynomial's *coefficients* are real, then any complex roots occur in *complex conjugate pairs*. This means, for example, that if $3 + 5i$ is a root, then $3 - 5i$ is also a root. A polynomial can have *repeated* or *multiple* roots. For example, the polynomial $x^3 + 19x^2 + 115x + 225$ has two repeated roots: $x = -5, -5$. Its third root is $x = -9$.

The *quadratic* formula gives the roots of the second-degree polynomial, $ax^2 + bx + c$, called the quadratic. The formula is

$$x = \frac{-b \pm \sqrt{b^2 - 4ac}}{2a}$$

Formulas exist for the roots of polynomials up to and including degree 4. However, these formulas are much more complicated to use than the quadratic formula. No formulas exist for degree 5 and higher, and so these polynomials must be solved numerically (which MATLAB does with a sophisticated search technique).

Polynomial roots can be found with the `roots(a)` command, where a is the polynomial's coefficient array. The result is a *column* vector that contains the polynomial's roots. For example, to find the roots of $x^3 - 7x^2 + 40x - 34$, the session is

```
>>a = [1,-7,40,-34];
>>roots(a)
ans =
   3.0000 + 5.000i
   3.0000 - 5.000i
   1.0000
```

The roots are $x = 1$ and $x = 3 \pm 5i$. You can also combine the two commands into the single command roots([1,-7,40,-34]). You can check the answer with the polyval command; to do so, continue the preceding session by typing polyval([1,-7,40,-34],ans). The result of this command is three values, all very close to zero, which indicates that the roots are correct within the accuracy MATLAB uses in its calculations.

The poly(r) command computes the coefficients of the polynomial whose roots are specified by the array r. The result is a *row* vector that contains the polynomial's coefficients. (Note that the roots command returns a *column* vector.) For example, to find the polynomial whose roots are 1 and $3 \pm 5i$, the session is

```
>>r = [1,3+5i,3-5i];
>>poly(r)
ans =
     1     -7     40     -34
```

The polynomial is $x^3 - 7x^2 + 40x - 34$. The two commands could have been combined into the single command poly([1,3+5i,3-5i]).

Example 2.5–1 Earthquake-resistant building design
Buildings designed to withstand earthquakes must have natural frequencies of vibration that are not close to the oscillation frequency of the ground motion. A building's natural frequencies are determined primarily by the masses of its floors and by the lateral stiffness of its supporting columns (which act like horizontal springs). We can find these frequencies by solving for the roots of a polynomial called the structure's *characteristic* polynomial. Figure 2.5–1 shows the exaggerated motion of the floors of a three-story building. For such a building, if each floor has a mass m and the columns have stiffness k, the polynomial is

$$f^6 - 5\alpha f^4 + 6\alpha^2 f^2 - \alpha^3 = 0$$

where $\alpha = k/4m\pi^2$. The building's natural frequencies in cycles per second are the positive roots of this equation. Find the building's natural frequencies in cycles per second for the case where $m = 4000$ kg and $k = 5 \times 10^6$ newtons per meter.

Floor

Floor

Columns

Floor

Figure 2.5–1
Simple vibration model
of a building subjected to
ground motion.

Ground Motion

Solution:

The MATLAB session is

```
>>k = 5e+6;
>>m = 1000;
>>alpha = k/(4*m*pi^2);
>>roots([1,0,-5*alpha,0,6*alpha^2,0,- alpha^3])
ans =
    20.2789
   -20.2789
    14.0335
   -14.0335
     5.0085
    -5.0085
```

Thus the frequencies, rounded to the nearest integer, are 20, 14, and 5 cycles per second.

Note that the polynomial here is missing the f^5, f^3, and f terms. Thus it can be written as the following cubic in terms of the variable $x = f^2$:

$$x^3 - 5\alpha x^2 + 6\alpha^2 x - \alpha^3 = 0$$

The command `roots([1,-5*alpha,6*alpha^2,- alpha^3])` gives the answers $x = 411.2348, 196.9377, 25.0849$, which correspond to $f = \sqrt{x} = 20, 14$, and 5 after being rounded to the nearest integer.

Test Your Understanding

T2.5–1 Use MATLAB to confirm that

$$(20x^3 - 7x^2 + 5x + 10)(4x^2 + 12x - 3) =$$
$$80x^5 + 212x^4 - 124x^3 + 121x^2 + 105x - 30$$

T2.5–2 Use MATLAB to confirm that

$$\frac{12x^3 + 5x^2 - 2x + 3}{3x^2 - 7x + 4} = 4x + 11$$

with a remainder of $59x - 41$.

T2.5–3 Use MATLAB to confirm that

$$\frac{6x^3 + 4x^2 - 5}{12x^3 - 7x^2 + 3x + 9} = 0.7108$$

when $x = 2$.

T2.5–4 Find the roots of $5x^3 + 167x^2 + 174x + 2135 = 0$. Use the `polyval` command to confirm your answer.

T2.5-5 Find the polynomial whose roots are $-2 \pm 5i$, -3, -3, and 10. Use the `polyval` command to confirm your answer.

2.6

Summary

You should now be able to perform basic operations and use arrays in MATLAB. For example, you should be able to

- Perform arithmetic operations.
- Create, address, and edit arrays.
- Perform array operations including addition, subtraction, multiplication, division, and exponentiation.
- Perform matrix operations including addition, subtraction, multiplication, division, and exponentiation.
- Perform polynomial algebra and root finding.

You should be careful to distinguish between array (or element by element) operations and matrix operations. Each has its own applications.

Table 2.6–1 Guide to commands introduced in Chapter 2

Special characters	Use
%	Designates a comment.
'	Transposes a matrix, creating complex conjugate elements.
. '	Transposes a matrix without creating complex conjugate elements.
;	Suppresses screen printing; also denotes a new row in an array.
:	Represents an entire row or column of an array.
. . .	Continues a line.

Tables	
Special variables and constants	Table 2.1–1
Scalar arithmetic operations	Table 2.1–2
Order of precedence	Table 2.1–3
Commands for managing the work session	Table 2.1–4
Array commands	Table 2.2–1
Element-by-element operations	Table 2.3–1
Special matrices	Table 2.4–4
Special products	Table 2.4–5
Polynomial commands	Table 2.5–1

Table 2.6–1 is a reference guide to all the MATLAB commands introduced in this chapter.

Key Terms with Page References

Absolute value, **41**
Array, **36**
Array addressing, **38**
Array operations, **44**
Array size, **36**
Column vector, **34**
Comment, **29**
Complex conjugate, **32**
Empty array, **39**
Identity matrix, **62**

Length, **41**
Magnitude, **41**
Matrix, **36**
Matrix operations, **44**
Null matrix, **62**
Precedence, **30**
Row vector, **34**
Scalar, **28**
Transpose, **34**

Problems

You can find the answers to problems marked with an asterisk at the end of the text.

Section 2.1

1.* Suppose that $x = 2$ and $y = 5$. Use MATLAB to compute the following:

a. $\dfrac{yx^3}{x - y}$

b. $\dfrac{3x}{2y}$

   c. $\dfrac{3}{2}xy$

   d. $\dfrac{x^5}{x^5 - 1}$

2. Suppose that $x = 3$ and $y = 4$. Use MATLAB to compute the following:

   a. $\left(1 - \dfrac{1}{x^5}\right)^{-1}$

   b. $3\pi x^2$

   c. $\dfrac{3y}{4x - 8}$

   d. $\dfrac{4(y - 5)}{3x - 6}$

3. Use MATLAB to compute the following:

   a. $(3 + 6i)(-7 - 9i)$

   b. $\dfrac{5 + 4i}{5 - 4i}$

   c. $\dfrac{3}{2}i$

   d. $\dfrac{3}{2i}$

4.* Suppose that $x = -7 - 5i$ and $y = 4 + 3i$. Use MATLAB to compute the following:

   a. $x + y$

   b. xy

   c. x/y

Section 2.2

5. a. Use two methods to create the vector x having 100 regularly spaced values starting at 5 and ending at 28.
   b. Use two methods to create the vector x having a regular spacing of 0.2 starting at 2 and ending at 14.
   c. Use two methods to create the vector x having 50 regularly spaced values starting at -2 and ending at 5.

6. a. Create the vector x having 50 logarithmically spaced values starting at 10 and ending at 1000.
   b. Create the vector x having 20 logarithmically spaced values starting at 10 and ending at 1000.

7.* Use MATLAB to create an array x having six values between 0 and 10 (including the endpoints 0 and 10). Create an array A whose first row contains the values $3x$ and whose second row contains the values $5x - 20$.

8. Repeat Problem 7 but make the first column of A contain the values $3x$ and the second column contain the values $5x - 20$.

9. Type this matrix in MATLAB and use MATLAB to answer the following questions:

$$A = \begin{bmatrix} 3 & 7 & -4 & 12 \\ -5 & 9 & 10 & 2 \\ 6 & 13 & 8 & 11 \\ 15 & 5 & 4 & 1 \end{bmatrix}$$

a. Create a vector v consisting of the elements in the second column of A.
b. Create a vector w consisting of the elements in the second row of A.

10. Type this matrix in MATLAB and use MATLAB to answer the following questions:

$$A = \begin{bmatrix} 3 & 7 & -4 & 12 \\ -5 & 9 & 10 & 2 \\ 6 & 13 & 8 & 11 \\ 15 & 5 & 4 & 1 \end{bmatrix}$$

a. Create a 4×3 array B consisting of all elements in the second through fourth columns of A.
b. Create a 3×4 array C consisting of all elements in the second through fourth rows of A.
c. Create a 2×3 array D consisting of all elements in the first two rows and the last three columns of A.

11.* Compute the length and absolute value of the following vectors:
a. x = [2, 4, 7]
b. y = [2, -4, 7]
c. z = [5+3i, -3+4i, 2-7i]

12. Given the matrix

$$A = \begin{bmatrix} 3 & 7 & -4 & 12 \\ -5 & 9 & 10 & 2 \\ 6 & 13 & 8 & 11 \\ 15 & 5 & 4 & 1 \end{bmatrix}$$

a. Find the maximum and minimum values in each column.
b. Find the maximum and minimum values in each row.

13. Given the matrix

$$A = \begin{bmatrix} 3 & 7 & -4 & 12 \\ -5 & 9 & 10 & 2 \\ 6 & 13 & 8 & 11 \\ 15 & 5 & 4 & 1 \end{bmatrix}$$

a. Sort each column and store the result in an array B.
b. Sort each row and store the result in an array C.
c. Add each column and store the result in an array D.
d. Add each row and store the result in an array E.

14. (for MATLAB 5 only)

a. Create a three-dimensional array **D** whose three "layers" are these matrices:

$$\mathbf{A} = \begin{bmatrix} 3 & -2 & 1 \\ 6 & 8 & -5 \\ 7 & 9 & 10 \end{bmatrix} \quad \mathbf{B} = \begin{bmatrix} 6 & 9 & -4 \\ 7 & 5 & 3 \\ -8 & 2 & 1 \end{bmatrix} \quad \mathbf{C} = \begin{bmatrix} -7 & -5 & 2 \\ 10 & 6 & 1 \\ 3 & -9 & 8 \end{bmatrix}$$

b. Use MATLAB to find the largest element in each layer of **D** and the largest element in **D**.

Section 2.3

15.* Given the matrices

$$\mathbf{A} = \begin{bmatrix} -7 & 16 \\ 4 & 9 \end{bmatrix} \quad \mathbf{B} = \begin{bmatrix} 6 & -5 \\ 12 & -2 \end{bmatrix} \quad \mathbf{C} = \begin{bmatrix} -3 & -9 \\ 6 & 8 \end{bmatrix}$$

Use MATLAB to:
a. Find **A** + **B** + **C**.
b. Find **A** − **B** + **C**.
c. Verify the associative law

$$(\mathbf{A} + \mathbf{B}) + \mathbf{C} = \mathbf{A} + (\mathbf{B} + \mathbf{C})$$

d. Verify the commutative law

$$\mathbf{A} + \mathbf{B} + \mathbf{C} = \mathbf{B} + \mathbf{C} + \mathbf{A} = \mathbf{A} + \mathbf{C} + \mathbf{B}$$

16.* Given the matrices

$$\mathbf{A} = \begin{bmatrix} 64 & 32 \\ 24 & -16 \end{bmatrix} \quad \mathbf{B} = \begin{bmatrix} 16 & -4 \\ 6 & -2 \end{bmatrix}$$

Use MATLAB to:
a. Find the result of **A** times **B** using the array product.
b. Find the result of **A** divided by **B** using array right division.
c. Find **B** raised to the third power element by element.

17.* The mechanical work W done in using a force F to push a block through a distance D is $W = FD$. The following table gives data on the amount of force used to push a block through the given distance over five segments of a certain path. The force varies because of the differing friction properties of the surface.

	Path segment				
	1	2	3	4	5
Force (N)	400	550	700	500	600
Distance (m)	2	0.5	0.75	1.5	3

Use MATLAB to find (a) the work done on each segment of the path and (b) the total work done over the entire path.

18. The following table shows the hourly wages, hours worked, and output (number of widgets produced) in one week for five widget makers.

	Worker				
	1	2	3	4	5
Hourly wage ($)	5	5.50	6.50	6	6.25
Hours worked	40	43	37	50	45
Output (widgets)	1000	1100	1000	1200	1100

Use MATLAB to answer these questions:
a. How much did each worker earn in the week?
b. What is the total salary amount paid out?
c. How many widgets were made?
d. What is the average cost to produce one widget?
e. How many hours does it take to produce one widget on average?
f. Assuming that the output of each worker has the same quality, which worker is the most efficient? Which is the least efficient?

19. The potential energy stored in a spring is $kx^2/2$, where k is the spring constant and x is the compression in the spring. The force required to compress the spring is kx. The following table gives the data for five springs:

	Spring				
	1	2	3	4	5
Force (N)	11	7	8	10	9
Spring constant k (N/m)	1000	800	900	1200	700

Use MATLAB to find (a) the compression x in each spring and (b) the potential energy stored in each spring.

20. A company must purchase five kinds of material. The following table gives the price the company pays per ton for each material, along with the number of tons purchased in the months of May, June, and July:

Material	Price ($/ton)	Quantity purchased (tons)		
		May	June	July
1	300	5	4	6
2	550	3	2	4
3	400	6	5	3
4	250	3	5	4
5	500	2	4	3

Use MATLAB to answer these questions:

a. Create a 5 × 3 matrix containing the amounts spent on each item for each month.

b. What is the total spent in May? in June? in July?

c. What is the total spent on each material in the three-month period?

d. What is the total spent on all materials in the three-month period?

Section 2.4

21.* Use MATLAB to find the products **AB** and **BA** for the following matrices:

$$A = \begin{bmatrix} 11 & 5 \\ -9 & -4 \end{bmatrix} \quad B = \begin{bmatrix} -7 & -8 \\ 6 & 2 \end{bmatrix}$$

22. Given the matrices

$$A = \begin{bmatrix} 3 & -2 & 1 \\ 6 & 8 & -5 \\ 7 & 9 & 10 \end{bmatrix} \quad B = \begin{bmatrix} 6 & 9 & -4 \\ 7 & 5 & 3 \\ -8 & 2 & 1 \end{bmatrix} \quad C = \begin{bmatrix} -7 & -5 & 2 \\ 10 & 6 & 1 \\ 3 & -9 & 8 \end{bmatrix}$$

Use MATLAB to:

a. Verify the associative property

$$A(B + C) = AB + AC$$

b. Verify the distributive property

$$(AB)C = A(BC)$$

23. The following tables show the costs associated with a certain product and the production volume for the four quarters of the business year. Use MATLAB to find (a) the quarterly costs for materials, labor, and transportation; (b) the total material, labor, and transportation costs for the year; and (c) the total quarterly costs.

Product	Unit product costs ($ × 10³)		
	Materials	Labor	Transportation
1	7	3	2
2	3	1	3
3	9	4	5
4	2	5	4
5	6	2	1

Product	Quarterly production volume			
	Quarter 1	Quarter 2	Quarter 3	Quarter 4
1	16	14	10	12
2	12	15	11	13
3	8	9	7	11
4	14	13	15	17
5	13	16	12	18

24.* Aluminum alloys are made by adding other elements to aluminum to improve its properties, such as hardness or tensile strength. The following table shows the composition of five commonly used alloys, which are known by their alloy numbers (2024, 6061, and so on) [Kutz, 1986]. Obtain a matrix algorithm to compute the amounts of raw materials needed to produce a given amount of each alloy. Use MATLAB to determine how much raw material of each type is needed to produce 1000 tons of each alloy.

Composition of aluminum alloys					
Alloy	%Cu	%Mg	%Mn	%Si	%Zn
2024	4.4	1.5	0.6	0	0
6061	0	1	0	0.6	0
7005	0	1.4	0	0	4.5
7075	1.6	2.5	0	0	5.6
356.0	0	0.3	0	7	0

25. Vectors with three elements can represent position, velocity, and acceleration. A mass of 5 kg, which is 3 meters away from the x-axis, starts at $x = 2$ meters and moves with a speed of 10 meters per second parallel to the y-axis. Its velocity is thus described by $\mathbf{v} = [0, 10, 0]$, and its position is described by $\mathbf{r} = [2, 10t + 3, 0]$. Its angular momentum vector $\mathbf{L}$ is found from $\mathbf{L} = m(\mathbf{r} \times \mathbf{v})$, where m is the mass. Use MATLAB to:

   a. Compute a matrix $\mathbf{P}$ whose 11 rows are the values of the position vector $\mathbf{r}$ evaluated at the times $t = 0, 0.5, 1, 1.5, \ldots 5$ seconds.
   b. What is the location of the mass when $t = 5$ seconds?
   c. Compute the angular momentum vector $\mathbf{L}$. What is its direction?

26.* The *scalar triple product* computes the magnitude M of the moment of a force vector $\mathbf{F}$ about a specified line. It is $M = (\mathbf{r} \times \mathbf{F}) \cdot \mathbf{n}$, where $\mathbf{r}$ is the position vector from the line to the point of application of the force and $\mathbf{n}$ is a unit vector in the direction of the line.

   Use MATLAB to compute the magnitude M for the case where $\mathbf{F} = [10, -5, 4]$ N, $\mathbf{r} = [-3, 7, 2]$ m, and $\mathbf{n} = [6, 8, -7]$.

Section 2.5

27. Use MATLAB to find the following product:

$$(10x^3 - 9x^2 - 6x + 12)(5x^3 - 4x^2 - 12x + 8)$$

28.* Use MATLAB to find the quotient and remainder of

$$\frac{14x^3 - 6x^2 + 3x + 9}{5x^2 + 7x - 4}$$

29.* Use MATLAB to evaluate

$$\frac{8x^3 - 9x^2 - 7}{10x^3 + 5x^2 - 3x - 7}$$

at $x = 5$.

30.* Use MATLAB to find the roots of $13x^3 + 182x^2 - 184x + 2503 = 0$. Use MATLAB to confirm your answer.

31.* Use MATLAB to find the polynomial whose roots are $3 \pm 6i$, 8, 8, and 20. Use MATLAB to confirm your answer.

32. Refer to Example 2.5–1. The polynomial equation that must be solved to find the natural frequencies of a particular building is

$$f^6 - 5\alpha f^4 + 6\alpha^2 f^2 - \alpha^3 = 0$$

where $\alpha = k/4m\pi^2$. Suppose $m = 5000$ kg. Consider three cases: (1) $k = 4 \times 10^6$ N/m; (2) $k = 5 \times 10^6$ N/m; and (3) $k = 6 \times 10^6$ N/m. Use MATLAB to answer these questions:

a. Which case has the smallest natural frequency?
b. Which case has the largest natural frequency?
c. Which case has the smallest spread between the natural frequencies?

Courtesy Henry Guckel/Dept. of Electrical Engineering, University of Wisconsin.

Engineering in the 21st Century . . .

Nanotechnology

While large-scale technology is attracting much public attention, many of the engineering challenges and opportunities in the 21st century will involve the development of extremely small devices and even the manipulation of individual atoms. This technology is called *nanotechnology* because it involves processing materials whose size is about 1 nanometer, which is 10^{-9} meter, or 1/1,000,000 of a millimeter. The distance between atoms in single-crystal silicon is 0.5 nanometer.

Nanotechnology is in its infancy, although some working devices have been created. The micromotor with gear train shown above has a dimension of approximately 10^{-4} meter. This device converts electrical input power into mechanical motion. It was constructed using the magnetic properties of electroplated metal films.

While we are learning how to make such devices, another challenge is to develop innovative applications for them. Many of the applications proposed thus far are medical; small pumps for drug delivery and surgical tools are two examples. Researchers at the Lawrence Livermore Laboratory have developed a microgripper tool to treat brain aneurysms. It is about the size of a grain of sand and was constructed from silicon cantilever beams powered by a shape-memory alloy actuator. To design and apply these devices, engineers must first model the appropriate mechanical and electrical properties. The features of MATLAB provide excellent support for such analyses.

78

3

Files, Functions, and Data Structures

Outline

So far we have illustrated the MATLAB interactive mode only. In this mode you type a command at the prompt, press **Enter,** and obtain your results immediately. However, MATLAB also uses several types of files. For example, if you perform many operations, you might want to keep a record of your commands and the results. MATLAB enables you to store this information in a *diary* file, which you can edit and print after you complete your session. For problems involving more than a few commands, or when you do not need the interactive response of the command line, it is sometimes more convenient to store your commands in a *script* file, which can be saved for later use. When you execute the script file, all the commands in it are processed in sequence just as if

79

they were entered at the command prompt. Files can also store data for analysis with MATLAB. We discuss the creation and use of such files in this chapter.

MATLAB has many built-in functions, including trigonometric, logarithmic, and hyperbolic functions, as well as functions for processing arrays. In addition, you can define your own functions with a *function* file, and you can use them just as conveniently as the built-in functions. We explain this technique in section 3.5.

MATLAB 5 introduced two new data structures: *cell* arrays and *structure* arrays. These data structures enable one array to store different types of data (for example, string data, real numbers, and complex numbers). With cell arrays you can access such data by its location, but with structure arrays you can access it by name also. This feature enables you to create and use data bases having different types of information (for example, a list of people with their addresses and phone numbers). We introduce these new structures in sections 3.6 and 3.7.

3.1

Using Files

M-FILES

MAT-FILES

ASCII FILES

DATA FILE

The three types of files we will be using are M-files, MAT-files, and data files. M-files have the extension .m, such as file1.m, and are used for MATLAB programs and for some MATLAB functions. M-files are discussed in sections 3.2 and 3.5. MAT-files have the extension .mat and are used to save the names and values of variables created during a MATLAB session. We discuss MAT-files in this section.

ASCII files are files written in a specific format designed to make them usable to a wide variety of software. The ASCII abbreviation stands for American Standard Code for Information Interchange. M-files are ASCII files that are written in the MATLAB language. Because they are ASCII files, M-files can be created using just about any word processor—generically called a text editor—because the ASCII file format is the basic format that all word processing programs can recognize and create. M-files are machine independent. MAT-files are *binary* files, not ASCII files. Binary files are generally readable only by the software that created them, so you cannot read a MAT-file with a word processor, for example. In general, transferring binary files between machine types (MS Windows and Macintosh, for example) is not easy. However, MAT-files contain a machine signature that allows them to be transferred. Binary files provide more compact storage than ASCII files.

The third type of file we will be using is a data file, specifically an ASCII data file, that is, one created according to the ASCII format. You may need to use MATLAB to analyze data stored in such a file created by a spreadsheet program, a word processor, or a laboratory data acquisition system or in a file you share with someone else. A typical ASCII data file has one or more lines of text at the beginning. These might be comments that describe what the data represents, the date it was created, and who created the data, for example. These lines are called the *header*. One or more lines of data, arranged in rows and columns, follow the header. The numbers in each row might be separated by spaces or by commas. In this section we will discuss how to use such data files with MATLAB.

Directories and Search Path

It is important to know the location of the files you use with MATLAB. This requirement frequently causes problems for beginners. Suppose you use MATLAB on your home computer and save an M-file or a MAT-file to a floppy disk, as discussed later in this section. If you want to use that disk with MATLAB on another computer, say, in a school's computer lab, you must make sure that MATLAB knows how to find your files.

Files are stored in *directories*, which are called *folders* on some computer systems. Every directory has a name; for example, if MATLAB was installed on drive c:, the main MATLAB directory is c:\matlab on MS Windows systems. The M-file matlabrc.m, which is the startup file, is stored in this directory. Directories can have subdirectories below them. For example, the MATLAB program itself, matlab.exe, is stored in the subdirectory \bin under the directory c:\matlab. The *path* to this subdirectory is c:\matlab\bin. The path tells you and MATLAB how to find a particular file. In fact, the full name of a file consists of its path and its name; for example, c:\matlab\bin\matlab.exe.

DIRECTORIES

SEARCH PATH

Working with Floppy Disks

Suppose you saved the M-file problem1.m in the directory \homework on a floppy disk that you insert in drive a:. The path for this file is a:\homework. As MATLAB is normally installed, when you type problem1, the following activity occurs:

1. MATLAB determines whether problem1 is a variable; if so, MATLAB displays the value.
2. If not, MATLAB determines whether problem1 is one of its own built-in commands; if so, MATLAB executes the command.
3. If not, MATLAB looks in the directory c:\matlab, where the M-files are normally stored, and executes problem1 if it is there.
4. If not, MATLAB searches the directories in the search path to find problem1 and execute it.

You can display the search path by typing path. If problem1 is on the floppy disk only and if directory a: is not in the search path, MATLAB does not find the file and generates an error message. However, you tell MATLAB where to look by typing cd a:\homework, which stands for "change directory to a:\homework." This command forces MATLAB to look in the correct directory to find your file. The general syntax of this command is cd dirname, where dirname is the full path to the directory. The *main* directory on the floppy disk is a:, so if your file is in the main directory, be sure to include the colon and type cd a:.

An alternative to this procedure is to copy your file to the hard drive (in directory c:\matlab). However, this approach has several pitfalls: (1) If you change the file during your session, you might forget to copy the revised file back to your floppy disk, (2) the hard drive becomes cluttered (this problem often occurs in public computer labs), and (3) someone else can copy your work! You can determine the *current,* or *working,* directory (the one where MATLAB looks for your file) by typing pwd. To see a list of all the files in the current directory, type dir. To see the files in the directory dirname, type dir dirname. If any M-files or MAT-files are in the current directory, the what command displays a list of them. The what dirname command does the same for the directory dirname.

Recording Your Session

You can keep a log of your interactive sessions in a *diary* file by using the diary command. Type diary to store all your succeeding keystrokes (including your mistakes!) and the MATLAB responses in the ASCII file diary. (except for graphs). You can display this file later by typing type diary. (Be sure to include the period [.], or MATLAB, thinking you want to type the *command* diary, will give you an error message.) You can also load the diary. file into a word processor for editing (to remove your mistakes!) and for inclusion in another document, perhaps a report. Type diary again, or diary off, to stop the recording. Note that you cannot retrieve anything that appeared before you started the diary.

MATLAB will write over the diary file the next time you record a session, but you can save the diary in another file by typing diary filename to start recording the session in the file filename. The session is stored in an ASCII text file that any word processor can read. If you type diary off to stop recording and later type diary on, MATLAB appends the remainder of the session to the end of the file.

You can use the operator (%) to insert comments to document your log, and you can use the date command to insert the current date into the log.

Saving and Retrieving Your Workspace Variables

You cannot use a file created with the diary command to read into MATLAB the names and values of the variables you used in a session. Therefore, if you want to stop using MATLAB but continue the session at a later time, you must use the `save` and `load` commands. Typing `save` causes MATLAB to save the workspace variables, that is, the variable names, their sizes, and their values, in a binary file called `matlab.mat`, which MATLAB can read. To retrieve your workspace variables, type `load`. You can then continue your session as before. Of course, if you exited MATLAB after using the `save` command, you cannot recover your keystrokes or the MATLAB responses. These will be stored in the diary file. To save the workspace variables in another file named `filename.mat`, type `save filename`. To load the workspace variables, type `load filename`.

To load the workspace variables, the filename must have the extension `.mat` or no extension at all. If the filename does not have an extension, MATLAB assumes that it is `.mat`.

To save just some of your variables, say, `var1` and `var2`, in the file `filename.mat`, type `save filename var1 var2`. You need not type the variable names to retrieve them; just type `load filename`.

You can save the variables in ASCII single-precision (eight digits) format by typing `save filename -ASCII`. To save the variables in ASCII double-precision (16 digits) format, type `save filename -double`. ASCII files containing single-precision data are recognizable by their use of the E format to represent numbers. For example, the number 1.249×10^2 is represented as `1.249E+002`. ASCII files containing double-precision data use the D format; for example, `1.249D+002`.

Reading Data from Externally Generated Files

As explained in Chapter 2, you can enter data into MATLAB by typing it into an array. Or as the next section explains, you can enter and store the data in an M-file. However, either method is inconvenient when you have a lot of data. Such data is often generated by some other application. For example, you might be given a data file generated by a spreadsheet program, or you might have to analyze data collected by a laboratory instrumentation system. Many applications support the ASCII file format, so you are likely to receive a data file stored in this format. If the file has a header or the data is separated by commas, MATLAB will produce an error message. To correct this situation, first load the data file into a text editor, remove the header, and replace the commas with spaces (the number of spaces does not matter as long as there is at least one). To retrieve this data into MATLAB, type `load filename`. If the file has m lines with n values in each line, the data will be assigned to an $m \times n$ matrix having the same name as the file with the extension stripped off. For example, if your data file contains 10 lines and three columns of data and is named `force.dat`, typing `load force.dat` creates the 10×3

Table 3.1–1 System Commands

Command	Description
cd dirname	Changes the current directory to dirname.
date	Displays the date as a string using the format dd-mmm-yy.
diary	Stores the remainder of the work session in the file diary. Also switches off the diary recording if it is on.
diary filename	Stores the remainder of the work session in the file filename.
diary off	Switches off the diary recording.
diary on	Switches on the diary recording in the current diary file.
path	Displays the MATLAB directory search path.
pwd	Displays the current directory.

matrix force, which you can use in your MATLAB session just as you would use any other variable. Your data file can have any extension except .mat, so that MATLAB will not try to load the file as a workspace file.

Some spreadsheet programs store data in the .wk1 format. You can use the command M = wk1read('filename') to import this data into MATLAB and store it in the matrix M. You can use the MATLAB fopen and fread commands to load data files created by applications in their own special format. We do not cover this specialized topic.

Tables 3.1–1 and 3.1–2 summarize the commands discussed in this section.

Table 3.1–2 File Commands

Command	Description
delete filename	Deletes the file filename.
dir	Lists all files in the current directory.
dir dirname	Lists all files in the directory dirname.
load	Loads all the workspace variables from the file matlab.mat.
load filename	Loads all the workspace variables from the file filename.mat.
load filename.ext	Loads the data in the ASCII file filename.ext into a matrix named filename.
save	Saves all the workspace variables in the file matlab.mat.
save filename	Saves all the workspace variables in the file filename.mat.
save filename variables	Saves the workspace variables listed in variables in the file filename.mat.
save filename keywords	Saves the variables in the file filename.mat in ASCII format, using the characteristics specified in keywords, which may be -ascii for 8 digits, -double for 16 digits, and/or -tabs to separate the data with tab stops.
type filename	Displays the contents of the file filename. If no extension is used, MATLAB displays the file filename.m. Use type diary. to display the diary file.
what	Lists all MATLAB files in the current directory.
what dirname	Lists all MATLAB files in the directory dirname on the MATLAB search path.
M = wk1read('filename')	Reads a .wk1 spreadsheet file and stores it the matrix M.

T3.1–1 **1.** Start recording a diary session in the file `diary1.txt`.
   2. Enter the vectors `x = [1:5]` and `y = [0:2:8]` into MATLAB and compute the array product `x.*y`.
   3. Save the workspace variables in the file `session1` and type `clear x y` to confirm that these variables no longer exist.
   4. Load the file `session1` and type `x.*y` to confirm that these variables exist.
   5. Turn off the diary session and type `type diary1.txt` to display the session log.

3.2
Script Files

You can perform operations in MATLAB in two ways:

1. By using the interactive mode, in which all commands are entered directly in the Command window.
2. By running a MATLAB program stored in an M-file. This type of file has MATLAB commands in it so that running such a file is equivalent to typing all the commands—one at a time—at the command line. You can run the file by typing its name at the command line or by selecting **Run M-file** from the **File** menu.

Using the interactive mode is very similar to using a calculator, but it is convenient only for simpler problems. When the problem requires many commands, has arrays with many elements, or you need to repeat a set of commands several times, the interactive mode is inconvenient. Fortunately, MATLAB allows you to write your own programs to avoid this difficulty. You write and save MATLAB programs in M-files. MATLAB uses two types of M-files: *script* files and *function* files. A *script file* contains a sequence **SCRIPT FILE** of MATLAB commands and is useful when you need to use many commands or arrays with many elements. Because they contain commands, script files are sometimes called *command* files. You execute a script file at the command-line prompt by typing its name without the extension `.m`. Another type of M-file is a *function file*, which is useful when you need to repeat a set of commands several times. We discuss function files in section 3.5.

Script files may contain any valid MATLAB commands, including user-written functions. Typing the name of a script file at the command-line prompt gives the same results as typing at the command prompt all the commands stored in the script file, one at a time. When you type the name of the script file, you are

GLOBAL VARIABLE

"running the file," or "executing the file." The values of variables produced by running a script file are available in the workspace; thus we say the script file's variables are "global."

Creating and Using a Script File

Here is a simple example that illustrates how to create, save, and run a script file. The exact procedure for creating and saving files depends on the MATLAB version, the operating system (MS Windows, Macintosh, UNIX, or VMS), and the text editor you use. You need to know how to open, edit, and save a file with the text editor you are using. You also need to make sure your editor saves the file in a directory that is in the MATLAB search path. If you use the following procedure, your file will be saved in the correct directory.

This simple script file computes the matrix **C** = **AB** and displays it on the screen.

```
% Program 'prod_abc.m'
% This program computes the matrix product C = A*B, and
% displays the result.
A = [1,4;2,5];
B = [3,6;1,2];
C = A*B
```

To create this new M-file:

- In the MS Windows or Macintosh environment, select **New** from the **File** menu and then select **M-file**. You will see a new edit window. On MS Windows systems this window is the **Notepad** edit window with MATLAB 4 and the **M-file Editor/Debugger** window with MATLAB 5. The Macintosh screen is similar.
- In the UNIX environment, type `!vi prod_abc.m` or `!emacs prod_abc.m` at the MATLAB prompt to open an edit window in either the **vi** editor or the **emacs** editor.

Type in the script file as shown in the preceding example, using the editing commands of the particular editor you are using. Follow these instructions to save the file under the name `prod_abc.m`:

- In the MS Windows or Macintosh environment, select **Save As...** from the **File** menu. In the dialog box that appears, type the name of the document as `prod_abc.m`. You must save the file in the MATLAB current working directory or folder. For example, on MS Windows systems, this can be the floppy disk in drive a:. In this case you can either select drive a: in the dialog box or name the file `a:prod_abc.m` before saving. Click on **Save** to save the file. Then click on **File, Exit** to exit the editor and return to the MATLAB command window. (If you save the file on a floppy drive, be sure to make that drive the working directory by typing `cd a:` on MS Windows systems, for example.)

- In the UNIX environment, write and save the file using the appropriate commands of the editor you are using. Then quit the editor and return to MATLAB.

In the MATLAB command window type the script file's name `prod_abc` to execute the program. You should see the result displayed in the command window. The session looks like

```
>>prod_abc
C =
    7    14
   11    22
```

Figure 3.2–1 shows a MATLAB 4 MS Windows screen containing the resulting Command window display and the Notepad editor opened to display the script file. The Macintosh screen is similar except that the text editor is not Notepad. Figure 3.2–2 shows the MATLAB 5 screen with the M-file Editor.

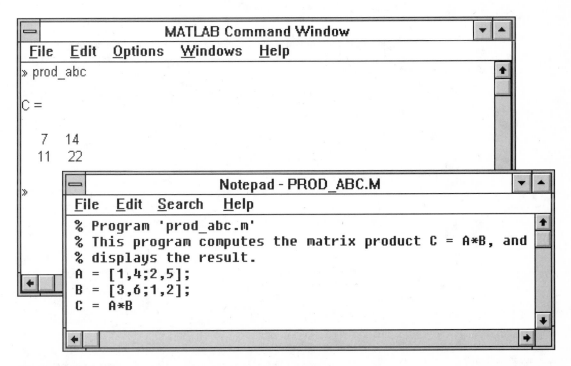

Figure 3.2–1
The MATLAB 4 Command window with the Notepad editor open.

Effective Use of Script Files

Here are some things to keep in mind when using script files:

1. The name of a script file must follow the MATLAB convention for naming variables; that is, the name must begin with a letter and may include digits and the underscore character, up to 19 characters.

2. Do not give a script file the same name as a variable it computes, because MATLAB will not be able to execute that script file more than once unless you clear the variable. Recall that typing a variable's name at the command prompt causes MATLAB to display the value of that variable. If there is no variable by that name, then MATLAB looks for a script file having that name. For example, if we had created the variable prod_abc = C(3,2) in the preceding script file having that name, then after the file is executed the first time, the variable prod_abc exists in the MATLAB workspace. If you modify the script file and run it a second time, MATLAB will display the value of prod_abc and will not execute the script file.

Figure 3.2–2
The MATLAB 5 Command window with the M-file Editor/Debugger window open.

3. Do not give a script file the same name as a MATLAB command or function. You can check to see whether a command, function, or filename already exists by using the `exist` command. For example, to see whether `prod_abc` already exists, type `exist('prod_abc')` *before* creating the file. This command returns one of the following values:
   - 0 if nothing has that name.
   - 1 if a variable has that name.
   - 2 if either a variable or an M-file has that name.
   - 3 if a MEX-file has that name (MEX-files are an advanced topic not covered in this text).
   - 4 if a compiled SIMULINK function has that name (SIMULINK is a simulation program not treated in this text).
   - 5 if a built-in MATLAB function has that name.

   The command `what` gives a directory listing of files.

4. As in interactive mode, all variables created by a script file are global variables and are left in the workspace. You can type `who` to see what variables are present. Typing `whos` instead gives a list of the variables present, their sizes, and whether or not they have nonzero imaginary parts.

5. Because all the variables in a script file are global, consider using a function file if you do not need access to all the variables. This approach avoids cluttering the workspace with variable names and reduces memory requirements.

6. You can use the `type` command to view an M-file without opening it with a text editor. For example, to view the file `prod_abc`, the command is `type prod_abc`.

Effective Use of the Command and Editor Windows

Here are some tips for using the Command and M-file Editor windows effectively:

- You can use the mouse to resize and move windows so that they can be viewed simultaneously. To activate a window, click on it.

- On MS Windows systems, use the **Alt-Tab** key combination to toggle quickly between the editor window and the Command window. Use the **up-arrow** key to retrieve the previously typed script filename, and press **Enter** to execute the script file. This technique allows you to debug your program quickly. After making changes in the script file, be sure to save it before switching to the Command window.

- To write a short report that includes your script file, results, and discussion—perhaps to present your solution to one of the chapter problems—use the mouse to highlight the results shown in the Command window and then copy and paste them to the editor window above or below your script file. Then, to save space, delete any extra blank lines, and perhaps the prompt symbol. Type your name and any other required information and add any discussion you wish; print the report from the editor window or save the report and import it into the word processor of your choice. (Change the filename or its extension if you intend to use the script file again!)

Debugging Script Files

Debugging a program is the process of finding and removing the "bugs," or errors, in a program. Such errors usually fall into one of the following categories:

- Syntax errors such as omitting a parenthesis or comma or spelling a command name incorrectly. MATLAB usually detects the more obvious errors and displays a message describing the error and its location.
- Errors due to an incorrect mathematical procedure. These are called *runtime errors.* They do not necessarily occur every time the program is executed; their occurrence often depends on the particular input data. A common example is division by zero.

The MATLAB error messages usually allow you to find syntax errors. However, runtime errors are more difficult to locate. To locate such an error, try the following:

1. Always test your program with a simple version of the problem, whose answers can be checked by hand calculations.
2. Display any intermediate calculations by removing semicolons at the end of statements.
3. Use the M-file Debugger (in MATLAB 5 only). Use of this debugger is not covered in this text, but you can access the MATLAB help facilities for more information. One of the advantages of MATLAB is that it can accomplish many tasks with relatively short programs. Thus you probably will not need to use the Debugger for the programs encountered in this text.

Programming Style

Comments can go anywhere in the script file. However, the first comment line before any executable statement is the line that is searched by the `lookfor` command (see Chapter 1). Therefore, if you intend to use the script file in the future, consider putting keywords that describe the script file in this first line (which is called the H1 line).

A suggested format for a script file follows.

```
% First comment contains key words and/or the program name.
% Author's name and the date created.
% Further description of program if needed.
Body of the file.
```

You might notice that the programs presented in this text do not follow this format. We usually omit the three comment lines to save space. They are also not necessary here because the text discussion associated with the program provides the required documentation (and besides, we all know who wrote these programs!).

Using M-Files to Store Data

You might have applications that require you to access the same set of data frequently. An example is a set of daily temperature measurements at a particular location, which are needed from time to time, for example, to compute the average temperature over some period. If there is not too much data to enter manually, you can store it in an array in a script file. For example, consider the single-line script file, whose name is mydata.m.

```
A = [2, 4; 7, 9]
```

A session to access this data from the command line and determine the maximum value in each column is

```
>>mydata
A =
    2    4
    7    9
>>x = max(A)
x =
    7    9
```

Note that the variable mydata is not in the workspace until you execute the script file by typing its name.

Test Your Understanding

T3.2–1 Create and run a script file that performs array multiplication of the vectors x = [0:10] and y = [2:2:22] and displays the (1, 5) element of the result.

T3.2–2 Create a script file called matrixa.m to store the matrix A = [2, 4; 7, 9]. Create another script file called asquared.m that runs matrixa.m and computes and displays A.^2.

3.3

Controlling Input and Output

MATLAB provides several useful commands for obtaining input from the user and for formatting the output (the results obtained by executing the MATLAB commands). Table 3.3–1 summarizes

Table 3.3–1 Input/Output Commands

Command	Description
disp(A)	Displays the contents, but not the name, of the array **A**.
disp('text')	Displays the text string enclosed within single quotes.
format	Controls the screen's output display format (see Table 3.3–2).
fprintf	Performs formatted writes to the screen or to a file (see Table 3.3–3).
x = input('text')	Displays the text in quotes, waits for user input from the keyboard, and stores the value in x.
x = input('text','s')	Displays the text in quotes, waits for user input from the keyboard, and stores the input as a string in x.
;	Suppresses screen printing when placed at the end of a line.

these commands. The methods presented in this section are particularly useful with script files.

The disp Command

You already know how to determine the current value of any variable by typing its name and pressing **Enter** at the command prompt. However, this method, which is useful in the interactive mode, is not useful for script files. The disp command (short for "display") can be used instead. Its syntax is disp(A), where A represents a MATLAB variable name. Thus typing disp(Speed) causes the value of the variable Speed to appear on the screen, but not the variable's name.

STRING

The disp command can also display text. You enclose the text within single quotes (this is called a *string*). For example, the command disp('The vehicle's predicted speed is:') causes the message to appear on the screen. This string can be used with the first form of the disp command in a script file as follows (assuming the value of Speed is 63):

```
disp('The vehicle's predicted speed is:')
disp(Speed)
```

When the file is run, these lines produce the following on the screen:

```
The vehicle's predicted speed is:
   63
```

Example 3.3–1 Design of a parallel-plate capacitor Capacitors are widely used in electric circuits. A capacitor stores energy by maintaining the charge separation produced

when a voltage is applied to the device. A parallel-plate capacitor is constructed from two or more parallel conducting plates, each having an area A and separated from each other by air or another dielectric material such as mica or paper. If the plates are separated by a distance d, the device's *capacitance C*, which is a measure of its energy storage capacity, can be computed from the formula

$$C = (n - 1)\frac{\epsilon A}{d}$$

where n is the number of plates and ϵ is the permittivity of the dielectric material. The unit of capacitance is the coulomb/volt and is called the *farad* (F).

Suppose we use plates having an area $A = 20$ cm^2, separated by a distance $d = 4$ mm with air, for which $\epsilon = 8.85 \times 10^{-12}$ F/m. Construct a table to select the number of plates needed to obtain a desired capacitance value. Assume that no more than 10 plates will be used.

Solution:

The following script file uses `disp` commands to display the table. The colon in `table(:,1)` represents all the rows in the first column of the matrix named `table`. The colon in `table(:,2)` represents all the rows in the second column of `table`. The transpose symbol ' converts `n` and `C` from row vectors to column vectors so that they can be used as columns in the array `table`. Lines 16 and 18 put the column vector `n'` in the first column of the matrix `table` and the column vector `C'` in the second column of `table`. The blank comment lines that separate the parts of the program help the reader to visualize the structure of the program.

```
% Program capacitr.m
% Generates a table of capacitance values.
%
% Define the values of the constants.
permittivity = 8.85e-12;
A = 20/100^2; % Convert A from centimeters to meters.
d = 4/1000; % Convert d from millimeters to meters.
%
% The vector n is the number of plates.
n = [2:10];
% The following generates the capacitance values.
% Multiply by 10^12 for display purposes.
C = ((n-1).*permittivity*A/d)*1e12;
%
% Create the first column in the table.
table(:,1) = n';
% Create the second column in the table.
table(:,2) = C';
```

```
% Display the table heading.
disp('No.   Plates Capacitance (F) X e12')
% Display the table.
disp(table)
```

When this program is run, it displays the following:

```
No.   Plates Capacitance (F) X e12
        2.0000   4.4250
        3.0000   8.8500
        4.0000  13.2750
        5.0000  17.7000
        6.0000  22.1250
        7.0000  26.5500
        8.0000  30.9750
        9.0000  35.4000
       10.0000  39.8250
```

To check the program, we pick a value for *n*, say, *n* = 2, and compute the capacitance from the formula $C = (2 - 1)(8.85 \times 10^{-12})(20/100^2)/(4/1000) = 4.425 \times 10^{-12}$. This answer agrees with the value computed by MATLAB except for the factor 10^{-12}, which was not displayed.

Formatting Commands

The `format` command controls how numbers appear on the screen. Table 3.3–2 gives the variants of this command. MATLAB uses many significant figures in its calculations, but we rarely need to see all of them. The default MATLAB display format is the `short` format, which uses four decimal digits. You can display more by typing `format long`, which gives 16 digits. To return to the default mode, type `format short`.

You can force the output to be in scientific notation by typing `format short e`, or `format long e`, where `e` stands for the number 10. Thus the output `6.3792e+03` stands for the number 6.3792×10^3. The output `6.3792e-03` stands for the number 6.3792×10^{-3}. Note that in this context `e` does *not* represent the

Table 3.3–2 Numeric Display Formats

Command	Description and Example
format short	four decimal digits (the default); 13.6745.
format long	16 digits; 17.27484029463547.
format short e	five digits (four decimals) plus exponent; 6.3792e+03.
format long e	16 digits (15 decimals) plus exponent; 6.379243784781294e−04.
format bank	two decimal digits; 126.73.
format +	Positive, negative, or zero; +.
format rat	Rational approximation; 43/7.
format compact	Suppresses some line feeds.
format loose	Resets to less compact display mode.

number e, which is the base of the natural logarithm. Here e stands for "exponent." It is a poor choice of notation, but MATLAB follows conventional computer programming standards that were established many years ago.

The fprintf command provides more control over the display format. Table 3.3–3 gives the syntax. Its use is best explained with a number of examples.

Suppose the variable Speed has the value 63.2. To display its value using three digits with one digit to the right of the decimal point, along with a message, the session is

```
>>fprintf('The speed is:  %3.1f\n',Speed)
The speed is:  63.2
```

Here the "field width" is 3, because there are three digits in 63.2. You may want to specify a wide enough field to provide blank spaces or to accommodate an unexpectedly large numerical value. The % sign tells MATLAB to interpret the following text as codes. The code \n tells MATLAB to start a new line after displaying the number.

The output can have more than one column, and each column can have its own format. For example,

```
>>r = [2.25:20:42.25];
>>circum = 2*pi*r;
>>y = [r;circum];
>>fprintf('%5.2f %11.5g\n',y)
  2.25       14.137
 22.25        139.8
 42.25       265.46
```

Table 3.3–3   Display Formats with the fprintf Command

Syntax	Description
fprintf('format',A, ...)	Displays the elements of the array **A**, and any additional array arguments, according to the format specified in the string 'format'.
'format' structure.	%[-][number1.number2]C, where number1 specifies the minimum field width, number2 specifies the number of digits to the right of the decimal point, and C contains control codes and format codes. Items in brackets are optional. [-] specifies left justified.

Control Codes		Format Codes	
Code	**Description**	**Code**	**Description**
\n	Start new line.	%e	Scientific format with lowercase e.
\r	Beginning of new line.	%E	Scientific format with uppercase E.
\b	Backspace.	%f	Decimal format.
\t	Tab.	%g	%e or %f, whichever is shorter.
"	Apostrophe.		
\\	Backslash.		

Note that the `fprintf` function displays the *transpose* of the matrix y.

Format code can be placed within text. For example, note how the period after the code `%6.3f` appears in the output at the end of the displayed text.

```
>>fprintf('The first circumference is %6.3f.\n',circum(1))
The first circumference is 14.137.
```

An apostrophe in displayed text requires two single quotes. For example:

```
>>fprintf('The second circle"s radius %15.3e is large.\n',r(2))
The second circle's radius     2.225e+001 is large.
```

A minus sign in the format code causes the output to be left justified within its field. Compare the following output with the preceding example:

```
>>fprintf('The second circle"s radius %-15.3e is large.\n',r(2))
The second circle's radius 2.225e+001      is large.
```

Control codes can be placed within the format string. The following example uses the tab code (\t).

```
>>fprintf('The radii are:%4.2f \t %4.2f \t %4.2f\n',r)
The radii are:  2.25      22.25      42.25
```

Note that in Example 3.3–1, the `disp` command displays more digits than necessary for the number of plates. We can improve the display by using the `fprintf` function instead of `disp`. Replacing the last three lines in the program with

```
E='';
fprintf('No.Plates Capacitance (F) X e12 %s\n',E)
fprintf('%2.0f \t \t \t %4.2f\n',table')
```

produces the following display:

```
No.Plates Capacitance (F) X e12
2           4.42
3           8.85
4          13.27
5          17.70
6          22.12
7          26.55
8          30.97
9          35.40
10         39.82
```

The empty matrix E is used because the syntax of the `fprintf` statement requires that a variable be specified. Because the first fprintf is needed to display the table title only, we need to fool MATLAB by supplying it with a variable whose value will not display.

Note that the fprintf command truncates the results, rather than rounding them. Note also that we must use the transpose operation to interchange the rows and columns of the table matrix in order to display it properly.

Only the real part of complex numbers will be displayed with the fprintf command. For example:

```
>>z = -4+9i;
>>fprintf('Complex number:  %2.2f \n',z)
Complex number:  -4.00
```

Instead you can display a complex number as a row vector. For example, if $w = -4 + 9i$:

```
>>w = [-4,9];
>>fprintf('Real part is %2.0f. Imaginary part is %2.0f. \n',w)
Real part is -4.  Imaginary part is 9.
```

User Input

The input command displays text on the screen, waits for the user to enter something from the keyboard, and then stores the input in the specified variable. For example, the command x = input('Please enter the value of x:') causes the message to appear on the screen. If you type 5 and press **Enter,** the variable x will have the value 5.

If you want to store a text string in a variable, use the other form of the input command. For example, the command Calendar = input('Enter the day of the week:', 'Calendar') prompts you to enter the day of the week. If you type Wednesday, this text will be stored in the variable Calendar.

Test Your Understanding

T3.3–1 Write a script file to compute and display a table to convert from radians to degrees. Use five values for the radian angle: 1, 2, 3, 4, and 5 radians. Be sure to label each column in the table.

T3.3–2 The volume V of a sphere depends on its radius r as follows: $V = 4\pi r^3/3$. Write a script file to compute and display a table showing the volume in cubic meters versus the radius in meters, for $1 \le r \le 2$, in increments of 0.1. Label each column and format the table to show the volume to three decimal places and the radius to one decimal place.

T3.3–3 The surface area A of a sphere depends on its radius r as follows: $A = 4\pi r^2$. Write a script file that prompts the user to enter a radius, computes the surface area, and displays the result.

3.4

**Elementary
Mathematical
Functions**

You can use the lookfor command to find functions that are relevant to your application. For example, type lookfor imaginary to get a list of the functions that deal with imaginary numbers. You will see listed:

imag   Complex imaginary part
i   Imaginary unit
j   Imaginary unit

Note that imaginary is not a MATLAB function, but the word is found in the help descriptions of the MATLAB function imag and the special symbols i and j. Their names and brief descriptions are displayed when you type lookfor imaginary. If you know the correct spelling of a MATLAB function—for example, disp—you can type help disp to obtain a description of the function. You can also access help from the **Help** menu at the top of the screen. You can then select either **Table of Contents** or **Index.**

Exponential and Logarithmic Functions

Table 3.4–1 summarizes some of the common elementary functions. An example is the square root function sqrt. To compute $\sqrt{9}$, you type sqrt(9) at the command line. When you press **Enter,** you see the result ans = 3. You can use functions with variables. For example, consider the session:

```
>>x = 9;
>>y = sqrt(x)
y =
   3
```

MATLAB automatically handles the square roots of negative numbers and returns a number with an imaginary part as the result. For example, typing sqrt(-9) gives the result ans = 0 + 3.0000i, which is the *positive* root.

Similarly, we can type exp(2) to obtain $e^2 = 7.3891$, where e is the base of the natural logarithms. Typing log(1) gives 2.7183, which is e. Note that in mathematics text, $\ln x$ denotes the *natural* logarithm, where $x = e^y$ implies that

$$\ln x = \ln(e^y) = y \ln e = y$$

Table 3.4–1 Some Common Mathematical Functions

Exponential

exp(x)	Exponential; e^x.
sqrt(x)	Square root; $\sqrt{x}$.

Logarithmic

log(x)	Natural logarithm; $\ln x$.
log10(x)	Common (base 10) logarithm; $\log x = \log_{10} x$.

Complex

abs(x)	Absolute value; $|x|$.
angle(x)	Angle of a complex number x.
conj(x)	Complex conjugate.
imag(x)	Imaginary part of a complex number x.
real(x)	Real part of a complex number x.

Numeric

ceil(x)	Round to the nearest integer toward ∞.
fix(x)	Round to the nearest integer toward zero.
floor(x)	Round to the nearest integer toward $-\infty$.
round(x)	Round toward the nearest integer.
sign(x)	Signum function: $+1$ if $x > 0$; 0 if $x = 0$; -1 if $x < 0$.

because $\ln e = 1$. However, this notation has not been carried over into MATLAB, which uses log(x) to represent $\ln x$.

The *common* (base 10) logarithm is denoted in text by $\log x$ or $\log_{10} x$. It is defined by the relation $x = 10^y$; that is,

$$\log_{10} x = \log_{10} 10^y = y \log_{10} 10 = y$$

because $\log_{10} 10 = 1$. The MATLAB common logarithm function is log10(x). A common mistake is to type log(x), instead of log10(x).

Another common error is to forget to use the array multiplication operator .*. Note that in the MATLAB expression y = exp(x).*log(x), we need to use the operator .* because both exp(x) and log(x) are arrays if x is an array.

Complex Number Functions

Chapter 2 explained how MATLAB easily handles complex number arithmetic. Several functions facilitate complex number operations. Figure 3.4–1 shows a graphical representation of a complex number in terms of a right triangle. The number $a + ib$ represents a point in the xy plane. In the *rectangular* representation $a + ib$, the number's real part a is the x coordinate of the point, and the imaginary part b is the y coordinate. The *polar* representation uses the distance M of the point from the origin, which is the length of the hypotenuse, and the angle θ the hypotenuse makes with the *positive real* axis. The pair (M, θ) is simply the polar coordinates of the point. In the polar representation the number is written as $M \angle \theta$. From the Pythagorean theorem, the length of

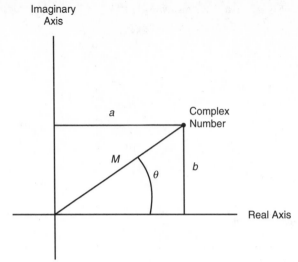

Figure 3.4–1
The rectangular and polar
representations of the
complex number *a* + *ib*.

the hypotenuse is given by

$$M = \sqrt{a^2 + b^2}$$

which is called the *magnitude* of the number. The angle θ can be found from the trigonometry of the right triangle. It is

$$\theta = \arctan(b/a)$$

Adding and subtracting complex numbers by hand is easy when they are in the rectangular representation. However, the polar representation facilitates multiplication and division of complex numbers by hand. We must enter complex numbers in MATLAB using the rectangular form, and its answers will be given in that form. We can obtain the rectangular representation from the polar representation as follows:

$$a = M \cos \theta \qquad b = M \sin \theta$$

The MATLAB abs(x) and angle(x) functions calculate the magnitude M and angle θ of the complex number x. The functions real(x) and imag(x) return the real and imaginary parts of x. The *complex conjugate* of the number $a + ib$ is $a - ib$. It can be shown that the complex conjugate of $M \angle \theta$ is $M \angle(-\theta)$. The function conj(x) computes the complex conjugate of x.

Note that when **x** is a vector, abs(x) gives a *vector* of absolute values. It does not give the magnitude of the vector. The magnitude of **x** is a *scalar* and is given by y = sqrt(x'*x). Thus abs(x) does not give y.

The magnitude of the product z of two complex numbers x and y is equal to the product of their magnitudes: $|z| = |x||y|$. The angle of the product is equal to the sum of the angles: $\angle z = \angle x + \angle y$. These facts are demonstrated below.

```
>>x = -3 + 4i;
>>y = 6 - 8i;
>>mag_x = abs(x)
mag_x =
    5.0000
>>mag_y = abs(y)
mag_y =
    10.0000
>>mag_product = abs(x*y)
    50.0000
>>angle_x = angle(x)
angle_x =
    2.2143
>>angle_y = angle(y)
angle_y =
    -0.9273
>>sum_angles = angle_x + angle_y
sum_angles =
    1.2870
>>angle_product = angle(x*y)
angle_product =
    1.2870
```

Similarly, for division, if $z = x/y$, then $|z| = |x|/|y|$ and $\angle z = \angle x - \angle y$.

Numeric Functions

Recall that one of the strengths of MATLAB is that it has been optimized to deal with arrays, and it will treat a variable as an array automatically. For example, to compute the square roots of 5, 7, and 15, type

```
>>x = [5,7,15];
>>y = sqrt(x)
y =
    2.2361    2.6361    3.8730
```

The square root function operates on every element in the array x.

The round function rounds to the nearest integer. Typing round(y) following the preceding session gives the results 2, 3, 4. The fix function truncates to the nearest integer toward zero. Typing fix(y) following the above session gives the results 2, 2, 3. The ceil function (which stands for "ceiling") rounds to the nearest integer toward ∞. Typing ceil(y) produces the answers 3, 3, 4.

Suppose $z = [-2.6, -2.3, 5.7]$. The floor function rounds to the nearest integer toward $-\infty$. Typing floor(z) produces the result -3, -3, 5. Typing fix(z) produces the answer -2, -2, 5. The abs function computes the absolute value. Thus abs(z) produces 2.6, 2.3, 5.7.

Test Your Understanding

T3.4–1 For several values of x and y, confirm that $\ln(xy) = \ln x + \ln y$.

T3.4–2 Find the magnitude, angle, real part, and imaginary part of the number $\sqrt{2 + 6i}$.

Trigonometric Functions

When writing mathematics in text, we use parentheses ( ), brackets [ ], and braces { } to improve the readability of expressions, and we have much latitude over their use. For example, we can write $\sin 2$ in text, but MATLAB requires parentheses surrounding the 2 (which is called the *function argument* or *parameter*). Thus **FUNCTION ARGUMENT** to evaluate $\sin 2$ in MATLAB, we type sin(2). The MATLAB function name must be followed by a pair of parentheses that surround the argument. To express in text the sine of the second element of the array x, we would type sin[x(2)]. However, in MATLAB you cannot use brackets or braces in this way, and you must type sin(x(2)).

You can include expressions and other functions as arguments. For example, to evaluate $\sin(x^2 + 5)$, you type sin(x.^2 + 5). To evaluate $\sin(\sqrt{x} + 1)$, you type sin(sqrt(x)+1). Using a function as an argument of another function is called *function composition*. Be sure to check the order of precedence and the number and placement of parentheses when typing such expressions. Every left-facing parenthesis requires a right-facing mate. However, this condition does not guarantee that the expression is correct!

Another common mistake involves expressions like $\sin^2 x$, which means $(\sin x)^2$. In MATLAB we write this expression as (sin(x))^2, *not* as sin^2(x), sin^2x, sin(x^2), or sin(x)^2!

Other commonly used functions are cos(x), tan(x), sec(x), and csc(x), which return $\cos x$, $\tan x$, $\sec x$, and $\csc x$, respectively. Table 3.4–2 lists the MATLAB trigonometric functions.

The MATLAB trigonometric functions operate in radian mode. Thus sin(5) computes the sine of 5 radians, not the sine of 5 degrees. To convert between degrees and radians, use the

Table 3.4–2 Trigonometric Functions

Trigonometric

cos(x)	Cosine; cos x.
cot(x)	Cotangent; cot x.
csc(x)	Cosecant; csc x.
sec(x)	Secant; sec x.
sin(x)	Sine; sin x.
tan(x)	Tangent; tan x.

Inverse trigonometric

acos(x)	Inverse cosine; arccos $x = \cos^{-1} x$.
acot(x)	Inverse cotangent; arccot $x = \cot^{-1} x$.
acsc(x)	Inverse cosecant; arccsc $x = \csc^{-1} x$.
asec(x)	Inverse secant; arcsec $x = \sec^{-1} x$.
asin(x)	Inverse sine; arcsin $x = \sin^{-1} x$.
atan(x)	Inverse tangent; arctan $x = \tan^{-1} x$.
atan2(y,x)	Four-quadrant inverse tangent.

relation $\theta_{radians} = (\pi/180)\theta_{degrees}$. Similarly, the inverse trigonometric functions return an answer in radians. The inverse sine, $\arcsin x = \sin^{-1} x$, is the value y that satisfies $\sin y = x$. To compute the inverse sine, type asin(x). For example, asin(.5) returns the answer: 0.5236 radians. Thus sin(0.5236) = 0.5.

MATLAB has two inverse tangent functions. The function atan(x) computes arctan x—the arctangent or inverse tangent—and returns an angle between $-\pi/2$ and $\pi/2$. Another correct answer is the angle that lies in the opposite quadrant. The user must be able to choose the correct answer. For example, atan(1) returns the answer 0.7854 radians, which corresponds to 45°. Thus tan 45° = 1. However, tan(45° + 180°) = tan 225° = 1 also. Thus arctan 225° = 1 is also correct. MATLAB provides the atan2(y,x) function to determine the arctangent unambiguously, where x and y are the coordinates of a point. The angle computed by atan2(y,x) is the angle between the positive real axis and line from the origin (0,0) to the point (x, y). For example, the point $x = 1, y = -1$ corresponds to $-45°$ or -0.7854 radians, and the point $x = -1$, $y = 1$ corresponds to 135° or 2.3562 radians. Typing atan2(-1,1) returns -0.7854, while typing atan2(1,-1) returns 2.3562. The atan2(y,x) function is an example of a function that has two arguments. The order of the arguments is important for such functions. For example, we have seen that atan2(-1,1) is not the same as atan2(1,-1).

Test Your Understanding

T3.4–3 For several values of x, confirm that $e^{ix} = \cos x + i \sin x$.

T3.4–4 For several values of x in the range $0 \le x \le 2\pi$, confirm that $\sin^{-1} x + \cos^{-1} x = \pi/2$.

T3.4–5 For several values of x in the range $0 \le x \le 2\pi$, confirm that $\tan(2x) = 2\tan x / (1 - \tan^2 x)$.

Hyperbolic Functions

The *hyperbolic functions* are the solutions of some common problems in engineering analysis. For example, the *catenary* curve, which describes the shape of a hanging cable supported at both ends, can be expressed in terms of the hyperbolic cosine, $\cosh x$, which is defined as

$$\cosh x = \frac{e^x + e^{-x}}{2}$$

The hyperbolic sine, $\sinh x$, is defined as

$$\sinh x = \frac{e^x - e^{-x}}{2}$$

The inverse hyperbolic sine, $\sinh^{-1} x$, is the value y that satisfies $\sinh y = x$. It can be expressed in terms of the natural logarithm as follows:

$$\sinh^{-1} x = \ln\left(x + \sqrt{x^2 + 1}\right) \qquad -\infty < x < \infty$$

Several other hyperbolic functions have been defined. Table 3.4–3 lists these hyperbolic functions and the MATLAB commands to obtain them.

Table 3.4–3 Hyperbolic Functions

Hyperbolic	
`cosh(x)`	Hyperbolic cosine; $\cosh x = (e^x + e^{-x})/2$.
`coth(x)`	Hyperbolic cotangent; $\cosh x / \sinh x$.
`csch(x)`	Hyperbolic cosecant; $1/\sinh x$.
`sech(x)`	Hyperbolic secant; $1/\cosh x$.
`sinh(x)`	Hyperbolic sine; $\sinh x = (e^x - e^{-x})/2$.
`tanh(x)`	Hyperbolic tangent; $\sinh x / \cosh x$.
Inverse hyperbolic	
`acosh(x)`	Inverse hyperbolic cosine; $\cosh^{-1} x = \ln(x + \sqrt{x^2 - 1})$, $x \ge 1$.
`acoth(x)`	Inverse hyperbolic cotangent; $\coth^{-1} x = \frac{1}{2}\ln\left(\frac{x+1}{x-1}\right)$, $x > 1$ or $x < -1$.
`acsch(x)`	Inverse hyperbolic cosecant; $\operatorname{csch}^{-1} x = \ln\left(\frac{1}{x} + \sqrt{\frac{1}{x^2} + 1}\right)$, $x \ne 0$.
`asech(x)`	Inverse hyperbolic secant; $\operatorname{sech}^{-1} x = \ln\left(\frac{1}{x} + \sqrt{\frac{1}{x^2} - 1}\right)$, $0 < x \le 1$.
`asinh(x)`	Inverse hyperbolic sine; $\sinh^{-1} x = \ln\left(x + \sqrt{x^2 + 1}\right)$, $-\infty < x < \infty$.
`atanh(x)`	Inverse hyperbolic tangent; $\tanh^{-1} x = \frac{1}{2}\ln\left(\frac{1+x}{1-x}\right)$, $-1 < x < 1$.

T3.4–6 For several values of x in the range $0 \leq x \leq 5$, confirm that $\sin(ix) = i \sinh x$.

Another type of M-file is a *function file*. Unlike a script file, all the variables in a function file are *local,* which means their values are available only within the function. Function files are useful when you need to repeat a set of commands several times. Function files are like functions in C, subroutines in FORTRAN and BASIC, and procedures in Pascal. They are the building blocks of larger programs. The first line in a function file must begin with a *function definition line* that has a list of inputs and outputs. This line distinguishes a function M-file from a script M-file. Its syntax is as follows:

FUNCTION FILE

LOCAL VARIABLE

FUNCTION DEFINITION LINE

```
function [output variables] = function_name(input variables);
```

Note that the output variables are enclosed in *square brackets,* while the input variables must be enclosed with *parentheses*. The `function_name` must be the same as the filename in which it is saved (with the `.m` extension). That is, if we name a function `drop`, it must be saved in the file `drop.m`. The function is "called" by typing its name (for example, `drop`) at the command line. The word `function` in the function definition line must be *lowercase*. Note also that even though MATLAB is case sensitive by default, your computer's operating system might not be case sensitive with regard to filenames. For example, while MATLAB would recognize `Drop` and `drop` as two different variables, your operating system might treat `Drop.m` and `drop.m` as the same file.

The following examples show permissible variations in the format of the function line. The differences depend on whether there is no output, a single output, or multiple outputs.

Function definition line	Filename
1. `function [area_square] = square(side);`	`square.m`
2. `function area_square = square(side);`	`square.m`
3. `function [volume_box] = box(height,width,length);`	`box.m`
4. `function [area_circle,circumf] = circle(radius);`	`circle.m`
5. `function sqplot(side);`	`sqplot.m`

Example 1 is a function with one input and one output. The square brackets are optional when there is only one output (see example 2). Example 3 has one output and three inputs. Example

4 has two outputs and one input. Example 5 has no output variable (for example, a function that generates a plot). In such cases the equal sign may be omitted.

Comment lines starting with the % sign can be placed anywhere in the function file. However, if you use `help` to obtain information about the function MATLAB displays all comment lines immediately following the function definition line. The first comment line can be accessed by the `lookfor` command.

We can call both built-in and user-defined functions either with the output variables explicitly specified, as in examples 1 through 4, or without any output variables specified. For example, we can call the function `square` as `square(side)` if we are not interested in its output variable `area_square`. (The function might perform some other operation that we want to occur, such as toggling `diary` on or off.) Note that if we omit the semicolon at the end of the function call statement, the first variable in the output variable list will be displayed using the default variable name `ans`.

The following function, called `drop`, computes a falling object's velocity and distance dropped. The input variables are the acceleration g, the initial velocity v_0, and the elapsed time t. Note that we must use the element-by-element operations for any operations involving function inputs that are arrays. Here we anticipate that t will be an array, so we use the element-by-element operator $(.\char`\^)$.

```
function [dist,vel] = drop(g,v0,t);
% Computes the distance travelled and the
% velocity of a dropped object, as functions
% of g, the initial velocity v0, and the time t.
vel = g*t + v0;
dist = 0.5*g*t.^2 + v0*t;
```

The following examples show various ways to call the function `drop`:

1. The variable names used in the function definition may, but need not, be used when the function is called:

```
a = 32.2;
initial_speed = 10;
time = 5;
[feet_dropped,speed] = drop(a,initial_speed,time)
```

2. The input variables need not be assigned values outside the function prior to the function call:

```
[feet_dropped,speed] = drop(32.2,10,5)
```

3. The inputs and outputs are assumed to be arrays:

```
[feet_dropped,speed]=drop(32.2,10,[0:1:5])
```

This function call produces the arrays `feet_dropped` and `speed`, each with six values corresponding to the six values of time in the array `time`.

Local Variables

The names of the input variables given in the function definition line are local to that function. This means that other variable names can be used when you call the function. All variables inside a function are erased after the function finishes executing, except when the same variable names appear in the output variable list used in the function call. For example, when using the `drop` function in a program, we can assign a value to the variable `dist` before the function call, and its value will be unchanged after the call because its name was not used in the output list of the call statement (the variable `feet_dropped` was used in the place of `dist`). This is what is meant by the function's variables being "local" to the function. This feature allows us to write generally-useful functions using variables of our choice, without being concerned that the calling program uses the same variable names for other calculations. This means that our function files are "portable," and need not be rewritten every time they are used in a different program.

You might find the M-file Debugger (in MATLAB 5 only) to be useful for locating errors in function files. Runtime errors in functions are more difficult to locate because the function's local workspace is lost when the error forces a return to the MATLAB base workspace. The Debugger provides access to the function workspace, and allows you to change values. It also enables you to execute lines one at a time and to set *breakpoints,* which are specific locations in the file where execution is temporarily halted. The applications in this text will probably not require use of the Debugger, which is useful mainly for very large programs, or programs containing *nested* functions (that is, functions that call other functions). For more information, consult the `help` facility or the MATLAB manual *Using MATLAB* [The MathWorks, 1997].

Applications

Some MATLAB commands act on functions. If the function of interest is not a simple function, it is more convenient to define the function in an M-file when using one of these commands.

Finding the Zeros of a Function

The `roots` command finds the zeros of polynomial functions only. Otherwise, you can use the `fzero` command to find the zero of a function of a single variable, which is denoted by x. One form of its syntax is `fzero('function', x0)`, where `function` is a string containing the name of the function. The `fzero` command returns a value of x that is near x0. It identifies only points where the function crosses the x-axis, not points where the function just touches the axis. For example, fzero('cos',2) returns the value $x = 1.5708$. However, to use this command to find the zeros of more complicated functions, it is more convenient to define the function in a function file. For example, if $y = x + 2e^{-x} - 3$, you define the following function file:

```
function y = f1(x)
y = x + 2*exp(-x) - 3;
```

Functions can have more than one zero, so it helps to plot the function first and then use fzero to obtain an answer that is more accurate than the answer read off the plot. Figure 3.5–1 shows the plot of this function, which has two zeros, one near $x = -0.5$ and one near $x = 3$. To find the zero near $x = -0.5$, type x = fzero('f1',-.5). The answer is $x = -0.5831$. To find the zero near $x = 3$, type x = fzero('f1',3). The answer is $x = 2.8887$.

Minimizing a Function of One Variable

The fmin command finds the minimum of a function of a single variable, which is denoted by x. One form of its syntax is fmin('function', x1, x2), where function is a string containing the name of the function. The fmin command returns a value of x that minimizes the function in the interval x1 ≤ x ≤ x2. For example, fmin('cos',0,4) returns the value $x = 3.1416$. However, to use this command to find the minimum of

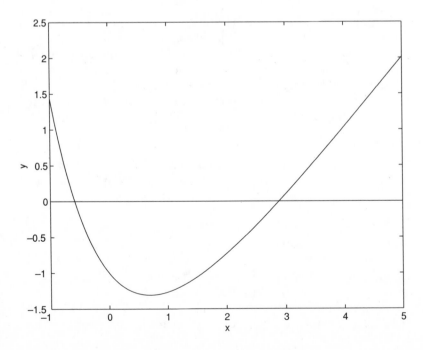

Figure 3.5–1
Plot of the function $y = x + 2e^{-x} - 3$.

more-complicated functions, it is more convenient to define the function in a function file. For example, if $y = 1 - xe^{-x}$, you define the following function file:

```
function y = f2(x)
y = 1-x.*exp(-x);
```

To find the value of x that gives a minimum of y for $0 \leq x \leq 5$, type `x = fmin('f2',0,5)`. The answer is $x = 1$. To find the minimum value of y, type `y = f2(x)`. The result is `y = 0.6321`.

To find the maximum of a function, use the `fmin` command with the negative of the function of interest. For example, to find the maximum of $y = xe^{-x}$ over the interval $0 \leq x \leq 5$, you must define the function file as follows:

```
function y = f3(x)
y = -x.*exp(-x);
```

Typing `fmin('f3',0,5)` gives the result $x = 1$. The function $y = xe^{-x}$ has a maximum at $x = 1$.

Whenever we use a minimization technique, we should check to make sure that the solution is a true minimum. For example, consider the following polynomial:

$$y = 0.025x^5 - 0.0625x^4 - 0.333x^3 + x^2$$

Its plot is shown in Figure 3.5–2. The function has two minimum points in the interval $-1 < x < 4$. The minimum near $x = 3$ is called a *relative* or *local* minimum because it forms a valley

Figure 3.5–2
Plot of the function $y = 0.025x^5 - 0.0625x^4 - 0.333x^3 + x^2$.

whose lowest point is higher than the minimum at $x = 0$. The minimum at $x = 0$ is the true minimum and is also called the *global* minimum. If we specify the interval $-1 \leq x \leq 4$ by typing

```
>>x = fmin('.025*x.^5-.0625*x.^4-.333*x.^3+x.^2',-1,4)
```

MATLAB gives the answer $x = 2.0438e-006$, which is essentially 0, the true minimum point. If we specify the interval $0.1 \leq x \leq 2.5$, MATLAB gives the answer $x = 0.1001$, which corresponds to the minimum value of y on the interval $0.1 \leq x \leq 2.5$. Thus we will miss the true minimum point if our specified interval does not include it. Also, fmin can give incorrect answers. If we specify the interval $1 \leq x \leq 4$, MATLAB gives the answer $x = 2.8236$, which corresponds to the "valley" shown in the plot, but which is not the minimum point on the interval $1 \leq x \leq 4$. On this interval the minimum point is at the boundary $x = 1$. The fmin procedure first looks for a minimum point corresponding to a zero slope; if it finds one, it stops. If it does not find one, it looks at the function values at the boundaries of the specified interval for x. In this example, MATLAB found a zero-slope minimum point and therefore missed the true minimum at the boundary.

No one has yet developed a numerical minimization method that works for every possible function. Therefore, we must use any such method with care. In practice, the best use of the fmin command is to determine precisely the location of a minimum point whose approximate location was found by other means, such as by plotting the function.

Minimizing a Function of Several Variables

To find the minimum of a function of more than one variable, use the fmins command. One form of its syntax is fmins('function', x0), where function is a string containing the name of the function. The vector x0 is a guess that must be supplied by the user. For example, to minimize the function $f = xe^{-x^2-y^2}$, we first define it in an M-file, using the vector x whose elements are x(1) = x and x(2) = y.

```
function f = f4(x)
f = x(1).*exp(-x(1).^2-x(2).^2);
```

Suppose we guess that the minimum is near $x = y = 0$. The session is

```
fmins('f4',[0,0])
ans =
    -0.7071      0.000
```

Thus the minimum occurs at $x = -0.7071, y = 0$.

Table 3.5–1 summarizes the fmin, fmins, and fzero commands.

Table 3.5–1 Minimization and Root-Finding Commands

Command	Description
fmin('function',x1,x2)	Returns a value of x in the interval x1 $\leq$ x $\leq$ x2 that corresponds to a minimum of the single-variable function described by the string 'function'.
fmins('function',x0)	Uses the starting vector x0 to find a minimum of the multivariable function described by the string 'function'.
fzero('function',x0)	Uses the starting value x0 to find a zero of the single-variable function described by the string 'function'.

Design Optimization

One way to improve engineering designs is by formulating the equations describing the design in the form of a minimization or maximization problem. This approach is called *design optimization*. Examples of quantities we would like to minimize are energy consumption and construction materials. Items we would like to maximize are useful life and capacity (such as the vehicle weight that can be supported by a bridge). The following example illustrates the concept of design optimization.

Example 3.5–1   Optimization of an irrigation channel
Figure 3.5–3 shows the cross-section of an irrigation channel. A preliminary analysis has shown that the cross-sectional area of the channel should be 100 ft² to carry the desired water-flow rate. To minimize the cost of concrete used to line the channel, we want to minimize the length of the channel's perimeter. Find the values of *d*, *b*, and θ that minimize this length.

Figure 3.5–3
Cross-section of an irrigation channel.

Solution:

The perimeter length *L* can be written in terms of the base *b*, depth *d*, and angle θ as follows:

$$L = b + \frac{2d}{\sin \theta}$$

The area of the trapezoidal cross-section is

$$100 = db + \frac{d^2}{\tan \theta}$$

The variables to be selected are b, d, and θ. We can reduce the number of variables by solving the latter equation for b to obtain

$$b = \frac{1}{d}\left(100 - \frac{d^2}{\tan \theta}\right)$$

Substitute this expression into the equation for L. The result is

$$L = \frac{100}{d} - \frac{d}{\tan \theta} + \frac{2d}{\sin \theta}$$

We must now find the values of d and θ to minimize L.

First define the function file for the perimeter length. Let the vector **x** be $[d \ \theta]$.

```
function L = channel(x)
L = 100./x(1) - x(1)./tan(x(2)) + 2*x(1)./sin(x(2));
```

Then use the `fmins` command. Using a guess of $d = 20$ and $\theta = 1$ radian, the session is

```
>>x = fmins('channel',[20,1])
x =
    7.5984    1.0472
```

Thus the minimum perimeter length is obtained with $d = 7.5984$ feet and $\theta = 1.0472$ radians, or $\theta = 60°$. Using a different guess, $d = 1$, $\theta = 0.1$, produces the same answer. The value of the base b corresponding to these values is $b = 8.7738$.

However, using the guess $d = 20$, $\theta = 0.1$ produces the physically meaningless result $d = -781$, $\theta = 3.1416$. The guess $d = 1$, $\theta = 1.5$ produces the physically meaningless result $d = 3.6058$, $\theta = -3.1416$.

The equation for L is a function of the two variables d and θ, and it forms a surface when L is plotted versus d and θ on a three-dimensional coordinate system. This surface might have multiple peaks, multiple valleys, and "mountain passes" called saddle points that can fool a minimization technique. Different initial guesses for the solution vector can cause the minimization technique to find different valleys and thus report different results. We can use the surface-plotting functions covered in Chapter 4 to look for multiple valleys, or we can use a large number of initial values for d and θ, say, over the physically realistic ranges $0 < d < 30$ and $0 < \theta < \pi/2$. If all the physically meaningful answers are identical, then we can be reasonably sure that we have found the minimum.

The fzero, fmin, and fmins commands have alternative forms not described here. With these forms you can specify the accuracy required for the solution, as well as the number of steps to use before stopping. Use the help facility to find out more about these commands.

Test Your Understanding

T3.5–1 The equation $e^{-0.2x} \sin(x + 2) = 0.1$ has three solutions in the interval $0 < x < 10$. Find these three solutions.

T3.5–2 The function $y = 1 + e^{-0.2x} \sin(x + 2)$ has two minimum points in the interval $0 < x < 10$. Find the values of x and y at each minimum.

T3.5–3 Find the depth d and angle θ to minimize the perimeter length of the channel shown in Figure 3.5–3 to provide an area of 200 ft^2. (Answer: $d = 10.7457$ ft, $\theta = 60°$.)

3.6

Cell Arrays

CELL ARRAY

The *cell array* is a new class of arrays introduced with MATLAB 5. Each element in a cell array is a *bin,* or *cell,* which can contain an array. You can store different classes of arrays in a cell array, and you can group data sets that are related but have different dimensions. You access cell arrays using the same indexing operations used with ordinary arrays.

Creating Cell Arrays

You can create a cell array by using assignment statements or by using the cell function (see Table 3.6–1). You can assign data to the cells by using either *cell indexing* or *content indexing*. To use cell indexing, enclose in parentheses the cell subscripts on

CELL INDEXING

Table 3.6–1 Cell Array Functions

Function	Description
C = cell(n)	Creates an $n \times n$ cell array C of empty matrices.
C = cell(n,m)	Creates an $n \times m$ cell array C of empty matrices.
celldisp(C)	Displays the contents of cell array C.
cellplot(C)	Displays a graphical representation of the cell array C.
C = num2cell(A)	Converts a numeric array A into a cell array C.
[X,Y, ...] = deal(A,B, ...)	Matches up the input and output lists. Equivalent to X = A, Y = B, ...
[X,Y, ...] = deal(A)	Matches up the input and output lists. Equivalent to X = A, Y = A, ...
iscell(C)	Returns a 1 if C is a cell array; otherwise, returns a 0.

the left side of the assignment statement and use the standard array notation. Enclose the cell contents on the right side of the assignment statement in braces { }.

Example 3.6–1   An environmental database

Data collection is important for early detection of changes in our environment. In order to detect such changes, we need to be able to analyze the database efficiently, and this effort requires a database that is set up for easy access. As a simple example, suppose you want to create a 2 × 2 cell array A, whose cells contain the location, the date, the air temperature (measured at 8 A.M., 12 noon, and 5 P.M.), and the water temperatures measured at the same time in three different points in a pond. The cell array looks like this:

Walden Pond	June 13, 1997
[60 72 65]	$\begin{bmatrix} 55 & 57 & 56 \\ 54 & 56 & 55 \\ 52 & 55 & 53 \end{bmatrix}$

Solution:

You can create this array by typing the following either in interactive mode or in a script file and running it.

```
A(1,1) = {'Walden Pond'};
A(1,2) = {'June 13, 1997'};
A(2,1) = {[60,72,65]};
A(2,2) = {[55,57,56;54,56,55;52,55,53]};
```

If you do not yet have contents for a particular cell, you can type a pair of empty braces { } to denote an empty cell, just as a pair of empty brackets [ ] denotes an empty numeric array. This notation creates the cell but does not store any contents in it.

CONTENT INDEXING   To use content indexing, enclose in braces the cell subscripts on the left side using the standard array notation. Then specify the cell contents on the right side of the assignment operator. For example:

```
A{1,1} = 'Walden Pond';
A{1,2} = 'June 13, 1997';
A{2,1} = [60,72,65];
A{2,2} = [55,57,56;54,56,55;52,55,53];
```

Type A at the command line. You will see

```
A =

    'Walden Pond'   'June 13, 1997'
    [1x3 double]    [3x3 double]
```

You can use the `celldisp` function to display the full contents. For example, typing `celldisp(A)` displays

```
A{1,1} =
    Walden Pond
A{2,1} =
    60  72  65
    .
    .
    .
    etc.
```

The `cellplot` function produces a graphical display of the cell array's contents in the form of a grid. Type `cellplot(A)` to see this display for the cell array A.

Use commas or spaces with braces to indicate columns of cells and use semicolons to indicate rows of cells (just as with numeric arrays). For example, typing

```
B = {[2,4], [6,-9;3,5]; [7;2], 10};
```

creates the following 2×2 cell array:

$$
\begin{array}{|c|c|}
\hline
[2 \quad 4] & \begin{bmatrix} 6 & -9 \\ 3 & 5 \end{bmatrix} \\
\hline
[7 \quad 2] & 10 \\
\hline
\end{array}
$$

You can preallocate empty cell arrays of a specified size by using the `cell` function. For example, type `C = cell(3,4)` to create the 3×4 cell array C and fill it with empty matrices. Once the array has been defined in this way, you can use assignment statements to enter the contents of the cells. For example, type `C(2,4) = {[6,-3,7]}` to put the 1×3 array in cell (2,4) and type `C(1,5) = {1:10}` to put the numbers from 1 to 10 in cell (1,5). Type `C(3,4) = {'30 mph'}` to put the string in cell (3,4).

Do not name a cell array with the same name as a previously used numeric array without first using the `clear` command to clear the name. Otherwise, MATLAB will generate an error. In addition, MATLAB does not clear a cell array when you make a single assignment to it. You can determine if an array is a cell array by using the `iscell` function. You can convert a numeric array to a cell array by using the `num2cell` function.

Accessing Cell Arrays

You can access the contents of a cell array by using either cell indexing or content indexing. For example, to use cell indexing to place the contents of cell (3,4) of the array C in the new variable Speed, type `Speed = C(3,4)`. To place the contents of the cells in rows 1 to 3, columns 2 to 5 in the new cell array D, type `D = C(1:3,2:5)`. The new cell array D will have three rows, four columns, and 12 arrays. To use content indexing to access some or all of the contents in a *single cell*, enclose the cell index expression in braces to indicate that you are assigning the contents, not the cells themselves, to a new variable. For example, typing `Speed = C{3,4}` assigns the contents `'30 mph'` in cell (3,4) to the variable Speed. You cannot use content indexing to retrieve the contents of more than one cell at a time. For example, the statements `G = C{1,:}` and `C{1,:} = var`, where var is some variable, are both invalid.

You can access subsets of a cell's contents. For example, to obtain the second element in the 1 × 3-row vector in the (2,4) cell of array C and assign it to the variable r, you type `r = C{2,4}(1,2)`. The result is `r = -3`.

The `deal` function accesses elements of a range of cells in a cell array. For example, with the preceding cell array B, x and y can be assigned to the elements in row 2 of B as follows:

```
[x,y] = deal(B{2,:})
x =
     7     2
y =
    10
```

Using Cell Arrays

You can use cell arrays in comma-separated lists just as you would use ordinary MATLAB variables. For example, suppose you create the 1 × 4 cell array H by typing

```
H = {[2,4,8], [6,-8,3], [2:6], [9,2,5]};
```

The expression H{2:4} is equivalent to a comma-separated list of the second through fourth cells in H. To create a numeric array J from the first, second, and fourth cells in the cell array H, you type

```
J = [H{1}; H{2}; H{4}]
```

The result is

$$J = \begin{bmatrix} 2 & 4 & 8 \\ 6 & -8 & 3 \\ 9 & 2 & 5 \end{bmatrix}$$

Typing H{2:3} displays the arrays in the second and third cells.

```
>>H{2:3}
ans =
    6    -8    3
ans =
    2    3    4    5    6
```

You can also use cell arrays in this manner in function input and output lists, and you can store the results in another cell array, say, K. For example,

```
>>[K{1:2}] = max(J)
K =
    [1x3 double]    [1x3 double]
```

Type K{1} to see the maximum values; type K{2} to see the corresponding indices.

```
>>K{1}
ans =
    9    4    8
>>K{2}
ans =
    3    1    1
```

You can apply functions and operators to cell contents. For example, suppose you create the 3×2 cell array L by typing

```
L = {[2,4,8], [6,-8,3]; [2:6], [9,2,5]; [1,4,5], [7,5,2]};
```

Then, for example:

```
>>max(L{3,2})
ans =
    7
```

Nested cell arrays have cells that contain cell arrays, which may also contain cell arrays, and so on. To create nested arrays, you can use nested braces, the cells function, or assignment statements. For example:

```
N(1,1) = {[2,7,5]};
N(1,2) = {{[5,9,1; 4,8,0], 'Case 1'; {5,8}, [7,3]}};
```

Typing N gives the result

```
N =
    [1x3 double]    {2x2 cell}
```

The following steps create the same array N using the `cell` function. The method assigns the output of `cell` to an existing cell.

```
% First create an empty 1x2 cell array.
N = cell(1,2)
% Then create a 2x2 cell array inside N(1,2).
N(1,2) = {cell(2,2)}
% Then fill N using assignment statements.
N(1,1) = {[2,7,5]};
N{1,2}(1,1) = {[5,9,1; 4,8,0]}
N{1,2}(1,2) = {'Case 1'}
N{1,2}{2,1}(1) = {5}
N{1,2}{2,1}(2) = {8}
N{1,2}(2,2) = {[7,3]}
```

Note that braces are used for subscripts to access cell contents until the lowest "layer" of subscripts is reached. Then parentheses are used because the lowest layer does not contain cell arrays.

As a final example, suppose you create the 3×2 cell array H by typing

```
H = {[2,4,8], [6,-8,3]; [2:6], [9,2,5]; [1,4,5], [7,5,2]};
```

You can create a numeric array J from the cell array H by typing

```
J = [H{1,1}; H{1,2}; H{2,2}]
```

The result is

$$J = \begin{bmatrix} 2 & 4 & 8 \\ 6 & -8 & 3 \\ 9 & 2 & 5 \end{bmatrix}$$

Typing H{2:3,:} displays the arrays in the second and third rows.

```
>>H{2:3,:}
ans =
    2    3    4    5    6
ans =
    9    2    5
ans =
    1    4    5
ans =
    7    5    2
```

Test Your Understanding

T3.6–1 Create the following cell array:

```
A = {[1:4], [0, 9, 2], [2:5], [6:8]}
```

What is `B = A{1:2}`? What is `C = [A{2}; A{4}]`? What is `D = min(A{2:3})`?

Structure arrays are composed of *structures*. This new class of arrays, introduced in MATLAB 5, enables you to store dissimilar arrays together. The elements in structures are accessed using *named fields*. This feature distinguishes them from cell arrays, which are accessed using the standard array indexing operations.

STRUCTURE ARRAY

A specific example is the best way to introduce the terminology of structures. Suppose you want to create a database of students in a course, and you want to include each student's name, Social Security number, e-mail address, and test scores. Figure 3.7–1 shows a diagram of this data structure. Each type of data (name, Social Security number, and so on) is a *field,* and its name is the *field name.* Thus our database has four fields. The first three fields each contain a text string, while the last field (the test scores) contains a vector having numerical elements. A *structure* consists of all this information for a single student. A *structure array* is an array of such structures for different students. The array shown in Figure 3.7–1 has two structures arranged in one row and two columns.

FIELD

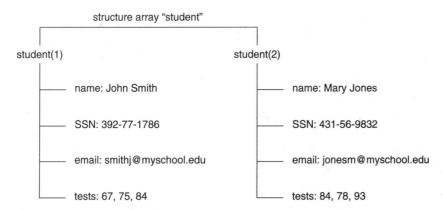

structure array "student"

student(1)
— name: John Smith
— SSN: 392-77-1786
— email: smithj@myschool.edu
— tests: 67, 75, 84

student(2)
— name: Mary Jones
— SSN: 431-56-9832
— email: jonesm@myschool.edu
— tests: 84, 78, 93

Figure 3.7–1
Arrangement of data in the structure array `student`.

Creating Structures

You can create a structure array by using assignment statements or by using the `struct` function. The following example uses assignment statements to build a structure. Structure arrays use the dot notation (.) to specify and to access the fields. You can type the commands either in the interactive mode or in a script file.

Example 3.7–1 A student database Create a structure array to contain the following types of student data:

- Student name.
- Social Security number.
- E-mail address.
- Test scores.

Enter the data shown in Figure 3.7–1 into the database.

Solution:

You can create the structure array by typing the following either in the interactive mode or in a script file. Start with the data for the first student.

```
student.name = 'John Smith';
student.SSN = '392-77-1786';
student.email = 'smithj@myschool.edu';
student.tests = [67,75,84];
```

If you then type

```
>>student
```

at the command line, you will see the following response:

```
name:  'John Smith'
SSN: = '392-77-1786'
email: = 'smithj@myschool.edu'
tests: = [67 75 84]
```

To determine the size of the array, type `size(student)`. The result is `ans = 1   1`, which indicates that it is a 1 × 1 structure array.

To add a second student to the database, use a subscript 2 enclosed in parentheses after the structure array's name and enter the new information. For example, type

```
student(2).name = 'Mary Jones';
student(2).SSN = '431-56-9832';
student(2).email = 'jonesm@myschool.edu';
student(2).tests = [84,78,93];
```

This process "expands" the array. Before we entered the data for the second student, the *dimension* of the structure array was 1 × 1 (it was a single structure). Now it is a 1 × 2 array consisting of two structures, arranged in one row and two columns. You can confirm this information by typing `size(student)`, which returns `ans = 1   2`. If you now type `length(student)`, you will get the result `ans = 2`, which indicates that the array has two elements (two structures). When a structure array has more than one structure, MATLAB does not display the individual field contents when you type the structure array's name. For example, if you now type `student`, MATLAB displays

```
>>student =

1x2 struct array with fields:
    name
    SSN
    email
    tests
```

You can also obtain information about the fields by using the `fieldnames` function (see Table 3.7–1). For example:

```
>>fieldnames(student)
ans =
    'name'
    'SSN'
    'email'
    'tests'
```

As you fill in more student information, MATLAB assigns the same number of fields and the same field names to each element. If you do not enter some information—for example, suppose you do not know someone's e-mail address—MATLAB assigns an empty matrix to that field for that student.

Table 3.7–1 Structure Functions

Function	Description
`names = fieldnames(S)`	Returns the field names associated with the structure array `S` as `names`, a cell array of strings.
`F = getfield(S,'field')`	Returns the contents of the field `'field'` in the structure array `S`. Equivalent to `F = S.field`.
`isfield(S,'field')`	Returns 1 if `'field'` is the name of a field in the structure array `S`, and 0 otherwise.
`isstruct(S)`	Returns 1 if the array `S` is a structure array, and 0 otherwise.
`S = rmfield(S,'field')`	Removes the field `'field'` from the structure array `S`.
`S = setfield(S,'field',V)`	Sets the contents of the field `'field'` to the value `V` in the structure array `S`.
`S = struct('f1','v1','f2','v2',...)`	Creates a structure array with the fields `'f1'`, `'f2'`, ... having the values `'v1'`, `'v2'`, ...

The fields can have different sizes. For example, each name field can contain a different number of characters, and the arrays containing the test scores can be different sizes, as would be the case if a certain student did not take the second test.

In addition to the assignment statement, you can also build structures using the `struct` function, which lets you "preallocate" a structure array. To build a structure array named `sa_1`, the syntax is

```
sa_1 = struct('field1','values1','field2','values2', ...)
```

where the arguments are the field names and their values. The values arrays `values1`, `values2`, ... must all be arrays of the same size, scalar cells, or single values. The elements of the values arrays are inserted into the corresponding elements of the structure array. The resulting structure array has the same size as the values arrays, or is 1×1 if none of the values arrays is a cell. For example, to preallocate a 1×1 structure array for the student database, you type

```
student = struct('name','John Smith', 'SSN',...
'392-77-1786','email','smithj@myschool.edu',...
'tests',[67,75,84])
```

Accessing Structure Arrays

To access the contents of a particular field, type a period after the structure array name, followed by the field name. For example, typing `student(2).name` displays the value `'Mary Jones'`. Of course, we can assign the result to a variable in the usual way. For example, typing `name2 = student(2).name` assigns the value `'Mary Jones'` to the variable `name2`. To access elements within a field, for example, John Smith's second test score, type `student(1).tests(2)`. This entry returns the value `75`. In general, if a field contains an array, you use the array's subscripts to access its elements. In this example the statement `student(1).tests(2)` is equivalent to `student(1,1).tests(2)` because `student` has one row.

To store all the information for a particular structure—say, all the information about Mary Jones—in another structure array named `M`, you type `M = student(2)`.

You can also assign or change values of field elements. For example, typing `student(2).test(2) = 81` changes Mary Jones's second test score from 78 to 81. Direct indexing is usually the best way to create or access field values. However, suppose you used the `fieldnames` function in an M-file to obtain a field name. You would know the field name only as a string. In this situation you can use the `setfield` and `getfield` functions for assigning and retrieving field values. For example, typing `setfield(M,'name', 'Mary Lee Jones')` inserts the new name. Typing `getfield(M,'name')` returns the result `ans = Mary Lee Jones`.

The preceding syntax for the `getfield` and `setfield` functions works on 1×1 arrays only. The alternate syntax, which works for an $i \times j$ array S, is

```
F = getfield(S, {i,j}, 'field', {k})
```

which is equivalent to `F = S(i,j).field(k)`. For example,

```
getfield(student, {1,1}, 'tests', {2})
```

returns the result `ans = 75`. Similarly,

```
S = setfield(S, {i,j}, 'field', {k})
```

is equivalent to `S(i,j).field(k) = S`.

Modifying Structures

Suppose you want to add phone numbers to the database. You can do this by typing the first student's phone number as follows:

```
student(1).phone = '555-1653'
```

All the other structures in the array will now have a `phone` field, but these fields will contain the empty array until you give them values.

To delete a field from every structure in the array, use the `rmfield` function. Its basic syntax is

```
new_struc = rmfield(array,'field');
```

where `array` is the structure array to be modified, `'field'` is the field to be removed, and `new_struc` is the name of the new structure array so created by the removal of the field. For example, to remove the Social Security field and call the new structure array `new_student`, type

```
new_student = rmfield(student,'SSN');
```

Using Operators and Functions with Structures

You can apply the MATLAB operators to structures in the usual way. For example, to find the maximum test score of the second student, you type `max(student(2).tests)`. The answer is 93.

The `isfield` function determines whether or not a structure array contains a particular field. Its syntax is `isfield(S,'field')`. It returns a value of 1 (which means "true") if `'field'` is the name of a field in the structure array S. For example, typing `isfield(student, 'name')` returns the result `ans = 1`.

The isstruct function determines whether or not an array is a structure array. Its syntax is isstruct(S). It returns a value of 1 if S is a structure array, and 0 otherwise. For example, typing isstruct(student) returns the result ans = 1, which is equivalent to "true."

Test Your Understanding

T3.7-1 Create the structure array student shown in Figure 3.7–1 and add the following information about a third student: name: Alfred E. Newman; SSN: 555-12-3456; e-mail: NewmanA@myschool.edu; tests: 55, 45, 58.

T3.7-2 Edit your structure array to change Mr. Newman's second test score from 45 to 53.

T3.7-3 Edit your structure array to remove the SSN field.

3.8

Summary

Now that you have finished this chapter you should be able to use M-files, MAT-files, and data files with MATLAB. Diary files are useful for recording your intermediate results. Script files are useful for creating longer programs. You should begin to use these for your more extensive assignments. Proper use of MATLAB input and output commands enable programs to obtain information from the user easily and to display results in a readable and useable form.

MATLAB functions fall into 20 main categories. In this chapter we introduced a number of commonly used mathematical functions. These are in the elementary function (elfun) category. In addition, you can create your own functions using function files.

If you are using MATLAB 5, you should now be able to create databases using cell and structure arrays. These allow you to

Table 3.8–1 Guide to Commands Introduced in Chapter 3

System commands	Table 3.1–1
File commands	Table 3.1–2
Input/output commands	Table 3.3–1
Numeric display formats	Table 3.3–2
Display formats with the fprintf command	Table 3.3–3
Elementary mathematical functions	Table 3.4–1
Trigonometric functions	Table 3.4–2
Hyperbolic functions	Table 3.4–3
Minimization and root-finding commands	Table 3.5–1
Cell array functions	Table 3.6–1
Structure functions	Table 3.7–1

cell arrays can be accessed by location, whereas data in structure
arrays can be accessed by name as well as by location.

Table 3.8–1 is a guide to all the commands introduced in this
chapter.

**Key Terms
with Page
References**

Problems

You can find the answers to problems marked with an asterisk at
the end of the text.

Section 3.1

1.   *a.* Start recording a diary session in the file `diary2.txt`.
   b. Enter the vector $x = [1:5]$ into MATLAB.
   c. Save the workspace variables in the file `session2`.
   d. Create the vector $x = [1:10]$.
   e. Load the file `session2` and compute the following expression:
   $z = 3x$. Is the result what you would expect? Explain.
   f. Turn off the diary session and type `type diary2.txt` to display
   the session log.

2. Determine which search path MATLAB is using on your computer. If you
   use a lab computer as well as a home computer, compare the two
   search paths.

3. If you use a spreadsheet program, determine whether it can save
   files in the `.wk1` format. If so, create and save a small spreadsheet
   containing some numbers. Then go to MATLAB; read the spreadsheet file
   into the matrix `M` and display it. It should be the same as the numbers
   in the rows and columns of your spreadsheet.

Sections 3.2 and 3.3

4. The amount of money in year k from an initial investment of $1000
   dollars, invested at 5.5 percent interest compounded annually, is given
   by $1000(1.055)^k$. Write a script file to compute and display the amount
   of money accumulated by year for 10 years. Label each column and
   use the `format bank` command.

5. Write a script file to compute and display a table to convert from degrees Fahrenheit (°F) to degrees Celsius (°C) over the temperature range 0 to 100 °F in increments of 10 degrees. The conversion relation is °C = 5(°F − 32)/9.

6. Write a script file that allows the user to input the three coefficients of the quadratic polynomial $ax^2 + bx + c$ and solves for both roots. Format the output appropriately and account for complex roots. Run the file for three cases: (1) $a = 2$, $b = 35$, $c = 100$; (2) $a = 3$, $b = 24$, $c = 48$; and (3) $a = 5$, $b = 24$, $c = 145$. Hand check the answers.

7. Redo Example 2.4–2 in Chapter 2 as a script file to allow the user to examine the effects of labor costs. Allow the user to input the four labor costs in the following table. When you run the file, it should display a labeled table of the quarterly costs and the category costs. Run the file for the case where the unit labor costs are $3000, $7000, $4000, and $8000 respectively.

Product Costs

| Product | Unit costs ($ \times 10^3$) | | |
	Materials	Labor	Transportation
1	6	2	1
2	2	5	4
3	4	3	2
4	9	7	3

Quarterly Production Volume

Product	Quarter 1	Quarter 2	Quarter 3	Quarter 4
1	10	12	13	15
2	8	7	6	4
3	12	10	13	9
4	6	4	11	5

8. Redo Problem 24 in Chapter 2 as a script file that allows the user to input any desired amount for each alloy. Be sure to label and format the output appropriately.

9. Users of Windows 95 or Windows NT might have a problem saving M-files because Windows automatically saves a text editor file with the extension.txt or .m.txt. If you register the .m extension, Notepad will no longer append the .txt extension. Follow these steps. (If you are using a lab computer, this process might have been done for you.)

1. Open **My Computer** and click on the **View** menu.
2. Choose **Options**; then choose the **File Types** tab.
3. Select **New Type** and type M-file in the Description of type field.
4. Type .m in the Associated extension field.
5. Click on **New** to open the Action field and type open with Notepad in that field.

6. Use the Browse button to find NOTEPAD.EXE for the **Application used to perform action** field.

7. Click on **OK** to close the **New Action** window.
8. Click on **OK** to close the **File Type** window.

You can then save text files with an .m extension. This information appears as solution 3166 under support/solutions on The Math-Works home page (http://www.mathworks.com).

Section 3.4

10.* Suppose that $y = -3 + ix$. For $x = 0, 1,$ and 2, use MATLAB to compute the following expressions. Hand check the answers.
 a. $|y|$
 b. $\sqrt{y}$
 c. $(-5 - 7i)y$
 d. $\frac{y}{6-3i}$

11.* Let $x = -5 - 8i$ and $y = 10 - 5i$. Use MATLAB to compute the following expressions. Hand check the answers.
 a. The magnitude and angle of xy.
 b. The magnitude and angle of $\frac{x}{y}$.

12.* Use MATLAB to find the angles corresponding to the following coordinates. Hand check the answers.
 a. $(x, y) = (5, 8)$
 b. $(x, y) = (-5, 8)$
 c. $(x, y) = (5, -8)$
 d. $(x, y) = (-5, -8)$

13. For several values of x, use MATLAB to confirm that $\sinh x = (e^x - e^{-x})/2$.

14. For several values of x, use MATLAB to confirm that $\sinh^{-1} x = \ln\left(x + \sqrt{x^2 + 1}\right)$, $-\infty < x < \infty$.

15.* Compute and display the 11 values of x and z in a two-column table, where

$$z = y^3 - 3y^2 + 4y + 10$$

$$y = \cos x$$

and $x = 0, 0.1, 0.2, \ldots, 1$.

16. The capacitance of two parallel conductors of length L and radius r, separated by a distance d in air, is given by

$$C = \frac{\pi \epsilon L}{\ln\left(\frac{d-r}{r}\right)}$$

where ϵ is the permittivity of air ($\epsilon = 8.854 \times 10^{-12}$ F/m).
 a. Compute and display a table of capacitance values versus d for $d = 0.003, 0.004, 0.005,$ and 0.01 meter; for $L = 1$ meter; and for $r = 0.001$ meter.
 b. Using $L = 1$ meter and $r = 0.01$ meter, write a script file that accepts user input for d and computes and displays C.

17.* When a belt is wrapped around a cylinder, the relation between the belt forces on each side of the cylinder is

$$F_1 = F_2 e^{\mu\beta}$$

where β is the angle of wrap of the belt and μ is the friction coefficient. Write a script file that first prompts a user to specify β, μ, and F_2 and then computes the force F_1. Test your program with the values $\beta = 130°$, $\mu = 0.3$, and $F_2 = 100$ newtons. (Hint: Be careful with β!)

Section 3.5

18. The MATLAB trigonometric functions expect their argument to be in radians. Write a function called sind that accepts an angle x in degrees and computes sin x. Test your function.

19. Write a function that accepts temperature in degrees F and computes the corresponding value in degrees C. The relation between the two is

$$T\,°C = \frac{5}{9}(T\,°F - 32)$$

Be sure to test your function.

20.* An object thrown vertically with a speed v_0 reaches a height h at time t, where

$$h = v_0 t - \frac{1}{2}gt^2$$

Write and test a function that computes the time t required to reach a specified height h, for a given value of v_0. The function's inputs should be h, v_0, and g. Test your function for the case where $h = 100$ meters, $v_0 = 50$ meters per second, and $g = 9.81$ meters per second². Interpret both answers.

Section 3.6

21. *a.* Use both cell indexing and content indexing to create the following 2 × 2 cell array:

Motor 28C	Test ID 6
$\begin{bmatrix} 3 & 9 \\ 7 & 2 \end{bmatrix}$	[6 5 1]

b. What are the contents of the (1,1) element in the (2,1) cell in this array?

22. The capacitance of two parallel conductors of length L and radius r, separated by a distance d in air, is given by

$$C = \frac{\pi \epsilon L}{\ln\left(\frac{d-r}{r}\right)}$$

where ϵ is the permittitivity of air ($\epsilon = 8.854 \times 10^{-12}$ F/m). Create a cell array of capacitance values versus d, L, and r for $d = 0.003$, 0.004, 0.005, and 0.01 meters; $L = 1, 2, 3$ meters; and $r = 0.001$, 0.002, 0.003 meters. Use MATLAB to determine the capacitance value for $d = 0.005$, $L = 2$, and $r = 0.001$.

Section 3.7

23. a. Create a structure array that contains the conversion factors for converting units of mass, force, and distance between the metric SI system and the British Engineering system.
    b. Use your array to compute the following:
    - The number of meters in 24 feet.
    - The number of feet in 65 meters.
    - The number of pounds equivalent to 18 Newtons.
    - The number of Newtons equivalent to 5 pounds.
    - The number of kilograms in 6 slugs.
    - The number of slugs in 15 kilograms.

24. Create a structure array that contains the following information fields concerning the road bridges in a town: bridge location, maximum load (tons), year built, year due for maintenance. Then enter the following data into the array:

Location	Max load	Year built	Due maintenance
Smith St.	80	1928	1997
Hope Ave.	90	1950	1999
Clark St.	85	1933	1998
North Rd.	100	1960	1998

25. Edit the structure array created in Problem 24 to change the maintenance data for the Clark St. bridge from 1998 to 2000.

26. Add the following bridge to the structure array created in Problem 24.

Location	Max load	Year built	Due maintenance
Shore Rd.	85	1997	2002

Photo courtesy of Flarecraft Corporation.

Engineering in the 21st Century . . .

Novel Designs

Sometimes just when we think a certain technical area is mature and the possibility of further development is unlikely, we get surprised by a novel design. Developments in other areas often allow a breakthrough in an area considered to be mature. Recent developments in aeronautics are examples of this phenomenon. Even though engineers have known for years that a human could generate enough power to propel an aircraft, the feat remained impossible until lightweight materials enabled the *Gossamer Condor* to fly across the English Channel in 1979. Ultralight aircraft and new aircraft that can stay aloft for more than a day are other examples.

These advances would have never occurred without the inventiveness of people willing to accept the challenge. Another example is the recent appearance of wing-in-ground effect (WIG) vehicles, such as the Flarecraft shown in the photo above. WIG vehicles make use of an air cushion to create lift. They are a hybrid between an aircraft and a hovercraft and most are intended for over-water flight only. A hovercraft rides on an air cushion created by fans, but the air cushion of a WIG vehicle is due to the air that is captured under its stubby wings. Associated technical problems include protecting the structure from high-speed wave impacts and achieving good pitching stability.

The Flarecraft is the first such commercially made vehicle. It seats five, cruises at 75 miles per hour, and has a range of 250 miles. It is intended for the water-taxi market, environmental monitoring, offshore hardware servicing, crew hauling, and wildlife rescue.

MATLAB's advanced graphics capabilities make it useful for visualizing flow patterns and for performing other aerodynamic studies needed to design such vehicles.

4

Plotting
with MATLAB

Outline

The popular phrase "A picture is worth a thousand words" emphasizes the importance of graphical representation in communicating information. It is easier to identify patterns in a plot than in a table of numbers. Engineers frequently use plots both to gain insight and to communicate their findings and ideas to others. Plotting, like any language, has a set of rules, standards, and practices that the engineer should follow to produce effective plots. Failure to do so will diminish one's reputation with colleagues, at least, and at worst, could lead others to draw incorrect conclusions about the data presented.

MATLAB has many functions that are useful for creating plots. In this chapter you will learn how to use them to create two-dimensional plots, which are also called *xy plots,* and three-dimensional plots called *xyz plots,* or *surface* plots. These plotting functions are described in the `plotxy` and `plotxyz` help categories in MATLAB 4, so typing `help plotxy` or `help plotxyz` will display a list of the relevant plotting functions. In MATLAB 5 the corresponding help categories are `graph2d` and `graph3d`.

This chapter also discusses the elements of a correct graph and how to use MATLAB to create effective graphs that convey

131

the desired information. An important application of plotting is *function discovery,* the technique for using data plots to obtain a mathematical function or "mathematical model" that describes the process that generated the data. This feature is very useful for engineering applications because engineers frequently need to use mathematical models to predict how their proposed designs will work.

4.1

xy Plotting Functions

ABSCISSA

ORDINATE

The most common plot is the xy plot. Its name assumes that we are plotting a function $y = f(x)$, although, of course, other symbols may be used. The x values are plotted on the horizontal axis (the *abscissa*), and the y values are plotted on the vertical axis (the *ordinate*). Usually the abscissa is used to plot the independent variable, which is the one more easily varied, and the ordinate is used to plot the dependent variable.

MATLAB has many functions and commands to produce various plots with special features. In this section we introduce the commands that are useful for making xy plots. In section 4.5 we treat three-dimensional plots.

The Anatomy of a Plot

SCALE

TICK MARK

AXIS LABEL

The "anatomy" and nomenclature of a typical xy plot is shown in Figure 4.1–1, in which the plot of a data set and a curve generated from an equation appear. The *scale* on each axis refers to the range and spacing of the numbers. Both axes in this plot are said to be "rectilinear"—often shortened to *linear*—because the spacing of the numbers is regular; for example, the distance between the numbers 2 and 3 is the same as the distance between the numbers 4 and 5. Another type of scale is the *logarithmic,* which we explain later in this chapter. *Tick marks* are placed on the axis to help visualize the numbers being plotted. The *tick-mark labels* are the numbers that correspond to the tick-mark locations. (Some plots will have tick-mark labels that are not numbers; for example, if we plot temperature versus time of year, the tick-mark labels on the horizontal axis could be the names of months.) The spacing of the tick marks and their labels is important. We cover this topic later in the chapter.

Each axis must have an *axis label*—also called an *axis title*. This label gives the name and units of the quantity plotted on that axis. An exception occurs when plotting a mathematical expression that has no physical interpretation; in that case the variables have no units. In addition, the plot often must have a plot title as well. The plot title is placed above the plot.

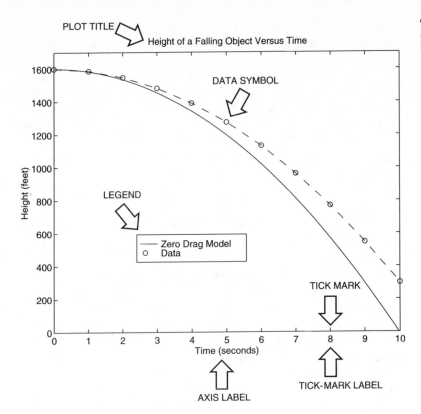

Figure 4.1–1
Nomenclature for a typical xy plot.

A plot can be made from measured data or from an equation. When data is plotted, each data point is plotted with a *data symbol,* or *point marker,* such as the small circle shown in Figure 4.1–1. A rare exception to this rule would be when there are so many data points that the symbols would be too densely packed. In that case, the data points should be plotted with a dot. However, when the plot is generated from an equation, data symbols must *never* be used! Lines are always used to plot an equation.

DATA SYMBOL

Sometimes data symbols are connected by lines to help the viewer visualize the data, especially if there are few data points. However, connecting the data points—especially with a solid line—might imply knowledge of what occurs between the data points, and thus you should be careful to prevent such misinterpretation.

When multiple curves or data sets are plotted, they must be distinguished from each other. One way of doing so is with a *legend,* which relates the data set symbol or the curve's line type to the quantity being plotted. Another method is to place a description (either text or an equation) near the curve or data symbols. We show examples of both methods later in the chapter.

LEGEND

Requirements for a Correct Plot

The following list describes the essential features of any plot:

1. Each axis must be labeled with the name of the quantity being plotted *and its units!* If two or more quantities having different units are plotted (such as when plotting both speed and distance versus time), indicate the units in the axis label if there is room, or in the legend or labels for each curve.

2. Each axis should have regularly spaced tick marks at convenient intervals—not too sparse, but not too dense—with a spacing that is easy to interpret and interpolate. For example, use 0.1, 0.2, and so on, rather than 0.13, 0.26, and so on.

3. If you are plotting more than one curve or data set, label each on its plot or use a legend to distinguish them.

4. If you are preparing multiple plots of a similar type or if the axes' labels cannot convey enough information, use a title.

5. If you are plotting measured data, plot each data point with a symbol such as a circle, square, or cross (use the same symbol for every point in the same data set). If there are many data points, plot them using the dot symbol.

6. Sometimes data symbols are connected by lines to help the viewer visualize the data, especially if there are few data points. However, connecting the data points, especially with a solid line, might be interpreted to imply knowledge of what occurs between the data points. Thus you should be careful to prevent such misinterpretation.

7. If you are plotting points generated by evaluating a function (as opposed to measured data), do *not* use a symbol to plot the points. Instead, connect the points with solid lines.

Plot, Label, and Title Commands

The MATLAB basic xy plotting function is `plot(x,y)`. If x and y are vectors, a single curve is plotted with the x values on the abscissa and the y values on the ordinate. The `xlabel` and `ylabel` commands put labels on the abscissa and the ordinate, respectively. The syntax is `xlabel('text')`, where `text` is the text of the label. Note that you must enclose the label's text in single quotes. The syntax for `ylabel` is the same. The `title` command puts a title at the top of the plot. Its syntax is `title('text')`, where `text` is the title's text.

The following MATLAB session plots $y = 0.4\sqrt{1.8x}$ for $0 \leq x \leq 52$, where y represents the height of a rocket after launch, in miles, and x is the horizontal (downrange) distance in miles.

```
>>x = [0:.1:52];
>>y = .4*sqrt(1.8*x);
>>plot(x,y)
```

```
>>xlabel('Distance (miles)')
>>ylabel('Height (miles)')
>>title('Rocket Height as a Function of Downrange Distance')
```

Figure 4.1–2 shows the plot. A spacing of 0.1 was selected for the x values to generate several hundred plotting points to produce a smooth curve. The plot(x,y) function in MATLAB automatically selects a tick-mark spacing for each axis and places appropriate tick labels. This feature is called autoscaling.

MATLAB also chose an upper limit for the x-axis, which is beyond the maximum value of 52 in the x values, to obtain a convenient spacing of 10 for the tick labels. A tick-label spacing of two would generate 27 labels, which gives a spacing so dense that the labels would overlap one another. A spacing of 13 would work, but is not as convenient as a spacing of 10. Later you will learn to override the values selected by MATLAB.

The axis labels and plot title are produced by the xlabel, ylabel, and title commands. The order of the xlabel, ylabel, and title commands does not matter, but we must place them *after* the plot command, either on separate lines using ellipses or on the same line separated by commas, as

```
>>x = [0:.1:52];
>>y = .4*sqrt(1.8*x);
>>plot(x,y),xlabel('Distance (miles)'),ylabel('Height (miles)'),...
title('Rocket Height as a Function of Downrange Distance')
```

Figure 4.1–2
The autoscaling feature in MATLAB selects tick-mark spacing.

The plot will appear in the figure window. You can obtain a hard copy of the plot in one of several ways:

1. Use the menu system. Select **Print** on the **File** menu in the figure window. Answer **OK** when you are prompted to continue the printing process.

2. Type `print` at the command line. This command sends the current plot directly to the printer.

3. Save the plot to a file to be printed later or imported into another application such as a word processor. You need to know something about graphics file formats to use this file properly. We do not cover this topic.

Type `help print` to obtain more information.

MATLAB assigns the output of the `plot` command to figure window number 1. When another `plot` command is executed, MATLAB overwrites the contents of the existing figure window with the new plot. Although you can keep more than one figure window active, we do not use this feature in this text.

When you have finished with the plot, close the figure window by selecting **Close** from the **File** menu in the figure window. Note that using the **Alt-Tab** key combination in Windows-based systems will return you to the Command window without closing the figure window.

`grid` **and** `axis` **Commands**

The `grid` command displays gridlines at the tick marks corresponding to the tick labels. Type `grid on` to add gridlines; type `grid off` to stop plotting gridlines. When used by itself, `grid` toggles this feature on or off, but you might want to use `grid on` and `grid off` to be sure.

AXIS LIMITS

You can use the `axis` command to override the MATLAB selections for the axis limits. The basic syntax is `axis([xmin xmax ymin ymax])`. This command sets the scaling for the x- and y-axes to the minimum and maximum values indicated. Note that, unlike an array, this command does not use commas to separate the values.

The `axis` command has the following variants:

- `axis square`, which selects the axes' limits so that the plot will be square.

- `axis equal`, which selects the scale factors and tick spacing to be the same on each axis. This variation makes `plot(sin(x), cos(x))` look like a circle, instead of an oval.

- `axis auto`, which returns the axis scaling to its default autoscaling mode in which the best axis limits are computed automatically.

For example, to add a grid and to change the axes limits on the previous plot to $0 \leq x \leq 52$ and $0 \leq y \leq 5$, the session would look like

```
>>x = [0:.1:52];
>>y = .4*sqrt(1.8*x);
>>plot(x,y),xlabel('Distance (miles)'),ylabel('Height (miles)'),...
title('Rocket Height as a Function of Downrange Distance'),...
grid on, axis([0 52 0 5])
```

Figure 4.1–3 shows this plot. Notice how MATLAB chose a tick label spacing of 5, not 13, for the x-axis.

This example illustrates how the printed plot can look different from the plot on the computer screen. MATLAB determines the number of tick-mark labels that can reasonably fit on the axis without being too densely spaced. A reasonable number for the computer screen is often different from the number for the printed output. In the preceding example, the screen plot showed labels on the x-axis at 0, 10, 20, . . . , whereas the printed plot had labels at the intervals 0, 5, 10, 15, 20, ... You can eliminate this effect by using the tick-mark commands discussed later in the chapter.

Plots of Complex Numbers

With only one argument, say, plot(y), the plot function will plot the values in the vector y versus their indices 1, 2, 3, . . . ,

Figure 4.1–3
The effects of the axis and grid commands.

and so on. If y is complex, plot(y) plots the imaginary parts versus the real parts. Thus plot(y) in this case is equivalent to plot(real(y),imag(y)). This situation is the only time when the plot function handles the imaginary parts; in all other variants of the plot function, it ignores the imaginary parts. For example, the script file

```
z = .1 + .9i;
n = [0:.01:10];
plot(z.^n),xlabel('Real'),ylabel('Imaginary')
```

generate the spiral shown in Figure 4.1–4. As you become more familiar with MATLAB, you will feel comfortable combining these three lines into the single line

```
plot((.1+.9i).^[0:.01:10]),xlabel('Real'),ylabel('Imaginary')
```

The Function Plot Command fplot

MATLAB has a "smart" command for plotting functions. The fplot command automatically analyzes the function to be plotted and decides how many plotting points to use so that the plot will show all the features of the function. Its syntax is fplot('string', [xmin xmax]), where 'string' is a text string that describes the function to be plotted and [xmin xmax] specifies the minimum and maximum values of the independent variable. The range of the dependent variable can also be specified. In this case the syntax is fplot('string', [xmin xmax ymin ymax]).

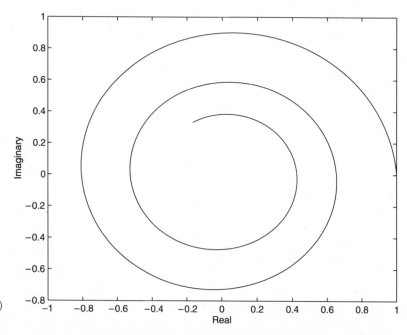

Figure 4.1–4
Application of the plot(y) function.

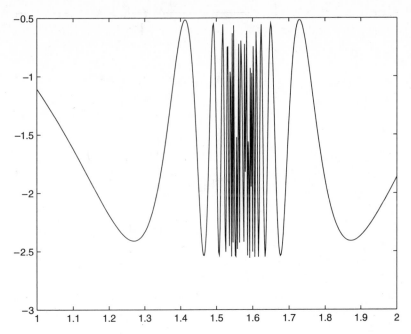

Figure 4.1–5
A plot generated with the `fplot` command.

For example, the session

```
>>f = 'cos(tan(x)) - tan(sin(x))';
>>fplot(f,[1 2])
```

produces the plot shown in Figure 4.1–5. The symbol x must be used for the independent variable. You may combine the two commands into a single command as follows: `fplot('cos(tan(x)) - tan(sin(x))',[1 2])`. Always remember to enclose the function in single quotes.

Contrast this plot with the one shown in Figure 4.1–6, which is given by the `plot` command using 100 plotting points.

```
>>x = [1:.01:2];
>>y = cos(tan(x)) - tan(sin(x));
>>plot(x,y)
```

We can see that the `fplot` command automatically chose enough plotting points to display all the variations in the function. We can achieve the same plot using the `plot` command, but we need to know how many values to use in specifying the x vector.

Another form is `[x,y] = fplot('string', limits)`, where `limits` may be either `[xmin xmax]` or `[xmin xmax ymin ymax]`. With this form the command returns the abscissa and ordinate values in the column vectors x and y, but no plot is produced. The returned values can then be used for other purposes, such as plotting multiple curves, which is the topic of the next section.

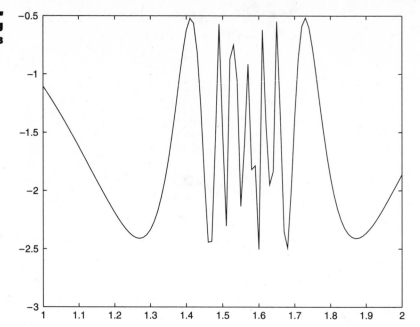

Figure 4.1–6
The function in Figure
4.1–5 generated with the
plot command.

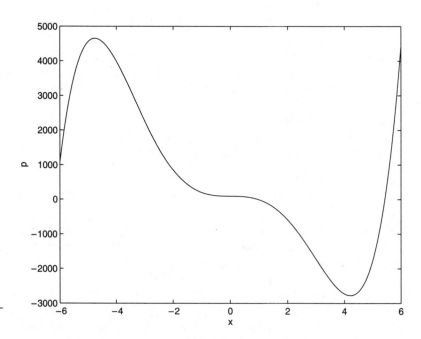

Figure 4.1–7
Plot of the polynomial
$3x^5 + 2x^4 - 100x^3 + 2x^2 - 7x + 90$ for $-6 \le x \le 6$.

Other commands can be used with the `fplot` command to enhance a plot's appearance, for example, the `title`, `xlabel`, and `ylabel` commands and the line type commands to be introduced in the next section.

Plotting Polynomials

We can plot polynomials more easily by using the `polyval` function, introduced in Chapter 2. This function evaluates the polynomial at specified values of the independent variable. It requires only the polynomial's coefficients and thus eliminates the need to type in the polynomial's expression. For example, to plot the polynomial $x^5 + 2x^4 - 100x^3 + 2x^2 - 7x + 90$ over the range $-6 \le x \le 6$ with a spacing of 0.01, you type

```
>>x = [-6:.01:6];
>>p = [3,2,-100,2,-7,90];
>>plot(x,polyval(p,x)),xlabel('x'),ylabel('p')
```

Figure 4.1–7 shows the resulting plot.

Test Your Understanding

T4.1–1 Redo the plot of the equation $y = 0.4\sqrt{1.8x}$ shown in Figure 4.1–2 for $0 \le x \le 35$ and $0 \le y \le 3.5$.

T4.1–2 Use the `fplot` command to investigate the function $\tan(\cos x) - \sin(\tan x)$ for $0 \le x \le 2\pi$. How many values of x are needed to obtain the same plot using the `plot` command? (Answer: 292 values.)

Table 4.1–1 Basic xy plotting commands

Command	Description
`axis([xmin xmax ymin ymax])`	Sets the minimum and maximum limits of the *x*- and *y*-axes.
`fplot('string', [xmin xmax])`	Performs intelligent plotting of functions, where `'string'` is a text string that describes the function to be plotted and `[xmin xmax]` specifies the minimum and maximum values of the independent variable. The range of the dependent variable can also be specified. In this case the syntax is `fplot('string', [xmin xmax ymin ymax])`.
`grid`	Displays gridlines at the tick marks corresponding to the tick labels. Type `grid on` to add gridlines; type `grid off` to stop plotting gridlines. When used by itself, `grid` switches this feature on or off.
`plot(x,y)`	Generates a plot of the array *y* versus the array *x* on rectilinear axes.
`plot(y)`	Plots the values of *y* versus their indices if *y* is a vector. Plots the imaginary parts of *y* versus the real parts if *y* is a vector having complex values.
`print`	Prints the plot in the figure window.
`title('text')`	Puts text in a title at the top of a plot.
`xlabel('text')`	Adds a text label to the *x*-axis (the abscissa).
`ylabel('text')`	Adds a text label to the *y*-axis (the ordinate).

T4.1–3 Plot the imaginary part versus the real part of the function $(0.2 + 0.8i)^n$ for $0 \leq n \leq 20$. Choose enough points to obtain a smooth curve. Label each axis and put a title on the plot. Use the axis command to change the tick-label spacing.

4.2

Subplots and Overlay Plots

SUBPLOT

OVERLAY PLOT

MATLAB can create figures that contain an array of plots, called *subplots*. These are useful when you want to compare the same data plotted with different axis types, for example. The MATLAB subplot command creates such figures.

We frequently need to plot more than one curve or data set on a single plot. Such a plot is called an *overlay plot*. This section describes several MATLAB commands for creating overlay plots.

Subplots

You can use the subplot command to obtain several smaller "subplots" in the same figure. The syntax is subplot(m,n,p). This command divides the figure window into an array of rectangular panes with m rows and n columns. The variable p tells MATLAB to place the output of the plot command following the subplot command into the pth pane. For example, subplot(3,2,5) creates an array of six panes, three panes

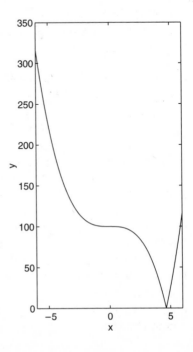

Figure 4.2–1
Application of the subplot command.

deep and two panes across, and directs the next plot to appear in the fifth pane (in the bottom-left corner). The following script file created Figure 4.2–1, which shows the plots of the functions $y = e^{-1.2x}\sin(10x + 5)$ for $0 \le x \le 5$ and $y = |x^3 - 100|$ for $-6 \le x \le 6$.

```
x = [0:.01:5];
y = exp(-1.2*x).*sin(10*x+5);
subplot(1,2,1)
plot(x,y),xlabel('x'),ylabel('y'),axis([0 5 -1 1])
x = [-6:.01:6];
y = abs(x.^3-100);
subplot(1,2,2)
plot(x,y),xlabel('x'),ylabel('y'),axis([-6 6 0 350])
```

When using the `subplot` function, you might wish to omit plot titles because the title from one subplot might be too close to the x-axis label of the preceding subplot.

Test Your Understanding

T4.2–1 Pick a suitable spacing for t and v, and use the `subplot` command to plot the function $z = e^{-0.5t}\cos(20t - 6)$ for $0 \le t \le 8$ and the function $u = 6\log_{10}(v^2 + 20)$ for $-8 \le v \le 8$. Label each axis.

Overlay Plots

You can use the following variants of the MATLAB basic plotting functions `plot(x,y)` and `plot(y)` to create overlay plots:

- `plot(A)` plots the columns of A versus their indices and generates n curves where A is a matrix with m rows and n columns.
- `plot(x,A)` plots the matrix A versus the vector x, where x is either a row vector or column vector and A is a matrix with m rows and n columns. If the length of x is m, then each *column* of A is plotted versus the vector x. There will be as many curves as there are columns of A. If x has length n, then each *row* of A is plotted versus the vector x. There will be as many curves as there are rows of A.
- `plot(A,x)` plots the vector x versus the matrix A. If the length of x is m, then x is plotted versus the *columns* of A. There will be as many curves as there are columns of A. If the length of x is n, then x is plotted versus the *rows* of A. There will be as many curves as there are rows of A.
- `plot(A,B)` plots the columns of the matrix B versus the columns of the matrix A.

Table 4.2–1 Specifiers for data markers, line types, and colors

Data markers		Line types		Colors	
Dot (·)	.	Solid line	-	Black	k
Asterisk (*)	*	Dashed line	- -	Blue	b
Cross (×)	x	Dash-dotted line	-.	Cyan	c
Circle (o)	o	Dotted line	:	Green	g
Plus sign (+)	+			Magenta	m
Square[†] (□)	Square			Red	r
Diamond[†] (◇)	Diamond			White	w
Five-pointed star[†] (★)	Pentagram			Yellow	y

[†] Available in MATLAB 5 only.

Data Markers and Line Types

To plot the vector y versus the vector x and mark each point with a data marker, enclose the symbol for the marker in single quotes in the `plot` function. Table 4.2–1 shows the symbols for the available data markers. For example, to use a small circle, which is represented by the lowercase letter o, type `plot(x,y, 'o')`. This notation results in a plot like the one on the left in Figure 4.2–2. To connect each data marker with a straight line, we must plot the data twice, by typing `plot(x,y,x,y,'o')`. See the plot on the right in Figure 4.2–2.

Suppose we have two curves or data sets stored in the vectors x, y, u, and v. To plot y versus x and v versus u on the same plot, type `plot(x,y,u,v)`. Both sets will be plotted with a solid line, which is the default line style. To distinguish the sets, we can plot

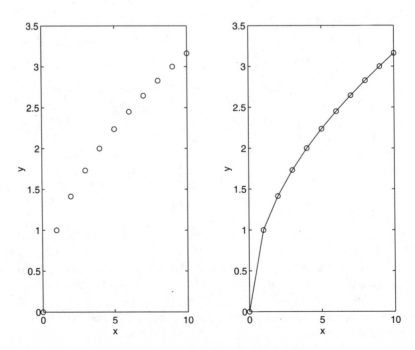

Figure 4.2–2
Use of data markers.

Figure 4.2–3
Data plotted using asterisks connected with a dotted line.

them with different linetypes. To plot y versus x with a solid line and u versus v with a dashed line, type `plot(x,y,u,v,'--')`, where the symbols `'--'` represent a dashed line. Table 4.2–1 gives the symbols for other line types. To plot y versus x with asterisks (∗) connected with a dotted line, you must plot the data twice by typing `plot(x,y,'*',x,y,':')`. See Figure 4.2–3.

You can obtain symbols and lines of different colors by using the color symbols shown in Table 4.2–1. The color symbol can be combined with the data-marker symbol and the line-type symbol. For example, to plot y versus x with green asterisks (∗) connected with a red dashed line, you must plot the data twice by typing `plot(x,y,'g*',x,y,'r--')`. (Do not use colors if you are going to print the plot on a black-and-white printer.)

Labeling Curves and Data

When more than one curve or data set is plotted on a graph, we must distinguish between them. If we use different data symbols or different line types, then we must either provide a legend or place a label next to each curve. To create a legend, use the `legend` command. The basic form of this command is `legend('string1','string2')`, where `string1` and `string2` are text strings of your choice. The `legend` command automatically obtains from the plot the line type used for each data set and displays a sample of this line type in the legend box next to the string you selected. The following script file produced the plot in Figure 4.2–4.

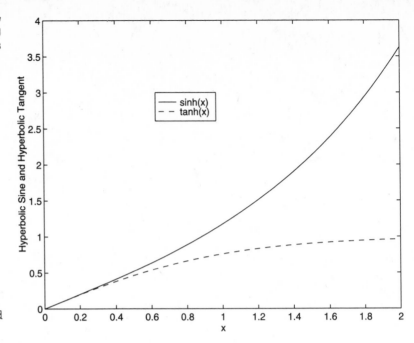

Figure 4.2–4
Application of the legend
command.

```
x = [0:.01:2];
y = sinh(x);
z = tanh(x);
plot(x,y,x,z,'--'),xlabel('x'), ...
ylabel('Hyperbolic Sine and Tangent'), ...
legend('sinh(x)','tanh(x)')
```

The legend command must be placed somewhere after the plot
command. When the plot appears in the figure window, use the
mouse to position the legend box. (Hold down the left button on a
two-button mouse to move the box.)

Gridlines can obscure the legend box. To prevent this situation,
instead of placing the legend command as shown in the preceding
session, type the following lines in the command window, after
the plot appears in the figure window but before printing the plot:

```
axes(legend('string1','string2'))
refresh
```

The first line makes the legend box act as the current set of drawing axes. The refresh command forces the plot to be redrawn
in the figure window. You can then print the plot. The axes command, not to be confused with the axis command, is a powerful
command with many features for manipulating figures in MATLAB.
However, this advanced topic is not covered in this text.

Another way to distinguish curves is to place a label next to
each. The label can be generated with either the gtext command,
which lets you place the label using the mouse, or with the text

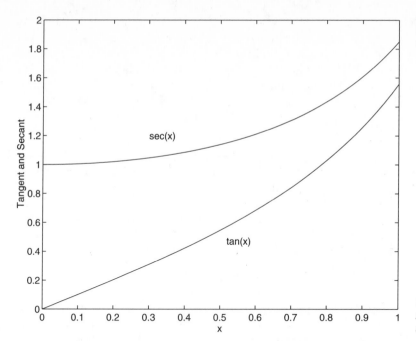

Figure 4.2–5
Application of the `gtext`
and `text` commands.

command, which requires you to specify the coordinates of the label. The syntax of the `gtext` command is `gtext('string')`, where `string` is a text string that specifies the label of your choice. When this command is executed, MATLAB waits for a mouse button or a key to be pressed while the mouse pointer is within the figure window; the label is placed at that position of the mouse pointer. You may use more than one `gtext` command for a given plot.

The `text` command, `text(x,y,'string')`, adds a text string to the plot at the location specified by the coordinates `x,y`. These coordinates are in the same units as the plot's data. The following script file illustrates the uses of the `gtext` and `text` commands and was used to create the plot shown in Figure 4.2–5.

```
x = [0:.01:1];
y = tan(x);
z = sec(x);
plot(x,y,x,z),xlabel('x'), ...
ylabel('Tangent and Secant'),gtext('tan(x)'), ...
text(.3,1.2,'sec(x)')
```

Of course, finding the proper coordinates to use with the `text` command usually requires some trial and error.

Graphical Solution of Equations

When we need to solve two equations in two unknown variables, we can plot the equations. The solution corresponds to the intersection of the two lines. If they do not intersect, there is no solution. If they intersect more than once, there are multiple solutions. A limitation of this approach is that we must know the approximate ranges of the two variables so that we can generate the plot. Another limitation is that the accuracy of the solution is limited by the accuracy with which we can read the plot. Of course, we can always expand the plot to increase the accuracy.

Example 4.2–1   Load-line analysis of electrical circuits

Figure 4.2–6 is a representation of an electrical system with a power supply and a load. The power supply produces the fixed voltage v_1 and supplies the current i_1 required by the load, whose voltage drop is v_2. The current-voltage relationship for a specific load is found from experiments to be

$$i_1 = 0.16\left(e^{0.12v_2} - 1\right) \tag{4.2–1}$$

Suppose that the supply resistance is $R_1 = 30\ \Omega$ and the supply voltage is $v_1 = 15$ V. To select or design an adequate power supply, we need to determine how much current will be drawn from the power supply when this load is attached. Find the voltage drop v_2 as well.

Figure 4.2–6
Circuit representation of a power supply and a load.

Solution:

Using Kirchhoff's voltage law, we obtain

$$v_1 - i_1 R_1 - v_2 = 0$$

Solve this for i_1.

$$i_1 = -\frac{1}{R_1}v_2 + \frac{v_1}{R_1} = -\frac{1}{30}v_2 + \frac{15}{30} \tag{4.2–2}$$

The plot of this equation is a straight line called the *load line*. The load line is so named because it shows how the current drawn by the load changes as the load's voltage changes. To find i_1 and v_2,

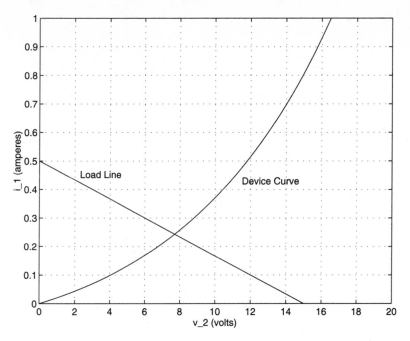

Figure 4.2-7
Plot of the load line and the device curve for Example 4.2-1.

we need to solve equations (4.2–1) and (4.2–2). Because of the term $e^{0.12v_2}$, it is not possible to obtain a solution using algebra. However, we can plot the curves corresponding to these equations and find their intersection. The MATLAB script file to do so follows, and Figure 4.2–7 shows the resulting plot.

```
v_2=[0:.01:20];
i_11=.16*(exp(.12*v_2)-1);
i_12=-(1/30)*v_2+.5;
plot(v_2,i_11,v_2,i_12),grid,xlabel('v_2 (volts)'),...
ylabel('i_1 (amperes)'),axis([0 20 0 1]),...
gtext('Load Line'),gtext('Device Curve')
```

From the figure we can see that the curves intersect at approximately $i_1 = 0.25$ amperes, $v_2 = 7.5$ volts. For a more accurate answer, change the axis statement to axis([7 8 .2 .3]) and obtain a new plot.

The hold Command

The hold command creates a plot that needs two or more plot commands. For example, suppose we wanted to plot $y = (3 + e^{-x}\sin 6x)/(4 + e^{-x}\cos 6x)$, $-1 \le x \le 1$ on the same plot with $z = (0.1 + 0.9i)^n$, where $0 \le n \le 10$. This plot requires two plot commands. The script file to create this plot using the hold command follows.

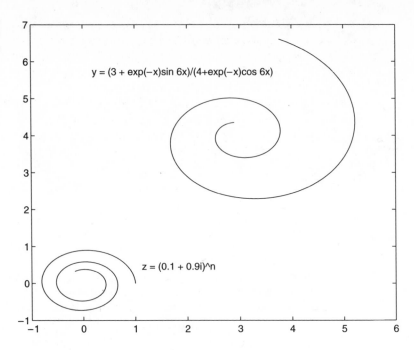

Figure 4.2–8
Application of the hold command.

```
x = [-1:.01:1];
y = (3+exp(-x).*sin(6*x))./(4+exp(-x).*cos(6*x));
plot((.1+.9i).^[0:.01:10]),hold,plot(x,y), ...
gtext('y =(3+exp(-x)sin 6x)/(4+exp(-x)cos 6x'), ...
gtext('z =(0.1 + 0.9i)^n')
```

Figure 4.2–8 shows the result.

Although it is not needed to generate multiple plots with the plot(x,y,u,v) type command, the hold command is especially

Table 4.2–2 Plot enhancement commands

Command	Description
axes	Creates axes objects.
gtext('text')	Places the string text in the figure window at a point specified by the mouse.
hold	Freezes the current plot for subsequent graphics commands.
legend('leg1','leg2', ...)	Creates a legend using the strings leg1, leg2, and so on and specifies its placement with the mouse.
plot(x,y,u,v)	Plots, on rectilinear axes, four arrays: y versus x and v versus u.
plot(x,y,'type')	Plots the array y versus the array x on rectilinear axes, using the line type, data marker, and colors specified in the string type. See Table 4.2–1.
plot(A)	Plots the columns of the $m \times n$ array A versus their indices and generates n curves.
plot(P,Q)	Plots array Q versus array P. See the text for a description of the possible variants involving vectors and/or matrices: plot(x,A), plot(A,x), and plot(A,B).
refresh	Redraws the current figure window.
subplot(m,n,p)	Splits the figure window into an array of subwindows with m rows and n columns and directs the subsequent plotting commands to the pth subwindow.
text(x,y,'text')	Places the string text in the figure window at a point specified by coordinates x, y.

useful with some of the advanced MATLAB toolbox commands that generate specialized plots. Some of these commands do not allow for more than one curve to be generated at a time, and so they must be executed more than once to generate multiple curves. The `hold` command is used to do this.

When more than one `plot` command is used, do not place any of the `gtext` commands before any `plot` command. Because the scaling changes as each `plot` command is executed, the label placed by the `gtext` command might end up in the wrong position. Table 4.2–2 summarizes the plot enhancement introduced in this section.

Test Your Understanding

T4.2–2 Plot the following two data sets on the same plot. For each set, $x = 0, 1, 2, 3, 4, 5$. Use a different data marker for each set. Connect the markers for the first set with solid lines. Connect the markers for the second set with dashed lines. Use a legend, and label the plot appropriately. The first set is $y = 11, 13, 8, 7, 5, 9$. The second set is $y = 2, 4, 5, 3, 2, 4$.

T4.2–3 Plot $y = \cosh x$ and $y = 0.5e^x$ on the same plot for $0 \leq x \leq 2$. Use different line types and a legend to distinguish the curves. Label the plot appropriately.

T4.2–4 Plot $y = \sinh x$ and $y = 0.5e^x$ on the same plot for $0 \leq x \leq 2$. Use a solid line type for each, the `gtext` command to label the $\sinh x$ curve, and the `text` command to label the $0.5e^x$ curve. Label the plot appropriately.

T4.2–5 Use the `hold` command and the `plot` command twice to plot $y = \sin x$ and $y = x - x^3/3$ on the same plot for $0 \leq x \leq 1$. Use a solid line type for each and use the `gtext` command to label each curve. Label the plot appropriately.

Text Enhancement in MATLAB 5

In MATLAB 5 you can create text, titles, and labels that contain mathematical symbols, Greek letters, and other effects such as italic. The new features are based on the TEX typesetting language [Lamport, 1994]. Here we give a summary of these features. For more information, including a list of the available characters, consult the online help for the `text` function.

The `text`, `gtext`, `title`, `xlabel`, and `ylabel` commands all require a string as their argument. For example, typing

```
>>title('A*exp(-t/tau)sin(omega t)')
```

produces a title that looks like `A*exp(-t/tau)sin(omega t)` but is supposed to represent the function $Ae^{-t/\tau}\sin(\omega t)$. The new features enable us to create a title that looks like the mathematical function by typing

```
>>title('Ae^{- t/\tau}sin(\omega t)')
```

The backslash character \ precedes all TEX character sequences. Thus the strings \tau and \omega represent the Greek letters τ and ω. Superscripts are created by typing ^; subscripts are created by typing _. To set multiple characters as superscripts or subscripts, enclose them in braces. For example, type `x_{13}` to produce x_{13}.

In mathematical text variables are usually set in italic, and functions, like sin, are set in roman type. To set a character, say, x, in italic using the TEX commands, you type {\it x}. To set the `title` function using these conventions, you would type

```
>>title('{\it Ae}^{-{\it t/\tau}}\sin({\it \omega t})
```

Hints for Improving Plots

The following actions, while not required, can nevertheless improve the appearance of your plots:

1. Start scales from zero whenever possible. This technique prevents a false impression of the magnitudes of any variations shown on the plot.

2. Use sensible tick-mark spacing. For example, if the quantities are months, choose a spacing of 12 because 1/10 of a year is not a convenient division. Space tick marks as close as is useful, but no closer. For example, if the data is given monthly over a range of 24 months, 48 tick marks would be too dense, and also unnecessary.

3. Minimize the number of zeros in the data being plotted. For example, use a scale in millions of dollars when appropriate, instead of a scale in dollars with six zeros after every number.

4. Determine the minimum and maximum data values for each axis before plotting the data. Then set the axis limits to cover the entire data range plus an additional amount to allow convenient tick-mark spacing to be selected. For example, if the data on the x-axis ranges from 1.2 to 9.6, a good choice for axis limits is 0 to 10. This choice allows you to use a tick spacing of 1 or 2.

5. Use a different line type for each curve when several are plotted on a single plot and they cross each other; for example, use a solid line, a dashed line, and combinations of lines and symbols. Beware of using colors to distinguish plots if you are going to make black-and-white printouts and copies.

6. Do not put many curves on one plot, particularly if they will be close to each other or cross one another.

7. Use the same scale limits and tick spacing on each plot if you need to compare information on more than one plot.

**Special
Plot Types**

153

In this section we show how to obtain logarithmic axes; how to change the default tick-mark spacing and labels; and how to produce stem, stairs, bar, and polar plots.

Logarithmic Plots

Thus far we have used only rectilinear scales. However, *logarithmic* scales are also widely used. (We often refer to them with the shorter term, *log* scale.) Two common reasons for choosing a log scale are (1) to represent a data set that covers a wide range of values and (2) to identify certain trends in data. As you will see, certain types of functional relationships appear as straight lines when plotted using a log scale. This method makes it easier to identify the function. A *log-log* plot has log scales on both axes. A *semilog* plot has a log scale on only one axis.

For example, Figures 4.3–1 and 4.3–2 show plots of the function:

$$y = \sqrt{\frac{100(1 - 0.01x^2)^2 + 0.02x^2}{(1 - x^2)^2 + 0.1x^2}}$$

The first plot uses rectilinear scales, and the second is a log-log plot. Because of the wide range in values on both the abscissa and ordinate, rectilinear scales do not reveal the important features.

Figure 4.3–1
Rectilinear scales cannot properly display variations over wide ranges.

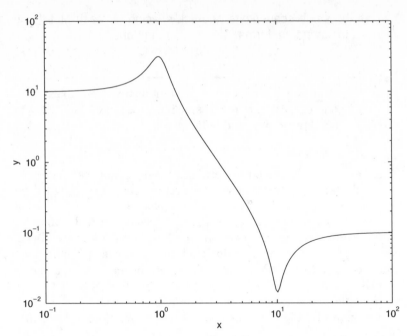

Figure 4.3–2
A log-log plot can display
wide variations in data
values.

It is important to remember the following points when using log scales:

1. You cannot plot negative numbers on a log scale, because the logarithm of a negative number is not defined.

2. You cannot plot the number 0 on a log scale, because $\log_{10} 0 = \ln 0 = -\infty$. You must choose an appropriately small number as the lower limit on the plot.

3. The tick-mark labels on a log scale are the actual values being plotted; they are not the logarithms of the numbers. For example, the range of x values in the plot in Figure 4.3–2 is from $10^{-1} = 0.1$ to $10^2 = 100$.

4. Equal distances on a log scale correspond to multiplication by the same constant (as opposed to addition of the same constant on a rectilinear scale). For example, all numbers that differ by a factor of 10 are separated by the same distance on a log scale. That is, the distance between 0.3 and 3 is the same as the distance between 30 and 300. This separation is referred to as a *decade* or *cycle*. The plot shown in Figure 4.3–2 covers three decades in x (from 0.1 to 100) and four decades in y and is thus called a *four-by-three-cycle plot*.

5. Gridlines and tick marks within a decade are unevenly spaced. If 8 gridlines or tick marks occur within the decade, they correspond to values equal to $2, 3, 4, \ldots, 8, 9$ times the value represented by the first gridline or tick mark of the decade.

MATLAB has three commands for generating plots having log scales. The appropriate command depends on which axis must have a log scale. Follow these rules:

1. Use the `loglog(x,y)` command to have both scales logarithmic.
2. Use the `semilogx(x,y)` command to have the *x* scale logarithmic and the *y* scale rectilinear.
3. Use the `semilogy(x,y)` command to have the *y* scale logarithmic and the *x* scale rectilinear.

We can plot multiple curves with these commands just as with the `plot` command. In addition, we can use the other commands, such as `grid`, `xlabel`, and `axis`, in the same manner.

Figure 4.3–3 shows plots made with the `plot` command and the three logarithmic plot commands. The same two data sets were used for each plot. The session follows.

```
>>x = [1,1.5,2,2.5,3,3.5,4];
>>y1 = [4,3.16,2.67,2.34,2.1,1.92,1.78];
>>y2 = [8.83,7.02,5.57,4.43,3.52,2.8,2.22];
>>subplot(2,2,1)
>>plot(x,y1,'o',x,y2,'x'),xlabel('x'),ylabel('y'),axis([1 4 0 10])
>>subplot(2,2,2)
>>semilogy(x,y1,'o',x,y2,'x'),xlabel('x'),ylabel('y')
>>subplot(2,2,3)
>>semilogx(x,y1,'o',x,y2,'x'),xlabel('x'),ylabel('y')
>>subplot(2,2,4)
>>loglog(x,y1,'o',x,y2,'x'),xlabel('x'),ylabel('y'), ...
axis([1 4 1 10])
```

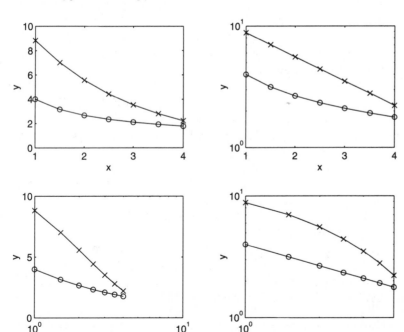

Figure 4.3–3
Two data sets plotted on four types of plots.

Note that the first data set lies close to a straight line only when plotted with both scales logarithmic, and the second data set nearly forms a straight line only on the semilog plot where the vertical axis is logarithmic. In section 4.4 we explain how to use these observations to derive a mathematical model for the data.

Frequency Response Plots and Filter Circuits

Many electrical applications use specialized circuits called *filters* to remove signals having certain frequencies. Filters work by responding only to signals that have the desired frequencies. These signals are said to "pass through" the circuit. The signals that do not pass through are said to be "filtered out." For example, a particular circuit in a radio is designed to respond only to signals having the broadcast frequency of the desired radio station. Other circuits, such as those constituting the graphic equalizer, enable the user to select certain musical frequencies such as bass or treble to be passed through to the speakers.

The mathematics required to design filter circuits is covered in upper-level engineering courses. However, a simple plot often describes the characteristics of filter circuits. Such a plot, called a *frequency-response plot*, is often provided when you buy a speaker-amplifier system.

Example 4.3–1   Frequency-response plot of a low-pass filter
The circuit shown in Figure 4.3–4 consists of a resistor and a capacitor and is thus called an RC circuit. If we apply a sinusoidal voltage v_i, called the input voltage, to the circuit as shown, then eventually the output voltage v_o will be sinusoidal also, with the same frequency but with a different amplitude and shifted in time relative to the input voltage. Specifically, if $v_i = A_i \sin \omega t$, then $v_o = A_o \sin(\omega t + \phi)$. The frequency-response plot is a plot of A_o/A_i versus frequency ω. It is usually plotted on logarithmic axes. Upper-level engineering courses explain that for the RC circuit shown, this ratio depends on ω and RC as follows:

$$\frac{A_o}{A_i} = \left| \frac{1}{RCs + 1} \right| \qquad (4.3\text{–}1)$$

Figure 4.3–4
An RC circuit.

where $s = \omega i$. For $RC = 0.1$ second, obtain the loglog plot of $|A_o/A_i|$ versus ω and use it to find the range of frequencies for which the output amplitude A_o is less than 70 percent of the input amplitude A_i.

Solution:

As with many graphical procedures, you must guess a range for the parameters in question. Here we must guess a range to use for the frequency ω. If we use $1 \leq \omega \leq 100$ radians per second, we will see the part of the curve that is of interest. The MATLAB script file is as follows:

```
RC = .1;
s = [1:100]*i;
M = abs(1./(RC*s+1));
loglog(imag(s),M),grid,xlabel('Frequency(rad/sec)'),...
ylabel('Output/Input Ratio'),...
title('Frequency Response of a Low-Pass RC Circuit (RC = 0.1)')
```

Figure 4.3–5 shows the plot. We can see that the output/input ratio A_o/A_i decreases as the frequency ω increases. The ratio is approximately 0.7 at $\omega = 10$ radians per second. The amplitude of any input signal having a frequency greater than this frequency will decrease by at least 30 percent. Thus this circuit is called a *low-pass* filter because it passes low-frequency signals better than it passes high-frequency signals. Such a circuit is often used to filter out noise from nearby electrical machinery.

Figure 4.3–5
Frequency-response plot of a low-pass RC circuit.

Controlling Tick-Mark Spacing and Labels

The MATLAB set command is a powerful command for changing the properties of MATLAB "objects," such as plots. We will not cover this command in depth, but will show how to use it to specify the spacing and labels of the tick marks. To explore this command further, type help set and help axes. Many of the properties that affect the appearance of plot axes are described under the axes command, which should not be confused with the axis command.

Up to now we changed the tick-mark spacing by using the axis command and hoped that the MATLAB autoscaling feature chose a proper tick-mark spacing. We can also use the following command to specify this spacing.

```
set(gca,'XTick',[xmin:dx:xmax],'YTick',[ymin:dy:ymax])
```

xmin and xmax are the x values that specify the placement of the first and the last tick marks on the x-axis, and dx specifies the spacing between tick marks. You would normally use the same values for xmin and xmax in both the set and axis commands. Similar definitions apply to the y axis values ymin, ymax, and dy. The term gca stands for "get current axes." It tells MATLAB to apply the new values to the axes currently used for plotting. For example, to plot $y = 0.25x^2$ for $0 \le x \le 2$, with tick marks spaced at intervals of 0.2 on the x-axis and 0.1 on the y-axis, you would type:

```
>>x = [0:.01:2]:
>>y =.25*x.^2;
>>plot(x,y),set(gca,'XTick',[0:.2:2],'YTick',[0:.1:1]), ...
xlabel('x'),ylabel('y')
```

The result appears in Figure 4.3–6.

The set command can also be used to change the tick-mark labels, for example, from numbers to text. Suppose we sell printers, and we want to plot the monthly sales in thousands of dollars from January to June. We can use the set command to label the x-axis with the names of the months, as shown in the following session. The vector x contains the number of the month, and the vector y contains the monthly sales in thousands of dollars.

```
>>x = [1:6];
>>y = [13,5,7,14,10,12];
>>plot(x,y,'o',x,y), ...
set(gca,'XTicklabel',['Jan';'Feb';'Mar';'Apr';'May';'Jun']),...
set(gca,'XTick',[1:6]),axis([1 6 0 15]),xlabel('Month'), ...
ylabel('Monthly Sales ($1000)'), ...
title('Printer Sales For January To June, 1997')
```

The plot appears in Figure 4.3–7. In MATLAB 4, use the plural 'XTickLabels'.

**Special
Plot Types**

Figure 4.3–6
An example of controlling
the tick-mark spacing with
the set command.

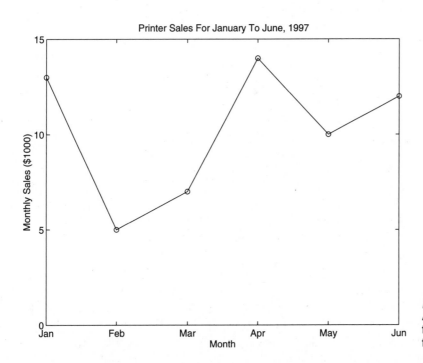

Figure 4.3–7
An example of controlling
the tick-mark labels with
the set command.

Note the labels in the `set` command must be enclosed in single quotes and are specified as a column vector; thus they are separated by semicolons. Another requirement is that all the labels must have the same number of characters (here, three characters). Table 4.3–2 summarizes the `set` command.

Stem, Stairs, and Bar Plots

STEM PLOTS

STAIRS PLOTS

BAR PLOTS

MATLAB has three other plot types that are related to xy plots. These are the stem, stairs, and bar plots. Their syntax is very simple; namely, `stem(x,y)`, `stairs(x,y)`, and `bar(x,y)`. If we replace the `plot(x,y,'o',x,y)` command in the preceding session with these commands, one at a time, we obtain the plots shown in Figures 4.3–8, 4.3–9, and 4.3–10, respectively.

Polar Plots

POLAR PLOTS

Polar plots are two-dimensional plots made using polar coordinates. If the polar coordinates are (θ, r), where θ is the angular coordinate and r is the radial coordinate of a point, then the command `polar(theta,r)` will produce the polar plot. A grid is automatically overlaid on a polar plot. This grid consists of concentric circles and radial lines every 30°. The `title` and `gtext` commands can be used to place a title and text. The variant command `polar(theta,r,'type')` can be used to specify the line type or data marker, just as with the `plot` command.

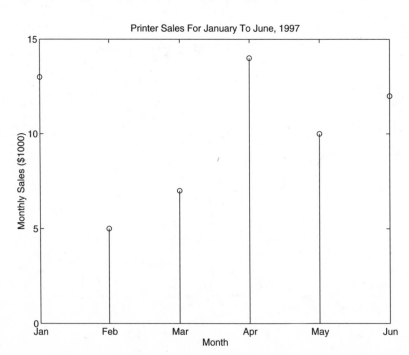

Figure 4.3–8
An example of a stem plot.

Printer Sales For January To June, 1997

Figure 4.3–9
An example of a stairs plot.

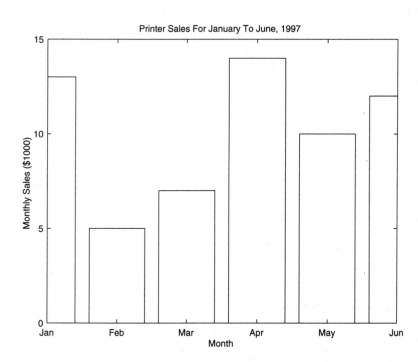

Printer Sales For January To June, 1997

Figure 4.3–10
An example of a bar plot.

Example 4.3–2 Plotting orbits   The equation

$$r = \frac{p}{1 - \epsilon \cos \theta}$$

describes the polar coordinates of an orbit measured from one of the orbit's two focal points. For objects in orbit around the sun, the sun is at one of the focal points. Thus r is the distance of the object from the sun. The parameters p and ϵ determine the size of the orbit and its eccentricity, respectively. A circular orbit has an eccentricity of 0; if $0 < \epsilon < 1$, the orbit is elliptical; and if $\epsilon > 1$, the orbit is hyperbolic. Obtain the polar plot that represents an orbit having $\epsilon = 0.5$ and $p = 2$ AU (AU stands for "astronomical unit"; 1 AU is the mean distance from the sun to Earth). How far away does the orbiting object get from the sun? How close does it approach Earth's orbit?

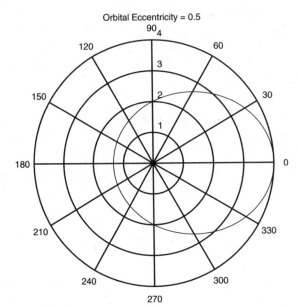

Figure 4.3–11
A polar plot showing an orbit having an eccentricity of 0.5.

Solution:

Figure 4.3–11 shows the polar plot of the orbit. The plot was generated by the following session.

```
>>theta = [0:pi/90:2*pi];
>>r = 2./(1-0.5*cos(theta));
>>polar(theta,r),title('Orbital Eccentricity = 0.5')
```

The sun is at the origin, and the plot's concentric circular grid enables us to determine that the closest and farthest distances the object is from the sun are approximately 1.3 and 4 AU. Earth's orbit, which is nearly circular, is represented by the innermost circle. Thus the closest the object gets to Earth's orbit is approximately 0.3 AU. The radial grid lines allow us to determine that when $\theta = 90°$ and $270°$, the object is 2 AU from the sun.

Test Your Understanding

T4.3–1 Obtain the plots shown in Figure 4.3–12. The power function is $y = 2/\sqrt{x}$, and the exponential function is $y = 10^{1-x}$.

T4.3–2 Plot the function $y = 8x^3$ for $-1 \le x \le 1$ with a tick spacing of 0.25 on the x-axis and 2 on the y-axis.

T4.3–3 The *spiral of Archimedes* is described by the polar coordinates (θ, r), where $r = a\theta$. Obtain a polar plot of this spiral for $0 \le \theta \le 4\pi$, with the parameter $a = 2$.

Figure 4.3–12
The power function $y = 2x^{-0.5}$ and the exponential function $y = 10^{1-x}$.

Table 4.3–1   Specialized plot commands

Command	Description
`bar(x,y)`	Creates a bar chart of *y* versus *x*.
`loglog(x,y)`	Produces a log-log plot of *y* versus *x*.
`polar(theta,r,'type')`	Produces a polar plot from the polar coordinates θ and *r*, using the line type, data marker, and colors specified in the string `type`.
`semilogx(x,y)`	Produces a semilog plot of *y* versus *x* with logarithmic abscissa scale.
`semilogy(x,y)`	Produces a semilog plot of *y* versus *x* with logarithmic ordinate scale.
`stairs(x,y)`	Produces a stairs plot of *y* versus *x*.
`stem(x,y)`	Produces a stem plot of *y* versus *x*.

Table 4.3–2   The `set` command

The `set` command specifies properties of objects such as axes. For example,

```
set(gca,'XTick',[xmin:dx:xmax],'YTick',[ymin:dy:ymax])
```

specifies the axis limits `xmin`, `xmax`, `ymin`, and `ymax` and the tick spacing `dx` and `dy`. The command

```
set(gca,'XTicklabel',['text'])
```

specifies the tick labels on the *x*-axis, where the string `text` is a column vector that specifies the tick labels. Each label must be enclosed in single quotes, and all labels must have the same number of characters. For more information, type `help axes`. In MATLAB 4, use the plural `'XTicklabels'`.

4.4

**Function
Discovery**

Function discovery is the process of finding, or "discovering," a function that can describe a particular set of data. The following three function types can often describe physical phenomena. For example, the *linear* function describes the voltage-current relation for a resistor ($V = iR$). The linear relation also describes the velocity versus time relation for an object with constant acceleration a ($v = at + v_0$). A *power* function describes the distance d traveled by a falling object versus time ($d = 0.5gt^2$). An *exponential* function can describe the temperature T of a cooling object ($T = T_0e^{-ct}$). The general forms of these functions are:

1. The *linear* function:

$$y(x) = mx + b \qquad\qquad (4.4-1)$$

Note that $y(0) = b$.

2. The *power* function:

$$y(x) = bx^m \qquad\qquad (4.4-2)$$

Note that $y(0) = 0$ if $m \geq 0$, and $y(0) = \infty$ if $m < 0$.

3. The *exponential* function:

$$y(x) = b(10)^{mx} \qquad \text{(4.4–3)}$$

or its equivalent form:

$$y = be^{mx} \qquad \text{(4.4–4)}$$

where e is the base of the natural logarithm ($\ln e = 1$). Note that $y(0) = b$ for both forms.

Each function gives a straight line when plotted using a specific set of axes:

1. The linear function $y = mx + b$ gives a straight line when plotted on rectilinear axes. Its slope is m and its intercept is b.
2. The power function $y = bx^m$ gives a straight line when plotted on log-log axes.
3. The exponential function $y = b(10)^{mx}$ and its equivalent form $y = be^{mx}$ give a straight line when plotted on a semilog plot whose y-axis is logarithmic.

These properties were illustrated in Figure 4.3–12, which shows the power function $y = 2x^{-0.5}$ and the exponential function $y = 10^{1-x}$.

We look for a straight line on the plot because it is relatively easy to recognize, and therefore we can easily tell whether the function will fit the data well. Using the following properties of base 10 logarithms, which are shared with natural logarithms, we have

$$\log_{10}(a\,b) = \log_{10} a + \log_{10} b$$

$$\log_{10}(a^m) = m \log_{10} a$$

Take the logarithm of both sides of the power equation $y = bx^m$ to obtain

$$\log_{10} y = \log_{10}(bx^m) = \log_{10} b + m \log_{10} x$$

This has the form

$$Y = B + mX$$

if we let $Y = \log_{10} y$, $X = \log_{10} x$, and $B = \log_{10} b$. Thus if we plot Y versus X on rectilinear scales, we will obtain a straight line whose slope is m and whose intercept is B. This process is the same as plotting $\log_{10} y$ versus $\log_{10} x$ on rectilinear scales, so we will obtain a straight line whose slope is m and whose intercept is $\log_{10} b$. This process is equivalent to plotting y versus x on *log-log* axes. Thus if the data can be described by the power function, it will form a straight line when plotted on log-log axes.

Taking the logarithm of both sides of the exponential equation $y = b(10)^{mx}$ we obtain

$$\log_{10} y = \log_{10}\left[b(10)^{mx}\right] = \log_{10} b + mx \log_{10} 10 = \log_{10} b + mx$$

because $\log_{10} 10 = 1$. This has the form

$$Y = B + mx$$

if we let $Y = \log_{10} y$ and $B = \log_{10} b$. Thus if we plot Y versus x on rectilinear scales, we will obtain a straight line whose slope is m and whose intercept is B. This process is the same as plotting $\log_{10} y$ versus x on rectilinear scales, so we will obtain a straight line whose slope is m and whose intercept is $\log_{10} b$. This is equivalent to plotting y on a log axis and x on a rectilinear axis (that is, *semilog* axes). Thus if the data can be described by the exponential function, it will form a straight line when plotted on semilog axes (with the log axis used for the ordinate).

Taking the logarithm of both sides of the equivalent exponential form $y = be^{mx}$ gives

$$\log_{10} y = \log_{10}(be^{mx}) = \log_{10} b + mx \log_{10} e$$

This has the form

$$Y = B + Mx$$

if we let $Y = \log_{10} y$, $B = \log 10b$, and $M = m \log_{10} e$. Thus if we plot Y versus x on rectilinear scales, we will obtain a straight line whose slope is M and whose intercept is B. This process is the same as plotting $\log_{10} y$ versus x on rectilinear scales, so we will obtain a straight line whose slope is $m \log_{10} e$ and whose intercept is $\log_{10} b$. This is equivalent to plotting y on a log axis and x on a rectilinear axis. Thus both equivalent exponential forms (4.4–3) and (4.4–4) will plot as a straight line on semilog axes.

Steps for Function Discovery

Here is a summary of the procedure to find a function that describes a given set of data. We assume that one of the three function types given above can describe the data. Fortunately, many applications generate data that these functions can describe.

1. Examine the data near the origin. The exponential function can never pass through the origin (unless of course $b = 0$, which is a trivial case). (See Figure 4.4–1 for examples with $b = 1$.) The linear function can pass through the origin only if $b = 0$. The power function can pass through the origin but only if $m > 0$. (See Figure 4.4–2 for examples with $b = 1$.)

2. Plot the data using rectilinear scales. If it forms a straight line, then it can be represented by the linear function and you are

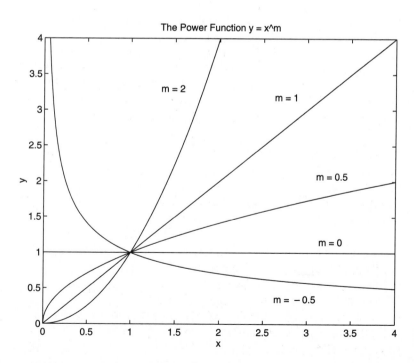

Figure 4.4–1
Examples of exponential
functions.

Figure 4.4–2
Examples of power
functions.

finished. Otherwise, if you have data at $x = 0$, then

a. If $y(0) = 0$, try the power function.
b. If $y(0) \neq 0$, try the exponential function.

If data is not given for $x = 0$, proceed to step 3.

3. If you suspect a power function, plot the data using log-log scales. Only a power function will form a straight line on a log-log plot. If you suspect an exponential function, plot the data using the semilog scales. Only an exponential function will form a straight line on a semilog plot. This method is the quickest way to identify the function.

4. In the function discovery application, we use the log-log and semilog plots *only* to identify the function type, but not to find the coefficients b and m. The reason is that it is difficult to interpolate on log scales.

    We can find the values of b and m with the MATLAB `polyfit` function. This function finds the coefficients of a polynomial of specified degree n that best fits the data, in the so-called least squares sense. You will see what this means in Chapter 5. The syntax appears in Table 4.4–1.

    Because we are assuming that our data will form a straight line on either a rectilinear, semilog, or log-log plot, we are interested only in a polynomial that corresponds to a straight line; that is, a first-degree polynomial, which we will denote as $w = p_1 z + p_2$. Thus referring to Table 4.4–1, we see that the vector p will be $[p_1, p_2]$ if n is 1. This polynomial has a different interpretation in each of the three cases:

    - **The linear function:** $y = mx + b$. In this case the variables w and z in the polynomial $w = p_1 z + p_2$ are the original data variables x and y, and we can find the linear function that fits the data by typing $p = polyfit(x,y,1)$. The first element p_1 of the vector p will be m, and the second element p_2 will be b.
    - **The power function:** $y = bx^m$. In this case

    $$\log_{10} y = m \log_{10} x + \log_{10} b \qquad (4.4\text{--}5)$$

    which has the form

    $$w = p_1 z + p_2$$

Table 4.4–1   The `polyfit` command

Command	Description
`p = polyfit(x,y,n)`	Fits a polynomial of degree n to data described by the vectors x and y, where x is the independent variable. Returns a row vector p of length $n + 1$ that contains the polynomial coefficients in order of descending powers.

where the polynomial variables w and z are related to the original data variables x and y by $w = \log_{10} y$ and $z = \log_{10} x$. Thus we can find the power function that fits the data by typing $p = \text{polyfit}(\log10(x),\log10(y),1)$. The first element p_1 of the vector p will be m, and the second element p_2 will be $\log_{10} b$. We can find b from $b = 10^{p_2}$.

• **The exponential function:** $y = b(10)^{mx}$. In this case

$$\log_{10} y = mx + \log_{10} b \tag{4.4--6}$$

which has the form

$$w = p_1 z + p_2$$

where the polynomial variables w and z are related to the original data variables x and y by $w = \log_{10} y$ and $z = x$. Thus we can find the exponential function that fits the data by typing $p = \text{polyfit}(x,\log10(y),1)$. The first element p_1 of the vector p will be m, and the second element p_2 will be $\log_{10} b$. We can find b from $b = 10^{p_2}$.

Applications

Function discovery is useful in all branches of engineering. Here we give three examples of applications in structural vibration, heat transfer, and fluid mechanics. The following example illustrates a common problem in structural engineering—the estimation of the deflection characteristics of a cantilever support beam.

Example 4.4–1   A cantilever beam-deflection model
The deflection of a cantilever beam is the distance its end moves in response to a force applied at the end (Figure 4.4–3).

Figure 4.4–3
An experiment to measure force and deflection in a cantilever beam.

The following table gives the deflection x that was produced in a particular beam by the given applied force f. Is there a set of axes (rectilinear, semilog, or log-log) with which the data plot is a straight line? If so, use that plot to find a functional relation between f and x.

Force f (pounds)	Deflection x (inches)
0	0
100	0.09
200	0.18
300	0.28
400	0.37
500	0.46
600	0.55
700	0.65
800	0.74

Solution:

The following MATLAB script file generates two plots on rectilinear axes. The data is entered in the arrays `deflection` and `force`.

```
% Enter the data.
deflection = [0,.09,.18,.28,.37,.46,.55,.65,.74];
force = [0:100:800];
%
% Plot the data on rectilinear scales.
subplot(2,1,1)
plot(force,deflection,'o'), ...
xlabel('Applied Force (lb)'),ylabel('Deflection (inches)'), ...
axis([0 800 0 .8])
```

The plot appears in the first subplot in Figure 4.4–4. The data points appear to lie on a straight line that can be described by the relation $f = kx$, where k is called the beam's *spring constant*. We can find the value of k by using the `polyfit` command as shown in the following script file which is a continuation of the preceding script file.

```
% Fit a straight line to the data.
p = polyfit(force,deflection,1);
k = 1/p(1);
fprintf('The spring constant k is %4.0f\n',k)
% Plot the fitted line and the data.
f = [0:2:800];
x = f/k;
subplot(2,1,2)
plot(f,x,force,deflection,'o'), ...
xlabel('Applied Force (lb)'),ylabel('Deflection (inches)'), ...
axis([0 800 0 .8])
```

Figure 4.4–4
Plots for the cantilever beam example.

This file computes the value of the spring constant to be $k = 1079$ pounds per inch. Thus the force is related to the deflection by $f = 1079x$. The second subplot in Figure 4.4–4 shows the data and the line x = f/k.

Heat Transfer

Engineers are often required to predict the temperatures that will occur in buildings and various industrial processes. This area of study is called *heat transfer*. The next example illustrates how we can use function discovery to predict the temperature dynamics of a cooling object.

Example 4.4–2 Temperature dynamics
The temperature of coffee cooling in a porcelain mug at room temperature (68°F) was measured at various times. The data follows.

Time t (sec)	Temperature T (°F)
0	145
620	130
2266	105
3482	90

Develop a model of the coffee's temperature as a function of time and use the model to estimate how long it will take the temperature to reach 120°F.

Figure 4.4–5
Temperature of a cooling
cup of coffee.

Solution:

Because $T(0)$ is finite but nonzero, the power function cannot describe this data, so we do not bother to plot the data on log-log axes. Figure 4.4–5 shows the plots used to solve the problem. The following MATLAB script file generates the first two plots. The time data is entered in the array `time`, and the temperature data is entered in `temp`.

```
% Enter the data.
time = [0,620,2266,3482];
temp = [145,130,105,90];
%
% Plot the data on rectilinear scales.
subplot(2,2,1)
plot((time,temp,time,temp,'o'),xlabel('Time (sec)'), ...
ylabel('Temperature (deg F)')
%
% Plot the data on semilog scales.
subplot(2,2,2)
semilogy((time,temp,time,temp,'o'),xlabel('Time (sec)'), ...
ylabel('Temperature (deg F)')
```

The data forms a straight line on the semilog plot only. Thus it can be described with the exponential function $T = b(10)^{mt}$. Using the `polyfit` command, the following lines can be added to the script file.

```
% Fit a straight line to the transformed data.
p = polyfit(time,log10(temp),1)
m = p(1);
b = 10^p(2)
fprintf('The m coefficient is:  %1.4e\n',m)
fprintf('The b coefficient is:  %1.4e\n',b)
```

The computed values are $m = -5.86 \times 10^{-5}$ and $b = 143.2$. Thus our derived model is $T = 143.2(10)^{-5.86 \times 10^{-5}t}$. To estimate how long it will take for the coffee to cool to 120°F, we must solve the equation $120 = b(10)^{mt}$ for t. The solution is $t = (\log_{10} 120 - \log_{10} b)/m$. The MATLAB command for this calculation is shown in the following script file, which produces the third and fourth subplots shown in Figure 4.4–5.

```
% Compute the time to reach 120 degrees.
t_120 = (log10(120)-log10(b))/m
fprintf('The time to reach 120 degrees is %3.0f\n',t_120)
% Show the derived curve and estimated point on semilog scales.
t = [0:10:4000];
T = b*10.^(m*t);
subplot(2,2,3)
semilogy(t,T,time,temp,'o',t_120,120,'+'),xlabel('Time (sec)'), ...
ylabel('Temperature (deg F)')
%
% Show the derived curve and estimated point on rectilinear scales.
subplot(2,2,4)
plot(t,T,time,temp,'o',t_120,120,'+'),xlabel('Time (sec)'),...
ylabel('Temperature (deg F)')
```

The computed value of `t_120` is 1311. Thus the time to reach 120° F is 1311 seconds. The plot of the model, along with the data and the estimated point (1311,120) marked with a + sign, is shown in the third and fourth subplots in Figure 4.4–5. Because the graph of our model lies near the data points, we can treat its prediction of 1311 seconds with some confidence.

Interpolation and Extrapolation

After we discover a functional relation that describes the data, we can use it to predict conditions that lie *within* the range of the original data. This process is called *interpolation*. For example, we can use the coffee cup model to estimate how long it takes for the coffee to cool to 120°F because we have data below and above 120°F. We can be fairly confident of this prediction because our model describes the temperature data very well.

INTERPOLATION

Extrapolation is the process of using the model to predict conditions that lie *outside* the original data range. Extrapolation might be used in the beam example to predict how much force would

EXTRAPOLATION

be required to bend the beam 1.2 inches. (The predicted value is found from the model to be $f = 1079(1.2) = 1295$ pounds.) We must be careful when using extrapolation because we usually have no reason to believe that the mathematical model is valid beyond the range of the original data. For example, if we continue to bend the beam, eventually the force is no longer proportional to the deflection and becomes much greater than that predicted by the linear model $f = kx$.

Extrapolation has a use in making tentative predictions, which must be backed up by testing. The next example describes an application of extrapolation.

Hydraulic Engineering

Torricelli's principle of hydraulic resistance states that the volume flow rate f of a liquid through a restriction—such as an opening or a valve—is proportional to the square root of the pressure drop p across the restriction; that is,

$$q = c \sqrt{p} \qquad (4.4-7)$$

where c is a constant. In many applications the weight of liquid in a tank causes the pressure drop (see Figure 4.4–6). In such situations Torricelli's principle states that the flow rate is proportional to the square root of the volume V of liquid in the tank. Thus

$$f = r \sqrt{V}$$

where r is a constant.

Torricelli's principle is widely used to design valves and piping systems for many applications, including water-supply engineering, hydraulically powered machinery, and chemical-processing systems. Here we apply it to a familiar item, a coffee pot.

Figure 4.4–6
An experiment to verify
Torricelli's principle.

Example 4.4–3 Hydraulic resistance

A 15-cup coffee pot (see Figure 4.4–6) was placed under a water faucet and filled to the 15-cup line. With the outlet valve open, the faucet's flow rate was adjusted until the water level remained constant at 15 cups, and the time for one cup to flow out of the pot was measured. This experiment was repeated with the pot filled to the various levels shown in the following table:

Liquid volume V (cups)	Time to fill one cup t (secs)
15	6
12	7
9	8
6	9

(a) Use the preceding data to verify Torricelli's principle for the coffee pot and to obtain a relation between the flow rate and the number of cups in the pot. (b) The manufacturer wants to make a 36-cup pot using the same outlet valve but is concerned that a cup will fill too quickly, causing spills. Extrapolate the relation developed in part (a) and predict how long it will take to fill one cup when the pot contains 36 cups.

Solution:

(a) Torricelli's principle in equation form is $f = rV^{1/2}$, where f is the flow rate through the outlet valve in cups per second, V is the volume of liquid in the pot in cups, and r is a constant whose value is to be found. We see that this relation is a power function where the exponent is 0.5. Thus if we plot $\log_{10}(f)$ versus $\log_{10}(V)$, we should obtain a straight line. The values for f are obtained from the reciprocals of the given data for t. That is, $f = 1/t$ cups per second.

The MATLAB script file follows. The resulting plots appear in Figure 4.4–7. The volume data is entered in the array `cups`, and the time data is entered in `meas_times`.

```
% Data for the problem.
cups = [6,9,12,15];
meas_times = [9,8,7,6];
meas_flow = 1./meas_times;
%
% Fit a straight line to the transformed data.
p = polyfit(log10(cups),log10(meas_flow),1);
coeffs = [p(1),10^p(2)];
m = coeffs(1);
b = coeffs(2);
fprintf('The m coefficient is %1.4e\n',m)
fprintf('The b coefficient is %1.4e\n',b)
%
```

Figure 4.4–7
Flow rate and fill time for a
coffee pot.

```
% Plot the data and the fitted line on a loglog plot to see
% how well the line fits the data.
x = [6:.01:40];
y = b*x.^m;
subplot(2,1,1)
loglog(x,y,cups,meas_flow,'o'),grid,xlabel('Volume (cups)'), ...
ylabel('Flow Rate (cups/sec)'),axis([5 15 .1 .3])
```

The computed values are $m = 0.433$ and $b = 0.0499$, and our derived relation is $f = 0.0499 V^{0.433}$. Because the exponent is 0.433, not 0.5, our model does not agree exactly with Torricelli's principle, but it is close. Note that the first plot in Figure 4.4–7 shows that the data points do not lie exactly on the fitted straight line. In this application it is difficult to measure the time to fill one cup with an accuracy greater than an integer second, so this inaccuracy could have caused our result to disagree with that predicted by Torricelli.

(b) Note that the fill time is $1/f$, the reciprocal of the flow rate. The remainder of the MATLAB script uses the derived flow rate relation $f = 0.0499 V^{0.433}$ to plot the extrapolated fill-time curve $1/f$ versus t.

```
% Plot the fill time curve extrapolated to 36 cups.
subplot(2,1,2)
plot(x,1./y,cups,meas_times,'o'),grid,xlabel('Volume(cups)'), ...
ylabel('Fill Time Per Cup (seconds)'),axis([5 36 0 10])
%
```

```
% Compute the fill time for V = 36 cups.
V = 36;
f_36 = b*V^m;
fprintf('The predicted fill time is (in seconds):  %1.1f\n',1/f_36)
```

The predicted fill time for one cup is 4.2 seconds. The manufacturer must now decide if this time is sufficient for the user to avoid overfilling. (In fact, the manufacturer did construct a 36-cup pot, and the fill time is approximately 4 seconds, which agrees with our prediction.)

Functions of two variables are sometimes difficult to visualize with a two-dimensional plot. Fortunately, MATLAB provides many functions for creating three-dimensional plots. Here we will summarize the basic functions to create three types of plots: line plots, surface plots, and contour plots. Information about the related functions is available in MATLAB help.

Three-Dimensional Line Plots

Lines in three-dimensional space can be plotted with the plot3 function. Its syntax is plot3(x,y,z). For example, the following equations generate a three-dimensional curve as the parameter t is varied over some range:

$$x = e^{-0.05t} \sin t$$

$$y = e^{-0.05t} \cos t$$

$$z = t$$

If we let t vary from $t = 0$ to $t = 10\pi$, the sin and cos functions will vary through five cycles, while the absolute values of x and y become smaller as t increases. This process results in the spiral curve shown in Figure 4.5–1, which was produced with the following session.

```
>>t = [0:pi/50:10*pi];
>>plot3(exp(-.05*t).*sin(t),exp(-.05*t).*cos(t),t),...
xlabel('x'),ylabel('y'),zlabel('z'),grid
```

Note that the grid and label functions work with the plot3 function, and that we can label the z-axis by using the zlabel function, which we have seen for the first time. Similarly, we can use the other plot-enhancement functions discussed in sections 4.1 and 4.2 to add a title and text and to specify line type and color.

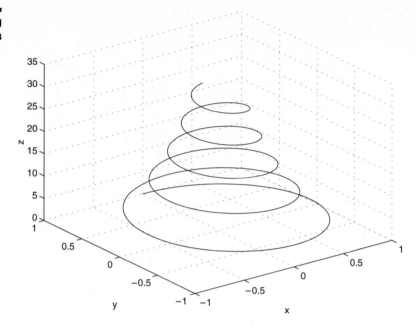

Figure 4.5–1
The curve $x = e^{-0.05t} \sin t$, $y = e^{-0.05t} \cos t, z = t$ plotted with the `plot3` function.

SURFACE MESH PLOT

Surface Mesh Plots

The function $z = f(x, y)$ represents a surface when plotted on xyz axes, and the `mesh` function provides the means to generate a surface plot. Before you can use this function, you must generate a grid of points in the xy plane, and then evaluate the function $f(x, y)$ at these points. The `meshgrid` function generates the grid. Its syntax is `[X,Y] = meshgrid(x,y)`. If `x = [xmin:xspacing:xmax]` and `y = [ymin:yspacing:ymax]`, then this function will generate the coordinates of a rectangular grid with one corner at $(xmin, ymin)$ and the opposite corner at $(xmax, ymax)$. Each rectangular panel in the grid will have a width equal to *xspacing* and a depth equal to *yspacing*. The resulting matrices X and Y contain the coordinate pairs of every point in the grid. These pairs are then used to evaluate the function.

The function `[X,Y] = meshgrid(x)` is equivalent to `[X,Y] = meshgrid(x,x)` and can be used if x and y have the same minimum values, the same maximum values, and the same spacing. Using this form, you can type `[X,Y] = meshgrid(min:spacing:max)`, where `min` and `max` specify the minimum and maximum values of both x and y and `spacing` is the desired spacing of the x and y values.

After the grid is computed, you create the surface plot with the `mesh` function. Its syntax is `mesh(x,y,z)`. The grid, label, and text functions can be used with the `mesh` function. The following session shows how to generate the surface plot of the function

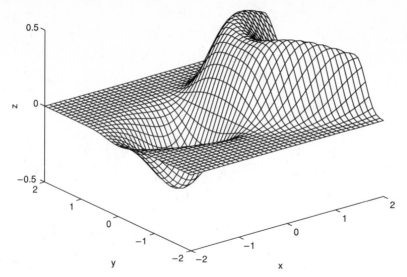

Figure 4.5–2
A plot of the surface $z = xe^{-[(x-y^2)^2+y^2]}$ created with the mesh function.

$z = xe^{-[(x-y^2)^2+y^2]}$, for $-2 \leq x \leq 2$ and $-2 \leq y \leq 2$, with a spacing of 0.1. This plot appears in Figure 4.5–2.

```
>>[X,Y] = meshgrid(-2:.1:2);
>>Z = X.*exp(-((X-Y.^2)^.2+Y.^2));
>>mesh(X,Y,Z),xlabel('x'),ylabel('y'),zlabel('z')
```

Be careful not to select too small a spacing for the x and y values for two reasons: (1) Small spacing creates small grid panels, which make the surface difficult to visualize, and (2) the matrices X and Y can become too large. (Users of the Student Edition of MATLAB are more likely to experience this second limitation than are users of the Professional Edition because of the smaller allowable array size.)

The surf and surfc functions are similar to mesh and meshc except that the former create a shaded surface plot.

Contour Plots

Topographic plots show the contours of the land by means of constant elevation lines. These lines are also called *contour lines*, and such a plot is called a *contour plot*. If you walk along a contour line, you remain at the same elevation. Contour plots can help you visualize the shape of a function. They can be created with the contour function, whose syntax is contour(X,Y,Z). You use this function the same way you use the mesh function; that is, first use the meshgrid function to generate the grid and then generate the function values. The following session generates the contour plot of the function whose surface plot is shown in Figure 4.5–2; namely, $z = xe^{-[(x-y^2)^2+y^2]}$, for $-2 \leq x \leq 2$ and

CONTOUR PLOT

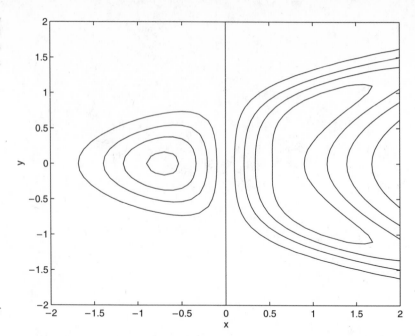

Figure 4.5–3
A contour plot of the
surface $z = xe^{-[(x-y^2)^2+y^2]}$
created with the contour
function.

$-2 \leq y \leq 2$, with a spacing of 0.1. This plot appears in Figure 4.5–3.

```
>>[X,Y] = meshgrid(-2:.1:2);
>>Z = X.*exp(-((X- Y.^2)^.2+Y.^2));
>>contour(X,Y,Z),xlabel('x'),ylabel('y')
```

Contour plots and surface plots can be used together to clarify the function. For example, unless the elevations are labeled on contour lines, you cannot tell whether there is a minimum or a maximum point. However, a glance at the surface plot will make this easy to determine. On the other hand, accurate measurements are not possible on a surface plot; these can be done on the contour plot because no distortion is involved. Thus a useful function is meshc, which shows the contour lines beneath the surface plot. The meshz function draws a series of vertical lines under the surface plot, while the waterfall function draws mesh lines in one direction only. The results of these functions are shown in Figure 4.5–4 for the function $z = xe^{-(x^2+y^2)}$.

Table 4.5–1 summarizes the functions introduced in this section.

Test Your Understanding

T4.5–1 Create a surface plot and a contour plot of the function
$z = (x - 2)^2 + 2xy + y^2$.

Figure 4.5–4
Plots of the surface
$z = xe^{-(x^2+y^2)}$ created
with the mesh function
and its variant forms:
meshc, meshz, and
waterfall.

Table 4.5–1 Three-dimensional plotting functions

Function	Description
contour(x,y,z)	Creates a contour plot.
mesh(x,y,z)	Creates a three-dimensional mesh surface plot.
meshc(x,y,z)	Same as mesh but draws a contour plot under the surface.
meshz(x,y,z)	Same as mesh but draws a series of vertical reference lines under the surface.
surf(x,y,z)	Creates a shaded three-dimensional mesh surface plot.
surfc(x,y,z)	Same as surf but draws a contour plot under the surface.
[X,Y] = meshgrid(x,y)	Creates the matrices X and Y from the vectors x and y to define a rectangular grid.
[X,Y] = meshgrid(x)	Same as [X,Y]= meshgrid(x,x).
waterfall(x,y,z)	Same as mesh but draws mesh lines in one direction only.

4.6

Summary

This chapter explained how to use the powerful MATLAB commands to create effective and pleasing two-dimensional and
three-dimensional plots. You learned an important application
of plotting—function discovery—which is the technique for using
data plots to obtain a mathematical function that describes the
data. This technique is widely used in engineering applications
because engineers frequently need to use mathematical models to
predict how their proposed designs will work.

  The following guidelines will help you create plots that effectively convey the desired information:

- Label each axis with the name of the quantity being plotted *and its
  units!*

Table 4.6–1 Guide to MATLAB commands introduced in Chapter 4

Basic xy plotting commands	Table 4.1–1
Data markers, line types, and colors	Table 4.2–1
Plot enhancement commands	Table 4.2–2
Specialized plot commands	Table 4.3–1
The set command	Table 4.3–2
Polynomial curve-fitting command	Table 4.4–1
Three-dimensional plotting functions	Table 4.5–1

- Use regularly spaced tick marks at convenient intervals along each axis.
- If you are plotting more than one curve or data set, label each on its plot or use a legend to distinguish them.
- If you are preparing multiple plots of a similar type or if the axes' labels cannot convey enough information, use a title.
- If you are plotting measured data, plot each data point in a given set with the same symbol, such as a circle, square, or cross.
- If you are plotting points generated by evaluating a function (as opposed to measured data), do *not* use a symbol to plot the points. Instead, connect the points with solid lines.

Table 4.6–1 is a guide to the MATLAB commands introduced in this chapter.

Key Terms with Page References

Abscissa, **132**	Ordinate, **132**
Axis label, **132**	Overlay plot, **142**
Axis limits, **136**	Polar plot, **160**
Bar plot, **160**	Scale, **132**
Contour plot, **179**	Stairs plot, **160**
Data symbol, **133**	Stem plot, **160**
Extrapolation, **173**	Subplot, **142**
Interpolation, **173**	Surface mesh plot, **178**
Legend, **133**	Tick mark, **132**

Problems

You can find the answers to problems marked with an asterisk at the end of the text.

Be sure to label and format properly any plots required by the following problems. Label each axis properly. Use a legend, data markers, or different line types as needed. Choose proper axis scaling and tick-mark spacing. Use a title, a grid, or both if they help to interpret the plot.

1.* *Breakeven analysis* determines the production volume at which the total production cost is equal to the total revenue. At the breakeven point, there is neither profit nor loss. In general, production costs consist of fixed costs and variable costs. Fixed costs include salaries of those not directly involved with production, factory maintenance costs, insurance costs, and so on. Variable costs depend on production volume and include material costs, labor costs, and energy costs. In the following analysis, assume that we produce only what we can sell; thus the production quantity equals the sales. Let the production quantity be Q, in gallons per year.

   Consider the following costs for a certain chemical product:

   Fixed cost: $3 million per year.

   Variable cost: 2.5 cents per gallon of product.

   The selling price is 5.5 cents per gallon.
   Use this data to plot the total cost and the revenue versus Q, and graphically determine the breakeven point. Fully label the plot and mark the breakeven point. For what range of Q is production profitable? For what value of Q is the profit a maximum?

2. Consider the following costs for a certain chemical product:

   Fixed cost: $2.045 million/year.

   Variable costs:

   Material cost: 62 cents per gallon of product.

   Energy cost: 24 cents per gallon of product.

   Labor cost: 16 cents per gallon of product.

   Assume that we produce only what we sell. Let P be the selling price in dollars per gallon. Suppose that the selling price and the sales quantity Q are interrelated as follows: $Q = 6 \times 10^6 - 1.1 \times 10^6 P$. Accordingly, if we raise the price, the product becomes less competitive and sales drop.
   Use this information to plot the fixed and total variable costs versus Q, and graphically determine the breakeven point(s). Fully label the plot and mark the breakeven points. For what range of Q is the production profitable? For what value of Q is the profit a maximum?

3.* Roots of polynomials appear in many engineering applications, such as electrical circuit design. Find the real roots of the polynomial equation

$$4x^5 + 3x^4 - 95x^3 + 5x^2 - 10x + 80 = 0$$

   in the range $-10 \le x \le 10$ by plotting the polynomial.

4. To compute the forces in structures, engineers sometimes must solve equations similar to the following. Use the `fplot` function to find all the positive roots of this equation:

$$x \tan x = 7$$

5.*   Cables are used to suspend bridge decks and other structures. If a heavy uniform cable hangs suspended from its two endpoints, it takes the shape of a *catenary* curve whose equation is

$$y = a \cosh\left(\frac{x}{a}\right)$$

where a is the height of the lowest point on the chain above some horizontal reference line, x is the horizontal coordinate measured to the right from the lowest point, and y is the vertical coordinate measured up from the reference line.

   Let $a = 10$ meters. Plot the catenary curve for $-20 \leq x \leq 30$ meters. How high is each endpoint?

Section 4.2

6.   Plot columns 2 and 3 of the following matrix **A** versus column 1. The data in column1 is time (seconds). The data in columns 2 and 3 is force (Newtons).

$$\mathbf{A} = \begin{bmatrix} 0 & -8 & 6 \\ 5 & -4 & 3 \\ 10 & -1 & 1 \\ 15 & 1 & 0 \\ 20 & 2 & -1 \end{bmatrix}$$

7.*   Many engineering applications use the following "small angle" approximation for the sine to obtain a simpler model that is easy to understand and analyze. This approximation states that $\sin x \approx x$, where x must be in radians. Investigate the accuracy of this approximation by creating three plots. For the first, plot $\sin x$ and x versus x for $0 \leq x \leq 1$. For the second, plot the approximation error $\sin(x) - x$ versus x for $0 \leq x \leq 1$. For the third, plot the percent error $[\sin(x) - x]/\sin(x)$ versus x for $0 \leq x \leq 1$. How small must x be for the approximation to be accurate within 5 percent?

8.   You can use trigonometric identities to simplify the equations that appear in many engineering applications. Confirm the identity $\tan(2x) = 2\tan x/(1 - \tan^2 x)$ by plotting both the left and the right sides versus x over the range $0 \leq x \leq 2\pi$.

9.   The complex number identity $e^{ix} = \cos x + i \sin x$ is often used to convert the solutions of engineering design equations into a form that is relatively easy to visualize. Confirm this identity by plotting the imaginary part versus the real part for both the left and right sides over the range $0 \leq x \leq 2\pi$.

10.   Use a plot over the range $0 \leq x \leq 5$ to confirm that $\sin(ix) = i \sinh x$.

11.*   The function $y(t) = 1 - e^{-bt}$, where t is time and $b > 0$, describes many engineering processes, such as the height of liquid in a tank as it is being filled and the temperature of an object being heated. Investigate the effect of the parameter b on $y(t)$. To do this, plot y versus t for several values of b on the same plot. How long will it take for $y(t)$ to reach 98 percent of its steady-state value?

12. The following functions describe the oscillations in electrical circuits and the vibrations of machines and structures. Plot these functions on the same plot. Because they are similar, decide how best to plot and label them to avoid confusion.

$$x(t) = 10e^{-0.5t} \sin(3t + 2)$$

$$y(t) = 7e^{-0.4t} \cos(5t - 3)$$

13. The data for a tension test on a steel bar appears in the following table. The *elongation* is the change in the bar's length. The bar was stretched beyond its *elastic limit* so that a permanent elongation remained after the tension force was removed. Plot the tension

Elongation (inches $\times 10^{-3}$)	Increasing tension force (lbs)	Decreasing tension force (lbs)
0	0	—
1	3500	0
2	6300	3000
3	9200	6000
4	11,500	8800
5	13,000	11,100
6	13,500	12,300
7	13,900	13,500
8	14,100	14,000
9	14,300	14,300
10	14,500	14,500

force versus the elongation. Be sure to label the parts of the curve that correspond to increasing and decreasing tension.

14. In certain kinds of structural vibrations, a periodic force acting on the structure will cause the vibration amplitude to repeatedly increase and decrease with time. This phenomenon, called *beating*, also occurs in musical sounds. A particular structure's displacement is described by

$$y(t) = \frac{1}{f_1^2 - f_2^2} [\cos(f_2 t) - \cos(f_1 t)]$$

where y is the displacement in inches and t is the time in seconds. Plot y versus t over the range $0 \leq t \leq 20$ for $f_1 = 8$ radians per second and $f_2 = 1$ radian per second. Be sure to choose enough points to obtain an accurate plot.

15.* The height $h(t)$ and horizontal distance $x(t)$ traveled by a ball thrown at an angle A with a speed v are given by

$$h(t) = vt \sin A - \frac{1}{2}gt^2$$

$$x(t) = vt \cos A$$

At Earth's surface the acceleration due to gravity is $g = 9.81$ meters per second^2.

a. Suppose the ball is thrown with a velocity $v = 10$ meters per second at an angle of 35°. Use MATLAB to compute how high the ball will go, how far it will go, and how long it will take to hit the ground.

b. Use the values of v and A given in (a) to plot the ball's *trajectory*; that is, plot h versus x for positive values of h.

c. Plot the trajectories for $v = 10$ meters per second corresponding to five values of the angle A: 20°, 30°, 45°, 60°, and 70°.

d. Plot the trajectories for $A = 45°$ corresponding to five values of the initial velocity v: 10, 12, 14, 16, and 18 meters per second.

16. The perfect gas law relates the pressure p, absolute temperature T, mass m, and volume V of a gas. It states that

$$pV = mRT$$

The constant R is the *gas constant*. The value of R for air is 286.7 Newton meter/kilogram degree Kelvin (N m/kg K). Suppose air is contained in a chamber at room temperature (20°C = 293°K). Create a plot having three curves of the gas pressure in N/m^2 versus the container volume V in m^3 for $20 \le V \le 100$. The three curves correspond to the following masses of air in the container: $m = 1$ kg; $m = 3$ kg; and $m = 7$ kg.

17. Oscillations in mechanical structures and electric circuits can often be described by the function

$$y(t) = e^{-t/\tau} \sin(\omega t + \phi)$$

where t is time and ω is the oscillation frequency in radians per unit time. The oscillations have a period of $2\pi/\omega$, and their amplitudes decay in time at a rate determined by τ, which is called the *time constant*. The smaller τ is, the faster the oscillations die out.

a. Use these facts to develop a criterion for choosing the spacing of the t values and the upper limit on t to obtain an accurate plot of $y(t)$. (Hint: Consider two cases: $4\tau > 2\pi/\omega$ and $4\tau < 2\pi/\omega$.)

b. Apply your criterion, and plot $y(t)$ for $\tau = 10$, $\omega = \pi$, and $\phi = 2$.

c. Apply your criterion, and plot $y(t)$ for $\tau = 0.1$, $\omega = 8\pi$, and $\phi = 2$.

18. When a constant voltage was applied to a certain motor initially at rest, its rotational speed $s(t)$ versus time was measured. The data appears in the following table:

Time (sec)	1	2	3	4	5	6	7	8	10
Speed (rpm)	1210	1866	2301	2564	2724	2881	2879	2915	3010

Determine whether the following function can describe the data. If so, find the values of the constants b and c.

$$s(t) = b(1 - e^{ct})$$

Section 4.3

19. The following table shows the average temperature for each year in a certain city. Plot the data as a stem plot, a bar plot, and a stairs plot.

Year	1990	1991	1992	1993	1994
Temperature (°C)	18	19	21	17	20

20. $10,000 invested at 5 percent interest compounded annually will grow according to the formula

$$y(k) = 10^4(1.05)^k$$

where k is the number of years ($k = 0, 1, 2 \ldots$). Plot the amount of money in the account for a 10-year period. Do this problem with four types of plots: the xy plot, the stem plot, the stairs plot, and the bar plot.

Section 4.4

21. The distance a spring stretches from its "free length" is a function of how much tension force is applied to it. The following table gives the spring length y that the given applied force f produced in a particular spring. The spring's free length is 4.7 inches. Find a functional relation between f and x, the extension from the free length ($x = y - 4.7$).

Force f (pounds)	Spring length y (inches)
0	4.7
0.47	7.2
1.15	10.6
1.64	12.9

22.* In each of the following problems, determine the best function $y(x)$ (linear, exponential, or power function) to describe the data. Plot the function on the same plot with the data. Label and format the plots appropriately.

a.

x	25	30	35	40	45
y	0	250	500	750	1000

b.

x	2.5	3	3.5	4	4.5	5	5.5	6	7	8	9	10
y	1500	1220	1050	915	810	745	690	620	520	480	410	390

c.

x	550	600	650	700	750
y	41.2	18.62	8.62	3.92	1.86

23. The population data for a certain country is

Year	1990	1991	1992	1993	1994	1995
Population (millions)	10	10.8	11.7	12.7	13.8	14.9

Obtain a function that describes this data. Plot the function and the data on the same plot. Estimate when the population will be double its 1990 size.

24.* The *half-life* of a radioactive substance is the time it takes to decay by half. The half-life of carbon 14, which is used for dating previously living things, is 5500 years. When an organism dies, it stops accumulating carbon 14. The carbon 14 present at the time of death decays with time. Let $C(t)/C(0)$ be the fraction of carbon 14 remaining at time t. In radioactive carbon dating, scientists usually assume that the remaining fraction decays exponentially according to the following formula:

$$\frac{C(t)}{C(0)} = e^{-bt}$$

a. Use the half-life of carbon 14 to find the value of the parameter b, and plot the function.

b. If 90 percent of the original carbon 14 remains, estimate how long ago the organism died.

c. Suppose our estimate of b is off by $\pm$ 1 percent. How does this error affect the age estimate in (*b*)?

25. *Quenching* is the process of immersing a hot metal object in a bath for a specified time to obtain certain properties such as hardness. A copper sphere 25 millimeters in diameter, initially at 300°C, is immersed in a bath at 0°C. The following table gives measurements of the sphere's temperature versus time. Find a functional description of this data. Plot the function and the data on the same plot.

188

Time (seconds)	0	1	2	3	4	5	6
Temperature (°C)	300	150	75	35	12	5	2

26. The useful life of a machine bearing depends on its operating temperature, as the following data shows. Obtain a functional description of this data. Plot the function and the data on the same plot. Estimate a bearing's life if it operates at 150°F.

Temperature (°F)	100	120	140	160	180	200	220
Bearing life (hours $\times 10^3$)	28	21	15	11	8	6	4

27. A certain electric circuit has a resistor and a capacitor. The capacitor is initially charged to 100 volts. When the power supply is detached, the capacitor voltage decays with time, as the following data table shows. Find a functional description of the capacitor voltage v as a function of time t. Plot the function and the data on the same plot.

Time (seconds)	0	0.5	1	1.5	2	2.5	3	3.5	4
Voltage (volts)	100	62	38	21	13	7	4	2	3

Section 4.5

28. The popular amusement ride known as the corkscrew has a helical shape. The parametric equations for a circular helix are

$$x = a\cos t$$

$$y = a\sin t$$

$$z = bt$$

where a is the radius of the helical path and b is a constant that determines the "tightness" of the path. In addition, if $b > 0$, the helix has the shape of a right-handed screw; if $b < 0$, the helix is left-handed.

Obtain the three-dimensional plot of the helix for the following three cases and compare their appearance with one another. Use $0 \le t \le 10\pi$ and $a = 1$.

a. $b = 0.1$

b. $b = 0.2$

c. $b = -0.1$

29. A robot rotates about its base at two revolutions per minute while lowering its arm and extending its hand. It lowers its arm at the rate of 120° per minute and extends its hand at the rate of 5 meters per minute. The arm is 0.5 meters long. The *xyz* coordinates of the hand are given by

$$x = (0.5 + 5t) \sin\left(\frac{2\pi}{3}t\right) \cos(4\pi t)$$

$$y = (0.5 + 5t) \sin\left(\frac{2\pi}{3}t\right) \sin(4\pi t)$$

$$z = (0.5 + 5t) \cos\left(\frac{2\pi}{3}t\right)$$

where *t* is time in minutes.

Obtain the three-dimensional plot of the path of the hand for $0 \leq t \leq 0.2$ minutes.

30. Obtain the surface and contour plots for the function $z = x^2 - 2xy + 4y^2$, showing the minimum at $x = y = 0$.

31. Obtain the surface and contour plots for the function $z = -x^2 + 2xy + 3y^2$. This surface has the shape of a saddle. At its saddlepoint at $x = y = 0$, the surface has zero slope, but this point does not correspond to either a minimum or a maximum. What type of contour lines correspond to a saddlepoint?

32. Obtain the surface and contour plots for the function $z = (x - y^2)(x - 3y^2)$. This surface has a singular point at $x = y = 0$, where the surface has zero slope, but this point does not correspond to either a minimum or a maximum. What type of contour lines correspond to a singular point?

33. A square metal plate is heated to 80° C at the corner corresponding to $x = y = 1$. The temperature distribution in the plate is described by

$$T = 80e^{-(x-1)^2} e^{-3(y-1)^2}$$

Obtain the surface and contour plots for the temperature. Label each axis. What is the temperature at the corner corresponding to $x = y = 0$?

34. The following function describes oscillations in some mechanical structures and electric circuits:

$$z(t) = e^{-t/\tau} \sin(\omega t + \phi)$$

In this function *t* is time, and ω is the oscillation frequency in radians per unit time. The oscillations have a period of $2\pi/\omega$, and their amplitudes decay in time at a rate determined by τ, which is called the *time constant*. The smaller τ is, the faster the oscillations die out.

Suppose that $\phi = 0$, $\omega = 2$, and τ can have values in the range $0.5 \leq \tau \leq 10$ seconds. Then the preceding equation becomes

$$z(t) = e^{-t/\tau} \sin(2t)$$

Obtain a surface plot and a contour plot of this function to help visualize the effect of τ for $0 \leq t \leq 15$ seconds. Let the x variable be time t and the y variable be τ.

Courtesy the Boeing Company.

Engineering in the 21st Century...

Virtual Prototyping

To many people computer-aided design (CAD) or computer-aided engineering (CAE) means creating engineering drawings. However, it means much more. Engineers can use computers to determine the forces, voltages, currents, and so on a proposed design might encounter. Then they can use this information to make sure the hardware can withstand the predicted forces or supply the required voltages or currents. Engineers are just beginning to use the full potential of CAE.

The normal stages in the development of a new vehicle, such as an aircraft, formerly consisted of aerodynamic testing a scale model; building a full-size wooden *mock-up* to check for pipe, cable, and structural interferences; and finally building and testing a *prototype,* the first complete vehicle. CAE is changing the traditional development cycle. The new Boeing 777 shown above is the first aircraft to be designed and built using CAE, without the extra time and expense of building a mockup. The design teams responsible for the various subsystems, such as aerodynamics, structures, hydraulics, and electrical systems, all had access to the same computer database that described the aircraft. Thus when one team made a design change, the database was updated, allowing the other teams to see whether the change affected their subsystem. This process of designing and testing with a computer model has been called *virtual prototyping.* In addition to saving time and expense, the use of virtual prototyping in developing the Boeing 777 enabled it to be certified immediately for overwater flights, something that earlier two-engine aircraft did not achieve until they had accumulated one year of flying experience.

MATLAB is a powerful tool for many CAE applications. It complements geometric modeling packages because it can do advanced calculations that such packages cannot do.

5

Linear Algebraic Equations

Outline

Linear algebraic equations such as

$$5x - 2y = 13$$

$$7x + 3y = 24$$

occur in many engineering applications. For example, electrical engineers use them to predict the power requirements for circuits; civil, mechanical, and aerospace engineers use them to design structures and machines; chemical engineers use them to compute material balances in chemical processes; and industrial engineers apply them to design schedules and operations. The examples and homework problems in this chapter explore some of these applications.

Linear algebraic equations can be solved "by hand" using pencil and paper, by calculator, or with software such as MATLAB. The choice depends on the circumstances. For equations with only two unknown variables, hand solution is easy and adequate. Some calculators can solve equation sets that have many variables. However, the greatest power and flexibility is obtained by using software. For example, MATLAB can obtain and plot equation solutions as we vary one or more parameters.

Without giving a formal definition of the term *linear algebraic equations,* let us simply say that their unknown variables never appear raised to a power other than unity and never appear as products, ratios, or in transcendental functions such as $\ln(x)$, e^x, and $\cos x$. The simplest linear equation is $ax = b$, which has the solution $x = b/a$ if $a \neq 0$.

In contrast, the following equations are nonlinear:

$$x^2 = 3$$

which has the solutions $x = \pm\sqrt{3}$, and

$$\sin x = 0.5$$

which has the solutions $x = 30°, 150°, 390°, 510°, \ldots$ In contrast to most nonlinear equations, these particular nonlinear equations are easy to solve. For example, we cannot solve the equation $x + 2e^{-x} - 3 = 0$ in "closed form"; that is, we cannot express the solution as a function. We must obtain this solution numerically, as explained in section 3.5. The equation has two solutions: $x = -0.5831$ and $x = 2.8887$ to four significant figures.

Sets of equations are linear if all the equations are linear. They are nonlinear if at least one of the equations is nonlinear. For example, the set

$$8x - 3y = 1$$

$$6x + 4y = 32$$

is linear because both equations are linear, whereas the set

$$6xy - 2x = 44$$

$$5x - 3y = -2$$

is nonlinear because of the product term xy.

Systematic solution methods have been developed for sets of linear equations. However, no systematic methods are available for nonlinear equations because the nonlinear category covers such a wide range of equations. In this chapter we first review methods for solving linear equations by hand, and we use these methods to develop an understanding of the potential pitfalls that can occur when solving linear equations. Then we introduce some matrix notation that is required for use with MATLAB and that is also useful for expressing solution methods in a compact way. The conditions for the existence and uniqueness of solutions are then introduced. Methods using MATLAB are then treated in three sections: Section 5.2 covers equation sets that have unique solutions; sections 5.3 and 5.4 explain how to determine whether a set has a unique solution, multiple solutions, or no solution at all.

You are sure to encounter situations in which MATLAB is not available (such as on a test!), and thus you should become familiar with the hand-solution methods. In addition, understanding these methods will help you understand the MATLAB responses and the pitfalls that can occur when obtaining a computer solution. Finally, hand solutions are sometimes needed when the numerical values of one or more coefficients are unspecified. In this section we cover hand-solution methods; later in the chapter we introduce the MATLAB methods for solving linear equations.

Several methods are available for solving linear algebraic equations by hand. The appropriate choice depends on user preference, on the number of equations, and on the structure of the equations to be solved. Here we will demonstrate two methods: (1) successive elimination of variables and (2) Cramer's method. The MATLAB method is based on the successive elimination technique, but Cramer's method gives us some insight into the existence and uniqueness of solutions and into the effects of numerical inaccuracy.

Successive Elimination of Variables

An efficient way to eliminate variables is to multiply one equation by a suitable factor and then add or subtract the resulting equation from another equation in the set. If the factor is chosen properly, the new equation so obtained will contain fewer variables. This process is continued with the remaining equations until only one unknown and one equation remain. A systematic method of doing this is *Gauss elimination*. With this method you   GAUSS ELIMINATION
multiply the first equation (called the *pivot* equation) by a suitable factor and add the result to one of the other equations in the set to cancel one variable. Repeat the process with the other equations in the set, using the same pivot equation. This step generates a new set of equations, with one less variable. Select the new pivot to be the first equation in this new set and repeat the process until only one variable and one equation remain. This method is suitable for computer implementation, and it forms the basis for many computer methods for solving linear equations. (It is the method used by MATLAB.)

Example 5.1–1   Gauss elimination   Solve the following set using Gauss elimination:

$$-x + y + 2z = 2 \qquad (5.1\text{--}1)$$

$$3x - y + z = 6 \qquad (5.1\text{--}2)$$

$$-x + 3y + 4z = 4 \qquad (5.1\text{--}3)$$

Solution:

The solution proceeds as follows:

1. Equation (5.1–1) is the pivot equation. Multiply it by -1 and add the result to (5.1–3) to obtain $2y + 2z = 2$, which is equivalent to $y + z = 1$. Next multiply (5.1–1) by 3 and add the result to (5.1–2) to obtain $2y + 7z = 12$. Thus we have a new set of two equations in two unknowns:

$$y + z = 1 \qquad (5.1\text{–}4)$$

$$2y + 7z = 12 \qquad (5.1\text{–}5)$$

2. Equation (5.1–4) is the new pivot equation. Multiply it by -2 and add the result to (5.1–5) to obtain $5z = 10$, or $z = 2$. Substitute this value into (5.1–4) to obtain $y + 2 = 1$, or $y = -1$. Then substitute the values of y and z into (5.1–1) to obtain $-x - 1 + 4 = 2$, or $x = 1$.

Test Your Understanding

T5.1–1 Solve the following equations using Gauss elimination:

$$6x - 3y + 4z = 41$$

$$12x + 5y - 7z = -26$$

$$-5x + 2y + 6z = 14$$

(Answer: $x = 2, y = -3, z = 5$)

Singular and Ill-Conditioned Problems

Figure 5.1–1 shows the graphs of the following equations:

$$3x - 4y = 5$$

$$6x - 10y = 2$$

Note that the two lines intersect, and therefore the equations have a solution, which is given by the intersection point: $x = 7$, $y = 4$. A *singular* problem refers to a set of equations having either no unique solution or no solution at all. For example, the set

$$3x - 4y = 5$$

$$6x - 8y = 10$$

SINGULAR PROBLEM

is singular and has no unique solution because the second equation is identical to the first equation, multiplied by 2. The graphs

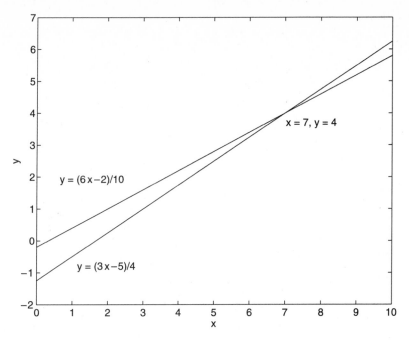

x = 7, y = 4

y = (6x−2)/10

y = (3x−5)/4

Figure 5.1–1
The graphs of two equations
intersect at the solution.

of these two equations are identical. All we can say is that the solution must satisfy $y = (3x - 5)/4$, which describes an infinite number of solutions.

On the other hand, the set

$$3x - 4y = 5 \qquad\qquad \textbf{(5.1–6)}$$

$$6x - 8y = 3 \qquad\qquad \textbf{(5.1–7)}$$

is singular and has no solution. The graphs of these two equations are distinct but *parallel* (see Figure 5.1–2). Since they do not intersect, no solution exists.

Homogeneous Equations

As another example, consider the following set of *homogeneous equations* (which means that their right sides are all zero)

$$6x + ay = 0 \qquad\qquad \textbf{(5.1–8)}$$

$$2x + 4y = 0 \qquad\qquad \textbf{(5.1–9)}$$

where a is a parameter. Multiply the second equation by 3 and subtract the result from the first equation to obtain

$$(a - 12)y = 0 \qquad\qquad \textbf{(5.1–10)}$$

The solution is $y = 0$ *only if* $a \neq 12$; substituting $y = 0$ into either (5.1–8) or (5.1–9) shows that $x = 0$. However, if $a = 12$, (5.1–10) implies that $0y = 0$, which is satisfied for any finite value

HOMOGENEOUS
EQUATIONS

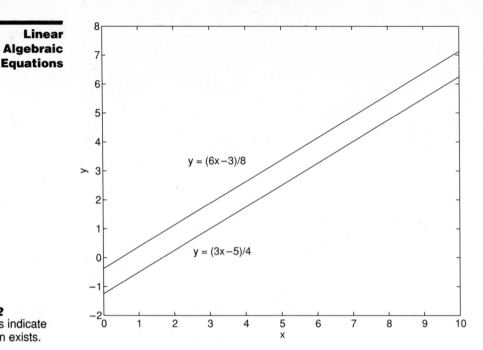

Figure 5.1–2
Parallel graphs indicate that no solution exists.

of y; in this case both (5.1–8) and (5.1–9) give $x = -2y$. Thus if $a = 12$, there are an infinite number of solutions for x and y, where $x = -2y$.

Ill-Conditioned Equations

**ILL-CONDITIONED
EQUATIONS**

An *ill-conditioned* set of equations is a set that is close to being singular (for example, two equations whose graphs are close to being parallel). The following set would be considered an ill-conditioned set if we carry only two significant figures in our calculations:

$$3x - 4y = 5$$

$$6x - 8.002y = 3$$

To see why, solve the first equation for y to obtain

$$y = \frac{3x - 5}{4}$$

and solve the second equation to obtain

$$y = \frac{6x - 3}{8.002} = \frac{3x - 1.5}{4.001}$$

If we had carried only two significant figures, we would have rounded the denominator of the latter expression to 4.0, and thus the two expressions for y would have the same slope and their graphs would be parallel. Thus we see that the ill-conditioned

status depends on the accuracy with which the solution calculations are made. Of course, MATLAB uses more than two significant
figures in its calculations. However, no computer can represent a
number with infinitely many significant figures, and so a given
set of equations can appear to be singular if the accuracy required
to solve them is greater than the number of significant figures
used by the software. If we carry four significant figures in our
calculations, we would find that the solution is $x = 4668$ and
$y = 3500$.

Test Your Understanding

T5.1–2 Show that the following set has no solution.

$$-4x + 5y = 10$$

$$12x - 15y = 8$$

Cramer's Method

Cramer's method is a systematic method for solving equations, but
it is not used as a basis for computer packages because it can be
slow and very sensitive to numerical round-off error, especially for
a large number of equations. We introduce it here to gain insight
into the requirements for a set of equations to have a solution. We
will use the following set of two equations to illustrate Cramer's
method:

CRAMER'S METHOD

$$a_{11}x + a_{12}y = b_1 \qquad (5.1\text{–}11)$$

$$a_{21}x + a_{22}y = b_2 \qquad (5.1\text{–}12)$$

To solve these equations, we can multiply the first equation by a_{22}
and the second equation by $-a_{12}$ to obtain

$$a_{22}(a_{11}x + a_{12}y) = a_{22}b_1$$

$$-a_{12}(a_{21}x + a_{22}y) = -a_{12}b_2$$

When these two equations are added, the y terms cancel and we
obtain the solution for x:

$$x = \frac{b_1 a_{22} - b_2 a_{12}}{a_{22}a_{11} - a_{12}a_{21}} \qquad (5.1\text{–}13)$$

We can cancel the x terms in a similar way and obtain the
following solution for y:

$$y = \frac{a_{11}b_2 - a_{21}b_1}{a_{22}a_{11} - a_{12}a_{21}} \qquad (5.1\text{–}14)$$

Note that both solutions have the same denominator, which we denote by $D = a_{22}a_{11} - a_{12}a_{21}$. If this denominator is zero, the above solutions are not valid because we cannot divide by zero. In that case all we can say is that

$$0x = b_1 a_{22} - b_2 a_{12}$$

$$0y = a_{11} b_2 - a_{21} b_1$$

So if $D = 0$, but $b_1 a_{22} - b_2 a_{12} \neq 0$, x is undefined. If $D = 0$ and $b_1 a_{22} - b_2 a_{12} = 0$, there are infinitely many solutions for x (because any finite value of x will satisfy the equation $0x = 0$).

Similarly, if $D = 0$, but $a_{11} b_2 - a_{21} b_1 \neq 0$, y is undefined, and if $a_{22} b_1 - a_{12} b_2 = 0$, there are infinitely many solutions for y.

Determinants

Cramer's method expresses the above solutions in terms of *determinants*. A determinant is a special square array that, unlike a matrix, can be reduced to a single number. The determinant D (called *Cramer's determinant*) formed from the coefficients of equations (5.1–11) and (5.1–12) is as follows:

$$D = \begin{vmatrix} a_{11} & a_{12} \\ a_{21} & a_{22} \end{vmatrix} \qquad \text{(5.1–15)}$$

Vertical bars denote a determinant, whereas square brackets denote a matrix. A determinant having two rows and two columns is a 2×2 determinant. The rule for reducing a 2×2 determinant to a single number follows.

$$D = \begin{vmatrix} a_{11} & a_{12} \\ a_{21} & a_{22} \end{vmatrix} = a_{11}a_{22} - a_{12}a_{21} \qquad \text{(5.1–16)}$$

Note that this expression is identical to the denominator of the solutions for x and y given by (5.1–13) and (5.1–14).

If we form a determinant D_1 by replacing the first column of D with the coefficients on the right side of the equation set (5.1–11) and (5.1–12), we obtain

$$D_1 = \begin{vmatrix} b_1 & a_{12} \\ b_2 & a_{22} \end{vmatrix} = b_1 a_{22} - b_2 a_{12}$$

This expression is identical to the numerator of the solution (5.1–13). Thus the solution can be expressed as the ratio of the two determinants $x = D_1/D$.

Next form the determinant D_2 by replacing the second column of D with the coefficients on the right side of the equation set. Thus

$$D_2 = \begin{vmatrix} a_{11} & b_1 \\ a_{21} & b_2 \end{vmatrix} = a_{11}b_2 - a_{21}b_1$$

This expression is identical to the numerator of the solution (5.1–14). Thus $y = D_2/D$.

Cramer's method expresses the solutions as ratios of determinants, and thus it can be extended to equations with more than two variables by using determinants having the appropriate dimension. Before using Cramer's method, be sure the variables are lined up in a consistent order (for example, x, y, z) in each equation and move all constants to the right side. Equations (5.1–1) through (5.1–3) from Example 5.1–1 illustrate this process.

$$-x + y + 2z = 2$$

$$3x - y + z = 6$$

$$-x + 3y + 4z = 4$$

Cramer's determinant for this set is

$$D = \begin{vmatrix} -1 & 1 & 2 \\ 3 & -1 & 1 \\ -1 & 3 & 4 \end{vmatrix}$$

The value of a 3×3 determinant can be expressed in terms of 2×2 determinants as follows:

$$\begin{vmatrix} a_{11} & a_{12} & a_{13} \\ a_{21} & a_{22} & a_{23} \\ a_{31} & a_{32} & a_{33} \end{vmatrix} = a_{11} \begin{vmatrix} a_{22} & a_{23} \\ a_{32} & a_{33} \end{vmatrix} - a_{12} \begin{vmatrix} a_{21} & a_{23} \\ a_{31} & a_{33} \end{vmatrix} + a_{13} \begin{vmatrix} a_{21} & a_{22} \\ a_{31} & a_{32} \end{vmatrix}$$

$$(5.1–17)$$

The result for the previous determinant D is $D = 10$. Rules exist to evaluate $n \times n$ determinants by hand, but we will shortly see how to use MATLAB to evaluate determinants.

One advantage of Cramer's method is that you can find one of the unknowns directly if that is all you want. For example, the first unknown is found from $x = D_1/D$, where D_1 is the determinant formed by replacing the first column in the determinant D with the coefficients on the right side of the equation set:

$$D_1 = \begin{vmatrix} 2 & 1 & 2 \\ 6 & -1 & 1 \\ 4 & 3 & 4 \end{vmatrix}$$

This determinant has the value $D_1 = 10$, and thus $x = D_1/D = 10/10 = 1$. Similarly, $y = D_2/D = -10/10 = -1$ and $z = D_3/D = 20/10 = 2$, where

$$D_2 = \begin{vmatrix} -1 & 2 & 2 \\ 3 & 6 & 1 \\ -1 & 4 & 4 \end{vmatrix} \qquad D_3 = \begin{vmatrix} -1 & 1 & 2 \\ 3 & -1 & 6 \\ -1 & 3 & 4 \end{vmatrix}$$

Cramer's Determinant and Singular Problems

When the number of variables equals the number of equations, a singular problem can be identified by computing Cramer's determinant D. If the determinant is zero, the equations are singular because D appears in the denominator of the solutions. For example, for the set

$$3x - 4y = 5$$

$$6x - 8y = 3$$

Cramer's determinant is

$$D = \begin{vmatrix} 3 & -4 \\ 6 & -8 \end{vmatrix} = 3(-8) - 6(-4) = 0$$

Thus the equation set is singular.

Another example is given by the following homogeneous set:

$$6x + ay = 0$$

$$2x + 4y = 0$$

We saw earlier that any finite values of x and y, such that $x = -2y$, are solutions of this set if $a = 12$. If $a \neq 12$, the only solution is $x = y = 0$. Cramer's determinant is

$$D = \begin{vmatrix} 6 & a \\ 2 & 4 \end{vmatrix} = 6(4) - 2a = 24 - 2a$$

and $D = 0$ if $a = 12$. Thus the set is singular if $a = 12$.

In general, for a set of homogeneous linear algebraic equations that contains the same number of equations as unknowns, a *nonzero* solution exists only if the set is singular; that is, if Cramer's determinant is *zero;* furthermore, the solution is not unique. If Cramer's determinant is not zero, the homogeneous set has a zero solution; that is, all the unknowns are zero.

Cramer's determinant gives some insight into ill-conditioned problems, which are close to being singular. A Cramer's determinant close to zero indicates an ill-conditioned problem.

MATLAB and Determinants

To use MATLAB to compute determinants, first enter the determinant as an array. Then use the det command to evaluate the determinant. For example, a MATLAB session to compute the determinant

$$D = \begin{vmatrix} 3 & -4 & 1 \\ 6 & 10 & 2 \\ 9 & -7 & 3 \end{vmatrix}$$

looks like

```
>>D = [3,-4,1;6,10,2;9,-7,3];
>>det(D)
ans =
    0
```

Test Your Understanding

T5.1–3 Use Cramer's method to solve for x and y in terms of the parameter b. For what value of b is the set singular?

$$4x - by = 5$$

$$-3x + 6y = 3$$

(Answer: $x = (10+b)/(8-b), y = 9/(8-b)$ unless $b = 8$.)

T5.1–4 For what value of b will the following set have a solution in which both x and y are nonzero? Find the relation between x and y.

$$4x - by = 0$$

$$-3x + 6y = 0$$

(Answer: If $b = 8$, $x = 2y$. If $b \neq 8$, $x = y = 0$.)

T5.1–5 Use Cramer's method to solve for y. Use MATLAB to evaluate the determinants.

$$2x + y + 2z = 17$$

$$3y + z = 6$$

$$2x - 3y + 4z = 19$$

(Answer: $y = 1$.)

Sets of linear algebraic equations can be expressed in matrix notation, a standard and compact method that is useful for expressing solutions and for developing software applications with an arbitrary number of variables. This section describes the use of matrix notation.

As you saw in Chapter 2, a *matrix* is an ordered array of rows and columns containing numbers, variables, or expressions. A *vector* is a special case of a matrix that has either one row or one column. A *row* vector has one row. A *column* vector has one column. In this chapter a vector is taken to be a column vector unless otherwise specified. Usually, when printed in text, lowercase boldface letters denote a vector, and uppercase boldface letters denote a matrix.

Matrix notation enables us to represent multiple equations as a single matrix equation. For example, consider the following set:

$$2x_1 + 9x_2 = 5 \qquad (5.2\text{--}1)$$

$$3x_1 - 4x_2 = 7 \qquad (5.2\text{--}2)$$

This set can be expressed in vector-matrix form as

$$\begin{bmatrix} 2 & 9 \\ 3 & -4 \end{bmatrix} \begin{bmatrix} x_1 \\ x_2 \end{bmatrix} = \begin{bmatrix} 5 \\ 7 \end{bmatrix}$$

which can be represented in the following compact form

$$\mathbf{Ax} = \mathbf{b} \qquad (5.2\text{--}3)$$

where we have defined the following matrices and vectors:

$$\mathbf{A} = \begin{bmatrix} 2 & 9 \\ 3 & -4 \end{bmatrix} \qquad \mathbf{x} = \begin{bmatrix} x_1 \\ x_2 \end{bmatrix} \qquad \mathbf{b} = \begin{bmatrix} 5 \\ 7 \end{bmatrix}$$

The matrix $\mathbf{A}$ corresponds in an ordered fashion to the coefficients of x_1 and x_2 in (5.2–1) and (5.2–2). Note that the first row in $\mathbf{A}$ consists of the coefficients of x_1 and x_2 on the left side of (5.2–1), and the second row contains the coefficients on the left side of (5.2–2). The vector $\mathbf{x}$ contains the variables x_1 and x_2, and the vector $\mathbf{b}$ contains the right sides of (5.2–1) and (5.2–2).

Cramer's determinant for the preceding set is

$$\begin{vmatrix} 2 & 9 \\ 3 & -4 \end{vmatrix} = 2(-4) - 3(9) = -35$$

This determinant is not the same as the matrix $\mathbf{A}$, but is said to be the "determinant of the matrix $\mathbf{A}$." A matrix with equal numbers of rows and columns is a *square* matrix. The determinant of a matrix $\mathbf{A}$ is the determinant formed by the rows and columns of $\mathbf{A}$. It is denoted by the symbol $|\mathbf{A}|$. If $|\mathbf{A}| = 0$, the matrix $\mathbf{A}$ is *singular.*

SINGULAR MATRIX

In general, the set of m equations in n unknowns

$$a_{11}x_1 + a_{12}x_2 + \cdots + a_{1n}x_n = b_1$$

$$a_{21}x_1 + a_{22}x_2 + \cdots + a_{2n}x_n = b_2$$

$$\cdots \cdots \qquad (5.2\text{--}4)$$

$$a_{m1}x_1 + a_{m2}x_2 + \cdots + a_{mn}x_n = b_m$$

can be written in the form (5.2–3), where

$$\mathbf{A} = \begin{bmatrix} a_{11} & a_{12} & \cdots & a_{1n} \\ a_{21} & a_{22} & \cdots & a_{2n} \\ \cdot & \cdot & \cdots & \cdot \\ a_{m1} & a_{m2} & \cdots & a_{mn} \end{bmatrix} \qquad (5.2\text{--}5)$$

$$\mathbf{x} = \begin{bmatrix} x_1 \\ x_2 \\ \vdots \\ x_n \end{bmatrix} \qquad (5.2\text{--}6)$$

$$\mathbf{b} = \begin{bmatrix} b_1 \\ b_2 \\ \vdots \\ b_m \end{bmatrix} \qquad (5.2\text{--}7)$$

The matrix $\mathbf{A}$ has m rows and n columns, so its dimension is expressed as $m \times n$.

Matrix Inverse

The solution of the scalar equation $ax = b$ is $x = b/a$ if $a \neq 0$. The division operation of scalar algebra has an analogous operation in matrix algebra. For example, to solve the matrix equation

$$\mathbf{Ax} = \mathbf{b} \qquad (5.2\text{--}8)$$

for $\mathbf{x}$, we must somehow "divide" $\mathbf{b}$ by $\mathbf{A}$. This procedure is developed from the concept of a *matrix inverse*. The inverse of   **MATRIX INVERSE** a matrix $\mathbf{A}$ is defined only if $\mathbf{A}$ is square and nonsingular. It is denoted by $\mathbf{A}^{-1}$ and has the property that

$$\mathbf{A}^{-1}\mathbf{A} = \mathbf{A}\mathbf{A}^{-1} = \mathbf{I} \qquad (5.2\text{--}9)$$

where $\mathbf{I}$ is the identity matrix. Using this property, we multiply both sides of (5.2–8) from the left by $\mathbf{A}^{-1}$ to obtain

$$\mathbf{A}^{-1}\mathbf{Ax} = \mathbf{A}^{-1}\mathbf{b}$$

Because $\mathbf{A}^{-1}\mathbf{Ax} = \mathbf{Ix} = \mathbf{x}$, we obtain

$$\mathbf{x} = \mathbf{A}^{-1}\mathbf{b} \qquad (5.2\text{--}10)$$

Evidently, the solution for $\mathbf{x}$ is given by (5.2–10). We now need to find out how to compute $\mathbf{A}^{-1}$.

Calculating a matrix inverse by hand is tedious. The inverse of a 3×3 matrix requires us to evaluate nine 2×2 determinants. We do not give the general procedure here because we will soon explain how to use MATLAB to compute a matrix inverse. The details of computing a matrix inverse can be found in many texts; for example, see [Kreyzig, 1993]. However, the inverse of a 2×2 matrix is easy to find. If $\mathbf{A}$ is given by

$$\mathbf{A} = \begin{bmatrix} a_{11} & a_{12} \\ a_{21} & a_{22} \end{bmatrix}$$

its inverse is given by

$$\mathbf{A}^{-1} = \frac{1}{|\mathbf{A}|}\begin{bmatrix} a_{22} & -a_{12} \\ -a_{21} & a_{11} \end{bmatrix} \tag{5.2–11}$$

Calculation of $\mathbf{A}^{-1}$ can be checked by determining whether $\mathbf{A}^{-1}\mathbf{A} = \mathbf{I}$. Note that the preceding formula shows that $\mathbf{A}^{-1}$ does not exist if $|\mathbf{A}| = 0$ (that is, if $\mathbf{A}$ is singular).

Example 5.2–1 The matrix inverse method

Solve the following equations using the matrix inverse:

$$2x + 9y = 5$$

$$3x - 4y = 7$$

Solution:

The matrix $\mathbf{A}$ is

$$\mathbf{A} = \begin{bmatrix} 2 & 9 \\ 3 & -4 \end{bmatrix}$$

Its determinant is $|\mathbf{A}| = 2(-4) - 9(3) = -35$, and its inverse is

$$\mathbf{A}^{-1} = \frac{1}{-35}\begin{bmatrix} -4 & -9 \\ -3 & 2 \end{bmatrix} = \frac{1}{35}\begin{bmatrix} 4 & 9 \\ 3 & -2 \end{bmatrix}$$

The solution is

$$\mathbf{x} = \mathbf{A}^{-1}\mathbf{b} = \frac{1}{35}\begin{bmatrix} 4 & 9 \\ 3 & -2 \end{bmatrix}\begin{bmatrix} 5 \\ 7 \end{bmatrix} = \frac{1}{35}\begin{bmatrix} 83 \\ 1 \end{bmatrix}$$

or $x = 83/35 = 2.3714$ and $y = 1/35 = 0.0286$.

The Matrix Inverse in MATLAB

The MATLAB command `inv(A)` computes the inverse of the matrix $\mathbf{A}$. The following MATLAB session solves the equations given in Example 5.2–1 using MATLAB.

```
>>A = [2,9;3,-4];
>>b = [5;7]
>>x = inv(A)*b
x =
    2.3714
    0.0286
```

If you attempt to solve a singular problem using the `inv` command, MATLAB displays an error message.

Test Your Understanding

T5.2–1 Use the matrix inverse method to solve the following set by hand and by using MATLAB:

$$3x - 4y = 5$$

$$6x - 10y = 2$$

(Answer: $x = 7, y = 4$.)

T5.2–2 Use the matrix inverse method to solve the following set by hand and by using MATLAB:

$$3x - 4y = 5$$

$$6x - 8y = 2$$

(Answer: no solution)

The Left-Division Method

The inverse matrix method works only if the matrix $\mathbf{A}$ is square; that is, if the number of unknowns equals the number of equations. Even if $\mathbf{A}$ is square, the method does not work for singular problems where $|\mathbf{A}| = 0$ because the matrix inverse $\mathbf{A}^{-1}$ does not exist for such cases. The same limitation applies to Cramer's method; it cannot solve equation sets when the number of unknowns does not equal the number of equations or when $|\mathbf{A}| = 0$.

MATLAB provides another method for solving the equation set $\mathbf{Ax} = \mathbf{b}$. The *left-division method* is based on Gauss elimination. An advantage of the left-division method is that it uses fewer internal multiplications and divisions than the matrix inverse method. Thus the left-division method is faster and more accurate than the matrix inverse method, especially when the number of variables is large. To use the left-division method to solve for $\mathbf{x}$, type x = A\b. This method also works in some cases where the number of unknowns does not equal the number of equations. However, this section focuses on problems in which the number of equations equals the number of unknowns. In sections 5.3 and 5.4, we examine other cases.

LEFT-DIVISION METHOD

If the number of equations equals the number of unknowns and if $|\mathbf{A}| \neq 0$, then the equation set has a solution and it is unique. The following methods give the solution for such cases: elimination of variables, Cramer's, matrix inverse, and left division. Simply check first to see whether $|\mathbf{A}| \neq 0$ before using any of these methods. If $|\mathbf{A}| = 0$ or if the number of equations does not equal the number of unknowns, then you must use the methods presented in section 5.3.

Example 5.2–2 Left-division method with three unknowns

Use the left-division method to solve the following set:

$$3x + 2y - 9z = -65$$

$$-9x - 5y + 2z = 16$$

$$6x + 7y + 3z = 5$$

Solution:

The matrix **A** is

$$A = \begin{bmatrix} 3 & 2 & -9 \\ -9 & -5 & 2 \\ 6 & 7 & 3 \end{bmatrix}$$

We can use MATLAB to check the determinant of **A** to see whether the problem is singular. The session looks like this:

```
>> A = [3,2,-9;-9,-5,2;6,7,3];
>> det(A)
ans =
    288
```

Because $|A| \neq 0$, a unique solution exists. It is obtained as follows:

```
>>b = [-65;16;5];
>>A\b
ans =
    2.0000
   -4.0000
    7.0000
```

This answer gives the vector **x**, which corresponds to the solution $x = 2$, $y = -4$, $z = 7$. It can be checked by determining whether **Ax** gives the vector **b**, by typing

```
>>A*ans
ans =
   -65.0000
    16.0000
     5.0000
```

which is the vector **b**. Thus the answer is correct.

The backward slash (\) is used for left division. Be careful to distinguish between the *backward* slash (\) and the forward slash (/) which is used for *right* division. Sometimes equation sets are written as $\mathbf{xC} = \mathbf{d}$, where $\mathbf{x}$ and $\mathbf{d}$ are *row* vectors. In that case you can use right division to solve the set $\mathbf{xC} = \mathbf{d}$ for $\mathbf{x}$ by typing x = d/C, or you can convert the equations to the form $\mathbf{Ax} = \mathbf{b}$. For example, the matrix equation

$$[x_1 \quad x_2]\begin{bmatrix} 6 & 2 \\ 3 & 5 \end{bmatrix} = [3 \quad -19]$$

corresponds to the equations

$$6x_1 + 3x_2 = 3$$

$$2x_1 + 5x_2 = -19$$

These equations can be written as

$$\begin{bmatrix} 6 & 3 \\ 2 & 5 \end{bmatrix}\begin{bmatrix} x_1 \\ x_2 \end{bmatrix} = \begin{bmatrix} 3 \\ -19 \end{bmatrix}$$

which is in the form $\mathbf{Ax} = \mathbf{b}$.

Applications

Linear equations are useful in many engineering fields. Electrical circuits are a common source of linear equation models. The circuit designer must be able to solve them to predict the currents that will exist in the circuit. This information is often needed to determine the power supply requirements, among other things.

Example 5.2–3 An electrical-resistance network
The circuit shown in Figure 5.2–1 has five resistances and two applied voltages. Assuming that the positive directions of current flow are in the directions shown in the figure, Kirchhoff's voltage law applied to each loop in the circuit gives

Figure 5.2–1
An electrical-resistance network.

$$-v_1 + R_1 i_1 + R_4 i_4 = 0$$

$$-R_4 i_4 + R_2 i_2 + R_5 i_5 = 0$$

$$-R_5 i_5 + R_3 i_3 + v_2 = 0$$

Conservation of charge applied at each node in the circuit gives

$$i_1 = i_2 + i_4$$

$$i_2 = i_3 + i_5$$

You can use these two equations to eliminate i_4 and i_5 from the first three equations. The result is:

$$(R_1 + R_4)i_1 - R_4 i_2 = v_1$$

$$-R_4 i_1 + (R_2 + R_4 + R_5)i_2 - R_5 i_3 = 0$$

$$R_5 i_2 - (R_3 + R_5)i_3 = v_2$$

Thus we have three equations in three unknowns: i_1, i_2, and i_3.

Write a MATLAB script file that uses given values of the applied voltages v_1 and v_2 and given values of the five resistances to solve for the currents i_1, i_2, and i_3. Use the program to find the currents for the case $R_1 = 5$, $R_2 = 100$, $R_3 = 200$, $R_4 = 150$, $R_5 = 250$ kΩ, $v_1 = 100$, and $v_2 = 50$ volts. (Note that 1 k$\Omega = 1000\ \Omega$.)

Solution:

Because there are as many unknowns as equations, there will be a unique solution if $|A| \neq 0$; in addition, the left-division method will generate an error message if $|A| = 0$. The following script file, named resist.m, uses the left-division method to solve the three equations for i_1, i_2, and i_3.

```
% File resist.m
% Solves for the currents i_1, i_2, i_3
R = [5,100,200,150,250]*1000;
v1 = 100; v2 = 50;
A1 = [R(1) + R(4), -R(4), 0];
A2 = [-R(4), R(2) + R(4) + R(5), -R(5)];
A3 = [0, R(5), -(R(3) + R(5))];
A = [A1; A2; A3];
b=[v1; 0; v2];
current = A\b;
disp('The currents are:')
disp(current)
```

The row vectors A1, A2, and A3 were defined to avoid typing the lengthy expression for A in one line. This script is executed from the command prompt as follows:

```
>>resist
The currents are:
   1.0e-003*
   0.9544
   0.3195
   0.0664
```

Because MATLAB did not generate an error message, the solution is unique. The currents are $i_1 = 0.9544$, $i_2 = 0.3195$, and $i_3 = 0.0664$ ma, where 1 ma = 1 milliamp = 0.001 ampere.

Linearity

The matrix equation $\mathbf{Ax} = \mathbf{b}$ possesses the *linearity* property. The solution $\mathbf{x}$ is $\mathbf{x} = \mathbf{A}^{-1}\mathbf{b}$, and thus $\mathbf{x}$ is proportional to the vector $\mathbf{b}$. We can use this fact to obtain a more generally useful algebraic solution in cases where the right sides are all multiplied by the same scalar. For example, suppose the matrix equation is $\mathbf{Ay} = \mathbf{b}c$, where c is a scalar. The solution is $\mathbf{y} = \mathbf{A}^{-1}\mathbf{b}c = \mathbf{x}c$. Thus if we obtain the solution to $\mathbf{Ax} = \mathbf{b}$, the solution to $\mathbf{Ay} = \mathbf{b}c$ is given by $\mathbf{y} = \mathbf{x}c$. We demonstrate the usefulness of this fact in Example 5.2–4.

When designing structures, engineers must be able to predict how much force will be exerted on each part of the structure so that they can properly select the part's size and material to make it strong enough. The engineers often must solve linear equations to determine these forces. These equations are obtained by applying the principles of statics, which state that the vector sums of forces and moments must be zero if the structure does not move.

Example 5.2–4 Calculation of cable tension

A mass m is suspended by three cables attached at the three points B, C, and D, as shown in Figure 5.2–2. Let T_1, T_2, and T_3 be the tensions in the three cables AB, AC, and AD, respectively. If the mass m is stationary, the sum of the tension components in the x, in the y, and in the z directions must each be zero. This requirement gives the following three equations:

$$\frac{T_1}{\sqrt{35}} - \frac{3T_2}{\sqrt{34}} + \frac{T_3}{\sqrt{42}} = 0$$

$$\frac{3T_1}{\sqrt{35}} - \frac{4T_3}{\sqrt{42}} = 0$$

$$\frac{5T_1}{\sqrt{35}} + \frac{5T_2}{\sqrt{34}} + \frac{5T_3}{\sqrt{42}} - mg = 0$$

Figure 5.2–2
A mass suspended by
three cables.

Use MATLAB to find T_1, T_2, and T_3 in terms of an unspecified value of
the weight mg.

Solution:

If we set $mg = 1$, the equations have the form $\mathbf{Ax} = \mathbf{b}$ where

$$
\mathbf{A} = \begin{bmatrix} \dfrac{1}{\sqrt{35}} & -\dfrac{3}{\sqrt{34}} & \dfrac{1}{\sqrt{42}} \\[2mm] -\dfrac{3}{\sqrt{35}} & 0 & -\dfrac{4}{\sqrt{42}} \\[2mm] \dfrac{5}{\sqrt{35}} & \dfrac{5}{\sqrt{34}} & \dfrac{5}{\sqrt{42}} \end{bmatrix} \qquad \mathbf{x} = \begin{bmatrix} T_1 \\ T_2 \\ T_3 \end{bmatrix} \qquad \mathbf{b} = \begin{bmatrix} 0 \\ 0 \\ 1 \end{bmatrix}
$$

We can use the following MATLAB script file to solve this system for $\mathbf{x}$
and then multiply the result by mg to obtain the desired result.

```
% File cable.m
% Computes the tensions in three cables.
A1 = [1/sqrt(35), -3/sqrt(34), 1/sqrt(42)];
A2 = [3/sqrt(35), 0, -4/sqrt(42)];
A3 = [5/sqrt(35), 5/sqrt(34), 5/sqrt(42)];
A = [A1; A2; A3];
b = [0; 0; 1];
x = A\b;
disp('The tension T_1 is:')
disp(x(1))
disp('The tension T_2 is:')
disp(x(2))
disp('The tension T_3 is:')
disp(x(3))
```

When this file is executed by typing `cable`, the result is stored in the array x, which gives the values $T_1 = 0.5071$, $T_2 = 0.2915$, and $T_3 = 0.4166$. Because MATLAB does not generate an error message when the file is executed, the solution is unique. Using the linearity property, we multiply these results by mg and obtain the following solution to the set $\mathbf{Ay} = \mathbf{b}mg$: $T_1 = 0.5071mg$, $T_2 = 0.2915mg$, and $T_3 = 0.4166mg$.

Underdetermined Systems

You have seen how to use the the matrix inverse method $\mathbf{x} = \mathbf{A}^{-1}\mathbf{b}$ to solve the equation set $\mathbf{Ax} = \mathbf{b}$. However, this method works only if the matrix $\mathbf{A}$ is square; that is, if the number of unknowns equals the number of equations. Even if $\mathbf{A}$ is square, the method will not work if $|\mathbf{A}| = 0$ because the matrix inverse $\mathbf{A}^{-1}$ does not exist. The same limitation applies to Cramer's method; it cannot solve equation sets where the number of unknowns does not equal the number of equations.

This section explains how to use MATLAB to solve problems in which the matrix $\mathbf{A}$ is square but $|\mathbf{A}| = 0$ and problems in which $\mathbf{A}$ is not square. The left-division method works for square and nonsquare $\mathbf{A}$ matrices. However, as you will see, if $\mathbf{A}$ is not square, the left-division method can give answers that might be misinterpreted. We explain how to interpret MATLAB results correctly.

An *underdetermined system* does not contain enough information to solve for all of the unknown variables, usually because it has fewer equations than unknowns. Thus an infinite number of solutions can exist, with one or more of the unknowns dependent on the remaining unknowns. For such systems the matrix inverse method and Cramer's method will not work. When there are more equations than unknowns, the left-division method will give a solution with some of the unknowns set equal to zero. A simple example is given by the equation $x + 3y = 6$. All we can do is solve for one of the unknowns in terms of the other; for example, $x = 6 - 3y$. An infinite number of solutions satisfy this equation. The left-division method gives one of these solutions, the one with y set equal to zero: $x = 6, y = 0$.

UNDERDETERMINED SYSTEM

```
>>A = [1,3];
>>b = 6;
>>x = A\b
x =
    6
    0
```

An infinite number of solutions might exist even when the number of equations equals the number of unknowns. This situation can occur when $|\mathbf{A}| = 0$. For such systems the matrix

214

**Linear
Algebraic
Equations**

PSEUDOINVERSE
METHOD

MINIMUM NORM
SOLUTION

inverse method and Cramer's method will not work, and the left-division method generates an error message warning us that the matrix **A** is singular. In such cases the *pseudoinverse method* x = pinv(A)*b gives one solution, the *minimum norm solution*. In cases that have an infinite number of solutions, some of the unknowns can be expressed in terms of the remaining unknowns, whose values are arbitrary. We can use the rref command to find these relations. We introduce these commands in this section and give examples showing how to interpret their results.

An equation set can be underdetermined even though it has as many equations as unknowns. For example, the set

$$2x - 4y + 5z = -4$$

$$-4x - 2y + 3z = 4$$

$$2x + 6y - 8z = 0$$

has three unknowns and three equations, but it is underdetermined and has infinitely many solutions. This condition occurs because the set has only two independent equations; the third equation can be obtained from the first two. To obtain the third equation, add the first and second equations to obtain $-2x - 6y + 8z = 0$, which is equivalent to the third equation.

Determining whether all the equations are independent might not be easy, especially if the set has many equations. For this reason we now introduce a method that enables us to determine easily whether or not an equation set has a solution and whether or not it is unique. The method requires an understanding of the concept of the *rank* of a matrix.

Matrix Rank

Consider the following 3 × 3 determinant:

$$\begin{vmatrix} 3 & -4 & 1 \\ 6 & 10 & 2 \\ 9 & -7 & 3 \end{vmatrix}$$

If we eliminate one row and one column in the determinant, we are left with a 2 × 2 determinant. Depending on which row and column we eliminate, we can obtain any of nine possible 2 × 2 determinants. These elements are called *subdeterminants*. For example, if we eliminate row 1 and column 1, we obtain

$$\begin{vmatrix} 10 & 2 \\ -7 & 3 \end{vmatrix} = 10(3) - 2(-7) = 44$$

If we eliminate row 2 and column 3, we obtain

$$\begin{vmatrix} 3 & -4 \\ 9 & -7 \end{vmatrix} = 3(-7) - 9(-4) = 15$$

Subdeterminants can be used to define the *rank* of a matrix, which provides useful information concerning the existence and nature of solutions. The definition of *matrix rank* is as follows:

Matrix rank. An $m \times n$ matrix $\mathbf{A}$ has a rank $r \geq 1$ if and only if $|\mathbf{A}|$ contains a nonzero $r \times r$ determinant and every square subdeterminant with $r + 1$ or more rows is zero.

For example, the rank of

$$\mathbf{A} = \begin{bmatrix} 3 & -4 & 1 \\ 6 & 10 & 2 \\ 9 & -7 & 3 \end{bmatrix} \qquad \text{(5.3–1)}$$

is 2 because $|\mathbf{A}| = 0$ whereas $\mathbf{A}$ contains at least one nonzero 2×2 subdeterminant. For example, the subdeterminant obtained by eliminating row 1 and column 1 is nonzero and has the value 44.

MATLAB provides an easy way to determine the rank of a matrix. First define the matrix $\mathbf{A}$ as an array in the usual way. Then type rank(A). For example, the following MATLAB session determines the rank of the matrix given by (5.3–1).

```
>>A = [3,-4,1;6,10,2;9,-7,3];
>>rank(A)
ans =
   2
```

Existence and Uniqueness of Solutions

The following test determines whether a solution exists and whether or not it is unique. The test requires that we first form the so-called *augmented matrix* $[\mathbf{A}\ \mathbf{b}]$. The first n columns of the augmented matrix are the columns of $\mathbf{A}$. The last column of the augmented matrix is the column vector $\mathbf{b}$. For example, if

$$\mathbf{A} = \begin{bmatrix} 5 & 3 & -9 \\ -2 & 6 & 8 \end{bmatrix} \qquad \mathbf{b} = \begin{bmatrix} 7 \\ -10 \end{bmatrix}$$

then the augmented matrix is

$$[\mathbf{A}\ \mathbf{b}] = \begin{bmatrix} 5 & 3 & -9 & 7 \\ -2 & 6 & 8 & -10 \end{bmatrix}$$

The solution test can be stated as follows [Kreyzig, 1993]:

Existence and uniqueness of solutions. The set $\mathbf{Ax} = \mathbf{b}$ with m equations and n unknowns has solutions if and only if rank[$\mathbf{A}$] = rank[$\mathbf{A}\ \mathbf{b}$] (1). Let r = rank[$\mathbf{A}$]. If condition (1) is satisfied and if $r = n$, then the solution is unique. If condition (1) is satisfied but $r < n$, an infinite number of solutions exists and r unknown variables can be expressed as linear combinations of the other $n - r$ unknown variables, whose values are arbitrary.

Homogeneous case. The homogeneous set $\mathbf{Ax} = \mathbf{0}$ is a special case in which $\mathbf{b} = \mathbf{0}$. For this case rank$[\mathbf{A}]$ = rank$[\mathbf{A} \ \mathbf{b}]$ always, and thus the set always has the trivial solution $\mathbf{x} = \mathbf{0}$. A nonzero solution, in which at least one unknown is nonzero, exists if and only if rank$[\mathbf{A}] < n$. If $m < n$, the homogeneous set always has a nonzero solution.

Recall that if $|\mathbf{A}| = 0$, the equation set is singular. If you try to solve a singular set using MATLAB, it prints a message warning that the matrix is singular and does not try to solve the problem. An ill-conditioned set of equations is a set that is close to being singular. The ill-conditioned status depends on the accuracy with which the solution calculations are made. When the internal numerical accuracy used by MATLAB is insufficient to obtain a solution, MATLAB prints a message to warn you that the matrix is close to singular and that the results might be inaccurate.

Example 5.3–1 A set having a unique solution

Determine whether the following set has a unique solution, and if so, find it:

$$3x - 2y + 8z = 48$$

$$-6x + 5y + z = -12$$

$$9x + 4y + 2z = 24$$

Solution:

The matrices **A**, **b**, and **x** are

$$\mathbf{A} = \begin{bmatrix} 3 & -2 & 8 \\ -6 & 5 & 1 \\ 9 & 4 & 2 \end{bmatrix} \quad \mathbf{b} = \begin{bmatrix} 48 \\ -12 \\ 24 \end{bmatrix} \quad \mathbf{x} = \begin{bmatrix} x \\ y \\ z \end{bmatrix}$$

The following MATLAB session checks the ranks of **A** and [**A** **b**] and finds the solution.

```
>>A = [3,-2,8;-6,5,1;9,4,2];
>>b = [48;-12;24];
>>rank(A)
ans =
    3
>>rank([A  b])
ans =
    3
>>x = A\b
x =
    2
   -1
    5
```

Because **A** and [**A b**] have the same rank, a solution exists. Because this rank equals the number of unknowns (which is three), the solution is unique. The left-division method gives this solution, which is $x = 2$, $y = -1$, $z = 5$.

Test Your Understanding

T5.3–1 Use MATLAB to show that the following set has a unique solution and then find the solution:

$$3x + 12y - 7z = 5$$

$$5x - 6y - 5z = -8$$

$$-2x + 7y + 9z = 5$$

(Answer: The unique solution is $x = -1.0204$, $y = 0.5940$, $z = -0.1332$.)

Example 5.3–2 An underdetermined set

Show that the following set does not have a unique solution. How many of the unknowns will be undetermined? Interpret the results given by the left-division method.

$$2x - 4y + 5z = -4$$

$$-4x - 2y + 3z = 4$$

$$2x + 6y - 8z = 0$$

Solution:

A MATLAB session to check the ranks looks like

```
>>A = [2,-4,5;-4,-2,3;2,6,-8];
>>b = [-4;4;0];
>>rank(A)
ans =
    2
>>rank([A  b])
ans =
    2
```

Because the ranks of **A** and [**A b**] are equal, a solution exists. However, because the number of unknowns is three, and is one greater than the rank of **A**, one of the unknowns will be undetermined. An infinite number of solutions exists, and we can solve for only two of the unknowns in terms of the third unknown.

Note that even though the number of equations equals the number of unknowns here, the matrix **A** is singular. (We know this because its rank is less than three.) Thus we cannot use the matrix inverse method or Cramer's method for this problem.

If we use the left-division method, MATLAB returns a message warning that the problem is singular, rather than producing an answer.

The `pinv` Command and the Euclidean Norm

EUCLIDEAN NORM

The `pinv` command can obtain a solution of an underdetermined set. To solve the equation set $\mathbf{Ax} = \mathbf{b}$ using the `pinv` command, type `x = pinv(A)*b`. Underdetermined sets have an infinite number of solutions, and the pinv command produces a solution that gives the minimum value of the *Euclidean norm,* which is the magnitude of the solution vector **x**. The magnitude of a vector **v** in three-dimensional space, having components x, y, z, is $\sqrt{x^2 + y^2 + z^2}$. It can be computed using matrix multiplication and the transpose as follows:

$$\sqrt{\mathbf{v}^T\mathbf{v}} = \sqrt{[x \ y \ z]^T \begin{bmatrix} x \\ y \\ z \end{bmatrix}} = \sqrt{x^2 + y^2 + z^2}$$

The generalization of this formula to an n-dimensional vector **v** gives the magnitude of the vector and is the Euclidean norm N. Thus

$$N = \sqrt{\mathbf{v}^T\mathbf{v}} \qquad (5.3\text{--}2)$$

Example 5.3–3 shows how to apply the `pinv` command.

Example 5.3–3 A statically-indeterminate problem
Determine the forces in the three equally spaced supports that hold up a light fixture. The supports are 5 feet apart. The fixture weighs 400 pounds, and its mass center is 4 feet from the right end. (a) Solve the problem by hand. (b) Obtain the solution using the MATLAB left-division method and the pseudoinverse method.

Solution:

(a) Figure 5.3–1 shows the fixture and the free-body diagram, where T_1, T_2, and T_3 are the tension forces in the supports. For the fixture to be in equilibrium, the vertical forces must cancel, and the total moments about an arbitrary fixed point—say, the right endpoint—must be zero. These conditions give the two equations:

$$T_1 + T_2 + T_3 - 400 = 0$$

$$400(4) - 10T_1 - 5T_2 = 0$$

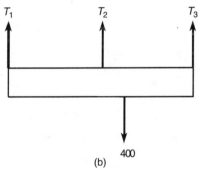

(a)

(b) 400

Figure 5.3–1
A light fixture and its free-body diagram.

or

$$T_1 + T_2 + T_3 = 400 \qquad \text{(5.3–3)}$$

$$10T_1 + 5T_2 + 0T_3 = 1600 \qquad \text{(5.3–4)}$$

Because there are more unknowns than equations, the set is underdetermined. These equations can be written in the matrix form $\mathbf{Ax} = \mathbf{b}$ as follows:

$$\begin{bmatrix} 1 & 1 & 1 \\ 10 & 5 & 0 \end{bmatrix} \begin{bmatrix} T_1 \\ T_2 \\ T_3 \end{bmatrix} = \begin{bmatrix} 400 \\ 1600 \end{bmatrix}$$

where

$$\mathbf{A} = \begin{bmatrix} 1 & 1 & 1 \\ 10 & 5 & 0 \end{bmatrix} \qquad \mathbf{b} = \begin{bmatrix} 400 \\ 1600 \end{bmatrix} \qquad \mathbf{x} = \begin{bmatrix} T_1 \\ T_2 \\ T_3 \end{bmatrix}$$

$$[\mathbf{A} \ \mathbf{b}] = \begin{bmatrix} 1 & 1 & 1 & 400 \\ 10 & 5 & 0 & 1600 \end{bmatrix}$$

Because we can find a nonzero 2×2 determinant in both $\mathbf{A}$ and $[\mathbf{A} \ \mathbf{b}]$, the ranks of $\mathbf{A}$ and $[\mathbf{A} \ \mathbf{b}]$ are both 2; thus a solution exists.

Because the number of unknowns is three, and is one greater than the rank of **A**, an infinite number of solutions exists and we can solve for only two of the forces in terms of the third force. Equation (5.3–4) gives

$$T_2 = \frac{1600 - 10T_1}{5} = 320 - 2T_1$$

Substitute this expression into (5.3–3) and solve for T_1 to find that $T_1 = T_3 - 80$. Thus the solution in terms of T_3 is

$$T_1 = T_3 - 80$$

$$T_2 = 320 - 2T_1 = 320 - 2(T_3 - 80) = 480 - 2T_3$$

We cannot determine numerical values for any of the forces. Such a problem, in which the equations of statics do not give enough equations to find all of the unknowns, is called *statically indeterminate*.

**STATICALLY
INDETERMINATE**

(b) A MATLAB session to check the ranks and to solve this problem using left division looks like

```
>>A = [1,1,1;10,5,0];
>>b = [400;1600];
>>rank(A)
ans =
   2
>>rank([A  b])
ans =
   2
>>A\b
ans =
   160.0000
   0
   240.0000
```

The answer corresponds to $T_1 = 160$, $T_2 = 0$, and $T_3 = 240$ pounds. This example illustrates how the MATLAB left-division operator produces a solution with one or more variables set to zero, for underdetermined sets having more unknowns than equations.

To use the pseudoinverse operator, type the command `pinv(A)*b`. The result is $T_1 = 93.3333$, $T_2 = 133.3333$, and $T_3 = 173.3333$ pounds. This answer is the minimum-norm solution for real values of the variables. The minimum-norm solution consists of the real values of T_1, T_2, and T_3 that minimize

$$N = \sqrt{T_1^2 + T_2^2 + T_3^2}$$

$$= \sqrt{(T_3 - 80)^2 + (480 - 2T_3)^2 + T_3^2}$$

$$= \sqrt{6T_3^2 - 2080T_3 + 236,800}$$

The smallest value N can have is zero. This result occurs when $T_3 = 173 \pm 97i$, which corresponds to $T_2 = 93 \pm 97i$ and $T_2 = 827 \pm 194i$. This result is a valid solution of the original equations, but is not the minimum-norm solution where T_1, T_2, and T_3 are restricted to real values (we know that the forces cannot be complex).

We can find the real value of T_3 that minimizes N by plotting N versus T_3 or by using calculus. The answer is $T_3 = 173.3333$, which gives $T_1 = 93.3333$ and $T_2 = 133.3333$. These values are the minimum norm solution given by the pseudoinverse method.

We must decide whether or not the solutions given by the left-division and the pseudoinverse methods are useful for applications that have an infinite number of solutions, and we must do so in the context of the specific application. For example, in the light-fixture application discussed in Example 5.3–3, only two supports are required, and the left-division solution (the solution with $T_2 = 0$) shows that if the middle support is eliminated, the forces in the end supports will be $T_1 = 160$ and $T_2 = 240$ pounds. Suppose we want to use three supports to reduce the load carried by each support. The pseudoinverse solution ($T_1 = 93$, $T_2 = 133$, $T_3 = 173$) is the solution that minimizes the sum of the squares of the support forces.

Many problems are statically indeterminate because the engineer has included more supports than necessary, usually for safety in case one support fails. In practice, when engineers are confronted with a statically indeterminate problem, they supplement the equations of statics with equations that describe the deformations of the supports as functions of the applied forces and moments. These additional equations allow the forces and moments within the structure to be determined unambiguously.

Test Your Understanding

T5.3–2 Use MATLAB to find two solutions to the following set:

$$x + 3y + 2z = 2$$

$$x + y + z = 4$$

(Answer: Minimum-norm solution: $x = 4.33$, $y = -1.67$, $z = 1.34$. Left-division solution: $x = 5, y = -1, z = 0$.)

The Reduced Row Echelon Form

We can express some of the unknowns in an underdetermined set as functions of the remaining unknowns. For example, in the statically indeterminate case of Example 5.3–3, we wrote the solutions for two of the forces in terms of the third:

$$T_1 = T_3 - 80$$

$$T_2 = 480 - 2T_3$$

These two equations are equivalent to

$$T_1 - T_3 = -80$$

$$T_2 + 2T_3 = 480$$

In matrix form these are

$$\begin{bmatrix} 1 & 0 & -1 \\ 0 & 1 & 2 \end{bmatrix} \begin{bmatrix} T_1 \\ T_2 \\ T_3 \end{bmatrix} = \begin{bmatrix} -80 \\ 480 \end{bmatrix}$$

The augmented matrix for the preceding set is

$$\begin{bmatrix} 1 & 0 & -1 & -80 \\ 0 & 1 & 2 & 480 \end{bmatrix}$$

Note that the first two columns form a 2×2 identity matrix. Therefore, the corresponding equations can be solved directly for T_1 and T_2 in terms of T_3.

We can always reduce an underdetermined set to such a form by multiplying the set's equations by suitable factors and adding the resulting equations to eliminate an unknown variable. The MATLAB rref command provides a procedure to reduce an equation set to this form, which is called the *reduced row echelon form*. Its syntax is rref([A b]). Its output is the augmented matrix [**C** **d**] that corresponds to the equation set **Cx** = **d**. This set is in reduced row echelon form.

**REDUCED ROW
ECHELON FORM**

Example 5.3–4   A singular set   The following under-determined equation set was analyzed in Example 5.3–2. There it was shown that an infinite number of solutions exists. Use the pinv and the rref commands to obtain solutions.

$$2x - 4y + 5z = -4$$

$$-4x - 2y + 3z = 4$$

$$2x + 6y - 8z = 0$$

Solution:
First use the pinv command. The MATLAB session follows.

```
>>A = [2,-4,5;-4,-2,3;2,6,-8];
>>b = [-4;4;0];
```

```
>>x = pinv(A)*b
ans =
   -1.2148
   0.2074
   -0.1481
```

Thus the pseudoinverse method gives the solution: $x = -1.2148$, $y = 0.2074$, $z = -0.1481$. This solution is valid, but it is not the general solution.

To obtain the general solution, we can use the `rref` command. The current MATLAB session continues as follows.

```
>>rref([A b])
ans =
   1      0      -0.1      -1.2000
   0      1      -1.3       0.4000
   0      0       0         0
```

The answer corresponds to the augmented matrix [**C d**], where

$$[\mathbf{C}\ \mathbf{d}] = \begin{bmatrix} 1 & 0 & -0.1 & -1.2 \\ 0 & 1 & -1.3 & 0.4 \\ 0 & 0 & 0 & 0 \end{bmatrix}$$

This matrix corresponds to the matrix equation **Cx** = **d**, or

$$x + 0y - 0.1z = -1.2$$

$$0x + y - 1.3z = 0.4$$

$$0x + 0y + 0z = 0$$

We can easily solve these expressions for x and y in terms of z as follows: $x = 0.1z - 1.2$ and $y = 1.3z + 0.4$. This result is the general solution to the problem, where z is taken to be the arbitrary variable.

Supplementing Underdetermined Systems

Often the linear equations describing the application are under-determined because not enough information has been specified to determine unique values of the unknowns. In such cases we might be able to include additional information, objectives, or con-straints to find a unique solution. We can use the `rref` command to reduce the number of unknown variables in the problem, as illustrated in the next two examples.

Example 5.3–5   Production planning   The follow-ing table shows how many hours reactors A and B need to produce 1 ton each of the chemical products 1, 2, and 3. The two reactors

are available for 40 hours and 30 hours per week, respectively. Determine how many tons of each product can be produced each week.

Hours	Product 1	Product 2	Product 3
Reactor A	5	3	3
Reactor B	3	3	4

Solution:

Let x, y, and z be the number of tons each of products 1, 2, and 3 that can be produced in one week. Using the data for reactor A, the equation for its usage in one week is

$$5x + 3y + 3z = 40$$

The data for reactor B gives

$$3x + 3y + 4z = 30$$

This system is underdetermined. The matrices for the equation $Ax = b$ are

$$A = \begin{bmatrix} 5 & 3 & 3 \\ 3 & 3 & 4 \end{bmatrix} \quad b = \begin{bmatrix} 40 \\ 30 \end{bmatrix} \quad x = \begin{bmatrix} x \\ y \\ z \end{bmatrix}$$

Here the rank(A) = rank([A b]) = 2, which is less than the number of unknowns. Thus an infinite number of solutions exists, and we can determine two of the variables in terms of the third.

Using the `rref` command `rref([A b])`, where A = [5,3,3;3,3,4] and b = [40;30], we obtain the following reduced echelon augmented matrix:

$$\begin{bmatrix} 1 & 0 & -0.5 & 5 \\ 0 & 1 & 1.8333 & 5 \end{bmatrix}$$

This matrix gives the reduced system

$$x - 0.5z = 5$$

$$y + 1.8333z = 5$$

which can be easily solved as follows:

$$x = 5 + 0.5z \tag{5.3–5}$$

$$y = 5 - 1.8333z \tag{5.3–6}$$

where z is arbitrary. However, z cannot be completely arbitrary if the solution is to be meaningful. For example, negative values of the variables have no meaning here; thus we require that $x \geq 0$, $y \geq 0$, and $z \geq 0$. Equation (5.3–5) shows that $x \geq 0$ if $z \geq -10$. From (5.3–6), $y \leq 0$ implies that $z \leq 5/1.8333 = 2.737$. Thus valid solutions are those given by (5.3–5) and (5.3–6), where $0 \leq z \leq 2.737$ tons. The choice of z within this range must be made on some other basis, such as profit.

For example, suppose we make a profit of $400, $600, and $100 per ton for products 1, 2, and 3, respectively. Then our total profit P is

$$P = 400x + 600y + 100z$$

$$= 400(5 + 0.5z) + 600(5 - 1.8333z) + 100z$$

$$= 5000 - 800z$$

Thus to maximize profit, we should choose z to be the smallest possible value; namely, $z = 0$. This choice gives $x = y = 5$ tons.

However, if the profits for each product were $3000, $600, and $100, the total profit would be $P = 18,000 + 500z$. Thus we should choose z to be its maximum; namely, $z = 2.737$ tons. From (5.3–5) and (5.3–6), we obtain $x = 6.36$ and $y = 0$ tons.

Example 5.3–6 Traffic engineering
A traffic engineer wants to know whether measurements of traffic flow entering and leaving a road network are sufficient to predict the traffic flow on each street in the network. For example, consider the network of one-way streets shown in Figure 5.3–2. The numbers in the figure give the measured traffic flows in vehicles per hour. Assume that no vehicles park anywhere within the network. If possible, calculate the traffic flows f_1, f_2, f_3, and f_4. If this is not possible, suggest how to obtain the necessary information.

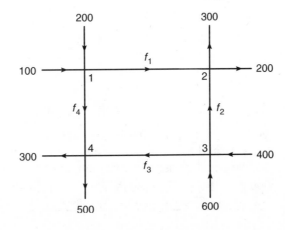

Figure 5.3–2
A network of one-way streets.

Solution:

The flow *into* intersection 1 must equal the flow *out* of the intersection, which gives us

$$100 + 200 = f_1 + f_4$$

Similarly, for the other three intersections, we have

$$f_1 + f_2 = 300 + 200$$

$$600 + 400 = f_2 + f_3$$

$$f_3 + f_4 = 300 + 500$$

Putting these expressions in the matrix form $\mathbf{Ax} = \mathbf{b}$, we obtain

$$\mathbf{A} = \begin{bmatrix} 1 & 0 & 0 & 1 \\ 1 & 1 & 0 & 0 \\ 0 & 1 & 1 & 0 \\ 0 & 0 & 1 & 1 \end{bmatrix} \quad \mathbf{b} = \begin{bmatrix} 300 \\ 500 \\ 1000 \\ 800 \end{bmatrix} \quad \mathbf{x} = \begin{bmatrix} f_1 \\ f_2 \\ f_3 \\ f_4 \end{bmatrix}$$

First check the ranks of $\mathbf{A}$ and $[\mathbf{A}\ \mathbf{b}]$ using the MATLAB rank command. Both have a rank of three, which is less than the number of unknowns, so we can determine three of the unknowns in terms of the fourth. Thus we cannot determine the traffic flows based on the given measurements. This example shows that it is not always possible to find a unique, exact solution even when the number of equations equals the number of unknowns.

Using the `rref([A b])` command produces the reduced augmented matrix

$$\begin{bmatrix} 1 & 0 & 0 & 1 & 300 \\ 0 & 1 & 0 & -1 & 200 \\ 0 & 0 & 1 & 1 & 800 \\ 0 & 0 & 0 & 0 & 0 \end{bmatrix}$$

which corresponds to the following reduced system:

$$f_1 + f_4 = 300$$

$$f_2 - f_4 = 200$$

$$f_3 + f_4 = 800$$

We can easily solve this system as follows: $f_1 = 300 - f_4$, $f_2 = 200 + f_4$, and $f_3 = 800 - f_4$.

If we could measure the flow on one of the internal roads, say, f_4, then we could compute the other flows. So we recommend that the engineer arrange to make this additional measurement.

T5.3–3 Use the `rref` and `pinv` commands and the left-division method to solve the following set:

$$3x + 5y + 6z = 6$$

$$8x - y + 2z = 1$$

$$5x - 6y - 4z = -5$$

(Answer: The set has an infinite number of solutions. The result obtained with the `rref` command is $x = 0.2558 - 0.3721z$, $y = 1.0465 - 0.9767z$, z arbitrary. The `pinv` command gives $x = 0.0571, y = 0.5249, z = 0.5340$. The left-division method generates an error message.)

T5.3–4 Use the `rref` and `pinv` commands and the left-division method to solve the following set:

$$3x + 5y + 6z = 4$$

$$x - 2y - 3z = 10$$

(Answer: The set has an infinite number of solutions. The result obtained with the `rref` command is $x = 0.2727z + 5.2727, y = -1.3636z - 2.2626$, z arbitrary. The solution obtained with left division is $x = 4.8000, y = 0, z = -1.7333$. The pseudoinverse method gives $x = 4.8394, y = -0.1972, z = -1.5887$.)

An *overdetermined system* is a set of equations that has more independent equations than unknowns. For such a system the matrix inverse method and Cramer's method will not work, because the **A** matrix is not square. However, some overdetermined systems have exact solutions, and they can be obtained with the left-division method `x = A\b`. For other overdetermined systems, no exact solution exists. In some of these cases, the left-division method does not yield an answer, while in other cases the left-division method gives an answer that satisfies the equation set only in a "least squares" sense, as explained in Example 5.4–1. When MATLAB gives an answer to an overdetermined set, it does not tell us whether the answer is the exact solution. We must determine this information ourselves, as shown in Example 5.4–2.

OVERDETERMINED
SYSTEM

Example 5.4–1 The least squares method

Suppose we have the following three data points, and we want to find the straight line $y = mx + b$ that best fits the data in some sense.

x	y
0	2
5	6
10	11

(a) Find the coefficients m and b by using the least squares criterion. (b) Find the coefficients by using MATLAB to solve the three equations (one for each data point) for the two unknowns m and b. Compare the answers from (a) and (b).

Solution:

(a) Because two points define a straight line, unless we are extremely lucky, our data points will not lie on the same straight line. A common criterion for obtaining the straight line that best fits the data is the *least squares* criterion. According to this criterion, the line that minimizes J, the sum of the squares of the vertical differences between the line and the data points, is the "best" fit (see Figure 5.4–1). Here J is

LEAST SQUARES METHOD

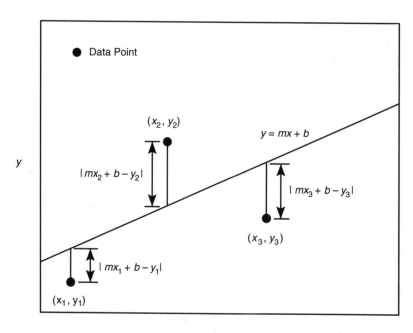

Figure 5.4–1
Illustration of the least squares criterion.

$$J = \sum_{i=1}^{i=3}(mx_i + b - y_i)^2$$

Substituting the data values (x_i, y_i), this expression becomes

$$J = (0m + b - 2)^2 + (5m + b - 6)^2 + (10m + b - 11)^2$$

You can use the `fmins` command to find the values of m and b that minimize J. On the other hand, if you are familiar with calculus, you know that the values of m and b that minimize J are found by setting the partial derivatives $\partial J/\partial m$ and $\partial J/\partial b$ equal to zero:

$$\frac{\partial J}{\partial m} = 2(5m + b - 6)(5) + 2(10m + b - 11)(10)$$

$$= 250m + 30b - 280 = 0$$

$$\frac{\partial J}{\partial b} = 2(b - 2) + 2(5m + b - 6) + 2(10m + b - 11)$$

$$= 30m + 6b - 38 = 0$$

These give the following equations for the two unknowns m and b:

$$250m + 30b = 280$$

$$30m + 6b = 38$$

The solution is $m = 0.9$ and $b = 11/6$. The best straight line in the least squares sense is $y = 0.9x + 11/6 = 0.9x + 1.8333$. It appears in Figure 5.4–2, along with the data points.

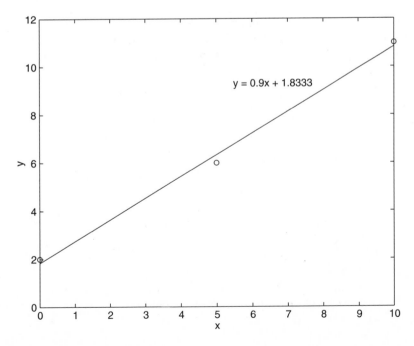

Figure 5.4–2
The least squares fit for the example data.

(b) Evaluating the equation $y = mx + b$ at each data point gives the following three equations:

$$0m + b = 2 \qquad (5.4-1)$$

$$5m + b = 6 \qquad (5.4-2)$$

$$10m + b = 11 \qquad (5.4-3)$$

This set is overdetermined because it has more equations than unknowns. These equations can be written in the matrix form $\mathbf{Ax} = \mathbf{b}$ as follows:

$$\begin{bmatrix} 0 & 1 \\ 5 & 0 \\ 10 & 1 \end{bmatrix} \begin{bmatrix} m \\ b \end{bmatrix} = \begin{bmatrix} 2 \\ 6 \\ 11 \end{bmatrix}$$

where

$$\mathbf{A} = \begin{bmatrix} 0 & 1 \\ 5 & 1 \\ 10 & 1 \end{bmatrix} \qquad \mathbf{x} = \begin{bmatrix} m \\ b \end{bmatrix} \qquad \mathbf{b} = \begin{bmatrix} 2 \\ 6 \\ 11 \end{bmatrix}$$

$$[\mathbf{A} \ \mathbf{b}] = \begin{bmatrix} 0 & 1 & 2 \\ 5 & 1 & 6 \\ 10 & 1 & 11 \end{bmatrix}$$

Because we can find a nonzero 2×2 determinant in $\mathbf{A}$, its rank is two. However $|\mathbf{A} \ \mathbf{b}| = -5 \neq 0$, so its rank is three. Thus no exact solution exists for m and b. The following MATLAB session uses left division.

```
>>A = [0,1;5,1;10,1];
>>b = [2;6;11];
>>rank(A)
ans =
    2
>>rank([A b])
ans =
    3
>>A\b
ans =
    0.9000
    1.8333
```

This result agrees with the least squares solution obtained previously: $m = 0.9$, $b = 11/6 = 1.8333$.

If we now type A*ans, MATLAB yields this result:

```
ans =
    1.833
    6.333
   10.8333
```

These values are the y values generated by the line $y = 0.9 + 1.8333x$ at the x data values $x = 0, 5, 10$. These values are different from the right sides of the original three equations (5.4–1) through (5.4–3). This result is not unexpected because the least squares solution is not an exact solution of the equations.

Some overdetermined systems have an exact solution. The left-division method sometimes gives an answer for overdetermined systems, but it does not indicate whether the answer is the exact solution. We need to check the ranks of **A** and [**A b**] to know whether the answer is the exact solution. The next example illustrates this situation.

Example 5.4–2 An overdetermined set   (a) Solve the following equations by hand and (b) solve them using MATLAB. Discuss the solution for two cases: $c = 9$ and $c = 10$.

$$x + y = 1$$

$$x + 2y = 3$$

$$x + 5y = c$$

Solution:
(a) To solve these equations by hand, subtract the first equation from the second to obtain $y = 2$. Substitute this value into the first equation to obtain $x = -1$. Substituting these values into the third equation gives $-1 + 10 = c$, which is satisfied only if $c = 9$. Thus a solution exists if and only if $c = 9$.

(b) The coefficient matrix and the augmented matrix for this problem are

$$\mathbf{A} = \begin{bmatrix} 1 & 1 \\ 1 & 2 \\ 1 & 5 \end{bmatrix} \qquad [\mathbf{A}\ \mathbf{b}] = \begin{bmatrix} 1 & 1 & 1 \\ 1 & 2 & 3 \\ 1 & 5 & c \end{bmatrix}$$

In MATLAB, enter the array A = [1,1;1,2;1,5]. For $c = 9$, type b = [1;3;9]; the rank(**A**) and rank([**A b**]) commands give the result that rank(**A**) = rank([**A b**]) = 2. Thus the system has a solution and, because the number of unknowns (two) equals the rank of **A**, the solution is unique. The left-division method **A** \ **b** gives this solution, which is $x = -1$ and $y = 2$.

For $c = 10$, type b = [1;3;10]; the rank(**A**) and rank([**A b**]) commands give the result that rank(**A**) $= 2$, but rank([**A b**]) $= 3$. Because rank(**A**) $\neq$ rank([**A b**]), no solution exists. However, the left-division method **A** \ **b** gives $x = -1.3846$ and $y = 2.2692$, which is *not* a solution! This conclusion can be verified by substituting these values into the original equation set. This answer is the solution to the equation set in a least squares sense. That is, these values are the values of x and y that minimize J, the sum of the squares of the differences between the equations' left and right sides.

$$J = (x + y - 1)^2 + (x + 2y - 3)^2 + (x + 5y - 10)^2$$

The MATLAB left-division operator sometimes gives the least squares solution when we use the operator to solve problems for which there is no exact solution. A solution exists when $c = 9$, but no solution exists when $c = 10$. The left-division method gives the exact solution when $c = 9$ but gives the least squares solution when $c = 10$.

To interpret MATLAB answers correctly for an overdetermined system, first check the ranks of **A** and [**A b**] to see whether an exact solution exists; if one does not exist, then you know that the left-division answer is a least squares solution.

Test Your Understanding

T5.4–1 Use MATLAB to solve the following set:

$$x - 3y = 2$$

$$3x + 5y = 7$$

$$70x - 28y = 153$$

(Answer: The unique solution, $x = 2.2143$, $y = 0.0714$, is given by the left-division method.)

T5.4–2 Use MATLAB to solve the following set:

$$x - 3y = 2$$

$$3x + 5y = 7$$

$$5x - 2y = -4$$

(Answer: no exact solution)

Once you have finished this chapter, you should be able to solve by hand systems of linear algebraic equations that have few variables and use MATLAB to solve systems that have many variables. If the number of equations in the set *equals* the number of unknown variables, the matrix **A** is square and MATLAB provides two ways of solving the equation set $\mathbf{Ax = b}$:

1. The matrix inverse method; solve for **x** by typing $x = inv(A)*b$.
2. The matrix left-division method; solve for **x** by typing $x = A\backslash b$.

If **A** is square and if MATLAB does not generate an error message when you use one of these methods, then the set has a unique solution, which is given by the left-division method. You can always check the solution for x by typing Ax to see if the result is the same as b. If so, the solution is correct. If you receive an error message, the set is underdetermined, and either it does not have a solution or it has more than one solution. In such a case, if you need more information, you must use the following procedures.

For underdetermined and overdetermined sets, MATLAB provides three ways of dealing with the equation set $\mathbf{Ax = b}$. (Note that the matrix inverse method will never work with such sets.)

1. The matrix left-division method; solve for **x** by typing $x = A\backslash b$.
2. The pseudoinverse method; solve for **x** by typing $x = pinv(A)*b$.
3. The reduced row echelon form (RREF) method. This method uses the MATLAB command $rref$ to obtain a solution.

Table 5.5–1 summarizes the four methods. You should be able to determine whether a unique solution, an infinite number of solutions, or no solution exists. You can get this information by testing for existence and uniqueness of solutions using the following test.

Table 5.5–1 Matrix commands for solving linear equations

Command	Description
det(A)	Computes the determinant of the array **A**.
inv(A)	Computes the inverse of the matrix **A**.
pinv(A)	Computes the pseudoinverse of the matrix **A**.
rank(A)	Computes the rank of the matrix **A**.
rref([A b])	Computes the reduced row echelon form corresponding to the augmented matrix [**A** **b**].
x = inv(A)*b	Solves the matrix equation **Ax** = **b**, using the matrix inverse.
x = A\b	Solves the matrix equation **Ax** = **b**, using left division.
x = d/C	Solves the matrix equation **xC** = **d**, using right division.

Existence and Uniqueness of Solutions

The set $\mathbf{Ax} = \mathbf{b}$ with m equations and n unknowns has solutions if and only if rank$[\mathbf{A}]$ = rank$[\mathbf{A}\ \mathbf{b}]$ (1). Let r = rank$[\mathbf{A}]$. If condition (1) is satisfied and if $r = n$, then the solution is unique. If condition (1) is satisfied but $r < n$, an infinite number of solutions exists and r unknown variables can be expressed as linear combinations of the other $n - r$ unknown variables, whose values are arbitrary.

Homogeneous case. The homogeneous set $\mathbf{Ax} = \mathbf{0}$ is a special case in which $\mathbf{b} = \mathbf{0}$. For this case rank$[\mathbf{A}]$ = rank$[\mathbf{A}\ \mathbf{b}]$ always, and thus the set always has the trivial solution $\mathbf{x} = \mathbf{0}$. A nonzero solution, in which at least one unknown is nonzero, exists if and only if rank$[\mathbf{A}] < n$. If $m < n$, the homogeneous set always has a nonzero solution.

Underdetermined Systems

In an *underdetermined* system not enough information is given to determine the values of all the unknown variables.

- An infinite number of solutions might exist in which one or more of the unknowns are dependent on the remaining unknowns.
- For such systems Cramer's method and the matrix inverse method will not work because either $\mathbf{A}$ is not square or because $|\mathbf{A}| = 0$.
- The left-division method will give a solution with some of the unknowns arbitrarily set equal to zero, but this solution is not the general solution.
- An infinite number of solutions might exist even when the number of equations equals the number of unknowns. The left-division method fails to give a solution in such cases.
- In cases that have an infinite number of solutions, some of the unknowns can be expressed in terms of the remaining unknowns, whose values are arbitrary. The `rref` command can be used to find these relations.

Overdetermined Systems

An *overdetermined* system is a set of equations that has more independent equations than unknowns.

- For such a system Cramer's method and the matrix inverse method will not work because the $\mathbf{A}$ matrix is not square.
- Some overdetermined systems have exact solutions, which can be obtained with the left-division method `A\b`.
- For overdetermined systems that have no exact solution, the answer given by the left-division method satisfies the equation set only in a least squares sense.

- When we use MATLAB to solve an overdetermined set, the program does not tell us whether the solution is exact. We must determine this information ourselves. The first step is to check the ranks of **A** and [**A b**] to see whether a solution exists; if no solution exists, then we know that the left-division solution is a least squares answer.

Key Terms with Page References

Augmented matrix, **215**

Cramer's determinant, **200**

Cramer's method, **199**

Determinant, **200**

Euclidean norm, **218**

Gauss elimination, **195**

Homogeneous equations, **197**

Ill-conditioned equations, **198**

Least squares method, **228**

Left-division method, **207**

Matrix inverse, **205**

Matrix rank, **215**

Minimum norm solution, **214**

Overdetermined system, **227**

Pseudoinverse method, **214**

Reduced row echelon form, **222**

Singular matrix, **204**

Singular problem, **196**

Statically indeterminate problem, **220**

Subdeterminant, **214**

Underdetermined system, **213**

Problems

You can find answers to problems marked with an asterisk at the end of the text.

Section 5.1

1. Solve the following problems by hand. For each of the following problems, find the unique solution if one exists. If a unique solution does not exist, determine whether no solution exists or a nonunique solution exists.

   a. $-5x + y = -6$

   $x + y = 6$

   b. $-2x + y = -5$

   $-2x + y = 3$

   c. $-2x + y = 3$

   $-8x + 4y = 12$

   d. $-2x + y = -5$

   $-2x + y = -5.00001$

2. Use elimination of variables to solve the following problem by hand:

$$12x - 5y = 11$$

$$-3x + 4y + 7z = -3$$

$$6x + 2y + 3z = 22$$

3.* Use elimination of variables to solve the following problem by hand:

$$6x - 3y + 4z = 41$$

$$12x + 5y - 7z = -26$$

$$-5x + 2y + 6z = 14$$

4. (*a*) Solve the following problem by hand for x, y, and z in terms of the parameter r. (*b*) For what value of r will a solution *not* exist?

$$3x + 2y - rz = 1$$

$$-x + 3y + 2z = 1$$

$$x - y - z = 1$$

Section 5.2
━━━━

5. Use matrix inversion to solve the following problems. Check your solutions by computing $A^{-1}A$:

    a. $2x + y = 5$

        $3x - 9y = 2$

    b. $-8x - 5y = 4$

        $-2x + 7y = 10$

    c. $12x - 5y = 11$

        $-3x + 4y + 7z = -3$

        $6x + 2y + 3z = 22$

    d. $6x - 3y + 4z = 41$

        $12x + 5y - 7z = -26$

        $-5x + 2y + 6z = 14$

6.* *a.* Solve the following matrix equation for the matrix **C**:

$$A(BC + A) = B$$

    b. Evaluate the solution obtained in part (*a*) for the case:

$$A = \begin{bmatrix} 3 & 9 \\ -2 & 4 \end{bmatrix} \qquad B = \begin{bmatrix} 2 & -3 \\ 7 & 6 \end{bmatrix}$$

7. Use MATLAB to solve the following problems:

   a. $-2x + y = -5$

      $-2x + y = 3$

   b. $-2x + y = 3$

      $-8x + 4y = 12$

   c. $-2x + y = -5$

      $-2x + y = -5.00001$

   d. $x_1 + 5x_2 - x_3 + 6x_4 = 19$

      $2x_1 - x_2 + x_3 - 2x_4 = 7$

      $-x_1 + 4x_2 - x_3 + 3x_4 = 20$

      $3x_1 - 7x_2 - 2x_3 + x_4 = -75$

8. The circuit shown in Figure P8 has five resistances and one applied voltage. Kirchhoff's voltage law applied to each loop in the circuit shown gives

$$v - R_2 i_2 - R_4 i_4 = 0$$

$$-R_2 i_2 + R_1 i_1 + R_3 i_3 = 0$$

$$-R_4 i_4 - R_3 i_3 + R_5 i_5 = 0$$

Conservation of charge applied at each node in the circuit gives

$$i_6 = i_1 + i_2$$

$$i_2 + i_3 = i_4$$

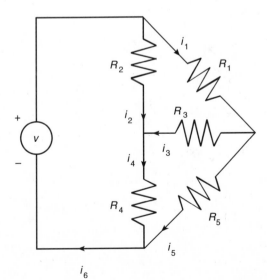

Figure P8

$$i_1 = i_3 + i_5$$

$$i_4 + i_5 = i_6$$

a. Write a MATLAB script file that uses given values of the applied voltage v and the values of the five resistances to solve for the six currents.

b. Use the program developed in part (a) to find the currents for the case: $R_1 = 1$, $R_2 = 5$, $R_3 = 2$, $R_4 = 10$, $R_5 = 5\,k\Omega$, and $v = 100$ volts. ($1\,k\Omega = 1000\,\Omega$).

9.* a. Use MATLAB to solve the following equations for x, y, and z as functions of the parameter c:

$$x - 5y - 2z = 11c$$

$$6x + 3y + z = 13c$$

$$7x + 3y - 5z = 10c$$

b. Plot the solutions for x, y, and z versus c on the same plot for $-10 \leq c \leq 10$.

10. Fluid flows in pipe networks can be analyzed in a manner similar to that used for electric-resistance networks. Figure P10 shows a network with three pipes. The volume flow rates in the pipes are q_1, q_2, and q_3. The pressures at the pipe ends are p_a, p_b, and p_c. The pressure at the junction is p_1. Under certain conditions, the pressure-flow rate relation in a pipe has the same form as the voltage-current relation in a resistor. Thus for the three pipes, we

(a)   (b)

Figure P10

$$q_1 = \frac{1}{R_1}(p_a - p_1)$$

$$q_2 = \frac{1}{R_2}(p_1 - p_b)$$

$$q_3 = \frac{1}{R_3}(p_1 - p_c)$$

where the R_i are the pipe resistances. From conservation of mass, $q_1 = q_2 + q_3$.

a. Set up these equations in a matrix form $\mathbf{Ax} = \mathbf{b}$ suitable for solving for the three flow rates q_1, q_2, and q_3, and the pressure p_1, given the values of the pressures p_a, p_b, and p_c, and the values of the resistances R_1, R_2, and R_3. Find the expressions for $\mathbf{A}$ and $\mathbf{b}$.

b. Use MATLAB to solve the matrix equations obtained in part (a) for the case: $p_a = 4320$ pounds/foot^2, $p_b = 3600$ pounds/foot^2, and $p_c = 2880$ pounds/foot^2. These correspond to 30, 25, and 20 psi, respectively (1 psi = 1 pound/inch^2. Atmospheric pressure is 14.7 psi). Use the resistance values $R_1 = 10,000$; $R_2 = R_3 = 14,000$ lb second/foot^5. These values correspond to fuel oil flowing through pipes 2 feet long, with 2 inch and 1.4 inch diameters, respectively. The units of the answers will be feet^3/second for the flow rates and pounds/foot^2 for pressure.

11. Figure P11 illustrates a robot arm that has two "links" connected by two "joints": a shoulder, or base, joint and an elbow joint. There is a motor at each joint. The joint angles are θ_1 and θ_2. The (x, y) coordinates of the hand at the end of the arm are given by

$$x = L_1 \cos \theta_1 + L_2 \cos(\theta_1 + \theta_2)$$

$$y = L_1 \sin \theta_1 + L_2 \sin(\theta_1 + \theta_2)$$

where L_1 and L_2 are the lengths of the links.

Polynomials are used for controlling the motion of robots. If we start the arm from rest with zero velocity and acceleration, the following polynomials are used to generate commands to be sent to the joint motor controllers.

$$\theta_1(t) = \theta_1(0) + a_1 t^3 + a_2 t^4 + a_3 t^5$$

$$\theta_2(t) = \theta_2(0) + b_1 t^3 + b_2 t^4 + b_3 t^5$$

where $\theta_1(0)$ and $\theta_2(0)$ are the starting values at time $t = 0$. The angles $\theta_1(t_f)$ and $\theta_2(t_f)$ are the joint angles corresponding to the desired destination of the arm at time t_f. The values of $\theta_1(0)$, $\theta_2(0)$, $\theta_1(t_f)$, and $\theta_2(t_f)$ can be found using trigonometry if the starting and ending (x, y) coordinates of the hand are specified.

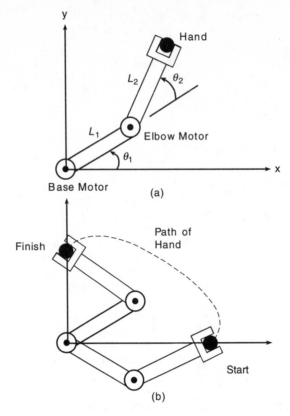

Hand

L_2

θ_2

L_1

Elbow Motor

θ_1

x

Base Motor

(a)

Path of
Hand

Finish

Start

(b)

a. Set up a matrix equation to be solved for the coefficients a_1, a_2, and a_3, given values for $\theta_1(0)$, $\theta_1(t_f)$, and t_f. Obtain a similar equation to be solved for the coefficients b_1, b_2, and b_3, given values for $\theta_2(0)$, $\theta_2(t_f)$, and t_f.

b. Use MATLAB to solve for the polynomial coefficients given the values $t_f = 2$ seconds, $\theta_1(0) = -19°$, $\theta_2(0) = 44°$, $\theta_1(t_f) = 43°$, and $\theta_2(t_f) = 151°$. (These values correspond to a starting hand location of $x = 6.5$, $y = 0$ feet and a destination location of $x = 0$, $y = 2$ feet for $L_1 = 4$ and $L_2 = 3$ feet.)

c. Use the results of part (b) to plot the path of the hand.

12.* Engineers use the concept of *thermal resistance R* to predict the rate of heat loss through a building wall in order to determine the heating system's requirements. This concept relates the heat flow rate q through a material to the temperature difference ΔT across the material: $q = \Delta T/R$. This relation is like the voltage-current relation for an electrical resistor: $i = v/R$. So the heat flow rate plays the role of electrical current, and the temperature difference plays the role of the voltage difference v. The SI unit for q is watt/meter^2. A watt is is 1 joule/second.

The wall shown in Figure P12 consists of four layers: an inner layer of plaster/lathe 10 millimeters thick, a layer of fiberglass insulation 125 millimeters thick, a layer of wood 60 millimeters

(a)

(b)

Figure P12

thick, and an outer layer of brick 50 millimeters thick. If we assume that the inner and outer temperatures T_i and T_o have remained constant for some time, then the heat energy stored in the layers is constant; thus the heat flow rate through each layer is the same. Applying conservation of energy gives the following equations:

$$q = \frac{1}{R_1}(T_i - T_1) = \frac{1}{R_2}(T_1 - T_2) = \frac{1}{R_3}(T_2 - T_3) = \frac{1}{R_4}(T_3 - T_o)$$

The thermal resistance of a solid material is given by $R = D/k$ where D is the material's thickness and k is the material's *thermal conductivity*. For the given materials, the resistances for a wall area of 1 meter^2 are $R_1 = 0.036$, $R_2 = 4.01$, $R_3 = 0.408$, and $R_4 = 0.038\,°K/watt$.

Suppose that $T_i = 20$ and $T_o = -10°C$. Find the other three temperatures and the heat loss rate q in watts/meter^2. Compute the heat loss rate in watts if the wall's area is 10 meters^2.

13. The concept of thermal resistance described in Problem 12 can be used to find the temperature distribution in the flat square plate shown in Figure P13a. The plate's edges are insulated so that no heat can escape, except at two points where the edge temperature is heated to T_a and T_b, respectively. The temperature varies through the plate, so no single point can describe the plate's temperature. One way to estimate the temperature distribution is to imagine that the plate consists of four subsquares and to compute the temperature in each subsquare. Let R be the thermal resistance of the material between the centers of adjacent subsquares. Then

(a)

(b)

Figure P13

we can think of the problem as a network of electrical resistors, as shown in Figure P13b. Let q_{ij} be the heat flow rate between the points whose temperatures are T_i and T_j. If T_a and T_b remain constant for some time, then both the heat energy stored in each subsquare and the heat flow rate between each subsquare are constant. Under these conditions conservation of energy says that the heat flow into a subsquare equals the heat flow out. Applying this principle to each subsquare gives the following equations:

$$q_{a1} = q_{12} + q_{13}$$

$$q_{12} = q_{24}$$

$$q_{13} = q_{34}$$

$$q_{34} + q_{24} = q_{4b}$$

Substituting $q_{ij} = (T_i - T_j)/R$, we find that R can be canceled out of every equation, and the equations can be rearranged as follows:

$$T_1 = \frac{1}{3}(T_a + T_2 + T_3)$$

$$T_2 = \frac{1}{2}(T_1 + T_4)$$

$$T_3 = \frac{1}{2}(T_1 + T_4)$$

$$T_4 = \frac{1}{3}(T_2 + T_3 + T_b)$$

These equations tell us that the temperature of each subsquare is the average of the temperatures in the adjacent subsquares!

Solve these equations for the case where $T_a = 150°C$ and $T_b = 20°C$.

14. Use the averaging principle developed in Problem 13 to find the temperature distribution of the plate shown in Figure P14, using the 3×3 grid and the given values $T_a = 150°C$ and $T_b = 20°C$.

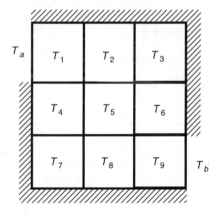

Figure P14

Section 5.3

15.* Use MATLAB to solve the following problem:

$$7x + 9y - 9z = 22$$

$$3x + 2y - 4z = 12$$

$$x + 5y - z = -2$$

16. The following table shows how many hours reactors A and B need to produce 1 ton each of the chemical products 1, 2, and 3. The two reactors are available for 35 hours and 40 hours per week, respectively.

Hours	Product 1	Product 2	Product 3
Reactor A	6	2	10
Reactor B	3	5	2

Let x, y, and z be the number of tons each of products 1, 2, and 3 that can be produced in one week.

a. Use the data in the table to write two equations in terms of x, y, and z. Determine whether or not a unique solution exists. If not, use MATLAB to find the relations between x, y, and z.

b. Note that negative values of x, y, and z have no meaning here. Find the allowable ranges for x, y, and z.

c. Suppose the profits for each product are $200, $300, and $100 for products 1, 2, and 3, respectively. Find the values of x, y, and z to maximize the profit.

d. Suppose the profits for each product are $200, $500, and $100 for products 1, 2, and 3, respectively. Find the values of x, y, and z to maximize the profit.

17. See Figure P17. Assume that no vehicles stop within the network. A traffic engineer wants to know whether the traffic flows f_1, $f_2, \ldots, f_7$ (in vehicles per hour) can be computed given the measured flows shown in the figure. If not, then determine how many more traffic sensors need to be installed and obtain the expressions for the other traffic flows in terms of the measured quantities.

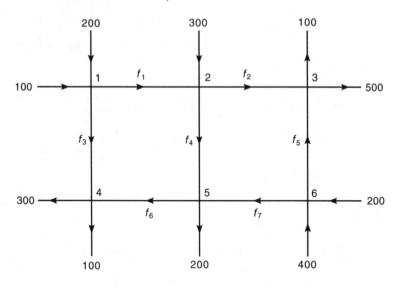

Figure P17

Section 5.4

18.* Use MATLAB to solve the following problem:

$$x - 3y = 2$$

$$x + 5y = 18$$

$$4x - 6y = 20$$

19.* Use MATLAB to solve the following problem:

$$x - 3y = 2$$

$$x + 5y = 18$$

$$4x - 6y = 10$$

20. *a.* Use MATLAB to find the coefficients of the quadratic polynomial $y = ax^2 + bx + c$ that passes through these three points: $(x, y) = (1, 4)$, $(4, 73)$, $(5, 120)$.

　　b. Use MATLAB to find the coefficients of the cubic polynomial $y = ax^3 + bx^2 + cx + d$ that passes through the three points given in part *(a)*.

Courtesy Jet Propulsion Lab/NASA.

Engineering in the 21st Century...

Robot-Assisted Microsurgery

Y ou need not be a medical doctor to participate in the exciting developments now taking place in the health field. Many advances in medicine and surgery are really engineering achievements, and many engineers are contributing their talents in this area. Recent achievements include

- Laparoscopic surgery in which a fiber-optic scope guides a small surgical device. This technology eliminates the need for large incisions and the resulting long recuperation.
- Computerized axial tomography (CAT) scans and magnetic resonance imaging (MRI), which provide noninvasive tools for diagnosing medical problems.
- Medical instrumentation, such as a fingertip sensor for continuously measuring oxygen in the blood and automatic blood pressure sensors.

As we move into the 21st century, an exciting challenge will be the development of robot-assisted surgery in which a robot, supervised by a human, performs operations requiring precise, steady motions. Robots have already assisted in hip surgery on animals, but much more development is needed. Another developing technology is *telesurgery* in which a surgeon uses a television interface to remotely guide a surgical robot. This technology would allow delivery of medical services to remote areas.

Robot-assisted microsurgery, which uses a robot capable of very small, precise motions, shows great promise. One application is in eye surgery, and the photo above shows a test of such a device on a dummy head. Designing such devices requires geometric analysis, control system design, and image processing. The MATLAB Image Processing toolbox and the several MATLAB toolboxes dealing with control system design are useful for such applications.

246

6

Programming with MATLAB

Outline

The MATLAB interactive mode is very useful for simple problems, but more complex problems require a script file. Such a file can be called a *computer program,* and writing such a file is called *programming.* The usefulness of MATLAB is greatly increased by the use of decision-making functions in its programs. These functions enable you to write programs whose operations depend on the results of calculations made by the program. The first three sections of the chapter deal with these decision-making functions.

MATLAB can also repeat calculations a specified number of times or until some condition is satisfied. This feature enables engineers to solve problems of great complexity or requiring numerous calculations. These "loop" structures are covered in section 6.4.

New in MATLAB 5 is the switch structure that enhances the MATLAB decision-making capabilities. This topic is covered in section 6.5.

Section 6.6 discusses "simulation," a major application of MATLAB programs that enables us to study the operation of complicated systems, processes, and organizations. Tables summarizing the MATLAB commands introduced in this chapter appear

247

throughout the chapter, and Table 6.7–1 will help you locate the information you need.

6.1

Relational Operators

RELATIONAL OPERATOR

ASSIGNMENT OPERATOR

MATLAB has six *relational* operators to make comparisons between arrays. These operators are shown in Table 6.1–1. Note that the *equal to* operator consists of two = signs, not a single = sign as you might expect. The single = sign is the *assignment,* or *replacement,* operator in MATLAB. For example, to increment the value of the scalar x by 2, you type x = x + 2. This statement creates the new value of x by "replacing" the previous value with the value x + 2.

The result of a comparison using the relational operators is either 0 (if the comparison is *false*), or 1 (if the comparison is *true*), and the result can be used as a variable. For example, if x = 2 and y = 5, typing z = x < y returns the value z = 1 and typing u = x==y returns the value u = 0. To make the statements more readable, we can group the logical operations using parentheses. For example, z = (x < y) and u = (x==y).

When used to compare arrays, the relational operators compare the arrays on an element-by-element basis. The arrays being compared must have the same dimension. The only exception occurs when we compare an array to a scalar. In that case all the elements of the array are compared to the scalar. For example, suppose that x = [6,3,9] and y = [14,2,9]. The following MATLAB session shows some examples.

```
>>z = (x < y)
z =
   1   0   0
>>z = (x > y)
z =
   0   1   0
>>z = (x ~= y)
z =
   1   1   0
>>z = (x == y)
z =
   0   0   1
>>z = (x > 8)
z =
   0   0   1
```

The relational operators can be used for array addressing. For example, with x = [6,3,9] and y = [14,2,9], typing z = x(x<y) finds all the elements in x that are less than the corresponding elements in y. The result is z = 6.

Table 6.1–1   Relational operators

Relational operator	Meaning
<	Less than.
<=	Less than or equal to.
>	Greater than.
>=	Greater than or equal to.
==	Equal to.
~=	Not equal to.

The arithmetic operators +, -, *, /, and \ have precedence over the relational operators. Thus the statement z = 5 > 2 + 7 is equivalent to z = 5 > (2+7) and returns the result z = 0. We can use parentheses to change the order of precedence; for example, z = (5 > 2) + 7 evaluates to z = 8.

Test Your Understanding

T6.1–1 Suppose that x = [-5,-4,7,8,9] and y = [-3,-4, 9,8,7]. What is the result of the following operations? Use MATLAB to check your answer.

  a. z = (x < y)
  b. z = (x > y)
  c. z = (x ~= y)
  d. z = (x == y)
  e. z = (x > 8)

MATLAB has four *logical operators,* which are sometimes called *Boolean* operators (see Table 6.2–1). These operators perform element-by-element operations. With the exception of the NOT operator (~), they have a lower precedence than the arithmetic and relational operators (see Table 6.2–2). The NOT symbol is called the *tilde.*

The NOT operation ~A returns an array of the same dimension as A; the new array has ones where A is zero and zeros where A is nonzero. For example, if x = [6,3,9] and y = [14,2,9], then z = ~x returns the array z = [0,0,0] and the statement z = ~x > y returns the result z = [0,0,0]. This expression is equivalent to z = (~x) > y, whereas z = ~(x > y) gives the result z = [1,0,1]. This expression is equivalent to z = (x <= y).

The &, |, and xor operators compare two arrays of the same dimension. The only exception, as with the relational operators, is that an array can be compared to a scalar. The AND operator

Table 6.2–1 Logical operators

Operator	Name	Definition
~	NOT	~A returns an array the same dimension as A; the new array has ones where A is zero and zeros where A is nonzero.
&	AND	A & B returns an array the same dimension as A and B; the new array has ones where both A and B have nonzero elements and zeros where either A or B is zero.
|	OR	A|B returns an array the same dimension as A and B; the new array has ones where at least one element in A or B is nonzero and zeros where A and B are both zero.
xor(A,B)	EXCLUSIVE OR	xor(A,B) returns an array the same dimension as A and B; the new array has ones where either A or B is nonzero, but not both, and zeros where A and B are either both nonzero or both zero.

& returns ones where both A and B have nonzero elements and zeros where any element of A or B is zero. The expression z = 0&3 returns z = 0, z = 2&3 returns z = 1, z = 0&0 returns z = 0, and z = [5,-3,0,0]&[2,4,0,5] returns z = [1,1,0,0]. Because of operator precedence, z = 1&2+3 is equivalent to z = 1&(2+3), which returns z = 1. Similarly, z = 5<6&1 is equivalent to z = (5<6)&1, which returns z = 1.

Let x and y be as before, and let a = [4,3,12]. The expression

    (x>y) & a

gives z = [0,1,0], and

    z = (x>y)&(x>a)

returns the result z = [0,0,0]. This is equivalent to

    z = x>y&x>a

which is much less readable.

Be careful when using the logical operators with inequalities. For example, note that ~(4 < 5) is equivalent to 5>=4. It is *not* equivalent to 5 > 4. As another example, the relation $5 < x < 10$ must be written as

    (5 < x) & (x < 10)

in MATLAB.

Table 6.2–2 Order of precedence for operator types

Precedence	Operator type
First	Parentheses; evaluated starting with the innermost pair.
Second	Arithmetic operators and NOT (~); evaluated from left to right.
Third	Relational operators; evaluated from left to right.
Fourth	Logical operators; evaluated from left to right.

The OR operator | returns ones where at least one of A and B has nonzero elements and zeros where both A and B are zero. The expression z = 0|3 returns z = 1, the expression z = 0|0 returns z = 0, and

    z = [5,-3,0,0]|[2,4,0,5]

returns z = [1,1,0,1]. Because of operator precedence,

    z = 3<5|4==7

is equivalent to

    z =(3<5)|(4==7)

which returns z = 1. Similarly, z = 1|0&1 is equivalent to z = (1|0)&1, which returns z = 1, while z = 1|0&0 returns z = 0, and z = 0&0|1 returns z = 1.

Because of the precedence of the NOT operator, the statement

    z = ~3==7|4==6

returns the result z = 0, which is equivalent to

    z = ((~3)==7)|(4==6)

The EXCLUSIVE OR operator xor(A,B) returns zeros where A and B are either both nonzero or both zero, and ones where either A or B is nonzero, *but not both*. The expression

    z = xor([3,0,6],[5,0,0])

returns z =[0,0,1], whereas

    z = [3,0,6]|[5,0,0]

returns z = [1,0,1], and

    z = [5,-3,0,0]&[2,4,0,5]

returns z = [1,1,0,1].

Table 6.2–3 is a so-called *truth table* that defines the operations of the logical operators. Until you acquire more experience with the logical operators, you should use this table to check your statements. Remember that *true* is equivalent to 1, and *false* is equivalent to 0. We can test the truth table by building its numerical equivalent as follows. Let x and y represent the first two columns of the truth table in terms of ones and zeros.

TRUTH TABLE

Table 6.2–3 Truth table for logical operators

x	y	~x	x|y	x&y	xor(x,y)
true	true	false	true	true	false
true	false	false	true	false	true
false	true	true	true	false	true
false	false	true	false	false	false

The following MATLAB session generates the truth table in terms of ones and zeros.

```
>>x = [1,1,0,0]';
>>y = [1,0,1,0]';
>>Truth_Table = [x,y,~x,x|y,x&y,xor(x,y)]
Truth_Table =
    1 1 0 1 1 0
    1 0 0 1 0 1
    0 1 1 1 0 1
    0 0 1 0 0 0
```

Table 6.2–4 lists several useful logical functions. You learned about the find function in Chapter 2.

Test Your Understanding

T6.2–1 If x = [5,-3,18,4] and y = [-9,13,7,4], what will be the result of the following operations? Use MATLAB to check your answer.

    a. z = ~y > x

    b. z = x&y

    c. z = x|y

    d. z = xor(x,y)

Table 6.2–4 Logical functions

Logical function	Definition
any(x)	Returns a scalar, which is 1 if any of the elements in the vector x is nonzero and 0 otherwise.
any(A)	Returns a row vector having the same number of columns as A and containing ones and zeros, depending on whether or not the corresponding column of the matrix A contains any nonzero elements.
all(x)	Returns a scalar, which is 1 if all the elements in the vector x are nonzero and 0 otherwise.
all(A)	Returns a row vector having the same number of columns as the matrix A and containing ones and zeros, depending on whether or not the corresponding column of A has all nonzero elements.
find(A)	Computes an array containing the indices of the nonzero elements of the array A.
[u,v,w] = find(A)	Computes the arrays u and v containing the row and column indices of the nonzero elements of the array A and computes the array w containing the values of the nonzero elements. The array w may be omitted.
finite(A)	Returns an array of the same dimension as A with ones where the elements of A are finite and zeros elsewhere.
isnan(A)	Returns an array of the same dimension as A with ones where A has 'NaN' and zeros elsewhere. ('NaN' stands for "not a number," which means an undefined result.)
isinf(A)	Returns an array of the same dimension as A, with ones where A has 'inf' and zeros elsewhere.
isempty(A)	Returns a 1 if A is an empty matrix and 0 otherwise.
isreal(A)	Returns a 1 if A has no elements with imaginary parts and 0 otherwise.

Example 6.2–1 Height and speed of a projectile

The height and speed of a projectile (such as a thrown ball) launched with a speed of v_0 at an angle A to the horizontal are given by

$$h(t) = v_0 t \sin A - 0.5gt^2$$

$$v(t) = \sqrt{v_0^2 - 2v_0 gt \sin A + g^2 t^2}$$

where g is the acceleration due to gravity. The projectile will strike the ground when $h(t) = 0$, which gives the time to hit, $t_{hit} = 2(v_0/g) \sin A$. Suppose that $A = 40°$, $v_0 = 20$ meters/second, and $g = 9.81$ meters/second^2. Use the MATLAB relational and logical operators to find the times when the height is no less than 6 meters and the speed is simultaneously no greater than 16 meters/second. In addition, discuss another approach to obtaining a solution.

Solution:

The key to solving this problem with relational and logical operators is to use the `find` command to determine the times at which the logical expression `(h >= 6) & (v <= 16)` is true. First we must generate the vectors `h` and `v` corresponding to times t_1 and t_2 between $0 \le t \le t_{hit}$, using a spacing for time t that is small enough to achieve sufficient accuracy for our purposes. We will choose a spacing of $t_{hit}/100$, which provides 101 values of time. The program follows. When computing the times t_1 and t_2, we must subtract 1 from `u(1)` and from `length(u)` because the first element in the array `t` corresponds to $t = 0$ (that is, `t(1)` is 0).

```
% Set the values for initial speed, gravity, and angle.
v0 = 20; g = 9.81; A = 40*pi/180;
% Compute the time to hit.
t_hit = 2*v0*sin(A)/g;
% Compute the arrays containing time, height, and speed.
t = [0:t_hit/100:t_hit];
h = v0*t*sin(A) - 0.5*g*t.^2;
v = sqrt(v0^2 - 2*v0*g*sin(A)*t + g^2*t.^2);
% Determine when the height is no less than 6,
% and the speed is no greater than 16.
u = find(h>=6&v<=16);
% Compute the corresponding times.
t_1 = (u(1)-1)*(t_hit/100)
t_2 = u(length(u)-1)*(t_hit/100)
```

The results are $t_1 = 0.8649$ and $t_2 = 1.7560$. Between these two times $h \ge 6$ meters and $v \le 16$ meters per second.

We could have solved this problem by plotting $h(t)$ and $v(t)$, but the accuracy of the results would be limited by our ability to pick points off the graph; in addition, if we had to solve many such problems, the graphical method would be more time-consuming.

T6.2-2 Consider the problem given in Example 6.2–1. Use relational and logical operators to find the times for which either the projectile's height is less than 4 meters or the speed is greater than 17 meters per second. Plot $h(t)$ and $v(t)$ to confirm your answer.

6.3

Conditional Statements

In everyday language we describe our decision making by using conditional phrases such as, If I get a raise, I will buy a new car. If the statement, I get a raise, is true, the action indicated (buy a new car) will be executed. Here is another example: If I get at least a $100 per week raise, I will buy a new car; else, I will put the raise into savings. A slightly more involved example is: If I get at least a $100 per week raise, I will buy a new car; else, if the raise is greater than $50, I will buy a new stereo; otherwise, I will put the raise into savings.

We can illustrate the logic of the first example as follows:

If I get a raise,
   I will buy a new car
. (period)

Note how the period marks the end of the statement.
   The second example can be illustrated as follows:

If I get at least a $100 per week raise,
   I will buy a new car;
else,
   I will put the raise into savings
. (period)

   The third example follows.

If I get at least a $100 per week raise,
   I will buy a new car;
else, if the raise is greater than $50,
   I will buy a new stereo;
otherwise,
   I will put the raise into savings
. (period)

The MATLAB *conditional statements* enable us to write programs that make decisions. Conditional statements contain one or more of the if, else, and elseif statements. The end statement denotes the end of a conditional statement, just as the period was used in the preceding examples. These conditional statements have a form similar to the examples, and they read somewhat like their English-language equivalents.

The if Statement

The if statement's basic form is

```
if logical expression
    statements
end
```

Every if statement must have an accompanying end statement. The end statement marks the end of the *statements* that are to be executed if the *logical expression* is true. A space is required between the if and the *logical expression,* which may be a scalar, a vector, or a matrix.

For example, suppose that x is a scalar and that we want to compute $y = \sqrt{x}$ only if $x \geq 0$. In English, we could specify this procedure as follows: If x is greater than or equal to zero, compute y from $y = \sqrt{x}$. The following if statement implements this procedure in MATLAB.

```
if x >= 0
    y = sqrt(x)
end
```

If x is negative, the program takes no action. The *logical expression* here is x >= 0, and the *statement* is the single line y = sqrt(x).

The if structure may be written on a single line; for example:

```
if x >= 0, y = sqrt(x), end
```

However, this form is less readable than the previous form. The usual practice is to indent the *statements* to clarify which statements belong to the if and its corresponding end and thereby improve readability.

The *logical expression* may be a compound expression; the *statements* may be a single command or a series of commands separated by commas or semicolons or on separate lines. For example:

```
z = 0;w = 0;
if (x >= 0)&(y >=0)
    z = sqrt(x) + sqrt(y)
    w = log(x) - 3*log(y)
end
```

The values of z and w are computed only if both x and y are nonnegative. Otherwise, z and w retain their values of zero.

We may "nest" if statements, as shown by the following example.

```
if logical expression 1
    statement group 1
    if logical expression 2
        statement group 2
    end
end
```

Note that each if statement has an accompanying end statement.

Program Documentation, Charts, and Pseudocode

Documenting programs properly is very important, even if you never give your programs to other people. If you need to modify one of your programs, you will find that it is often very difficult to recall how it operates if you have not used it for some time. The following elements can help you develop effective documentation:

- Variable names that indicate the quantities they represent.
- Comments within the program.
- A verbal description of the program, often in pseudocode.
- A flowchart that provides a graphical description of the operation of the program.
- A structure chart that provides a graphical description of how the parts of the program are connected.

The advantage of using suitable variable names and comments is that they reside with the program; anyone who gets a copy of the program will see such documentation. However, the names and comments often do not provide enough of an overview of the program. The latter three elements can provide such an overview.

PSEUDOCODE

Pseudocode is a text description that uses English-like phrases, perhaps with some MATLAB terms, to explain the operation of the program. As its name implies, pseudocode is an imitation of the actual computer code. In addition to providing documentation, pseudocode is useful for outlining a program before writing the detailed code, which takes longer to write because it must conform to the strict rules of MATLAB. The above description of two nested if statements is actually pseudocode, because no specific MATLAB commands were used to describe the *logical expressions* and the *statement groups*. Here is another example of pseudocode, which is a pseudocode description of the algorithm used to compute z and w earlier.

Pseudocode example: If both x and y are nonnegative, then compute z and w from

$$z = \sqrt{x} + \sqrt{y}$$

$$w = \log x - 3\log y$$

A *flowchart* uses special geometric symbols to represent calculations, decision points, and input/output operations. For example, a parallelogram represents an input or output operation, a rectangle represents calculations, and a diamond represents a decision point. The symbols are connected with arrows that show the "flow," or sequence, of calculations. The flowchart representation of the `if` statement appears in Figure 6.3–1. Figure 6.3–2 is a flowchart of the process described by the previous pseudocode example.

FLOWCHART

A *structure chart* displays the organization of a program without showing the details of the calculations and decision processes. For example, we can create program modules using function files that do specific, readily identifiable tasks. Larger programs are usually composed of a main program that calls upon the modules to do their specialized tasks as needed. A structure chart shows the connection between the main program and the modules. For example, suppose you want to write a program that plays a game,

STRUCTURE CHART

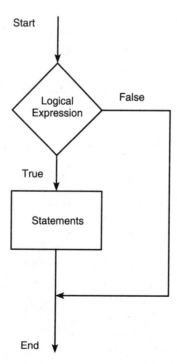

Figure 6.3–1
Flowchart representation
of the `if` statement.

Figure 6.3–2
Flowchart corresponding
to the pseudocode
example.

say, Tic-Tac-Toe. You would need a module to allow the human player to input a move, a module to update and display the game grid, and a module that contains the computer's strategy for selecting its moves. Figure 6.3–3 shows the structure chart of such a program.

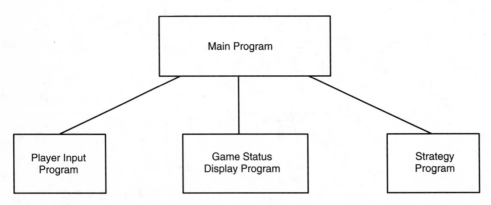

Figure 6.3–3
Structure chart of a game program.

Flowcharts are useful for developing and documenting programs that contain conditional statements because the flowcharts can display the various paths (called *branches*) that a program can take, depending on how the conditional statements are executed. We have not used flowcharts before this chapter, because none of the programs involved branching.

The usefulness of flowcharts and structure charts is limited by their size. Drawing such charts might be impractical for large, more complicated programs, and pseudocode might be used instead. Nevertheless, for smaller projects, sketching a flowchart, a structure chart, or both can help you organize your thoughts before beginning to write the specific MATLAB code. Pseudocode can also form the basis for any comments you insert into the program.

The `else` Statement

When more than one action can occur as a result of a decision, we can use the `else` and `elseif` statements along with the `if` statement. The basic structure for the use of the `else` statement is

```
if logical expression
    statement group 1
else
    statement group 2
end
```

Figure 6.3–4 shows the flowchart of this structure.

For example, suppose that $y = \sqrt{x}$ for $x \geq 0$ and that $y = e^x - 1$ for $x < 0$. The following statements will calculate y:

```
if x >= 0
    y = sqrt(x)
else
    y = exp(x) - 1
end
```

When the test, `if` *logical expression,* is performed, where the logical expression may be an array, the test returns a value of true only if *all* the elements of the logical expression are nonzero! For example, if we fail to recognize how the test works, the following statements do not perform the way we might expect.

```
x=[4,-9,25];
if x < 0
    disp('Some of the elements of x are negative.')
else
    y = sqrt(x)
end
```

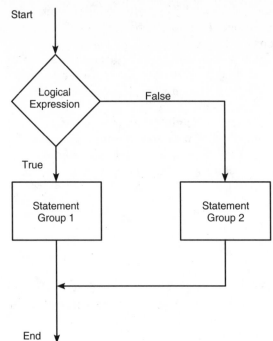

Figure 6.3–4
Flowchart of the `else`
structure.

When this program is run it gives the result

```
y =
    2      0 + 3.000i     5
```

The program does not test each element in x in sequence. Instead it tests the truth of the vector relation x < 0. The test if x < 0 returns a false value because it generates the vector [0,1,0]. Compare the preceding program with these statements.

```
x=[4,-9,25];
if x >= 0
    y = sqrt(x)
else
    disp('Some of the elements of x are negative.')
end
```

When executed, it produces the following result: Some of the elements of x are negative. The different conditional statements produce different values. The test if x < 0 is true, whereas the test if x >= 0 returns a false value because x >= 0 returns the vector [1,0,1].

We sometimes must choose between a program that is concise, but perhaps more difficult to understand, and one that uses more statements than is necessary. For example, the statements

```
if logical expression 1
    if logical expression 2
        statements
    end
end
```

can be replaced with the more concise program

```
if logical expression 1 & logical expression 2
    statements
end
```

The elseif Statement

The basic structure for the elseif statement is

```
if logical expression 1
    statement group 1
elseif logical expression 2
    statement group 2
end
```

Figure 6.3–5 is the flowchart for the elseif structure. For example, suppose that $y = \ln x$ if $x \geq 5$ and that $y = \sqrt{x}$ if $0 \leq x < 5$. The following statements will compute y.

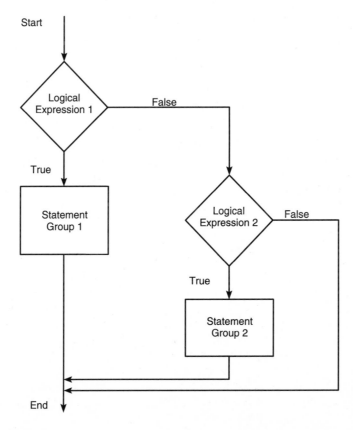

Figure 6.3–5
Flowchart for the elseif structure.

```
if x >= 5
   y = log(x)
else
   if x >= 0
      y = sqrt(x)
   end
end
```

If $x = -2$, for example, no action will be taken. If we use an elseif, we need fewer statements. For example:

```
if x >= 5
   y = log(x)
elseif x >= 0
   y = sqrt(x)
end
```

Note that the elseif statement does not require a separate end statement.

The else statement can be used with elseif to create detailed decision-making programs. For example, suppose that $y = \ln x$ for $x > 10$, $y = \sqrt{x}$ for $0 \le x \le 10$, and $y = e^x - 1$ for $x < 0$. The following statements will compute y.

```
if x > 10
   y = log(x)
elseif x >= 0
   y = sqrt(x)
else
   y = exp(x) - 1
end
```

Decision structures may be nested; that is, one structure can contain another structure, which in turn can contain another, and so on. The flowchart in Figure 6.3–6 describes the following code, which contains an example of nested if statements.

```
if x > 10
   y = log(x)
   if y >= 3
      z = 4*y
   elseif y >= 1
      z = 2*y
   else
      z = 0
   end
else
   y = 5*x
   z = 7*x
end
```

Figure 6.3–6
Flowchart illustrating nested if statements.

Note how the indentations emphasize the statement groups associated with each end statement. The flowchart required to represent this code is quite large. In practice, flowcharts often must be condensed by omitting some details to effectively describe the overall program.

***

Test Your Understanding

T6.3–1 Given a number x and the quadrant q ($q = 1, 2, 3, 4$), write a program to compute $\sin^{-1}(x)$ in degrees, taking into account the quadrant. The program should display an error message if $|x| > 1$.

***

Application

In Chapter 5 you saw that the set of linear algebraic equations $\mathbf{Ax} = \mathbf{b}$ with m equations and n unknowns has solutions if and only if (1) rank[$\mathbf{A}$] = rank[$\mathbf{A}$ $\mathbf{b}$]. Let r = rank[$\mathbf{A}$]. If condition (1)

Table 6.3–1   Pseudocode for the linear equation solver

If the rank of **A** equals the rank of [**A b**], then
 	
   determine whether the rank of **A** equals the number of unknowns. If so, there is a unique solution, which can be computed using left division. Display the results and stop.
 	
   Otherwise, there is an infinite number of solutions, which can be found from the augmented matrix. Display the results and stop.
 	
Otherwise (if the rank of **A** does not equal the rank of [**A b**]), then there are no solutions. Display this message and stop.

is satisfied and if $r = n$, then the solution is unique. If condition (1) is satisfied but $r < n$, an infinite number of solutions exists; in addition, r unknown variables can be expressed as linear combinations of the other $n - r$ unknown variables, whose values are arbitrary. In this case we can use the rref command to find the relations between the variables. The pseudocode in Table 6.3–1 can be used to outline the program before writing it.

A condensed flowchart appears in Figure 6.3–7. From this chart or the pseudocode, we can develop the script file shown in Table 6.3–2. The program uses the given arrays A and b to check the rank conditions, the left-division method to obtain the solution, if one exists, and the rref method if there is an infinite number of solutions. Note that the number of unknowns equals the number of columns in A, which is given by size_A(2), the second element in size_A. Note also that the rank of **A** cannot exceed the number of columns in **A**.

Table 6.3–2   MATLAB program to solve linear equations

```
% Script file lineq.m
% Solves the set Ax = b, given A and b.
% Check the ranks of A and [A  b].
if rank(A) == rank([A b])
    % The ranks are equal.
    size_A = size(A);
    % Does the rank of A equal the number of unknowns?
    if rank(A) == size_A(2)
        % Yes.  Rank of A equals the number of unknowns.
        disp('There is a unique solution, which is:')
        x = A\b % Solve using left division.
    else
        % Rank of A does not equal the number of unknowns.
        disp('There is an infinite number of solutions.')
        disp('The augmented matrix of the reduced system is:')
        rref([A b]) % Compute the augmented matrix.
    end
else
    % The ranks of A and [A  b] are not equal.
    disp('There are no solutions.')
end
```

Figure 6.3–7
Flowchart illustrating a program to solve linear equations.

Test Your Understanding

T6.3–2 Type in the preceding script file `lineq.m` given in Table 6.3–2 and run it for the following cases. Hand check the answers.
  a. A = [1,-1;1,1],b = [3;5]
  b. A = [1,-1;2,-2],b = [3;6]
  c. A = [1,-1;2,-2],b = [3;5]

Strings

A *string* is a variable that contains characters. Strings are useful for creating input prompts and messages and for storing and operating on data such as names and addresses. To create a string variable, enclose the characters in single quotes. For example, the string variable `name` is created as follows: **STRING**

```
>> name = 'Leslie Student'
name =
    Leslie Student
```

The following string number

```
>> number = '123'
number =
   123
```

is *not* the same as the variable number created by typing number = 123.

Strings are stored as row vectors in which each column represents a character. For example, the variable name has one row and 14 columns (each blank space occupies one column). Thus

```
>> size(name)
ans =
   1 14
```

We can access any column the way we access any other vector. For example, the letter S in the name Leslie Student occupies the eighth column in the vector name. It can be accessed as follows:

```
>> name(8)
ans =
   S
```

The colon operator can be used with string variables as well. For example:

```
>> first_name = name(1:6)
first_name =
   Leslie
```

We can manipulate the columns of string variables just as we do vectors. For example, to insert a middle initial, we type

```
>> full_name = [name(1:6),' C.',name(7:14)]
full_name =
   Leslie C. Student
full_name(8) = 'F'
full_name =
   Leslie F. Student
```

The findstr function (which stands for *find str*ing) is useful for finding the locations of certain characters. For example:

```
>> findstr(full_name,'e')
ans =
   2 6 15
```

This session tells us that the letter e occurs in the 2nd, 6th, and 15th columns.

Two string variables are equal if and only if every character is the same, including blank spaces. Note that uppercase and lowercase letters are *not* the same. Thus the strings 'Hello' and 'hello' are not equal, and the strings 'can not' and 'cannot' are not equal. The function strcmp (for *string compare*) determines whether two strings are equal. Typing strcmp('string1','string2') returns a 1 if the strings 'string1' and 'string2' are equal and 0 otherwise. The functions lower('string') and upper('string') convert 'string' to all lowercase or all uppercase letters. These functions are useful for accepting keyboard input without forcing the user to distinguish between lowercase and uppercase.

One of the most important applications for strings is to create input prompts and output messages. The following prompt program uses the isempty(x) function, which returns a 1 if the array x is empty and 0 otherwise. It also uses the input function, whose syntax is

```
x = input(' prompt' , 'string' )
```

This function displays the string *prompt* on the screen, waits for input from the keyboard, and returns the entered value in the string variable x. The function returns an empty matrix if you press the **Enter** key without typing anything.

The following prompt program is a script file that allows the user to answer Yes by typing either Y or y or by pressing the **Enter** key. Any other response is treated as a No answer.

```
response = input('Do you want to continue?  Y/N [Y]: ','s');
if (isempty(response))|(response == 'Y')|(response == 'y')
    response = 'Y'
else
    response = 'N'
end
```

Many more string functions are available in MATLAB. Type help strfun to obtain information on these.

A *loop* is a structure for repeating a calculation a number of times. Each repetition of the loop is a *pass*. MATLAB uses two types of explicit loops: the for loop, when the number of passes is known ahead of time, and the while loop, when the looping process must terminate when a specified condition is satisfied, and thus the number of passes is not known in advance.

for **Loops**

A simple example of a for loop is   FOR **LOOP**

```
for k = 5:10:35
    x = k^2
end
```

The *loop variable* k is initially assigned the value 5, and x is calculated from x = k^2. Each successive pass through the loop increments k by 10 and calculates x until k exceeds 35. Thus k takes on the values 5, 15, 25, and 35, and x takes on the values 25, 225, 625, and 1225. The program then continues to execute any statements following the end statement.

The typical structure of a for loop is

```
for loop variable = m:s:n
    statements
end
```

The expression m:s:n assigns an initial value of m to the loop variable, which is incremented by the value s—called the *step value* or *incremental value*. The *statements* are executed once during each pass, using the current value of the loop variable. The looping continues until the loop variable exceeds the *terminating value* n. For example, in the expression for k = 5:10:36, the final value of k is 35. Note that we need not place a semicolon after the for m:s:n statement to suppress printing k. Figure 6.4–1 shows the flowchart of a for loop.

Note that a for statement needs an accompanying end statement. The end statement marks the end of the *statements* that are to be executed. A space is required between the for and the *loop variable,* which may be a scalar, a vector, or a matrix, although the scalar case is by far the most common.

The for loop may be written on a single line; for example:

```
for x = 0:2:10, y = sqrt(x), end
```

However, this form is less readable than the previous form. The usual practice is to indent the *statements* to clarify which statements belong to the for and its corresponding end and thereby improve readability.

NESTED LOOPS

We may nest for loops, as shown by the following example. (Note that each for statement needs an accompanying end statement.)

```
m = 0;
% Outer loop:  increments q by 3.
for q = 0:3:6
    m = m + 1;
    n = 0;
    % Inner loop:  increments r by 5.
    for r = 0:5:15
        % Increment n by 1.
        n = n + 1;
        A(m,n) = r + q;
    end
        % End of inner loop.
end
% End of outer loop.
```

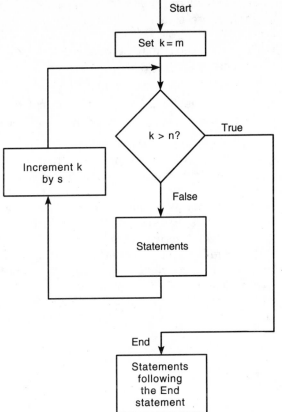

Figure 6.4–1
Flowchart of a for loop.

The result is the following 3×4 matrix:

$$\mathbf{A} = \begin{bmatrix} 0 & 5 & 10 & 15 \\ 3 & 8 & 13 & 18 \\ 6 & 11 & 16 & 21 \end{bmatrix}$$

Test Your Understanding

T6.4–1 Write a program similar to the preceding program to produce the following matrix:

$$\mathbf{A} = \begin{bmatrix} 4 & 8 & 12 \\ 10 & 14 & 18 \\ 16 & 20 & 24 \\ 22 & 26 & 30 \end{bmatrix}$$

Note the following rules when using for loops with the loop variable expression k = m:s:n:

- The step value s may be negative. For example, k = 10:-2:4 produces k = 10, 8, 6, 4.
- If s is omitted, the step value defaults to one.
- If s is positive, the loop will not be executed if m is greater than n.
- If s is negative, the loop will not be executed if m is less than n.
- If m equals n, the loop will be executed only once.
- If the step value s is not an integer, round-off errors can cause the loop to execute a different number of passes than intended.

You should not alter the value of the loop variable k within the *statements*. Doing so can cause unpredictable results.

A common practice in traditional programming languages like BASIC and Fortran is to use the symbols i and j as loop variables. However, this convention is not good practice in MATLAB, which uses these symbols for the imaginary unit $\sqrt{-1}$. For example, what do you think is the result of the following program? Try it and see!

```
x = 1;
y = 1;
for i = 1:5
    x = x + 6i
    y = y + 5/i
end
```

It is permissible to use an if statement to "jump" out of the loop before the loop variable reaches its terminating value. The break command, which terminates the loop but does not stop the entire program, can be used for this purpose. For example:

```
for k = 1:10
    x = 50 - k^2;
    if x < 0
        break
    end
    y = sqrt(x)
end
% The program execution jumps to here
% if the break command is executed.
```

However, it is usually possible to write the code to avoid using the break command. This can often be done with a while loop as explained in the next section.

It is permissible to use a matrix expression for the loop variable. In this case the loop variable is a vector that is set equal to the successive columns of the matrix expression during each pass. For example,

```
A = [1,2,3;4,5,6];
for v = A
    disp(v)
end
```

is equivalent to

```
A = [1,2,3;4,5,6];
n = 3;
for k = 1:n
    v = A(:,k)
end
```

The common expression $k = m:s:n$ is a special case of a matrix expression in which the columns of the expression are scalars, not vectors.

Implied Loops

Many MATLAB commands contain *implied loops*. For example, consider these statements.

IMPLIED LOOP

```
x = [0:5:100];
y = cos(x);
```

To achieve the same result using a for loop, we must type

```
for k = 1:21
    x = (k-1)*5;
    y(k) = cos(x);
end
```

The find command is another example of an implied loop. The statement $y = find(x>0)$ is equivalent to

```
j=0;
for i=1:length(x)
    if x(i)>0
        j = j + 1;
        y(j)=i;
    end
end
```

If you are familiar with a traditional programming language such as FORTRAN or BASIC, you might be inclined to solve problems in MATLAB using loops, instead of using the powerful MATLAB commands such as find. To use these commands and to maximize the power of MATLAB, you might need to adopt a new approach to problem solving. As the preceding example shows, you often can save many lines of code by using MATLAB commands, instead of using loops. Your programs will also run faster because MATLAB was designed for high-speed vector computations.

T6.4–2 Write a for loop that is equivalent to the command sum(A), where A is a matrix.

Example 6.4–1 Flight of an instrumented rocket

All rockets lose weight as they burn fuel; thus the mass of the system is variable. The following equations describe the speed v and height h of a rocket launched vertically, neglecting air resistance. They can be derived from Newton's law [Beer and Johnston 1997].

$$v(t) = u \ln \frac{m_0}{m_0 - qt} - gt \tag{6.4–1}$$

$$h(t) = \frac{u}{q}(m_0 - qt)\ln(m_0 - qt)$$
$$+ u(\ln m_0 + 1)t - \frac{gt^2}{2} - \frac{m_0 u}{q}\ln m_0 \tag{6.4–2}$$

where m_0 is the rocket's initial mass, q is the rate at which the rocket burns fuel mass, u is the exhaust velocity of the burned fuel relative to the rocket, and g is the acceleration due to gravity. Let b be the *burn time*, after which all the fuel is consumed. Thus the rocket's mass without fuel is $m_e = m_0 - qb$.

For $t > b$ the rocket engine no longer produces thrust, and the speed and height are given by

$$v(t) = v(b) - g(t - b) \tag{6.4–3}$$

$$h(t) = h(b) + v(b)(t - b) - \frac{g(t - b)^2}{2} \tag{6.4–4}$$

The time t_p to reach the peak height is found by setting $v(t) = 0$. The result is $t_p = b + v(b)/g$. Substituting this expression into the expression (6.4–4) for $h(t)$ gives the following expression for the peak height: $h_p = h(b) + v^2(b)/(2g)$. The time at which the rocket hits the ground is $t_{hit} = t_p + \sqrt{2h_p/g}$.

Suppose the rocket is carrying instruments to study the upper atmosphere, and we need to determine the amount of time spent above 50,000 feet as a function of the burn time b (and thus as a function of the fuel mass qb). Assume that we are given the following

Table 6.4–1 Pseudocode for Example 6.4–1

Enter data.
Increment burn time from 0 to 100. For each burn-time value:
> Compute m_0, v_b, h_b, h_p.
> If $h_p \geq h_{desired}$,
> > Compute t_p, t_{hit}.
> > Increment time from 0 to t_{hit}.
> > > Compute height as a function of time, using the appropriate equation, depending on whether burnout has occurred.
> > Compute the duration above desired height.
> > End of the time loop.
> If $h_p < h_{desired}$, set duration equal to zero.
End of the burn-time loop.
Plot the results.

Table 6.4–2 MATLAB program for Example 6.4–1

```
% Script file rocket1.m:
% Computes flight duration as a function of burn time.
% Basic data values.
m_e = 100; q = 1; u = 8000; g = 32.2;
dt = 0.1; h_desired = 50000;
for b = 1:100 % Loop over burn time.
    burn_time(b) = b;
    % The following lines implement the formulas in the text.
    m_0 = m_e + q*b; v_b = u*log(m_0/m_e) - g*b;
    h_b = ((u*m_e)/q)*log(m_e/(m_e+q*b))+u*b - 0.5*g*b^2;
    h_p = h_b + v_b^2/(2*g);
    if h_p >= h_desired
    % Calculate only if peak height > desired height.
        t_p = b + v_b/g; % Compute peak time.
        t_hit = t_p + sqrt(2*h_p/g); % Compute time to hit.
        for p = 0:t_hit/dt:t_hit
            % Use a loop to compute the height vector.
            k = p + 1; t = p*dt; time(k) = t;
            if t <= b
                % Burnout has not yet occurred.
                h(k) = (u/q)*(m0 - q*t)*log(m0 - q*t)...
                    + u*(log(m0) + 1)*t - 0.5*g*t^2 ...
                    - (m0*u/q)*log(m0);
            else
                % Burnout has occurred.
                h(k) = h_b - 0.5*g*(t - b)^2 + v_b*(t - b);
            end
        end
        % Compute the duration.
        duration(b) = length(find(h>=h_desired))*dt;
    else
        % Rocket did not reach the desired height.
        duration(b) = 0;
    end
end % Plot the results.
plot(burn_time,duration),xlabel('Burn Time (sec)'),...
ylabel('Duration (sec)'),title('Duration Above 50,000 Feet')
```

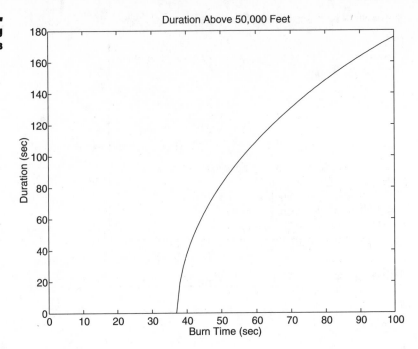

Figure 6.4–2
Duration above 50,000
feet as a function of the
burn time.

values: $m_e = 100$ slugs,[1] $q = 1$ slug per second, $u = 8000$ feet per second, and $g = 32.2$ feet per second[2]. If the rocket's maximum fuel load is 100 slugs, the maximum value of b is $100/q = 100$. Write a MATLAB program to solve this problem.

Solution:

Pseudocode for developing the program appears in Table 6.4–1. A `for` loop is a logical choice to solve this problem because we know the burn time b and t_{hit}, the time it takes to hit the ground. A MATLAB program to solve this problem appears in Table 6.4–2. It has two nested `for` loops. The inner loop is over time and evaluates the equations of motion at times spaced 1/10 of a second apart. This loop calculates the duration above 50,000 feet for a specific value of the burn time b. We can obtain more accuracy by using a smaller value of the time increment dt. The outer loop varies the burn time in integer values from $b = 1$ to $b = 100$. The final result is the vector of durations for the various burn times. Figure 6.4–2 gives the resulting plot.

`while` Loops

The `while` loop is used when the looping process terminates because a specified condition is satisfied, and thus the number

---

[1]A *slug* is the unit of mass in the British Engineering system of units. The mass of an object in slugs can be found by dividing its weight by g. At Earth's surface a mass of 1 slug weighs 32.2 pounds.

loop is

```
x = 5;
while x < 25
    disp(x)
    x = 2*x-1;
end
```

The results displayed by the `disp` statement are 5, 9, and 17. The *loop variable* x is initially assigned the value 5, and it has this value until the statement x = 2*x - 1 is encountered the first time. The value then changes to 9. Before each pass through the loop, x is checked to see whether its value is less than 25. If so, the pass is made. If not, the loop is skipped and the program continues to execute any statements following the `end` statement.

A principal application of `while` loops is when we want the loop to continue as long as a certain statement is true. Such a task is often more difficult to do with a `for` loop. For example:

```
x=1;
while x~= 5
    disp(x)
    x = x+1;
end
```

The statements between the `while` and the `end` are executed once during each pass, using the current value of the loop variable x. The looping continues until the condition x~=5 is false. The results displayed by the `disp` statement are 1, 2, 3, and 4.

The typical structure of a `while` loop follows.

```
while logical expression
    statements
end
```

MATLAB first tests the truth of the *logical expression*. A loop variable must be included in the *logical expression*. For example, x is the loop variable in the statement `while` x~=5. If the *logical expression* is true, the *statements* are executed. For the `while` loop to function properly, the following two conditions must occur:

1. The loop variable must have a value before the `while` statement is executed.
2. The loop variable must be changed somehow by the *statements*.

The *statements* are executed once during each pass, using the current value of the loop variable. The looping continues until the *logical expression* is false. Figure 6.4–3 shows the flowchart of the `while` loop.

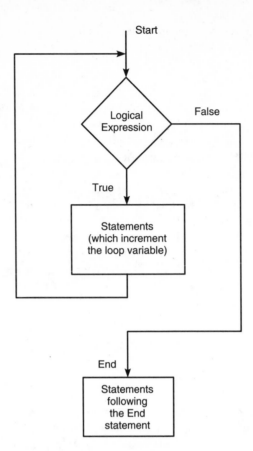

Start

Logical Expression

False

True

Statements (which increment the loop variable)

End

Statements following the End statement

Figure 6.4–3
Flowchart of the `while` loop.

Each `while` statement must be matched by an accompanying `end`. As with `for` loops, the *statements* should be indented to improve readability. You may nest `while` loops, and you may nest them with `for` loops and `if` statements.

Always make sure that the loop variable has a value assigned to it before the start of the loop. For example, the following loop can give unintended results if x has an overlooked previous value.

```
while x < 10
    x = x + 1;
    y = 2*x;
end
```

If x has not been assigned a value prior to the loop, an error message will occur. If we intend x to start at zero, then we should place the statement x = 0; before the `while` statement.

It is possible to create an *infinite loop,* which is a loop that never ends. For example:

```
x=8;
while x~=0
    x = x-3;
end
```

Within the loop the variable x takes on the values 5, 2, −1, −4, ..., and the condition x ~= 0 is always satisfied, so the loop never stops.

Example 6.4–2 Time to reach a specified height
Consider the variable-mass rocket treated in Example 6.4–1. Write a program to determine how long it takes for the rocket to reach 40,000 feet if the burn time is 50 seconds.

Solution:
The pseudocode appears in Table 6.4–3. Because we do not know the time required, a while loop is convenient to use. The program in Table 6.4–4 performs the task and is a modification of the program in Table 6.4–2. Note that the new program allows for the possibility that the rocket might not reach 40,000 feet. It is important to write your programs to handle all such foreseeable circumstances. The answer given by the program is 53 seconds.

Table 6.4–3   Pseudocode for Example 6.4–2

Enter data.
Compute m_0, v_b, h_b, h_p.
If $h_p \geq h_{desired}$,
    Use a while loop to increment time and compute height until desired height is reached.
        Compute height as a function of time, using the appropriate equation, depending on whether burnout has occurred.
    End of the time loop.
    Display the results.
If $h_p < h_{desired}$, rocket cannot reach desired height.

Test Your Understanding

T6.4–3 Rewrite the following code using a while loop to avoid using the break command.

```
for k = 1:10
    x = 50 - k^2;
    if x < 0
        break
    end
    y = sqrt(x)
end
```

T6.4–4 Find to two decimal places the largest value of x before the error in the series approximation $e^x \approx 1 + x + x^2/2 + x^3/6$ exceeds 1 percent (answer: $x = 0.83$).

Table 6.4–4 MATLAB program for Example 6.4–2

```
% Script file rocket2.m
% Computes time to reach desired height.
% Set the data values.
h_desired = 40000; m_e = 100; q = 1;
u = 8000; g = 32.2; dt = 0.1; b = 50;
% Compute values at burnout, peak time, and height.
m_0 = m_e + q*b; v_b = u*log(m_0/m_e) - g*b;
h_b = ((u*m_e)/q)*log(m_e/(m_e+q*b))+u*b- .5*g*b^2;
t_p = b + v_b/g;
h_p = h_b + v_b^2/(2*g);
% If h_p > h_desired, compute time to reached h_desired.
if h_p > h_desired
   h = 0; k = 0;
   while h < h_desired % Compute h until h = h_desired.
      t = k*dt; k = k + 1;
      if t <= b
         % Burnout has not yet occurred.
         h = (u/q)*(m_0 - q*t)*log(m_0 - q*t)...
             + u*(log(m_0) + 1)*t - 0.5*g*t^2 ...
             - (m_0*u/q)*log(m_0);
      else
         % Burnout has occurred.
         h = h_b - 0.5*g*(t - b)^2 + v_b*(t - b);
      end
   end
   % Display the results.
   disp('The time to reach the desired height is:')
   disp(t)
else
   disp('Rocket cannot achieve the desired height.')
end
```

6.5

The switch Structure

The switch structure is new with MATLAB 5. It provides an alternative to using the if, elseif, and else commands. Anything programmed using switch can also be programmed using if structures. However, for some applications the switch structure is more readable than code using the if structures. The syntax is

switch *input expression* (scalar or string)
    case *value1*
        statement group 1
    case *value2*
        statement group 2

           .
           .
           .

    otherwise
        statement group n
end

The *input expression* is compared to each case value. If they are the same, then the statements following that case statement are executed and processing continues with any statements after the end statement. If the *input expression* is a string, then it is equal to the case *value* if strcmp returns a value of 1 (true). Only the first matching case is executed. If no match occurs, the statements following the otherwise statement are executed. However, the otherwise statement is optional. If it is absent, execution continues with the statements following the end statement if no match exists. Each case *value* statement must be on a single line.

For example, suppose the variable angle has an integer value that represents an angle measured in degrees from North. The following switch block displays the point on the compass that corresponds to that angle.

```
switch angle
   case 45
      disp('Northeast')
   case 135
      disp('Southeast')
   case 225
      disp('Southwest')
   case 315
      disp('Northwest')
   otherwise
      disp('Direction Unknown')
end
```

The use of a string variable for the *input expression* can result in very readable programs. For example, in the following code the numeric vector x has values, and the user enters the value of the string variable response; its intended values are min, max, or sum. The code then either finds the minimum or maximum value of x or sums the elements of x, as directed by the user.

```
t = [0:100]; x = exp(-t).*sin(t);
response = input('Type min, max, or sum.','s')
response = lower('response');
switch response
   case min
      minimum = min(x)
   case max
      maximum = max(x)
   case sum
      total = sum(x)
   otherwise
      disp('You have not entered a proper choice.')
end
```

The `switch` statement can handle multiple conditions in a single `case` statement by enclosing the case *value* in a cell array. For example, the following `switch` block displays the corresponding point on the compass, given the integer angle measured from North.

```
switch angle
    case {0,360}
        disp('North')
    case {-180,180}
        disp('South')
    case {-270,90}
        disp('East')
    case {-90,270}
        disp('West')
    otherwise
        disp('Direction Unknown')
end
```

Test Your Understanding

T6.5–1 Write a program using the `switch` structure to input one angle, whose value may be 45, −45, 135, or −135 degrees, and display the quadrant (1, 2, 3, or 4) containing the angle.

6.6

Applications to Simulation

SIMULATION

OPERATIONS RESEARCH

Simulation is the process of building and analyzing the output of computer programs that describe the operations of an organization, process, or physical system. Such a program is called a *computer model*. Simulation is often used in *operations research*, which is the quantitative study of an organization in action, to find ways to improve the functioning of the organization. Simulation enables engineers to study the past, present, and future actions of the organization for this purpose. Operations research techniques are useful in all engineering fields. Common examples include airline scheduling, traffic-flow studies, and production lines. The MATLAB logical operators and loops are excellent tools for building simulation programs.

Example 6.6–1   A college enrollment model:
Part I   As an example of how simulation can be used for operations research, consider the following college enrollment model. A certain college wants to analyze the effect of admissions and freshman retention rate on the college's enrollment so that it can predict the future need for instructors and other resources. Assume that the

college has estimates of the percentages of students repeating a grade or leaving school before graduating. Develop a matrix equation on which to base a simulation model that can help in this analysis.

Solution:

Suppose that the current freshman enrollment is 500 students and the college decides to admit 1000 freshmen per year from now on. The college estimates that 10 percent of the freshman class will repeat the year. The number of freshmen in the following year will be $0.1(500) + 1000 = 1050$, then it will be $0.1(1050) + 1000 = 1150$, and so on. Let $x_1(k)$ be the number of freshmen in year k, where $k = 1, 2, 3, 4, 5, 6, \ldots$ Then in year $k + 1$, the number of freshmen is given by

$$x_1(k + 1) = 10 \text{ percent of previous freshman class}$$
$$\text{repeating freshman year}$$
$$+ 1000 \text{ new freshmen}$$
$$= 0.1x_1(k) + 1000 \qquad \text{(6.6–1)}$$

Because we know the number of freshmen in the first year of our analysis (which is 500), we can solve this equation step-by-step to predict the number of freshmen in the future.

Let $x_2(k)$ be the number of sophomores in year k. Suppose that 15 percent of the freshmen do not return and that 10 percent repeat freshman year. Thus 75 percent of the freshman class returns as sophomores. Suppose also 5 percent of the sophomores repeat the sophomore year and that 200 sophomores each year transfer from other schools. Then in year $k + 1$, the number of sophomores is given by

$$x_2(k + 1) = 0.75x_1(k) + 0.05x_2(k) + 200$$

To solve this equation we need to solve the "freshman" equation (6.6–1) at the same time, which is easy to do with MATLAB. Before we solve these equations, let us develop the rest of the model.

Let $x_3(k)$ and $x_4(k)$ be the number of juniors and seniors in year k. Suppose that 5 percent of the sophomores and juniors leave school and that 5 percent of the sophomores, juniors, and seniors repeat the grade. Thus 90 percent of the sophomores and juniors return and advance in grade. The models for the juniors and seniors are

$$x_3(k + 1) = 0.9x_2(k) + 0.05x_3(k)$$

$$x_4(k + 1) = 0.9x_3(k) + 0.05x_4(k)$$

These four equations can be written in the following matrix form:

$$
\begin{bmatrix} x_1(k+1) \\ x_2(k+1) \\ x_3(k+1) \\ x_4(k+1) \end{bmatrix} =
\begin{bmatrix} 0.1 & 0 & 0 & 0 \\ 0.75 & 0.05 & 0 & 0 \\ 0 & 0.9 & 0.05 & 0 \\ 0 & 0 & 0.9 & 0.05 \end{bmatrix}
\begin{bmatrix} x_1(k) \\ x_2(k) \\ x_3(k) \\ x_4(k) \end{bmatrix} +
\begin{bmatrix} 1000 \\ 200 \\ 0 \\ 0 \end{bmatrix}
$$

In Example 6.6–2 we will see how to use MATLAB to solve such equations.

T6.6-1 Suppose that 70 percent of the freshmen, instead of 75 percent, return for the sophomore year. How does the previous equation change?

Example 6.6-2 A college enrollment model: Part II To study the effects of admissions and transfer policies, generalize the enrollment model in Example 6.6–1 to allow for varying admissions and transfers.

Solution:

Let $a(k)$ be the number of new freshmen admitted in the spring of year k for the following year $k + 1$ and let $d(k)$ be the number of transfers into the following year's sophomore class. Then the model becomes

$$x_1(k + 1) = c_{11}x_1(k) + a(k)$$

$$x_2(k + 1) = c_{21}x_1(k) + c_{22}x_2(k) + d(k)$$

$$x_3(k + 1) = c_{32}x_2(k) + c_{33}x_3(k)$$

$$x_4(k + 1) = c_{43}x_3(k) + c_{44}x_4(k)$$

where we have written the coefficients c_{21}, c_{22}, and so on in symbolic, rather than numerical, form so that we can change their values if desired.

STATE TRANSITION DIAGRAM

This model can be represented graphically by a *state transition diagram,* like the one shown in Figure 6.6–1. Such diagrams are widely used to represent time-dependent and probabilistic processes. The arrows indicate how the model's calculations are updated for each new year. The enrollment at year k is described completely by the values of $x_1(k)$, $x_2(k)$, $x_3(k)$, and $x_4(k)$; that is, by the vector $\mathbf{x}(k)$, which is called the *state vector.* The elements of the state vector are the *state variables.* The state transition diagram shows how the new values of the state variables depend on both the previous values and the inputs $a(k)$ and $d(k)$.

The four equations can be written in the following matrix form:

$$
\begin{bmatrix} x_1(k+1) \\ x_2(k+1) \\ x_3(k+1) \\ x_4(k+1) \end{bmatrix} = \begin{bmatrix} c_{11} & 0 & 0 & 0 \\ c_{21} & c_{22} & 0 & 0 \\ 0 & c_{32} & c_{33} & 0 \\ 0 & 0 & c_{43} & c_{44} \end{bmatrix} \begin{bmatrix} x_1(k) \\ x_2(k) \\ x_3(k) \\ x_4(k) \end{bmatrix} + \begin{bmatrix} a(k) \\ d(k) \\ 0 \\ 0 \end{bmatrix}
$$

or more compactly as

$$\mathbf{x}(k + 1) = \mathbf{C}\mathbf{x}(k) + \mathbf{b}(k)$$

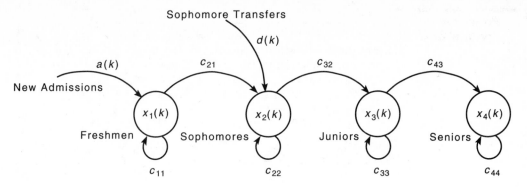

Figure 6.6–1
The state transition diagram for the college enrollment model.

where

$$\mathbf{x}(k) = \begin{bmatrix} x_1(k) \\ x_2(k) \\ x_3(k) \\ x_4(k) \end{bmatrix} \qquad \mathbf{b}(k) = \begin{bmatrix} a(k) \\ d(k) \\ 0 \\ 0 \end{bmatrix}$$

and

$$\mathbf{C} = \begin{bmatrix} c_{11} & 0 & 0 & 0 \\ c_{21} & c_{22} & 0 & 0 \\ 0 & c_{32} & c_{33} & 0 \\ 0 & 0 & c_{43} & c_{44} \end{bmatrix}$$

Suppose that the initial total enrollment of 1480 consists of 500 freshmen, 400 sophomores, 300 juniors, and 280 seniors. The college wants to study, over a 10-year period, the effects of increasing admissions by 100 each year and transfers by 50 each year until the total enrollment reaches 4000; then admissions and transfers will be held constant. Thus the admissions and transfers for the next 10 years are given by

$$a(k) = 900 + 100k$$

$$d(k) = 150 + 50k$$

for $k = 1, 2, 3, \ldots$ until the college's total enrollment reaches 4000; then admissions and transfers are held constant at the previous year's levels. We cannot determine when this event will occur without doing a simulation. Table 6.6–1 gives the pseudocode for solving this problem.

Because we know the length of the study (10 years), a `for` loop is a natural choice. We use an `if` statement to determine when to switch from the increasing admissions and transfer schedule to the constant schedule. A MATLAB script file to predict the enrollment for the next 10 years appears in Table 6.6–2. Figure 6.6–2 shows the resulting plot. Note that after year 4 there are more sophomores than

283

Table 6.6–1 Pseudocode for Example 6.6–2

Enter the coefficient matrix **C** and the initial enrollment vector **x**.
Enter the initial admissions and transfers, $a(1)$ and $d(1)$.
Set the first column of the enrollment matrix **E** equal to **x**.
Loop over years 2 to 10.
    If the total enrollment is $\leq$ 4000, increase admissions by 100 and transfers
    by 50 each year.
    If the total enrollment is $>$ 4000, hold admissions and transfers constant.
    Update the vector **x**, using **x** = **Cx** + **b**.
    Update the enrollment matrix **E** by adding another column composed of **x**.
End of the loop over years 2 to 10.
Plot the results.

Table 6.6–2 College enrollment model

```
% Script file enroll1.m.  Computes college enrollment.
% Model's coefficients.
C = [.1,0,0,0;.75,.05,0,0;0,.9,.05,0;0,0,.9,.05];
% Initial enrollment vector.
x = [500;400;300;280];
% Initial admissions and transfers.
a(1) = 1000; d(1) = 200;
% E is the 4 x 10 enrollment matrix.
E(:,1) = x;
% Loop over years 2 to 10.
for k = 2:10
    % The following describes the admissions
    % and transfer policies.
    if sum(x) <= 4000
        % Increase admissions and transfers.
        a(k) = 900+100*k;
        d(k) = 150+50*k;
    else
        % Hold admissions and transfers constant.
        a(k) = a(k-1);
        d(k) = d(k-1);
    end
    % Update enrollment matrix.
    b = [a(k);d(k);0;0];
    x = C*x+b;
    E(:,k) = x;
end
% Plot the results.
plot(E'),hold,plot(E(1,:),'o'),plot(E(2,:),'+'),plot(E(3,:),'*'),...
plot(E(4,:),'x'),xlabel('Year'),ylabel('Number of Students'),...
gtext('Frosh'),gtext('Soph'),gtext('Jr'),gtext('Sr'),...
title('Enrollments as a Function of Time')
```

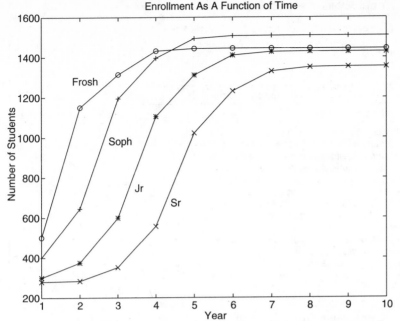

Enrollment As A Function of Time

Figure 6.6–2
Class enrollments versus time.

freshmen. The reason is that the increasing transfer rate eventually overcomes the effect of the increasing admission rate.

In actual practice this program would be run many times to analyze the effects of different admissions and transfer policies and to examine what happens if different values are used for the coefficients in the matrix **C** (indicating different dropout and repeat rates).

Test Your Understanding

T6.6–2 In the program in Table 6.6–2, lines 16 and 17 compute the values of a(k) and d(k). These lines are repeated here:

```
a(k) = 900+100*k
d(k) = 150+50*k;
```

Why does the program contain the line a(1) = 1000; d(1) = 200;?

6.7

Summary

Now that you have finished this chapter, you should be able to write programs that can perform decision-making procedures; that is, the program's operations depend on results of the program's calculations or on input from the user. The first three

Table 6.7–1 Guide to MATLAB commands introduced in Chapter 6

Relational operators	Table 6.1–1
Logical operators	Table 6.2–1
Order of precedence for operator types	Table 6.2–2
Truth table for logical operators	Table 6.2–3
Logical functions	Table 6.2–4

Miscellaneous commands		
Command	**Description**	**Section**
`break`	Terminates the execution of a `for` or a `while` loop.	6.4
`case`	Used with `switch` to direct program execution.	6.5
`else`	Delineates an alternate block of statements.	6.3
`elseif`	Conditionally executes statements.	6.3
`end`	Terminates `for`, `while`, and `if` statements.	6.3, 6.4
`findstr('s1','s2')`	For character strings `s1` and `s2`, finds the starting indices of any occurrences of the shorter string within the longer string of the pair.	6.3
`for`	Repeats statements a specific number of times.	6.4
`if`	Executes statements conditionally.	6.3
`switch`	Directs program execution by comparing the input expression with the associated `case` expressions.	6.5
`while`	Repeats statements an indefinite number of times.	6.4

sections of the chapter covered the necessary functions: the relational operators, the logical operators and functions, and the conditional statements.

You should also be able to use MATLAB loop structures to write programs that repeat calculations a specified number of times or until some condition is satisfied. This feature enables engineers to solve problems of great complexity or requiring numerous calculations. The `for` loop and `while` loop structures were covered in section 6.4.

Section 6.5 covered the `switch` structure, which is new with MATLAB 5. Section 6.6 presented an application of these methods to simulation, which enables engineers to study the operation of complicated systems, processes, and organizations.

Tables summarizing the MATLAB commands introduced in this chapter are located throughout the chapter. Table 6.7–1 will help you locate these tables. It also summarizes those commands not found in the other tables.

Key Terms with Page References

You can find answers to problems marked with an asterisk at the
end of the text.

Problems

Section 6.1

1.* Suppose that x = 6. Find the results of the following operations by
hand and use MATLAB to check your results.
    a. z = (x<10)   *b.* z = (x==10)
    c. z = (x>=4)   *d.* z = (x~=7)

2.* Find the results of the following operations by hand and use MATLAB to
check your results.
    a. z = 6>3+8   *b.* z = 6+3>8
    c. z = 4>(2+9)   *d.* z = (4<7)+3
    e. z = 4<7+3   *f.* z = (4<7)*5
    g. z = 4<(7*5)   *h.* z = 2/5>=5

3.* Suppose that x = [10, -2, 6, 5, -3] and y = [9, -3,
2, 5, -1]. Find the results of the following operations by hand
and use MATLAB to check your results.
    a. z = (x<6)   *b.* z = (x<=y)
    c. z = (x==y)   *d.* z = (x~=y)

4. For the arrays x and y given below, use MATLAB to find all the elements
in x that are greater than the corresponding elements in y.

x = [-3, 0, 0, 2, 6, 8]   y = [-5, -2, 0, 3, 4, 10]

5. The array price given below contains the price in dollars of a certain
stock over 10 days. Use MATLAB to determine how many days the price
was above $20.

price = [19, 18, 22, 21, 25, 19, 17, 21, 27, 29]

6. The arrays price_A and price_B given below contain the price in
dollars of two stocks over 10 days. Use MATLAB to determine how many
days the price of stock A was above the price of stock B.

price_A = [19, 18, 22, 21, 25, 19, 17, 21, 27, 29]

price_B = [22, 17, 20, 19, 24, 18, 16, 25, 28, 27]

7. The arrays price_A, price_C, and price_B given below contain
the price in dollars of three stocks over 10 days.
    a. Use MATLAB to determine how many days the price of stock A was
above both the price of stock B and the price of stock C.
    b. Use MATLAB to determine how many days the price of stock A was
above either the price of stock B or the price of stock C.
    c. Use MATLAB to determine how many days the price of stock A was
above either the price of stock B or the price of stock C, but not
both.

price_A = [19, 18, 22, 21, 25, 19, 17, 21, 27, 29]

price_B = [22, 17, 20, 19, 24, 18, 16, 25, 28, 27]

price_C = [17, 13, 22, 23, 19, 17, 20, 21, 24, 28]

Section 6.2

8.* Suppose that x = [-3, 0, 0, 2, 5, 8] and y = [-5, -2, 0, 3, 4, 10]. Find the results of the following operations by hand and use MATLAB to check your results.

a. z = y<~x   *b.* z = x&y

c. z = x|y   *d.* z = xor(x,y)

9. The height and speed of a projectile (such as a thrown ball) launched with a speed of v_0 at an angle A to the horizontal are given by

$$h(t) = v_0 t \sin A - 0.5gt^2$$

$$v(t) = \sqrt{v_0^2 - 2v_0 g t \sin A + g^2 t^2}$$

where g is the acceleration due to gravity. The projectile will strike the ground when $h(t) = 0$, which gives the time to hit $t_{hit} = 2(v_0/g)\sin A$.

Suppose that $A = 30°$, $v_0 = 40$ meters/second, and $g = 9.81$ meters/second^2. Use the MATLAB relational and logical operators to find the times when

a. The height is no less than 15 meters.

b. The height is no less than 15 meters and the speed is simultaneously no greater than 36 meters/second.

c. The height is less than 5 meters or the speed is greater than 35 meters/second.

10.* The price, in dollars, of a certain stock over a 10-day period is given in the following array.

```
price = [19, 18, 22, 21, 25, 19, 17, 21, 27, 29]
```

Suppose you owned 1000 shares at the start of the 10-day period, and you bought 100 shares every day the price was below $20 and sold 100 shares every day the price was above $25. Use MATLAB to compute (*a*) the amount you spent in buying shares, (*b*) the amount you received from the sale of shares, (*c*) the total number of shares you own after the 10th day, and (*d*) the net increase in the worth of your portfolio.

11. Let e1 and e2 be logical expressions. DeMorgan's laws for logical expressions state that

NOT(e1 AND e2) implies that (NOT e1) OR (NOT e2)

and

NOT(e1 OR e2) implies that (NOT e1) AND (NOT e2)

Use these laws to find an equivalent expression for each of the following expressions and use MATLAB to verify the equivalence.

a. ~((x < 10)&(x>=6))

b. ~((x == 2) | (x > 5))

12. Are these following expressions equivalent? Use MATLAB to check your answer for specific values of *a, b, c,* and *d*.

a. 1. (a==b)&((b==c)|(a==c))
     2. (a==b)|((b==c)&(a==c))

b. 1. (a<b)&((a>c)|(a>d))
     2. (a<b)&(a>c)|((a<b)&(a>d))

13. Rewrite the following statements to use only one `if` statement.

```
if x < y
   if z < 10
      w = x*y*z
   end
end
```

14. Figure P14a shows a mass-spring model of the type used to design packaging systems and vehicle suspensions, for example. The springs exert a force that is proportional to their compression, and the proportionality constant is the spring constant k. The two side springs provide additional resistance if the weight W is too heavy for the center spring. When the weight W is gently placed, it moves through a distance x before coming to rest. From statics, the weight force must balance the spring forces at this new position. Thus

$$W = k_1 x \qquad \text{if } x < d$$

$$W = k_1 x + 2k_2(x - d) \qquad \text{if } x \geq d$$

These relations can be used to generate the plot of W versus x, shown in Figure P14b.

(a)

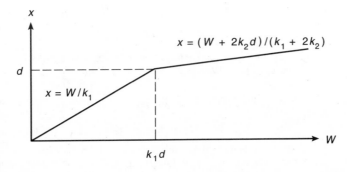

(b)

Figure P14

a. Create a function file that computes the distance x, using the input parameters W, k_1, k_2, and d. Test your function for the following two cases, using the values $k_1 = 10^4$ newtons/meter; $k_2 = 1.5 \times 10^4$ newtons/meter; $d = 0.1$ meter.

$$W = 500 \text{ newtons}$$

$$W = 2000 \text{ newtons}$$

b. Use your function to plot x versus W for $0 \leq W \leq 3000$ newtons for the values of k_1, k_2, and d given in part (a).

Section 6.4

15. We now want to analyze the mass-spring system discussed in Problem 14 for the case in which the weight W is dropped onto the platform attached to the center spring. If the weight is dropped from a height h above the platform, we can find the maximum spring compression x by equating the weight's gravitational potential energy Wh with the potential energy stored in the springs. Thus

$$Wh = \frac{1}{2}k_1 x^2 \qquad \text{if } x < d$$

which can be solved for x as

$$x = \sqrt{\frac{2Wh}{k_1}} \qquad \text{if } x < d$$

and

$$Wh = \frac{1}{2}k_1 x^2 + \frac{1}{2}(2k_2)(x-d)^2 \qquad \text{if } x \geq d$$

which gives the following quadratic equation to solve for x:

$$(k_1 + 2k_2)x^2 - 4k_2 dx + 2k_2 d^2 - 2Wh = 0 \qquad \text{if } x \geq d$$

a. Create a function file that computes the maximum compression x due to the falling weight. The function's input parameters are k_1, k_2, d, W, and h. Test your function for the following two cases, using the values $k_1 = 10^4$ newtons/meter; $k_2 = 1.5 \times 10^4$ newtons/meter; and $d = 0.1$ meter.

$$W = 100 \text{ newtons}, h = 0.5 \text{ meter}$$

$$W = 2000 \text{ newtons}, h = 0.5 \text{ meter}$$

b. Use your function file to generate a plot of x versus h for $0 \leq h \leq 2$ meters. Use $W = 100$ newtons and the preceding values for k_1, k_2, and d.

c. Use your function file to generate a surface mesh plot and a contour plot of x versus h and W for $0 \leq W \leq 500$ newtons and for $0 \leq h \leq 2$ meters. Use the preceding values for k_1, k_2, and d.

16. Electrical resistors are said to be connected "in series" if the same current passes through each and "in parallel" if the same voltage is applied across each. If in series, they are equivalent to a single

resistor whose resistance is given by

$$R = R_1 + R_2 + R_3 + \ldots + R_n$$

If in parallel, their equivalent resistance is given by

$$\frac{1}{R} = \frac{1}{R_1} + \frac{1}{R_2} + \frac{1}{R_3} + \ldots + \frac{1}{R_n}$$

Write an M-file that prompts the user for the type of connection (series or parallel) and the number of resistors n and then computes the equivalent resistance.

17. a. An *ideal* diode blocks the flow of current in the direction opposite that of the diode's arrow symbol. It can be used to make a *half-wave rectifier* as shown in Figure P17a. For the ideal diode, the voltage v_L across the load R_L is given by

$$v_L = \begin{cases} v_S & \text{if } v_S > 0 \\ 0 & \text{if } v_S \le 0 \end{cases}$$

Suppose the supply voltage is

$$v_S(t) = 3e^{-t/3}\sin(\pi t) \quad \text{volts}$$

where time t is in seconds. Write a MATLAB program to plot the voltage v_L versus t for $0 \le t \le 10$.

b. A more accurate model of the diode's behavior is given by the *offset diode* model, which accounts for the offset voltage inherent in semiconductor diodes. The offset model contains an ideal diode and a battery whose voltage equals the offset

(a)

(b)

Figure P17

voltage (which is approximately 0.6 V for silicon diodes) [Rizzoni, 1996]. The half-wave rectifier using this model is shown in Figure P17b. For this circuit,

$$v_L = \begin{cases} v_S - 0.6 & \text{if } v_S > 0.6 \\ 0 & \text{if } v_S \leq 0.6 \end{cases}$$

Using the same supply voltage given in part (a), plot the voltage v_L versus t for $0 \leq t \leq 10$; then compare the results with the plot obtained in part (a).

18.* Engineers in industry must continually look for ways to make their designs and operations more efficient. One tool for doing so is *optimization,* which uses a mathematical description of the design or operation to select the best values of certain variables. Many sophisticated mathematical tools have been developed for this purpose, and some are in the MATLAB Optimization toolbox. However, problems that have a limited number of possible variable values can use MATLAB loop structures to search for the optimum solution. This problem and the next two are examples of multivariable optimization that can be done with the basic MATLAB program.

A company wants to locate a distribution center that will serve six of its major customers in a 30 × 30-mile area. The locations of the customers relative to the southwest corner of the area are given below in terms of (x, y) coordinates (the x direction is east; the y direction is north) (see Figure P18). Also given is the volume in tons per week that must be delivered from the distribution center to each customer. The weekly delivery cost c_i for customer i depends on the volume V_i and the distance d_i from the distribution center. For simplicity we will assume that this distance is the straight-line distance. (This assumes that the road network is dense.) The weekly cost is given by $c_i = 0.5d_i V_i$; $i = 1, 2, \ldots, 6$.

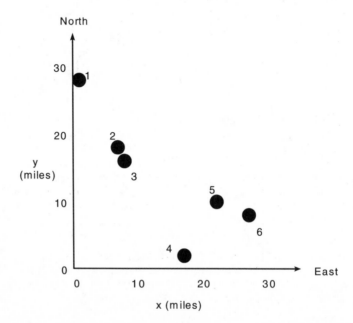

Figure P18

Customer	x location (miles)	y location (miles)	Volume (tons/week)
1	1	28	3
2	7	18	7
3	8	16	4
4	17	2	5
5	22	10	2
6	27	8	6

a. Find the location of the distribution center (to the nearest mile) that minimizes the total weekly cost to service all six customers.

b. To see how sensitive the cost is to location of the distribution center, obtain a surface plot and a contour plot of the total cost as a function of the x and y coordinates of the distribution center's location. How much would the cost increase if we located the center 1 mile in any direction from the optimal location?

19. A company has the choice of producing up to four different products with its machinery, which consists of lathes, grinders, and milling machines. The number of hours on each machine required to produce a product is given in the following table, along with the number of hours available per week on each type of machine. Assume that the company can sell everything it produces. The profit per item for each product appears in the last line of the table.

	Product				Hours available
	1	2	3	4	
Hours required					
Lathe	1	2	0.5	3	40
Grinder	0	2	4	1	30
Milling	3	1	5	2	45
Unit profit ($)	100	150	90	120	

a. Determine how many units of each product the company should make to maximize its total profit and then compute this profit. Remember, the company cannot make fractional units, so your answer must be in integers. (Hint: First estimate the upper limits on the number of products that can be produced without exceeding the available capacity.)

b. How sensitive is your answer? How much does the profit decrease if you make one more or one less item than the optimum?

20. A certain company makes televisions, stereo units, and speakers. Its parts inventory includes chassis, picture tubes, speaker cones, power supplies, and electronics. The inventory, required components, and profit for each product appear in the following table. Determine how many of each product to make in order to maximize the profit.

	Product			
	Television	Stereo unit	Speaker unit	Inventory
Requirements				
Chassis	1	1	0	450
Picture Tube	1	0	0	250
Speaker Cone	2	2	1	800
Power Supply	1	1	0	450
Electronics	2	2	1	600
Unit profit ($)	80	50	40	

21.* Use a loop in MATLAB to determine how long it will take to accumulate $1,000,000 in a bank account if you deposit $10,000 initially and $10,000 at the end of each year; the account pays 6 percent annual interest.

22. A weight W is supported by two cables anchored a distance D apart (see Figure P22). The cable length L_{AB} is given, but the length L_{AC} is to be selected. Each cable can support a maximum tension force equal to W. For the weight to remain stationary, the total horizontal force and total vertical force must each be zero. This principle gives the equations

$$-T_{AB} \cos \theta + T_{AC} \cos \phi = 0$$

$$T_{AB} \sin \theta + T_{AC} \sin \phi = W$$

We can solve these equations for the tension forces T_{AB} and T_{AC} if we know the angles θ and ϕ. From the law of cosines

$$\theta = \cos^{-1}\left(\frac{D^2 + L_{AB}^2 - L_{AC}^2}{2DL_{AB}}\right)$$

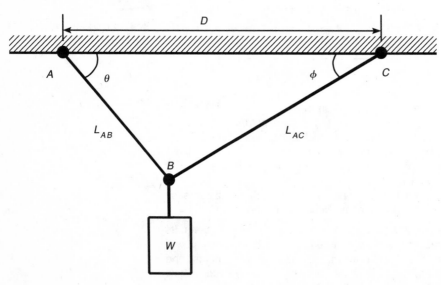

Figure P22

From the law of sines

$$\phi = \sin^{-1}\left(\frac{L_{AB}\sin\theta}{L_{AC}}\right)$$

For the given values $D = 6$ feet, $L_{AB} = 3$ feet, and $W = 2000$ pounds, use a loop in MATLAB to find L_{ACmin}, the shortest length L_{AC} we can use without T_{AB} or T_{AC} exceeding 2000 pounds. Note that the largest L_{AC} can be is 6.7 feet (which corresponds to $\theta = 90°$). Plot the tension forces T_{AB} and T_{AC} on the same graph versus L_{AC} for $L_{ACmin} \le L_{AC} \le$ 6.7.

23.* In the structure in Figure P23a, six wires support three beams. Wires 1 and 2 can support no more than 1200 newtons each, wires 3 and 4 can support no more than 400 newtons each, and wires

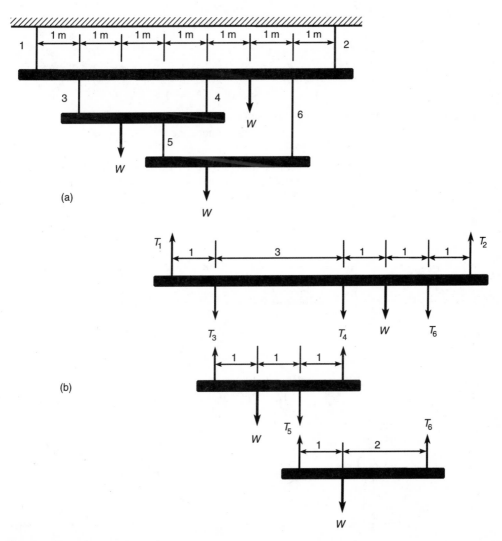

(a)

(b)

Figure P23

5 and 6 no more than 200 newtons each. Three equal weights W are attached at the points shown. Assuming that the structure is stationary and that the weights of the wires and the beams are very small compared to W, the principles of statics applied to a particular beam state that the sum of vertical forces is zero and that the sum of moments about any point is also zero. Applying these principles to each beam using the free-body diagrams shown in Figure P23b, we obtain the following equations. Let the tension force in wire i be T_i. For beam 1

$$T_1 + T_2 = T_3 + T_4 + W + T_6$$

$$-T_3 - 4T_4 - 5W - 6T_6 + 7T_2 = 0$$

For beam 2

$$T_3 + T_4 = W + T_5$$

$$-W - 2T_5 + 3T_4 = 0$$

For beam 3

$$T_5 + T_6 = W$$

$$-W + 3T_6 = 0$$

Find the maximum value of the weight W the structure can support. Remember that the wires cannot support compression, so T_i must be nonnegative.

24. The electrical resistance network analyzed in Example 5.2–3 is shown again in Figure P24. The equations describing the circuit were derived in that example and are repeated here.

$$-v_1 + R_1 i_1 + R_4 i_4 = 0$$

$$-R_4 i_4 + R_2 i_2 + R_5 i_5 = 0$$

$$-R_5 i_5 + R_3 i_3 + v_2 = 0$$

$$i_1 = i_2 + i_4$$

$$i_2 = i_3 + i_5$$

Figure P24

a. The given values of the resistances and the voltage v_1 are $R_1 = 5$, $R_2 = 100$, $R_3 = 200$, $R_4 = 150$, $R_5 = 250$ kΩ, and $v_1 = 100$ volts. (Note that 1 kΩ = 1000 Ω.) Suppose that each resistance is rated to carry a current of no more than 1 milliamperes (= 0.001 amperes). Determine the allowable range of positive values for the voltage v_2.

b. Suppose we want to investigate how the resistance R_3 limits the allowable range for v_2. Obtain a plot of the allowable limit on v_2 as a function of R_3 for $150 \le R_3 \le 250$ kΩ.

25. Many applications require us to know the temperature distribution in an object. For example, this information is important for controlling the material properties, such as hardness, when cooling an object formed from molten metal. In a heat transfer course, the following description of the temperature distribution in a flat, rectangular metal plate is often derived. The temperature is held constant at T_1 on three sides, and at T_2 on the fourth side (see Figure P25). The temperature $T(x, y)$ as a function of the xy coordinates shown is given by

$$T(x, y) = (T_2 - T_1)w(x, y) + T_1$$

where

$$w(x, y) = \frac{2}{\pi} \sum_{n\ \text{odd}}^{\infty} \frac{2}{n} \sin\left(\frac{n\pi x}{L}\right) \frac{\sinh(n\pi y/L)}{\sinh(n\pi W/L)}$$

Use the following data: $T_1 = 70°F$, $T_2 = 200°F$, and $W = L = 2$ feet.

a. The terms in the preceding series become smaller in magnitude as n increases. Write a MATLAB program to verify this fact for $n = 1$, ..., 19 for the center of the plate ($x = y = 1$).

b. Using $x = y = 1$, write a MATLAB program to determine how many terms are required in the series to produce a temperature calculation that is accurate to within 1 percent. (That is, for what

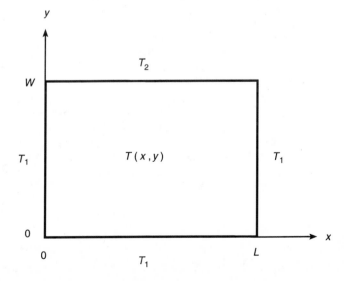

Figure P25

value of n will the addition of the next term in the series produce a change in T of less than 1 percent.) Use your physical insight to determine whether this answer gives the correct temperature at the center of the plate.

c. Modify the program from part (b) to compute the temperatures in the plate; use a spacing of 0.2 for both x and y.

d. Use the program from part (c) to generate a surface mesh plot and a contour plot of the temperature distribution.

Section 6.5

26. (For MATLAB 5 only) The following table gives the approximate values of the static coefficient of friction μ for various materials.

Materials	μ
Metal on metal	0.20
Wood on wood	0.35
Metal on wood	0.40
Rubber on concrete	0.70

To start a weight W moving on a horizontal surface, you must push with a force F, where $F = \mu W$. Write a MATLAB program that uses the switch structure to compute the force F. The program should accept as input the value of W and the type of materials.

27. (For MATLAB 5 only) The height and speed of a projectile (such as a thrown ball) launched with a speed of v_0 at an angle A to the horizontal are given by

$$h(t) = v_0 t \sin A - 0.5gt^2$$

$$v(t) = \sqrt{v_0^2 - 2v_0 gt \sin A + g^2 t^2}$$

where g is the acceleration due to gravity. The projectile will strike the ground when $h(t) = 0$, which gives the time to hit $t_{hit} = 2(v_0/g) \sin A$.

Use the switch structure to write a MATLAB program to compute either the maximum height reached by the projectile, the total horizontal distance traveled, or the time to hit. The program should accept as input the user's choice of which quantity to compute and the values of v_0, A, and g. Test the program for the case where $v_0 = 40$ meters/second, $A = 30°$, and $g = 9.81$ meters/second^2.

28. (For MATLAB 5 only) Use the switch structure to write a MATLAB program to compute how much money accumulates in a savings account in one year. The program should accept the following input: the initial amount of money deposited in the account; the frequency of interest compounding (monthly, quarterly, semiannually, or annually); and the interest rate. Run your program for a $1000 initial deposit for each case; use a 5 percent interest rate. Compare the amounts of money that accumulate for each case.

Section 6.6

29. Consider the college enrollment model discussed in Example 6.6–2. Suppose the college wants to limit freshmen admissions to 120

percent of the current sophomore class and limit sophomore transfers to 10 percent of the current freshman class. Rewrite and run the program given in the example to examine the effects of these policies over a 10-year period. Plot the results.

30. Suppose you project that you will be able to deposit the following monthly amounts into a savings account for a period of five years. The account initially has no money in it.

Year	1	2	3	4	5
Monthly deposit ($)	300	350	350	350	400

At the end of each year in which the account balance is at least $3000, you withdraw $2000 to buy a certificate of deposit (CD), which pays 6 percent interest compounded annually.

Write a MATLAB program to compute how much money will accumulate in five years in the account and in any CD's you buy. Run the program for two different interest rates: 4 percent and 5 percent.

31.* A certain company manufactures and sells golf carts. At the end of each week, the company transfers the carts produced that week into storage (inventory). All carts that are sold are taken from the inventory. A simple model of this process is

$$I(k + 1) = P(k) + I(k) - S(k)$$

where

$P(k)$ = the number of carts produced in week k

$I(k)$ = the number of carts in inventory in week k

$S(k)$ = the number of carts sold in week k

The projected weekly sales for 10 weeks are

Week	1	2	3	4	5	6	7	8	9	10
Sales	50	55	60	70	70	75	80	80	90	55

Suppose the weekly production is based on the previous week's sales so that $P(k) = S(k - 1)$. Assume that the first week's production is 50 carts; that is, $P(1) = 50$. Write a MATLAB program to compute and plot the number of carts in inventory for each of the 10 weeks or until the inventory drops below zero. Run the program for two cases: (*a*) an initial inventory of 50 carts so that $I(1) = 50$, and (*b*) an initial inventory of 30 carts so that $I(1) = 30$.

32. Redo Problem 31 with the restriction that the next week's production is set to zero if the inventory exceeds 40 carts.

Courtesy of NASA.

Engineering in the 21st Century...

International Engineering

The end of the Cold War has resulted in increased international cooperation. A vivid example of this is the cooperation between the Russian and American space agencies. The photo shows the American space shuttle Atlantis docked with the Russian space station Mir while orbiting over a typhoon. Now Russia, the United States, and several other countries are collaborating on a more ambitious space project: the International Space Station (ISS). The launch of the first element of the station, a Russian-built cargo block, is scheduled for late 1998. Already, hundreds of U.S. engineers have spent months in Russia and the U.S., working on the project with engineers from the participating countries. The station will have a crew of seven, will weigh over 1,000,000 pounds, and will be 290 feet long and 356 feet wide. To assemble it will require 28 U.S. shuttle flights and 41 Russian flights over a period of 5 years.

The new era of international cooperation has resulted in increased integration of national economies into one global economy. For example, many components for cars assembled in the United States are supplied by companies in other countries. In the next century improved communications and computer networks will enable engineering teams in different countries to work simultaneously on different aspects of the product's design, employing a common design database. To prepare for such a future in international engineering, students need to become familiar with other cultures and languages, as well as proficient in computer-aided design.

MATLAB is available in international editions and has been widely used in Europe for many years. Thus engineers familiar with MATLAB will already have a head start in preparing for a career in international engineering.

7 Statistics, Regression, and Interpolation

Outline

This chapter is unlike the first six chapters in that it covers relatively few MATLAB functions. These functions are easy to use and have widespread and important uses in statistics and data analysis; however, their proper application requires informed judgment and experience. Here we present enough of the mathematical foundations of these methods to allow you to apply them properly.

We begin with an introduction to basic statistics and probability in section 7.1. You will see how to obtain and interpret *histograms,* which are specialized plots for displaying statistical results. The *normal distribution,* commonly called the *bell-shaped curve,* forms the basis of many statistical methods and is covered in section 7.2. As you saw in Chapter 6, MATLAB is useful for programming simulations. In section 7.3 you will see how to include random processes in your simulation programs. In many applications you need to use measured data to develop a mathematical model of a process or device. Section 7.4 shows you how to find functions that adequately describe the data. In section 7.5 you will see how to use interpolation with data tables to estimate values that are not in the table. An interesting application of this method is in machine control, and we give an example of controlling a robot arm.

When you have finished this chapter, you should be able to use MATLAB to do the following:

- Solve basic problems in statistics and probability.
- Create simulations incorporating random processes.
- Develop functional descriptions of data.
- Apply interpolation techniques.

7.1

Statistics, Histograms, and Probability

MEAN
MEDIAN

In all likelihood you have computed an *average,* for example, the average of all your test scores in a course. To find your average, you add your scores and divide by the number of tests. The mathematical term for this average is the *mean.* On the other hand, the *median* is the value in the middle of the data if the number of data points is odd. For example, if the test scores on a particular test in a class of 27 students have a median of 74, then 13 students scored below 74, 13 scored above 74, and one student obtained a grade of 74. If the number of data points is even, the median is the mean of the two values closest to the middle. The mean need not be the same as the median. For example, for the data 60, 65, 68, 74, 88, 95, the mean is 75, whereas the median is the mean of 68 and 74, or 71.

MATLAB provides the mean(x) and median(x) functions to perform these computations. If x is a vector, the mean (or median) value of the vector's values is returned. However, if x is a matrix, a row vector is returned containing the mean (or median) value of each column of x. These functions do not require the elements in x to be sorted in ascending or descending order.

In many applications, the mean and the median do not adequately describe a data set. Two data sets can have the same mean (or the same median) yet be very different. For example, the test scores 60, 65, 68, 74, 88, 95 have the same mean as the scores 71, 72, 73, 77, 78, 79, but the two sets describe very different test outcomes. The first set of scores vary over a large range, whereas in the second set the scores are tightly grouped about the mean.

HISTOGRAM

The way the data are spread around the mean can be described by a *histogram* plot. A *histogram* is a plot of the frequency of occurrence of data values versus the values themselves. For example, suppose that in a class of 20 students the 20 scores on the first test were

```
61  61  65  67  69  72  74  74  76  77
83  83  85  88  89  92  93  93  95  98
```

Figure 7.1–1
Histograms of test scores for 20 students.

On this test there are five scores in the 60–69 range, five in the
70–79 range, five in the 80–89 range, and five in the 90–100
range. The histogram for these scores is shown in the top graph
in Figure 7.1–1. It is a bar plot of the number of scores that
occur within each range, with the bar centered in the middle of
the range (for example, the bar for the range 60–69 is centered
at 64.5, and the asterisk on the plot's abscissa shows the bar's
center).

Suppose that on the second test the following 20 scores were
achieved:

66 69 72 74 75 76 77 78 78 79
79 80 81 83 84 85 87 88 90 94

On this test there are two scores in the 60–69 range, nine in the
70–79 range, seven in the 80–89 range, and two in the 90–100
range. The histogram for these scores is shown in the bottom
graph in Figure 7.1–1. The mean on both tests is identical and
is 79.75. However, the distribution of the scores is very different.
On the first test we say that the scores are evenly, or "uniformly,"
distributed between 60 and 100, whereas on the second test the
scores are more clustered around the mean.

To plot a histogram, you must group the data into subranges, called *bins*. In this example the four bins are the ranges 60–69, 70–79, 80–89, and 90–100. The choice of the bin width and bin center can drastically change the shape of the histogram. If the number of data values is relatively small, the bin width cannot be small, because some of the bins will contain no data and the resulting histogram might not usefully illustrate the distribution of the data.

To obtain a histogram, first sort the data if it has not yet been sorted (you can use the sort function here). Then choose the bin ranges and bin centers and count the number of values in each bin. Use the bar command to plot the number of values in each bin versus the bin centers. The MATLAB script file that generates Figure 7.1–1 follows. We have selected the bin centers to be in the middle of the ranges 60–69, 70–79, 80–89, 90–99.

```
% Collect the scores in each bin.
test1 = [5,5,5,5];
test2 = [2,9,7,2];
% Specify the bin centers.
x = [64.5,74.5,84.5,94.5];
subplot(2,1,1)
bar(x,test1),axis([60 100 0 10]),...
title('Histogram of Scores for Test 1'),...
xlabel('Score Range'),ylabel('Number of Scores')
subplot(2,1,2)
bar(x,test2),axis([60 100 0 10]),...
title('Histogram of Scores for Test 2'),...
xlabel('Score Range'),ylabel('Number of Scores')
```

MATLAB provides the hist command to generate a histogram. This command has several forms. Its basic form is hist(y), where y is a vector containing the data. This form aggregates the data into 10 bins evenly spaced between the minimum and maximum values in y. The second form is hist(y,n), where n is a user-specified scalar indicating the number of bins. The third form is hist(y,x), where x is a user-specified vector that determines the location of the bin centers; the bin widths are the distances between the centers.

Example 7.1–1 Breaking strength of thread

To ensure proper quality control, a thread manufacturer selects samples and tests them for breaking strength. Suppose that 20 thread samples are pulled until they break, and the breaking force is measured in newtons rounded off to integer values. The breaking force values recorded were 92, 94, 93, 96, 93, 94, 95, 96, 91, 93, 95, 95, 95, 92, 93, 94, 91, 94, 92, and 93. Plot the histogram of the data.

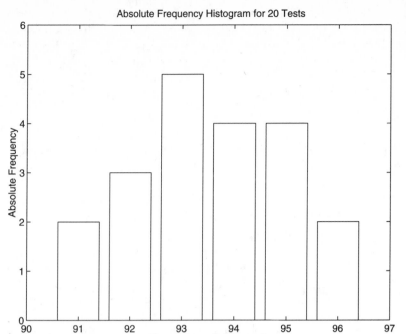

Figure 7.1–2
Histogram for 20 tests of thread strength.

Solution:

Store the data in the vector y, which is shown in the following script file. Because there are six outcomes (91, 92, 93, 94, 95, 96 newtons), we choose six bins. However, if you use hist(y,6), the bins will not be centered at 91, 92, 93, 94, 95, and 96. So use the form hist(y,x), where x = [91:96]. The following script file generates the histogram shown in Figure 7.1–2.

```
% Thread breaking strength data for 20 tests.
y = [92,94,93,96,93,94,95,96,91,93,...
95,95,95,92,93,94,91,94,92,93];
% The six possible outcomes are 91,92,93,94,95,96
x=[91:96];
hist(y,x),axis([90 97 0 6]),ylabel('Absolute Frequency'),...
xlabel('Thread Strength (newtons)'),...
title('Absolute Frequency Histogram For 20 Tests')
```

The *absolute frequency* is the number of times a particular outcome occurs. For example, in 20 tests this data shows that a 95 occurred four times. The absolute frequency is 4, and its *relative frequency* is 4/20, or 20% of the time.

ABSOLUTE FREQUENCY

RELATIVE FREQUENCY

When there is a large amount of data, you can avoid typing in every data value by first aggregating the data. The following example shows how this is done using the ones function. The following data was generated by testing 100 thread samples. The number of times 91, 92, 93, 94, 95, or 96 newtons was measured is 13, 15, 22, 19, 17, and 14, respectively.

```
% Thread strength data for 20 tests.
y = [91*ones(1,13),92*ones(1,15),93*ones(1,22),...
94*ones(1,19),95*ones(1,17),96*ones(1,14)];
x=[91:96];
hist(y,x),ylabel('Absolute Frequency'),...
xlabel('Thread Strength (newtons)'),...
title('Absolute Frequency Histogram For 100 Tests')
```

The result appears in Figure 7.1–3.

The hist function is somewhat limited in its ability to produce useful histograms. Unless all the outcome values are the same as the bin centers (as is the case with the thread examples), the graph produced by the hist function will not be satisfactory. This case occurs when you want to obtain a *relative* frequency histogram. In such cases you can use the bar function to generate the histogram. The bar function was introduced in Chapter 4. The

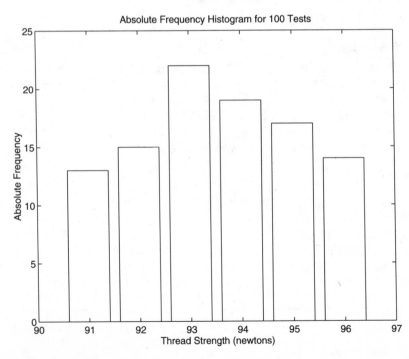

Figure 7.1–3
Absolute frequency histogram for 100 thread tests.

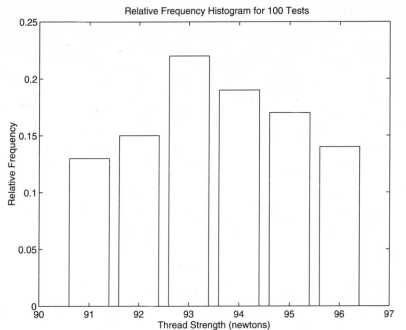

Figure 7.1–4
Relative frequency histogram for 100 thread tests.

following script file generates the relative frequency histogram
for the 100 thread tests. Note that if you use the bar function,
you must aggregate the data first.

```
% Relative frequency histogram using the bar function.
tests = 100;
y=[13,15,22,19,17,14]/tests;
x=[91:96];
bar(x,y),ylabel('Relative Frequency'),...
xlabel('Thread Strength (newtons)'),...
title('Relative Frequency Histogram For 100 Tests')
```

The result appears in Figure 7.1–4.

The fourth, fifth, and sixth forms of the hist function do not
generate a plot, but are used to compute the frequency counts
and bin locations. The bar function can then be used to plot the
histogram. The syntax of the fourth form is [z,x] = hist(y),
where z is the returned vector containing the frequency count and
x is the returned vector containing the bin locations. The fifth and
sixth forms are [z,x] = hist(y,n) and [z,x] = hist(y,x).
In the latter case the returned vector x is the same as the user-
supplied vector. The following script file shows how the sixth form
can be used to generate a relative frequency histogram for the
thread example with 100 tests.

Table 7.1–1 Histogram functions

Command	Description
`bar(x,y)`	Creates a bar chart of y versus x.
`hist(y)`	Aggregates the data in the vector y into 10 bins evenly spaced between the minimum and maximum values in y.
`hist(y,n)`	Aggregates the data in the vector y into n bins evenly spaced between the minimum and maximum values in y.
`hist(y,x)`	Aggregates the data in the vector y into bins whose center locations are specified by the vector x. The bin widths are the distances between the centers.
`[z,x] = hist(y)`	Same as `hist(y)` but returns two vectors z and x that contain the frequency count and the bin locations.
`[z,x] = hist(y,n)`	Same as `hist(y,n)` but returns two vectors z and x that contain the frequency count and the bin locations.
`[z,x] = hist(y,x)`	Same as `hist(y,x)` but returns two vectors z and x that contain the frequency count and the bin locations. The returned vector x is the same as the user-supplied vector x.

```
tests = 100;
y = [91*ones(1,13),92*ones(1,15),93*ones(1,22),...
94*ones(1,19),95*ones(1,17),96*ones(1,14)];
x=[91:96];
[z,x]=hist(y,x);bar(x,z/tests),...
ylabel('Relative Frequency'),xlabel('Thread Strength (newtons)'),...
title('Relative Frequency Histogram For 100 Tests')
```

The plot generated by this M-file will be identical to that shown in Figure 7.1–4. These commands are summarized in Table 7.1–1.

Test Your Understanding

T7.1–1 In 50 tests of thread, the number of times 91, 92, 93, 94, 95, or 96 newtons was measured was 7, 8, 10, 6, 12, and 7, respectively. Obtain the absolute and relative frequency histograms.

Probability

Probability is expressed as a number between 0 and 1 or as a percentage between 0 percent and 100 percent. For example, because there are six possible outcomes from rolling a single die, the probability of obtaining a specific number on one roll is 1/6, or 16.67 percent. Thus if you roll the die a large number of times, you expect to obtain a 2 one-sixth of the time. Figure 7.1–5 shows the theoretical uniform probabilities for rolling a single die, and the relative frequency histogram for the data from 100 die rolls. The number of times a 1, 2, 3, 4, 5, or 6 occurred was 21, 14, 18, 16, 19, and 12 respectively. The plots of the theory and the data are very similar, but not identical. In general, if you had rolled

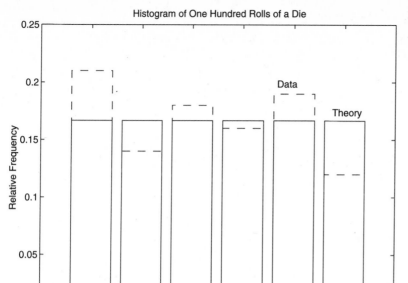

Figure 7.1–5
Comparison of theory and experiment for 100 rolls of a single die.

the die 1000 times instead of 100 times, the histogram would look even more like the theoretical probability plot.

If you roll two balanced dice, each roll has 36 possible outcomes because each die can produce six numbers. There is only one way to obtain a sum of 2, but there are two ways to obtain a sum of 3, and so on. Thus the probability of rolling a sum of 2 is 1/36, and the probability of rolling a sum of 3 is 1/36 + 1/36 = 2/36. Continuing this line of reasoning, you can obtain the theoretical probabilities for the sum of two dice, as shown in the following table.

Probabilities for the sum of two dice											
Sum	2	3	4	5	6	7	8	9	10	11	12
Probability (× 36)	1	2	3	4	5	6	5	4	3	2	1

An experiment was performed by rolling two dice 100 times and recording the sums. The data follows.

Data for two dice											
Sum	2	3	4	5	6	7	8	9	10	11	12
Frequency	5	5	8	11	20	10	8	12	7	10	4

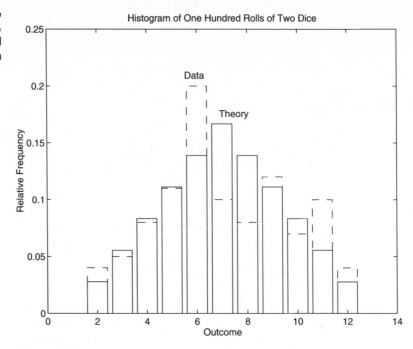

Figure 7.1–6
Comparison of theory and experiment for 100 rolls of two dice.

Figure 7.1–6 shows the relative frequency histogram and the theoretical probabilities on the same plot. If you had collected more data, the histogram would have been closer to the theoretical probabilities.

The theoretical probabilities can be used to predict the outcome of an experiment. Note that the sum of the theoretical probabilities for two dice equals 1, because it is 100 percent certain to obtain a sum between 2 and 12. The sum of the probabilities corresponding to the outcomes 3, 4, and 5 is $2/36 + 3/36 + 4/36 = 1/4$. This result corresponds to a probability of 25 percent. Thus if you roll two dice many times, you would expect to obtain a sum of either 3, 4, or 5 twenty-five percent of the time.

In many applications the theoretical probabilities are not available because the underlying causes of the process are not understood well enough. In such applications you can use the histogram to make predictions. For example, if you did not have the theoretical probabilities for the sum of two dice, you could use the data to estimate the probability. Using the previously given data from 100 rolls, you can estimate the probability of obtaining a sum of either 3, 4, or 5 by summing the relative frequencies of these three outcomes. This sum is $(5 + 8 + 11)/100 = 0.24$, or 24 percent. Thus based on the data from 100 rolls, you can estimate that you would obtain a sum of either 3, 4, or 5 twenty-four percent of the time. The accuracy of the estimates so obtained is highly dependent on the number of trials used to collect the data; the more trials, the better. Many sophisticated statistical methods are available to assess the accuracy of such predictions; these methods are covered in advanced courses.

T7.1–2 If you roll a pair of balanced dice 200 times, how many times would you expect to obtain a sum of 7? How many times would you expect to obtain a sum of either 9, 10, or 11? How many times would you expect to obtain a sum less than 7?

(Answer: 33 times, 50 times, and 106 times.)

Rolling a die is an example of a process whose possible outcomes are a limited set of numbers; namely, the integers from 1 to 6. For such processes the probability is a function of a discrete-valued variable, that is, a variable having a limited number of values. For example, the following table gives the measured heights of 100 men 20 years of age. The heights were recorded to the nearest 1/2 inch, so the height variable is discrete valued.

Height (inches)	Frequency	Height (inches)	Frequency
64	1	70	9
64.5	0	70.5	8
65	0	71	7
65.5	0	71.5	5
66	2	72	4
66.5	4	72.5	4
67	5	73	3
67.5	4	73.5	1
68	8	74	1
68.5	11	74.5	0
69	12	75	1
69.5	10		

Scaled Frequency Histogram

You can plot the data as a histogram using either the absolute or relative frequencies. However, another useful histogram uses data scaled so that the total area under the histogram's rectangles is 1. This *scaled frequency histogram* is the absolute frequency histogram divided by the total area of that histogram. The area of each rectangle on the absolute frequency histogram equals the bin width times the absolute frequency for that bin. Because all the rectangles have the same width, the total area is the bin width times the sum of the absolute frequencies. The following M-file produces the scaled histogram shown in Figure 7.2–1.

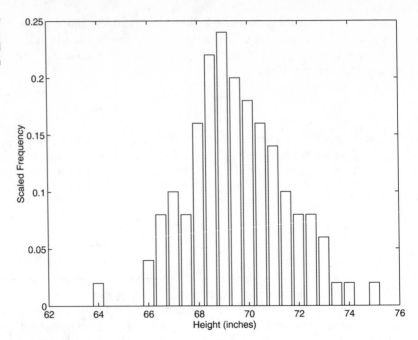

Figure 7.2-1
Scaled histogram of the height data.

```
% Absolute frequency data.
y_abs=[1,0,0,0,2,4,5,4,8,11,12,10,9,8,7,5,4,4,3,1,1,0,1];
binwidth=.5;
% Compute scaled frequency data.
area=binwidth*sum(y_abs);
y_scaled=y_abs/area;
% Define the bins.
bins=[64:binwidth:75];
% Plot the scaled histogram.
bar(bins,y_scaled),...
ylabel('Scaled Frequency'),xlabel('Height (inches)')
```

Because the total area under the scaled histogram is 1, the fractional area corresponding to a range of heights gives the probability that a randomly selected 20-year-old man will have a height in that range. For example, the heights of the scaled histogram rectangles corresponding to heights of 67 through 69 inches are 0.1, 0.08, 0.16, 0.22, and 0.24. Because the bin width is 0.5, the total area corresponding to these rectangles is $(0.1 + 0.08 + 0.16 + 0.22 + 0.24)(0.5) = 0.4$. Thus 40 percent of the heights lie between 67 and 69 inches.

Continuous Approximation to the Scaled Histogram

In the height data given previously, there was a limited number of possible outcomes because the heights were measured to within 1/2 inch. That is, if a particular man's height is between 66 and

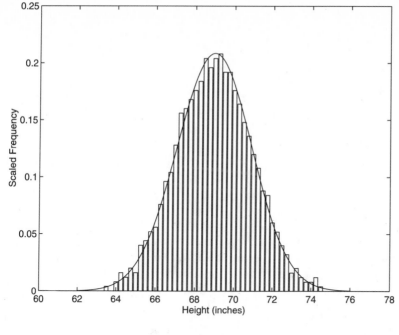

Figure 7.2–2
Scaled histogram of
height data for very many
measurements.

66.5, we would measure and record his height as either 66 or
66.5. The number of possible outcomes is doubled if we were
to measure the heights to within 1/4 inch. Other processes can
have an infinite set of possible outcomes. For example, you could
obtain an infinite number of possible height measurements in
the human population if you could measure a person's height to
enough decimal places. For example, an infinite number of values
exist between 66 inches and 66.5 inches.

Figure 7.2–2 shows the scaled histogram for very many height
measurements taken to within 1/4 inch. For many processes,
as we decrease the bin width and increase the number of measurements, the tops of the rectangles in the scaled histogram
often form a smooth bell-shaped curve such as the one shown in
Figure 7.2–2.

For processes having an infinite number of possible outcomes,
the probability is a function of a *continuous* variable and is plotted
as a curve rather than as rectangles. It is based on the same
concept as the scaled histogram; that is, the total area under
the curve is 1, and the fractional area gives the probability of
occurrence of a specific range of outcomes. A probability function
that describes many processes is the *normal* or *Gaussian* function, **NORMAL OR GAUSSIAN**
which is shown in Figure 7.2–3. This function is also known **FUNCTION**
as the "bell-shaped curve." Outcomes that can be described by
this function are said to be "normally distributed." The normal **NORMALLY DISTRIBUTED**
probability function is a two-parameter function; one parameter,
μ, is the mean of the outcomes, and the other parameter, σ, is
the *standard deviation*. The mean μ locates the peak of the curve **STANDARD DEVIATION**
and is the most likely value to occur. The width, or spread, of

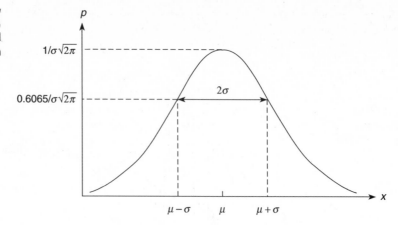

Figure 7.2–3
The basic shape of the
normal distribution curve.

VARIANCE

the curve is described by the parameter σ. Sometimes the term *variance* is used to describe the spread of the curve. The variance is the square of the standard deviation σ.

The normal probability function is described by the following equation:

$$p(x) = \frac{1}{\sigma\sqrt{2\pi}}e^{-(x-\mu)^2/2\sigma^2} \qquad (7.2\text{–}1)$$

Figure 7.2–4 is a plot of this function for three cases having the same mean, $\mu = 10$, but different standard deviations: $\sigma = 1, 2,$

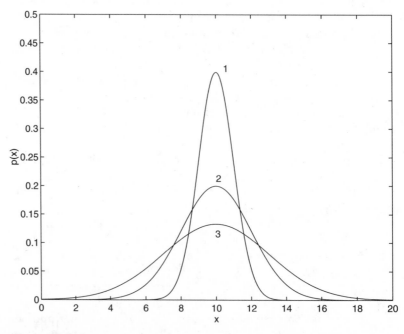

Figure 7.2–4
The effect on the normal distribution curve of increasing σ. For this case $\mu = 10$, and the three curves correspond to $\sigma = 1$, $\sigma = 2$, and $\sigma = 3$.

and 3. Note how the peak height decreases as σ is increased. The reason is that the area under the curve must equal 1 (because the value of the random variable x must certainly lie between $-\infty$ and $+\infty$).

Recall that the fractional area under a scaled histogram gives the probability that a range of outcomes will occur. The fractional area under a probability function curve also gives this probability. It can be shown that 68.3 percent, or approximately 68 percent, of the area lies between the limits of $\mu - \sigma \leq x \leq \mu + \sigma$. Consequently, if a variable is normally distributed, there is a 68 percent chance that a randomly selected sample will lie within one standard deviation of the mean. In addition, 95.5 percent, or approximately 96 percent, of the area lies between the limits of $\mu - 2\sigma \leq x \leq \mu + 2\sigma$, and 99.7 percent, or practically 100 percent, of the area lies between the limits of $\mu - 3\sigma \leq x \leq \mu + 3\sigma$. So there is a 96 percent chance that a randomly selected sample will lie within two standard deviations of the mean, and a 99.7 percent chance that a randomly selected sample will lie within three standard deviations of the mean. Figure 7.2–5 illustrates the areas

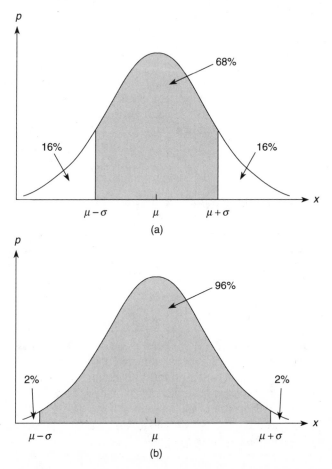

(a)

(b)

Figure 7.2–5
Probability interpretation of (a) the $\mu \pm \sigma$ and (b) the $\mu \pm 2\sigma$ limits.

Table 7.2–1 Mean and Standard Deviation Functions

Command	Description
mean(x)	Calculates the mean of the data stored in the vector x.
median(x)	Calculates the median of the data stored in the vector x.
std(x)	Uses equation (7.2–3) to calculate the standard deviation of the data stored in the vector x.

associated with the $\mu \pm \sigma$ and $\mu \pm 2\sigma$ limits. For example, if the variable is normally distributed with a mean equal to 20 and a standard deviation equal to 2, there is a 68 percent chance that a randomly selected sample will lie between 18 and 22, a 96 percent chance that it will lie between 16 and 24, and a 99.7 percent chance that it will lie between 14 and 26.

Estimating the Mean and Standard Deviation

In most applications you do not know the mean or variance of the distribution of possible outcomes, but must estimate them from experimental data. An estimate of the mean μ is denoted by $\bar{x}$ and is found in the same way you compute an average, namely,

$$\bar{x} = \frac{1}{n}(x_1 + x_2 + x_3 + \cdots + x_n) = \frac{1}{n}\sum_{i=1}^{n}x_i \qquad (7.2\text{–}2)$$

where the n data values are $x_1, x_2, \cdots, x_n$. The variance of a set of data values is the average of their squared deviations from their mean $\bar{x}$. Thus the standard deviation σ is computed from a set of n data values as follows:

$$\sigma = \sqrt{\frac{\sum_{i=1}^{n}(x_i - \bar{x})^2}{n-1}} \qquad (7.2\text{–}3)$$

You would expect that the divisor should be n rather than $n-1$. However, using $n-1$ gives a better estimate of the standard deviation when the number of data points n is small. The MATLAB function mean(x) uses (7.2–2) to calculate the mean of the data stored in the vector x. The function std(x) uses (7.2–3) to calculate the standard deviation. Table 7.2–1 summarizes these functions.

Example 7.2–1   Mean and standard deviation of heights
Statistical analysis of data on human proportions is required in many engineering applications. For example, designers of submarine crew quarters need to know how small they can make bunk lengths without eliminating a large percentage of prospective crew members. Use MATLAB to estimate the mean and standard deviation for the preceding height data.

Solution:

The script file follows. The data given in the table is the absolute frequency data and is stored in the vector y_abs. A bin width of 1/2 inch is used because the heights were measured to the nearest 1/2 inch. The vector bins contains the heights in 1/2 inch increments.

To compute the mean and standard deviation, reconstruct the original (raw) height data from the absolute frequency data. Note that this data has some zero entries. For example, none of the 100 men had a height of 65 inches. Thus to reconstruct the raw data, start with a null vector y_raw and fill it with the height data obtained from the absolute frequencies. The for loop checks to see whether the absolute frequency for a particular bin is nonzero. If it is nonzero, append the appropriate number of data values to the vector y_raw. If the particular bin frequency is 0, y_raw is left unchanged.

```
% Absolute frequency data.
y_abs=[1,0,0,0,2,4,5,4,8,11,12,10,9,8,7,5,4,4,3,1,1,0,1];
binwidth=.5;
% Define the bins.
bins=[64:binwidth:75];
% Fill the vector y_raw with the raw data.
% Start with a null vector.
y_raw=[];
for i=1:length(y_abs)
    if y_abs(i)>0
        new=bins(i)*ones(1,y_abs(i));
    else
        new=[];
    end
y_raw=[y_raw,new];
end
% Compute the mean and standard deviation.
mu=mean(y_raw),sigma=std(y_raw)
```

When you run this program, you will find that the mean is $\mu = 69.3$ inches and the standard deviation is $\sigma = 1.96$ inches.

As discussed earlier, you can use the 1σ, 2σ, and 3σ points to estimate the 68.3 percent, 95.5 percent, and 99.7 percent probabilities, respectively. Thus for the preceding height data, 68.3 percent of 20-year-old men will be between $\mu - \sigma = 67.3$ and $\mu + \sigma = 71.3$ inches tall.

If you need to compute the probability at other points, you can use the erf function. Typing erf(x) returns the area to the left of the value $t = x$ under the curve of the function $2e^{-t^2} / \sqrt{\pi}$. This area, which is a function of x, is known as the *error function*, and is written as erf(x). The probability that the random variable x is less than or equal to b is written as $P(x \leq b)$ if the outcomes are

ERROR FUNCTION

normally distributed. This probability can be computed from the error function as follows [Kreyzig, 1993]:

$$P(x \leq b) = \frac{1}{2}\left[1 + \mathrm{erf}\left(\frac{b - \mu}{\sigma \sqrt{2}}\right)\right] \qquad (7.2\text{--}4)$$

The probability that the random variable x is no less than a and no greater than b is written as $P(a \leq x \leq b)$. It can be computed as follows:

$$P(a \leq x \leq b) = \frac{1}{2}\left[\mathrm{erf}\left(\frac{b - \mu}{\sigma \sqrt{2}}\right) - \mathrm{erf}\left(\frac{a - \mu}{\sigma \sqrt{2}}\right)\right] \qquad (7.2\text{--}5)$$

These equations are useful for computing probabilities of outcomes for which the data is scarce or missing altogether.

Example 7.2–2   Estimation of height distribution

Use the results of Example 7.2–1 to estimate how many twenty-year old men are no taller than 68 inches. How many are within 3 inches of the mean?

Solution:

In Example 7.2–1 the mean and standard deviation were found to be $\mu = 69.3$ inches and $\sigma = 1.96$ inches. In the preceding table of heights, note that few data points are available for heights less than 68 inches. However, if you assume that the heights are normally distributed, you can use equation (7.2–4) to estimate how many men are shorter than 68 inches. Use (7.2–4) with $b = 68$; that is,

$$P(x \leq 68) = \frac{1}{2}\left[1 + \mathrm{erf}\left(\frac{68 - 69.3}{1.96 \sqrt{2}}\right)\right]$$

To determine how many men are within 3 inches of the mean, use (7.3–5) with $a = \mu - 3 = 66.3$ and $b = \mu + 3 = 72.3$; that is,

$$P(66.3 \leq x \leq 72.3) = \frac{1}{2}\left[\mathrm{erf}\left(\frac{3}{1.96 \sqrt{2}}\right) - \mathrm{erf}\left(\frac{-3}{1.96 \sqrt{2}}\right)\right]$$

In MATLAB these expressions are computed in a script file as follows:

```
mu=69.3;
sigma=1.96;
% How many are no taller than 68 inches?
b1=68;
P1=(1+erf((b1-mu)/(sigma*sqrt(2))))/2
% How many are within 3 inches of the mean?
a2=66.3;
b2=72.3;
P2=(erf((b2-mu)/(sigma*sqrt(2)))-erf((a2- mu)/(sigma*sqrt(2))))/2
```

When you run this program, you obtain the results P1 = 0.2536 and P2 = 0.8741. Thus 25 percent of twenty-year-old men are estimated to be 68 inches or less in height, and 87 percent are estimated to be between 66.3 and 72.3 inches tall.

Test Your Understanding

T7.2–1 Suppose that 10 more height measurements are obtained so that the following numbers must be *added* to the preceding height table.

Height (inches)	Additional data
64.5	1
65	2
66	1
67.5	2
70	2
73	1
74	1

(a) Plot the scaled frequency histogram. (b) Find the mean and standard deviation. (c) Use the mean and standard deviation to estimate how many 20-year-old men are no taller than 69 inches. (d) Estimate how many are between 68 and 72 inches tall.

(Answers: (b) mean = 69.4 inches, standard deviation = 2.14 inches; (c) 43 percent; (d) 63 percent)

Sums and Differences of Random Variables

It can be proved that the mean of the sum (or difference) of two independent normally distributed random variables equals the sum (or difference) of their means, but the variance is always the sum of the two variances. That is, if x and y are normally distributed with means μ_x and μ_y, and variances σ_x^2 and σ_y^2, and if $u = x + y$ and $v = x - y$, then

$$\mu_u = \mu_x + \mu_y \qquad (7.2\text{–}6)$$

$$\mu_v = \mu_x - \mu_y \qquad (7.2\text{–}7)$$

$$\sigma_u^2 = \sigma_v^2 = \sigma_x^2 + \sigma_y^2 \qquad (7.2\text{–}8)$$

These properties are applied in some of the homework problems.

Random Number Generation

We often do not have a simple probability distribution to describe the distribution of outcomes in many engineering applications. For example, the probability that a circuit consisting of many components will fail is a function of the number and the age of the components, but we often cannot obtain a function to describe the failure probability. In such cases engineers often resort to simulation to make predictions. The simulation program is executed many times, using a random set of numbers to represent the failure of one or more components, and the results are used to estimate the desired probability.

Uniformly Distributed Numbers

UNIFORMLY DISTRIBUTED In a sequence of *uniformly distributed* random numbers, all values within a given interval are equally likely to occur. The MATLAB function rand generates random numbers uniformly distributed over the interval [0,1]. Type rand to obtain a single random number in the interval [0, 1]. Typing rand again generates a different number because the MATLAB algorithm used for the rand function requires a "seed" value to start. MATLAB obtains this seed value from the computer's CPU clock. Thus every time the rand function is used, a different result will be obtained. For example,

```
rand
ans =
   0.6161
rand
ans =
   0.5184
```

Type rand(n) to obtain an $n \times n$ matrix of uniformly distributed random numbers in the interval [0, 1]. Type rand(m,n) to obtain an $m \times n$ matrix of random numbers. For example, to create a 1-×-100-row vector y having 100 random values in the interval [0, 1], type y = rand(1,100). Using the rand function this way is equivalent to typing rand 100 times. Even though there is a single call to the rand function, the rand function's calculation has the effect of using a different seed value to obtain each of the 100 numbers so that they will be random.

To generate the same sequence of random numbers so that you can compare the results of two or more simulations, you must use the same seed value. The seed value for the uniform number generator can be specified to be s by typing rand('seed',s). To obtain the current value of the seed, type rand('seed'). The rand function generates the same random value every time it is used with the same seed value. Table 7.3–1 summarizes these functions.

Table 7.3–1 Random Number Functions

Command	Description
rand	Generates a single uniformly distributed random number between 0 and 1.
rand(n)	Generates an $n \times n$ matrix containing uniformly distributed random numbers between 0 and 1.
rand(m,n)	Generates an $m \times n$ matrix containing uniformly distributed random numbers between 0 and 1.
rand('seed',s)	Sets the value of the seed of the uniformly-distributed random number generator to s.
rand('seed')	Returns the current value of the seed of the uniformly-distributed random number generator.
randn	Generates a single normally distributed random number having a mean of 0 and a standard deviation of 1.
randn(n)	Generates an $n \times n$ matrix containing normally distributed random numbers having a mean of 0 and a standard deviation of 1.
rand(m,n)	Generates an $m \times n$ matrix containing normally distributed random numbers having a mean of 0 and a standard deviation of 1.
randn('seed',s)	Sets the value of the seed of the normally-distributed random number generator to s.
randn('seed')	Returns the current value of the seed of the normally-distributed random number generator.

You can use the rand function to generate random numbers in an interval other than [0, 1]. For example, to generate values in the interval [2, 10], first generate a random number between 0 and 1, multiply it by 8 (the difference between the upper and lower bounds), and then add the lower bound (2). The result is a value that is uniformly distributed in the interval [2, 10]. The general formula for generating a uniformly distributed random number y in the interval $[a, b]$ is

$$y = (b - a)x + a \qquad \text{(7.3–1)}$$

where x is a random number uniformly distributed in the interval [0, 1]. For example, to generate a vector y containing 1000 uniformly distributed random numbers in the interval [2, 10], you type y = 8*rand(1,1000) + 2. You can check the results with the mean, min, and max functions. You should obtain values close to 6, 2, and 10, respectively.

Test Your Understanding

T7.3–1 Use MATLAB to generate a vector y containing 1500 uniformly distributed random numbers in the interval [-5, 15]. Check your results with the mean, min, and max functions.

Simulations Using Random Numbers

Simulations using random number generators can be used to analyze and find solutions to problems that are difficult or impossible to solve using standard mathematics. The following example illustrates this method.

321

Example 7.3–1   Optimal production quantity

You have recently taken a position as the engineer in charge of your company's seasonal product, which is manufactured during the off-season. You want to determine the optimum production level. If you can produce more units than you can sell, your profit will not be as large as it could be; if you produce too many units, the unsold units at the end of the season will hurt profits. A review of the company's records shows that the fixed cost of production is $30,000 per season, no matter how many units are made, and that it costs $2000 above the fixed cost to make one unit. In addition, past sales have fluctuated between 25 and 50 units per season, with no increasing or decreasing trend in the sales data. Your sales force estimates that you cannot raise the price above $4000 because of the competition.

Determine the optimal number of units to produce for each season. Assume a selling price of $4000 during the season. Assume also that at the end of the season all unsold units can be sold at $1000 each.

Solution:

Given that the previous sales were always between 25 and 50 units per season, with no trend in the data, the most reasonable model for the sales is a uniform distribution over the interval [25, 50]. In the following script file, the vector `cost` is the cost as a function of production level (the number of units produced). The loop over k computes the profit for each of the 26 production levels starting with 25 and ending with 50. The loop over m does a random number simulation to compute the profit for a particular production level. The variable `demand` represents the demand for the product; it is a uniformly distributed number in the interval [25, 50]. If the demand is greater than the number of units produced, then all the units will be sold and the income is $4000 times the number produced. If the demand is less than the number of units produced, then the income is $4000 times the number sold plus $1000 times the number unsold, which is the number produced minus the demand. For each random demand, the profit is computed as the difference between the income and the cost. This amount is the scalar `profit`. The cumulative profit `cum_profit` is the sum of profits for all the random simulations for a particular production level. The expected profit `expected_profit` for a particular production level is the profit for that level averaged over all the random simulations.

```
n = 5000; % number of random simulations
level = [25:50]; % initialize the production level vector
cost = 30000+2000*level;
for k = 1:26
    cum_profit = 0;
    for m = 1:n
        demand = floor(rand*(50-25)+26);
```

```
        if demand >= level(k)
            income = 4000*level(k);
        else
            income = 4000*demand+1000*(level(k)-demand);
        end
        profit = income-cost(k);
        cum_profit = cum_profit+profit;
    end
    expected_profit = cum_profit/n;
    p(k,1) = level(k);
    p(k,2) = expected_profit;
end
plot(p(:,1),p(:,2),'o',p(:,1),p(:,2),'-'),...
xlabel('No. of Units'),ylabel('Profit ($)')
```

The choice of 5000 simulations was a somewhat arbitrary compromise between accuracy and the amount of time required to do the calculations. The more simulations, the more accurate the results, but the program will take longer to finish. The results are shown in Figure 7.3–1. The maximum profit is attained for a production level in the range of 39 to 43 units per season. The profit is nearly $38,000 per season, which is much more than the profit obtained by a conservative production level of 25 units per season.

You should try different values of n and compare the results.

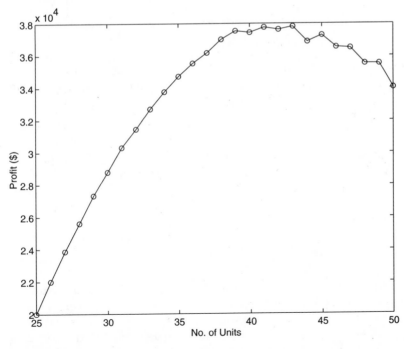

Figure 7.3–1
Profit versus quantity plot for 5000 simulations.

T7.3–2 In Example 7.3–1, what is the optimum production level and resulting profit if we sell unsold units at the end of the season at cost ($2000), instead of below cost?

(Answer: Optimum production level = 50 units per season; profit = $46,000.)

Normally Distributed Random Numbers

In a sequence of normally distributed random numbers, the values near the mean are more likely to occur. We have noted that the outcomes of many processes can be described by the normal distribution. Although a uniformly distributed random variable has definite upper and lower bounds, a normally distributed random variable does not.

The MATLAB function randn will generate a single number that is normally distributed with a mean equal to 0 and a standard deviation equal to 1. Type randn(n) to obtain an $n \times n$ matrix of such numbers. Type randn(m,n) to obtain an $m \times n$ matrix of random numbers. Type randn('seed') to obtain the current value of the seed for the normally distributed number generator. You can use the function randn('seed',s) to specify the seed for the generator. Table 7.3–1 summarizes these functions.

You can generate a sequence of normally distributed numbers having a mean μ and standard deviation σ from a normally distributed sequence having a mean of 0 and a standard deviation of 1. You do this by multiplying the values by σ and adding μ to each result. Thus if x is a random number with a mean of 0 and a standard deviation of 1, use the following equation to generate a new random number y having a standard deviation of σ and a mean of μ.

$$y = \sigma x + \mu \qquad (7.3\text{–}2)$$

For example, to generate a vector y containing 2000 random numbers normally distributed with a mean of 5 and a standard deviation of 3, you type y = 3*randn(1,2000) + 5. You can check the results with the mean and std functions. You should obtain values close to 5 and 3, respectively.

Test Your Understanding

T7.3–3 Use MATLAB to generate a vector y containing 1800 random numbers normally distributed with a mean of 7 and a standard deviation of 10. Check your results with the mean and std functions. Why can't you use the min and max functions to check your results?

Functions of random variables.

If y and x are linearly related, as

$$y = bx + c \qquad (7.3\text{--}3)$$

and if x is normally distributed with a mean μ_x and standard deviation σ_x, it can be shown that the mean and standard deviation of y are given by

$$\mu_y = b\mu_x + c \qquad (7.3\text{--}4)$$

$$\sigma_y = |b|\sigma_x \qquad (7.3\text{--}5)$$

However, it is easy to see that the means and standard deviations do not combine in a straightforward fashion when the variables are related by a nonlinear function. For example, if x is normally distributed with a mean of 0, and if $y = x^2$, it is easy to see that the mean of y is not 0, but is positive. In addition, y is not normally distributed.

Some advanced methods are available for deriving a formula for the mean and variance of $y = f(x)$, but for our purposes, the simplest way is to use random number simulation.

It was noted in the previous section that the mean of the sum (or difference) of two independent normally distributed random variables equals the sum (or difference) of their means, but the variance is always the sum of the two variances. However, if z is a nonlinear function of x and y, then the mean and variance of z cannot be found with a simple formula. In fact, the distribution of z will not even be normal. This outcome is illustrated by the following example.

Example 7.3–2 Statistical analysis and manufacturing tolerances
Suppose you must cut a triangular piece off the corner of a square plate by measuring the distances x and y from the corner (see Figure 7.3–2). The desired value of x is 10 inches, and the desired value of θ is 20°. This requires that $y = 3.64$

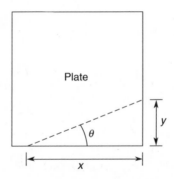

Plate

θ

y

x

Figure 7.3–2
Dimensions of a triangular cut.

inches. We are told that measurements of x and y are normally distributed with means of 10 and 3.64, respectively, with a standard deviation equal to 0.05 inch. Determine the standard deviation of θ and plot the relative frequency histogram for θ.

Solution:

From Figure 7.3–2, we see that the angle θ is determined by $\theta = \tan^{-1}(y/x)$. We can find the statistical distribution of θ by creating random variables x and y that have means of 10 and 3.64, respectively, with a standard deviation of 0.05. The random variable θ is then found by calculating $\theta = \tan^{-1}(y/x)$ for each random pair (x, y). The following script file shows this procedure.

```
s = .05; % standard deviation of x and y
n = 8000; % number of random simulations
x = 10+s*randn(1,n);
y = 3.64+s*randn(1,n);
theta = (180/pi)*atan(y./x);
mean_theta = mean(theta)
sigma_theta = std(theta)
xp = [19:.1:21];
z = hist(theta,xp);
yp = z/n;
bar(xp,yp),xlabel('Theta (degrees)'),ylabel('Relative Frequency')
```

The choice of 8000 simulations was a compromise between accuracy and the amount of time required to do the calculations. You should try different values of n and compare the results. The results gave a mean of 19.9993° for θ with a standard deviation of 0.2730°. The histogram is shown in Figure 7.3–3. Although the plot resembles

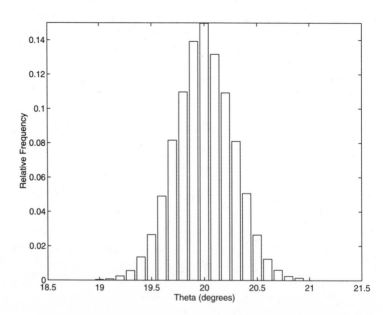

Figure 7.3–3
Scaled histogram of the
angle θ.

the normal distribution, the values of θ are not distributed normally. From the histogram we can calculate that approximately 65 percent of the values of θ lie between 19.8 and 20.2. This range corresponds to a standard deviation of 0.2°, not 0.273° as calculated from the simulation data. Thus the curve is not a normal distribution.

This example shows that the interaction of two of more normally distributed variables does not produce a result that is normally distributed. In general, the result is normally distributed if and only if the result is a linear combination of the variables.

We can distinguish between two types of analysis in experiments involving two variables, say, x and y. In the first type, called *correlation analysis*, both variables are random, and we are interested in finding the relation between them. An example is the analysis of the relation, if any, between the chemistry grades x and physics grades y of a group of students. We will not deal with correlation analysis in this text, because it is an advanced topic in statistics.

With the second type of analysis, called *regression analysis*, one of the variables, say, x, is regarded as an ordinary variable because we can measure it without error or assign it whatever values we want. The variable x is the *independent* or *controlled* variable. The variable y is a random variable. Regression analysis deals with the relationship between y and x. An example is the dependence of the outdoor temperature y on the time of day x.

REGRESSION ANALYSIS

In this section we use the MATLAB function `polyfit` to perform regression analysis with polynomials and other types of functions. The `polyfit` function is based on the least squares method, which we now discuss.

The Least Squares Method

In Chapter 5 (Example 5.4–1 on page 228) we found the coefficients of the straight line $y = mx + b$ that best fit the following data in the least squares sense.

x	y
0	2
5	6
10	11

According to the least squares criterion, the line that gives the best fit is the one that minimizes J, the sum of the squares of the vertical differences between the line and the data points (see Figure 7.4–1). These differences are called the *residuals*. Here there are three data points, and J is given by

RESIDUALS

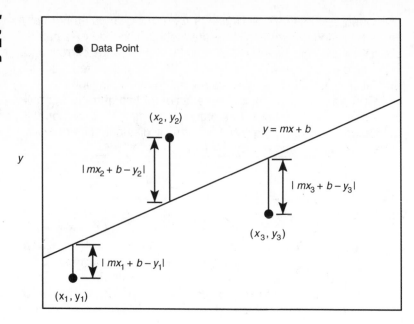

Figure 7.4–1
Illustration of the least
squares criterion.

$$J = \sum_{i=1}^{3} \left(m\,x_i + b - y_i\right)^2$$

Substituting the data values (x_i, y_i) given in the table, we obtain

$$J = (0m + b - 2)^2 + (5m + b - 6)^2 + (10m + b - 11)^2$$

The values of m and b that minimize J can be found from $\partial J/\partial m = 0$ and $\partial J/\partial b = 0$. These conditions give the following equations that must be solved for the two unknowns m and b.

$$250m + 30b = 280$$

$$30m + 6b = 38$$

The solution is $m = 0.9$ and $b = 11/6$. The best straight line in the least squares sense is $y = 0.9x + 11/6$. If we evaluate this equation at the data values $x = 0$, 5, and 10, we obtain the values $y = 1.833, 6.333, 10.8333$. These values are different from the given data values $y = 2$, 6, and 11 because the line is not a perfect fit to the data. The value of J is $J = (1.833 - 2)^2 + (6.333 - 6)^2 + (10.8333 - 11)^2 = 0.16656689$. No other straight line will give a lower value of J for this data. This line is shown in Figure 5.4–2 in Chapter 5.

Now suppose we want to fit a quadratic function $y = a_1x^2 + a_2x + a_3$ to a set of m data points. Then the expression for J is

$$J = \sum_{i=1}^{m} \left(a_1x_i^2 + a_2x_i + a_3 - y_i\right)^2$$

Using calculus (find the derivatives $\partial J/\partial a_1$, $\partial J/\partial a_2$, and $\partial J/\partial a_3$ and set them equal to 0), we can obtain the following equations that must be solved for a_1, a_2, and a_3:

$$a_1 \sum_{i=1}^{m} x_i^4 + a_2 \sum_{i=1}^{m} x_i^3 + a_3 \sum_{i=1}^{m} x_i^2 = \sum_{i=1}^{m} x_i^2 y_i$$

$$a_1 \sum_{i=1}^{m} x_i^3 + a_2 \sum_{i=1}^{m} x_i^2 + a_3 \sum_{i=1}^{m} x_i = \sum_{i=1}^{m} x_i y_i$$

$$a_1 \sum_{i=1}^{m} x_i^2 + a_2 \sum_{i=1}^{m} x_i + m\,a_3 = \sum_{i=1}^{m} y_i$$

These three linear equations are in terms of the three unknowns a_1, a_2, and a_3, and they can be solved easily in MATLAB.

In general, for the polynomial $a_1 x^n + a_2 x^{n-1} + \cdots + a_n x + a_{n+1}$, the sum of the squares of the residuals for m data points is

$$J = \sum_{i=1}^{m} \left(a_1 x^n + a_2 x^{n-1} + \cdots + a_n x + a_{n+1} - y_i \right)^2$$

The values of the $n+1$ coefficients a_i that minimize J can be found by solving a set of $n+1$ linear equations. The polyfit function provides this solution. Its syntax is p = polyfit(x,y,n). The function fits a polynomial of degree n to data described by the vectors x and y, where x is the independent variable. The result p is the row vector of length $n+1$ that contains the polynomial coefficients in order of descending powers. Table 7.4–1 summarizes the polyfit and polyval functions.

To illustrate the use of the polyfit function, consider the data set where $x = 1, 2, 3, \ldots, 9$ and $y = 5, 6, 10, 20, 28, 33, 34, 36, 42$. The following script file finds and plots the first- through fourth-degree polynomials for this data and evaluates J for each polynomial.

Table 7.4–1 Functions for polynomial regression

Command	Description
p = polyfit(x,y,n)	Fits a polynomial of degree n to data described by the vectors x and y, where x is the independent variable. Returns a row vector p of length $n+1$ that contains the polynomial coefficients in order of descending powers.
[p,s] = polyfit(x,y,n)	Fits a polynomial of degree n to data described by the vectors x and y, where x is the independent variable. Returns a row vector p of length $n+1$ that contains the polynomial coefficients in order of descending powers and a structure s for use with polyval to obtain error estimates for predictions (MATLAB 5 only).
[y,delta] = polyval(p,x,s)	Uses the optional output structure s generated by [p,s] = polyfit(x,y,n) to generate error estimates. If the errors in the data used with polyfit are independent and normally distributed with constant variance, at least 50 percent of the data will lie within the band $y \pm \textit{delta}$ (MATLAB 5 only).

```
x = [1:9];
y = [5,6,10,20,28,33,34,36,42];
xp = [1:.01:9];
for k = 1:4
    yp(k,:) = polyval(polyfit(x,y,k),xp);
    J(k) = sum((polyval(polyfit(x,y,k),x)-y).^2);
end
subplot(2,2,1)
plot(xp,yp(1,:),x,y,'o'),axis([0 10 0 50])
subplot(2,2,2)
plot(xp,yp(2,:),x,y,'o'),axis([0 10 0 50])
subplot(2,2,3)
plot(xp,yp(3,:),x,y,'o'),axis([0 10 0 50])
subplot(2,2,4)
plot(xp,yp(4,:),x,y,'o'),axis([0 10 0 50])
disp(J)
```

The plots are shown in Figure 7.4–2, and the J values are, to two significant figures, 72, 57, 42, and 4.7. Thus the value of J decreases as the polynomial degree is increased, as we would expect. The figure shows why the fourth-degree polynomial can fit the data better than the lower-degree polynomials. Because it has more coefficients, the fourth-degree polynomial can follow the "bends" in the data more easily than the other polynomials can.

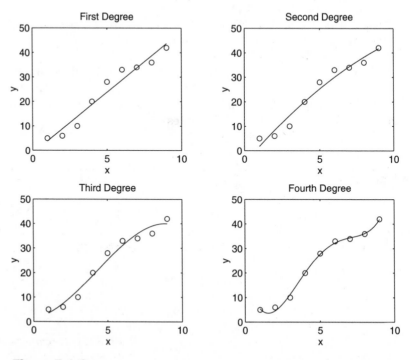

Figure 7.4–2
Regression using polynomials of first through fourth degree.

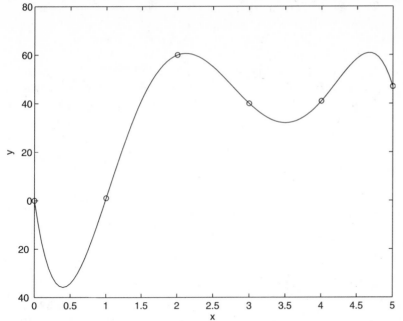

Figure 7.4–3
An example of a fifth-degree polynomial that passes through all six data points but exhibits large excursions between points.

The first-degree polynomial (a straight line) cannot bend at all, the quadratic polynomial has one bend, the cubic has two bends, and the quartic has three bends.

The polynomial coefficients in the preceding script file are contained in the vector `polyfit(x,y,k)`. If you need the polynomial coefficients, say, for the cubic polynomial, type `polyfit(x,y,3)` after the program has been run. The result is -0.1019, 1.3081, 0.7433, and 1.5556. These values correspond to the polynomial $-0.1019x^3 + 1.3081x^2 + 0.7433x + 1.5556$.

It is tempting to use a high-degree polynomial to obtain the best possible fit. However, there are two dangers in using high-degree polynomials. Figure 7.4–3 illustrates one of these dangers. The data is $x = 0, 1, \ldots, 5$, and $y = 0, 1, 60, 40, 41$, and 47. Because there are six data points, a fifth-degree polynomial (which has six coefficients) can be found that passes through all six points and thus its J value will be 0. This polynomial, which can be found using the `polyfit` function, is plotted in Figure 7.4–3 along with the data. Note how the polynomial makes large excursions between the first and the last pairs of data points. Thus we could get large errors if we were to use this polynomial to estimate y values for $0 < x < 1$ and for $4 < x < 5$. High-degree polynomials often exhibit large excursions between the data points and thus should be avoided if possible.

The second danger with using high-degree polynomials is that they can produce large errors if their coefficients are not represented with a large number of significant figures. We examine this issue later in this section.

In some cases it might not be possible to fit the data with a low-degree polynomial. In such cases we might be able to use several cubic polynomials. This method, called cubic splines, is covered in the next section.

Test Your Understanding

T7.4–1 Obtain and plot the first-through fourth-degree polynomials for the data given above; namely, $x = 0, 1, \ldots, 5$ and $y = 0, 1, 60, 40, 41$, and 47. Find the coefficients and the J values.

(Answer: The polynomials are $9.5714x + 7.5714$; $-3.6964x^2 + 28.0536x - 4.7500$; $0.3241x^3 - 6.1270x^2 + 32.4934x - 5.7222$; and $2.5208x^4 - 24.8843x^3 + 71.2986x^2 - 39.5304x - 1.4008$. The corresponding J values are 1534, 1024, 1017, and 495, respectively.)

Fitting Other Functions

In Chapter 4 (section 4.4) we used the `polyfit` function to fit power and exponential functions. We found the power function $y = bx^m$ that fits the data by typing `p = polyfit(log10(x), log10(y),1)`. The first element p_1 of the vector `p` will be m, and the second element p_2 will be $\log_{10} b$. We can find b from $b = 10^{p_2}$. We can find the exponential function $y = b(10)^{mx}$ that fits the data by typing `p = polyfit(x,log10(y),1)`. The first element p_1 of the vector `p` will be m, and the second element p_2 will be $\log_{10} b$. We can find b from $b = 10^{p_2}$.

Any function is a candidate for fitting data. However, it might be difficult to obtain and solve equations for the function's coefficients. Polynomials are used because their curves can take on many shapes and because they result in a set of linear equations that can be easily solved for the coefficients. As we have just seen, that power and exponential functions can be converted to first-degree polynomials by logarithmic transformations. Other functions can be converted to polynomials by suitable transformations.

Given the data (y, z), the logarithmic function

$$y = m \ln(z) + b$$

can be converted to a first-degree polynomial by transforming the z values into x values by the transformation $x = \ln(z)$. The resulting function is $y = mx + b$.

Given the data (y, z), the function

$$y = b(10)^{m/z}$$

can be converted to an exponential function by transforming the z values by the transformation $x = 1/z$. In MATLAB we can type `p = polyfit(1./z,log10(y),1)`. The first element p_1 of the vector `p` will be m, and the second element p_2 will be $\log_{10} b$. We can find b from $b = 10^{p_2}$.

Given the data (v, x), the function

$$v = \frac{1}{mx + b}$$

can be converted to a first-degree polynomial by transforming the v data values with the transformation $y = 1/v$. The resulting function is $y = mx + b$.

The Quality of a Curve Fit

In general, if the arbitrary function $y = f(x)$ is used to represent the data, then the error in the representation is given by $e_i = f(x_i) - y_i$, for $i = 1, 2, 3, \ldots, m$. The error (or residual) e_i is the difference between the data value y_i and the value of y obtained from the function, that is, $f(x_i)$. The least squares criterion used to fit a function $f(x)$ is the sum of the squares of the residuals J. It is defined as

$$J = \sum_{i=1}^{m} \left[f(x_i) - y_i \right]^2 \qquad \text{(7.4–1)}$$

We can use this criterion to compare the quality of the curve fit for two or more functions used to describe the same data. The function that gives the smallest J value gives the best fit.

We denote the sum of the squares of the deviation of the y values from their mean $\bar{y}$ by S, which can be computed from

$$S = \sum_{i=1}^{m} (y_i - \bar{y})^2 \qquad \text{(7.4–2)}$$

This formula can be used to compute another measure of the quality of the curve fit, the *coefficient of determination,* also known as the *r-squared value.* It is defined as

COEFFICIENT OF DETERMINATION

$$r^2 = 1 - \frac{J}{S} \qquad \text{(7.4–3)}$$

For a perfect fit, $J = 0$ and thus $r^2 = 1$. Thus the closer r^2 is to 1, the better the fit. The largest r^2 can be is 1. The value of S indicates how much the data is spread around the mean, and the value of J indicates how much of the data spread is unaccounted for by the model. Thus the ratio J/S indicates the fractional variation unaccounted for by the model. It is possible for J to be larger than S, and thus it is possible for r^2 to be negative. Such cases, however, are indicative of a very poor model that should not be used. As a rule of thumb, a good fit accounts for at least 99 percent of the data variation. This value corresponds to $r^2 \geq 0.99$.

For example, the following table gives the values of J, S, and r^2 for the first- through fourth-degree polynomials used above to fit the data $x = 1, 2, 3, \ldots, 9$ and $y = 5, 6, 10, 20, 28, 33, 34, 36, 42$.

Degree n	J	S	r^2
1	72	1490	0.952
2	57	1505	0.962
3	42	1520	0.972
4	4.7	1557	0.997

Because the fourth-degree polynomial has the largest r^2 value, it represents the data better than the representation from first- through third-degree polynomials, according to the r^2 criterion.

To calculate the values of S and r^2, add the following lines to the end of the script file shown on page 330.

```
mu = mean(y);
for k=1:4
    S(k) = sum((polyval(polyfit(x,y,k),x)- mu).^2);
    r2(k) = 1-J(k)/S(k);
end
S
r2
```

Regression and Numerical Accuracy

We mentioned that there are two dangers in using high-degree polynomials. The first danger is that high-degree polynomials often exhibit large excursions between the data points, and thus we could get large errors if we were to use a high-degree polynomial to estimate y values between the data points.

The second danger with using high-degree polynomials is that their coefficients often require a large number of significant figures to be represented accurately. Thus if you calculate these coefficients using the `polyfit` function and you intend to include these coefficients in a report for example, then you should display them with the `format long` or `format long e` commands. As an example, consider the data:

x	y	x	y	x	y
0	0.1	14	2.022	28	0.4308
2	1.884	16	1.65	30	0.203
4	2.732	18	1.5838	32	0.1652
6	3.388	20	1.35	34	-0.073
8	3.346	22	1.0082	36	-0.002
10	3	24	0.718	38	-0.1122
12	2.644	26	0.689	40	0.106

Using the `format long` command, a sixth-degree polynomial fit, `polyfit(x,y,6)`, gives the result

$$y = -2.217184 \times 10^{-8}x^6 + 3.99755011 \times 10^{-6}x^5$$

$$- 2.7743377123 \times 10^{-4}x^4 + 9.54858210731 \times 10^{-3}x^3$$

$$- 0.16883241225688x^2 + 1.27261806145996x$$

$$- 0.05640333772511 \qquad \textbf{(7.4-4)}$$

It is plotted along with the data in the top graph in Figure 7.4–4. The J and r^2 values are $J = 0.1859$ and $r^2 = 0.9935$.

Now suppose we keep only the first eight decimal places of the coefficients. The resulting polynomial is

$$y = -2 \times 10^{-8}x^6 + 4 \times 10^{-6}x^5$$

$$- 2.7743 \times 10^{-4}x^4 + 9.54858 \times 10^{-3}x^3$$

$$- 0.16883241x^2 + 1.27261806x - 0.05640334 \quad \textbf{(7.4-5)}$$

This polynomial is plotted in the bottom graph of Figure 7.4–4. Obviously, the polynomial deviates greatly from the data for

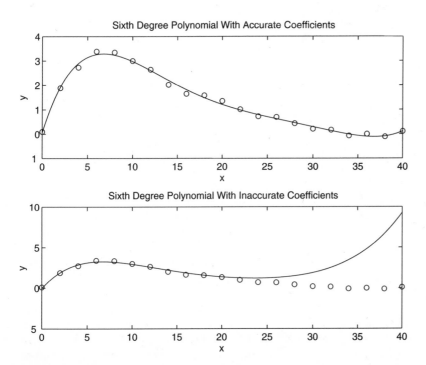

Figure 7.4–4
Effect of coefficient accuracy on a sixth-degree polynomial. The top graph shows the effect of 14 decimal-place accuracy. The bottom graph shows the effect of 8 decimal-place accuracy.

the larger values of x. The J and r^2 values are $J = 176.5$ and $r^2 = -0.351$. The negative value of r^2 indicates that the fit is so poor as to be useless. Polynomials whose coefficients have not been specified accurately enough are prone to large errors at large values of x.

High-degree polynomials have coefficients that not only must be displayed and stored with great accuracy but also are harder to compute accurately. As the polynomial degree increases, the number of linear equations to be solved also increases, and inaccuracies in the numerical solution of these equations become more significant.

An alternative to using a high-degree polynomial is to fit two or more functions to the data. To illustrate this approach, we will fit two cubics because a cubic has greater flexibility than a quadratic but is less susceptible to numerical inaccuracies than higher-degree polynomials. Examining the data plot in Figure 7.4–4, we see that the data has a bend near $x = 5$ and another bend near $x = 38$. The transition between the convex and concave parts of the data appears to be around $x = 15$. Thus we will fit one cubic over $0 \le x \le 15$ and another over $15 < x \le 40$. The necessary script file follows.

```
x1 = [0:2:14];x2 = [16:2:40]
y1 = [0.1, 1.884, 2.732, 3.388, 3.346, 3, 2.644, 2.022]
y2 = [1.65, 1.5838, 1.35, 1.0082, 0.718, 0.689, 0.4308,
0.203, 0.1652, -0.073, -0.002, -0.1122, 0.106]
x = [x1,x2];
y = [y1,y2];
% Create variables z1 and z2 to generate the curve.
z1 = [0:.01:15]; z2=[15:.01:40];
% Fit two cubics.
w1 = polyfit(x1,y1,3);
w2 = polyfit(x2,y2,3);
% Plot the results.
plot(z1,polyval(w1,z1),z2,polyval(w2,z2),x,y,'o'),...
xlabel('x'),ylabel('y')
% Compute the coefficient of determination.
mu1 = mean(y1);
mu2 = mean(y2);
S = sum((polyval(w1,x1)-mu1).^2) + sum((polyval(w2,x2)-mu2).^2)
J = sum((polyval(w1,x1)-y1).^2) + sum((polyval(w2,x2)-y2).^2)
r2 = 1-J/S
```

The values are $S = 12.7749$, $J = 0.0868$, and $r^2 = 0.9932$, which indicates a very good fit. The plot is shown in Figure 7.4–5. The curves are not tangent, but they need not be for this example. However, some applications require the curves to be tangent, and in the next section we develop a method for fitting cubics that are tangent. Here we estimated the transition point $x = 15$ at which

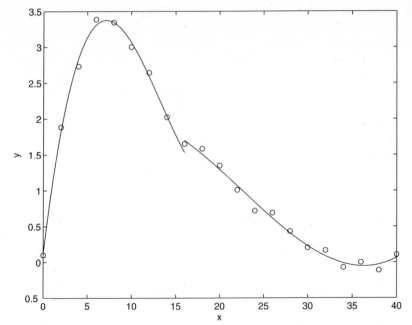

Figure 7.4–5
Use of two cubics to fit data.

to separate the two cubics. You can experiment with other values to improve the fit, although the fit we achieved is very good.

If we want to estimate a value of y for $0 \leq x \leq 15$, we use the first cubic, which is found from w1 and is

$$y = 0.00249494949495x^3 - 0.09924512987013x^2$$

$$+ 1.03759920634921x + 0.11742424242424$$

To estimate a value of y for $15 < x \leq 40$, we use the second cubic, which is found from w2 and is

$$y = 0.00020364219114x^3 - 0.01381168831169x^2$$

$$+ 0.19723598068598x + 1.24452447552445$$

Note that MATLAB reports the coefficients to 14 decimal places.

To demonstrate the robustness of the cubic polynomials, their coefficients were rounded off to eight decimal places. For these rounded coefficients, $S = 12.7754$, $J = 0.0868$, and $r^2 = 0.9932$; these values are identical to the results obtained with the more accurate coefficients.

Scaling the data: The effect of computational inaccuracies in computing the coefficients can be lessened by properly scaling the data so that the x and y data values do not differ by several orders of magnitude. For example, suppose you have the following sales data in millions of dollars for the years 1980 through 1989: 2.1, 3.4, 2.5, 5.3, 6.2, 4.7, 3.7, 6.1, 5.8, 4.7. You should not attempt to fit the data using the values $x = 1980, 1981, \ldots, 1989$ and $y = 2.1, 3.4, 2.5, 5.3, 6.2, 4.7, 3.7, 6.1, 5.8, 4.7$, because the x and y values differ by factors of almost 1000. Instead, you should subtract 1980 from the years and use the array $x = [0:9]$ to represent the years starting at 1980. Scaling the data becomes important for higher-degree polynomials and for problems involving many data points.

Constraining Models to Pass through a Given Point

Many applications require a model whose form is dictated by physical principles. For example, the force-extension model of a spring must pass through the origin $(0, 0)$ because the spring exerts no force when it is unstretched. Thus a linear spring model $f = a_1x + a_2$ must have a zero value for a_2. However, in general the polyfit function will give a nonzero value for a_2 because of the scatter or measurement error that is usually present in the data.

To obtain a zero-intercept model of the form $y = a_1x$, we must derive the equation for a_1 from basic principles. The sum of the squared residuals in this case is

$$J = \sum_{i=1}^{m} (a_1x_i - y_i)^2$$

Computing the derivative $\partial J / \partial a_1$ and setting it equal to 0 gives the result

$$a_1 \sum_{i=1}^{m} x_i^2 = \sum_{i=1}^{m} x_i y_i \qquad (7.4\text{--}6)$$

which can be easily solved for a_1.

For the quadratic model, $y = a_1x^2 + a_2x + a_3$, the coefficient a_3 must be 0 for the curve to pass through the origin. The sum of the squared residuals in this case is

$$J = \sum_{i=1}^{m} \left(a_1x_i^2 + a_2x_i - y_i \right)^2$$

Computing the derivatives $\partial J / \partial a_1$ and $\partial J / \partial a_2$ and setting them equal to 0 gives the equations:

$$a_1 \sum_{i=1}^{m} x_i^4 + a_2 \sum_{i=1}^{m} x_i^3 = \sum_{i=1}^{m} y_i x_i^2 \qquad (7.4\text{--}7)$$

$$a_1 \sum_{i=1}^{m} x_i^3 + a_2 \sum_{i=1}^{m} x_i^2 = \sum_{i=1}^{m} y_i x_i \qquad (7.4\text{--}8)$$

These can be solved for a_1 and a_2.

If the model is required to pass through a point not at the origin, say the point (x_0, y_0), subtract x_0 from all the x values, subtract y_0 from all the y values, and then use the above equations to find the coefficients. The resulting equations will be of the form

$$y = a_1(x - x_0) + y_0 \qquad \text{(7.4–9)}$$

and

$$y = a_1(x - x_0)^2 + a_2(x - x_0) + y_0 \qquad \text{(7.4–10)}$$

You can derive equations for other functions in a similar manner.

Multiple Linear Regression

Suppose that y is a linear function of two or more variables, x_1, x_2, ... For example,

$$y = a_0 + a_1 x_1 + a_2 x_2 \qquad \text{(7.4–11)}$$

To find the coefficient values a_0, a_1, and a_2 to fit a set of data (y, x_1, x_2) in the least squares sense, we can make use of the fact that the left-division method for solving linear equations uses the least squares method when the equation set is overdetermined (see Chapter 5, section 5.4). To use this method, let n be the number of data points and write the linear equation in matrix form as follows.

$$\mathbf{Xa} = \mathbf{y} \qquad \text{(7.4–12)}$$

where

$$\mathbf{a} = \begin{bmatrix} a_0 \\ a_1 \\ a_2 \end{bmatrix} \qquad \text{(7.4–13)}$$

$$\mathbf{X} = \begin{bmatrix} 1 & x_{11} & x_{21} \\ 1 & x_{12} & x_{22} \\ 1 & x_{13} & x_{23} \\ & \cdots & \\ 1 & x_{1n} & x_{2n} \end{bmatrix} \qquad \text{(7.4–14)}$$

$$\mathbf{y} = \begin{bmatrix} y_1 \\ y_2 \\ y_3 \\ \cdots \\ y_n \end{bmatrix} \qquad \text{(7.4–15)}$$

where x_{1i}, x_{2i}, and y_i are the data, $i = 1, \ldots, n$. The solution for the coefficients is given by $a = X \backslash y$.

Example 7.4–1 Breaking strength and alloy composition
The tension force y required to break a steel bar is a function of the percentage x_1 and x_2 of each of two alloying

elements present in the metal. The following table gives some pertinent data. Obtain a linear model $y = a_0 + a_1 x_1 + a_2 x_2$ to describe the relationship.

Breaking strength (kN) y	% of element 1 x_1	% of element 2 x_2
7.1	0	5
19.2	1	7
31	2	8
45	3	11

Solution:

The script file is as follows:

```
x1=[0:3]';x2=[5,7,8,11]';
y=[7.1,19.2,31,45]';
X=[ones(size(x1)) x1 x2];
a=X\y
yp=X*a;
Max_Percent_Error=100*max(abs((yp-y)./y))
```

The vector `yp` is the vector of breaking-strength values predicted by the model. The scalar `Max_Percent_Error` is the maximum percent error in the four predictions. The results are a = [0.8000, 10.2429, 1.2143]' and `Max_Percent_Error` = 3.2193. Thus the model is $y = 0.8 + 10.2429 x_1 + 1.2143 x_2$. The maximum percent error of the model's predictions, as compared to the given data, is 3.2193 percent.

7.5

Interpolation

INTERPOLATION

Engineering problems often require the analysis of data pairs. For example, the paired data might represent a *cause and effect*, or *input-output relationship*, such as the current produced in a resistor as a result of an applied voltage, or a *time history*, such as the temperature of an object as a function of time. Another type of paired data represents a *profile*, such as a road profile (which shows the height of the road along its length). In some applications we want to estimate a variable's value between the data points. This process is called *interpolation*. In other cases we might need to estimate the variable's value outside of the given data range. This process is *extrapolation*. Interpolation and extrapolation are greatly aided by plotting the data. Such plots, some perhaps using logarithmic axes, often help to discover a functional description of the data.

Suppose that x represents the independent variable in the data (such as the applied voltage in the preceding example), and y represents the dependent variable (such as the resistor current). In some applications the data set will contain only one value of y for each value of x. In other cases there will be several measured values of y for a particular value of x. This condition is called *data scatter*. For example, suppose we apply 10 volts to a resistor, and measure 3.1 ma of current. Then, repeating the experiment, suppose we measure 3.3 ma the second time. If we average the two results, the resulting data point will be $x = 10$ V, $y = 3.2$ ma, which is an example of *aggregating* the data. In this section we assume that the data have been aggregated if necessary, so only one value of y corresponds to a specific value of x. You can use the methods of sections 7.1 and 7.2 to aggregate the data by computing its mean. The data's standard deviation indicates how much the data is spread around the aggregated point.

Suppose we have the following temperature measurements, taken once an hour starting at 7:00 A.M. The measurements at 8 A.M. and 10 A.M. are missing for some reason, perhaps because of equipment malfunction.

Time	7 A.M.	9 A.M.	11 A.M.	12 noon
Temperature (°F)	49	57	71	75

A plot of this data is shown in Figure 7.5–1 with the data point connected by dashed lines. If we need to estimate the temperature

Figure 7.5–1
A plot of temperature data versus time.

at 10 A.M., we can read the value from the dashed line that connects the data points at 9 A.M. and 11 A.M.. From the plot we thus estimate the temperature at 8 A.M. to be 53° F and at 10 A.M. to be 64° F. We have just performed *linear interpolation* on the data to obtain an *estimate* of the missing data. Linear interpolation is so named because it is equivalent to connecting the data points with a linear function (a straight line).

Of course we have no reason to believe that the temperature follows the straight lines shown in the plot, and our estimate of 64° F will most likely be incorrect, but it might be close enough to be useful. When using interpolation, we must always keep in mind that our results will be approximate and should be used with caution. In general, the more closely spaced the data, the more accurate the interpolation. Plotting the data sometimes helps to judge the accuracy of the interpolation.

Using straight lines to connect the data points is the simplest form of interpolation. Another function could be used if we have a good reason to do so. In the next section we use polynomial functions to do the interpolation.

Linear interpolation in MATLAB is obtained with the `interp1` and `interp2` functions. Suppose that `x` is a vector containing the independent variable data and that `y` is a vector containing the dependent variable data. If `x_int` is a vector containing the value or values of the independent variable at which we wish to estimate the dependent variable, then typing `interp1(x,y,x_int)` produces a vector the same size as `x_int` containing the interpolated values of `y` that correspond to `x_int`. For example, the following session produces an estimate of the temperatures at 8 A.M. and 10 A.M. from the preceding data. The vectors `x` and `y` contain the times and temperatures, respectively.

```
≫x = [7, 9, 11, 12];
≫y = [49, 57, 71, 75];
≫x_int = [8, 10];
≫interp1(x,y,x_int)
 ans =
    53
    64
```

You must keep in mind two restrictions when using the `interp1` function. The values of the independent variable in the vector `x` must be in ascending order, and the values in the interpolation vector `x_int` must lie within the range of the values in `x`. Thus we cannot use the `interp1` function to estimate the temperature at 6 A.M., for example.

The `interp1` function can be used to interpolate in a table of values by defining `y` to be a matrix instead of a vector. For example, suppose we now have temperature measurements at three locations and that the measurements at 8 A.M. and 10 A.M. are missing for all three locations. The data is

Time	Temperatures (° F)		
	Location 1	Location 2	Location 3
7 A.M.	49	52	54
9 A.M.	57	60	61
11 A.M.	71	73	75
12 noon	75	79	81

We define x as before, but now we define y to be a matrix whose three columns contain the second, third, and fourth columns of the preceding table. The following session produces an estimate of the temperatures at 8 A.M. and 10 A.M. at each location.

```
≫x = [7, 9, 11, 12]';
≫y(:,1) = [49, 57, 71, 75]';
≫y(:,2) = [52, 60, 73, 79]';
≫y(:,3) = [54, 61, 75, 81]';
≫x_int = [8, 10]';
≫interp1(x,y,x_int)
 ans =
     53.0000      56.0000      57.5000
     64.0000      65.5000      68.0000
```

Thus the estimated temperatures at 8 A.M. at each location are 53, 56, and 57.5° F, respectively. At 10 A.M. the estimated temperatures are 64, 65.5, and 68. From this example we see that if the first argument x in the interp1(x,y,x_int) function is a *vector* and the second argument y is a *matrix*, the function interpolates between the rows of y and computes a matrix having the same number of columns as y and the same number of rows as the number of values in x_int.

Note that we need not define two separate vectors x and y. Rather, we can define a single matrix that contains the entire table. For example, by defining the matrix temp to be the preceding table, the session would look like this:

```
≫temp(:,1) = [7, 9, 11, 12]';
≫temp(:,2) = [49, 57, 71, 75]';
≫temp(:,3) = [52, 60, 73, 79]';
≫temp(:,4) = [54, 61, 75, 81]';
≫x_int = [8, 10]';
≫interp1(temp(:,1),temp(:,2:4),x_int)
 ans =
     53.0000      56.0000      57.5000
     64.0000      65.5000      68.0000
```

Figure 7.5–2
Temperature measurements
at four locations.

2-D Interpolation

Now suppose that we have temperature measurements at four locations at 7 A.M.. These locations are at the corners of a rectangle 1 mile wide and 2 miles long. Assigning a coordinate system origin $(0, 0)$ to the first location, the coordinates of the other locations are $(1, 0), (1, 2)$, and $(0, 2)$; see Figure 7.5–2. The temperature measurements are shown in the figure. The temperature is a function of two variables, the coordinates x and y. MATLAB provides the interp2 function to interpolate functions of two variables. If the function is written as $z = f(x, y)$ and we wish to estimate the value of z for $x = x_i$ and $y = y_i$, the syntax is interp2(x,y,z,x_i,y_i).

Suppose we want to estimate the temperature at the point whose coordinates are $(0.6, 1.5)$. Put the x coordinates in the vector x and the y coordinates in the vector y. Then put the temperature measurements in a matrix z such that going across a row represents an increase in x and going down a column represents an increase in y. The session to do this is as follows:

```
≫x=[0,1];
≫y=[0,2];
≫z=[49,54;53,57]
  z =
    49     54
    53     57
≫interp2(x,y,z,.6,1.5)
  ans =
      54.5500
```

Thus the estimated temperature is 54.55°.

Table 7.5–1 Linear interpolation commands

Command	Description
y_int=interp1(x,y,x_int)	Used to linearly interpolate a function of one variable: $y = f(x)$. Returns a linearly interpolated vector y_int at the specified value x_int, using data stored in x and y.
z_int=interp2(x,y,z,x_,y_int)	Used to linearly interpolate a function of two variables: $y = f(x, y)$. Returns a linearly interpolated vector z_int at the specified values x_int and y_int, using data stored in x, y, and z.

The syntax of the interp1 and interp2 functions is summarized in Table 7.5–1. MATLAB 5 also provides the interpn function for interpolating multidimensional arrays.

Cubic-Spline Interpolation

We have seen that the use of high-order polynomials can exhibit undesired behavior between the data points, and this behavior can make high-order polynomials unsuitable for interpolation. An alternative procedure that is widely used is to fit the data points using a lower-order polynomial between *each pair* of adjacent data points. This method is called *spline* interpolation and is so named for the splines used by illustrators to draw a smooth curve through a set of points. Such a device can be constructed from a length of lead coated with rubber or flexible plastic. It can be bent to provide a drawing guide passing through the data points.

Spline interpolation obtains an exact fit that is also smooth. The most common procedure uses cubic polynomials, called *cubic splines*, and thus is called *cubic-spline interpolation*. If the data is given as n pairs of (x, y) values, then $n - 1$ cubic polynomials are used. Each has the form

$$y_i(x) = a_i(x - x_i)^3 + b_i(x - x_i)^2 + c_i(x - x_i) + d_i$$

for $x_i \leq x \leq x_{i+1}$ and $i = 1, 2, \ldots, n - 1$. The coefficients a_i, b_i, c_i, and d_i for each polynomial are determined so that the following three conditions are satisfied for each polynomial:

1. The polynomial must pass through the data points at its endpoints at x_i and x_{i+1}.
2. The slopes of adjacent polynomials must be equal at their common data point and
3. The curvatures of adjacent polynomials must be equal at their common data point.

CUBIC SPLINES

For example, a set of cubic splines for the temperature data given earlier follows (y represents the temperature values, and x represents the hourly values). The data is repeated here.

x	7	9	11	12
y	49	57	71	75

We will shortly see how to use MATLAB to obtain these polynomials. For $7 \leq x \leq 9$,

$$y_1(x) = -0.35(x-7)^3 + 2.85(x-7)^2 - 0.3(x-7) + 49$$

For $9 \leq x \leq 11$,

$$y_2(x) = -0.35(x-9)^3 + 0.75(x-9)^2 + 6.9(x-9) + 57$$

For $11 \leq x \leq 12$,

$$y_3(x) = -0.35(x-11)^3 - 1.35(x-11)^2 + 5.7(x-11) + 71$$

MATLAB provides the `spline` command to obtain a cubic-spline interpolation. Its syntax is `y_int = spline(x,y,x_int)`, where `x` and `y` are vectors containing the data and `x_int` is a vector containing the values of the independent variable x at which we wish to estimate the dependent variable y. The result `y_int` is a vector the same size as `x_int` containing the interpolated values of y that correspond to `x_int`. The spline fit can be plotted by plotting the vectors `x_int` and `y_int`. For example, the following session produces and plots a cubic spline fit to the preceding data, using an increment of 0.01 in the x values.

```
>>x=[7,9,11,12];
>>y=[49,57,71,75];
>>x_int=[7:.01:12];
>>y_int=spline(x,y,x_int);
>>plot(x,y,'o',x,y,'-- ',x_int,y_int),...
xlabel('Time (hrs)'),ylabel('Temperature (deg F)',...
title('Temperature Measurements at a Single Location'),...
axis([7 12 45 80])
```

The plot is shown in Figure 7.5–3. The dashed lines represent linear interpolation, and the solid curve is the cubic spline. Note that if we use the spline plot to estimate the temperature at 8 A.M., we obtain approximately 51° F. If we evaluate the spline polynomial at $x = 8$, we obtain $y(8) = 51.2°$ F. In either case the estimate is different from the 53° F estimate obtained from linear interpolation. It is impossible to say which estimate is more accurate without having more understanding of the temperature dynamics.

Instead of plotting the cubic spline and estimating a point on the plot, we can obtain a more accurate calculation, more quickly, by using the following variation of the `interp1` function.

```
y_est = interp1(x,y,x_est,'spline')
```

Temperature Measurements at a Single Location

Figure 7.5–3
Linear and cubic-spline interpolation of temperature data.

In this form the function returns a column vector `y_est` that contains the estimated values of y that correspond to the x values specified in the vector `x_est`, using cubic-spline interpolation. For example, to estimate the value of y at $x = 8$ for the preceding data, we would type `interp1(x,y,8,'spline')`. MATLAB returns the answer 51.2. To estimate the value of y at two different points, say, $x = 8$ and $x = 10$, we would type `interp1(x,` `10],'spline')`. MATLAB returns the answers 51.2 and 64.3.

In some applications it is helpful to know the polynomial coefficients, but we cannot obtain the spline coefficients from the `interp1` function. However, we can use the form

```
[breaks, coeffs, m, n] = unmkpp(spline(x,y))
```

to obtain the coefficients of the cubic polynomials. The vector `breaks` contains the x values of the data, and the matrix `coeffs` is an $m \times n$ matrix containing the coefficients of the polynomials. The scalars m and n give the dimensions of the matrix `coeffs`; m is the number of polynomials, and n is the number of coefficients for each polynomial (MATLAB will fit a lower-order polynomial if possible, so there can be fewer than four coefficients). For example, using the same data, the following session produces the coefficients of the polynomials given earlier:

```
>>x=[7,9,11,12];
>>y=[49,57,71,75];
>>[breaks, coeffs, m, n] = unmkpp(spline(x,y));
 breaks =
    7    9    11    12
 coeffs =
    -0.3500   2.8500  -0.3000   49.0000
    -0.3500   0.7500   6.900    57.0000
    -0.3500  -1.3500   5.7000   71.0000
 m =
    3
 n =
    4
```

The first row of the matrix coeffs contains the coefficients of the first polynomial, and so on. These functions are summarized in Table 7.5–2.

Application to Robot Control

Cubic splines are used to control robotic devices such as the arm shown in Figure 7.5–4. This particular arm is a simple one that moves in a two-dimensional plane. It has a motor at its "shoulder" and a motor at its "elbow." When these two motors rotate through the proper angles, the arm can place its hand at a desired point in the plane. Robots have a supervisory computer that accepts user input, such as the desired location of the hand. The computer then calculates how much rotation each motor must produce to move the hand from its starting point to its desired final position. Then, at regular time intervals, the supervisory computer feeds the angular motion commands to the two smaller computers that

Table 7.5–2 Polynomial interpolation commands

Command	Description
y_est = interp1(x,y,x_est,'spline')	Returns a column vector y_est that contains the estimated values of y that correspond to the x values specified in the vector x_est, using cubic spline interpolation.
y_int = spline(x,y,x_int)	Computes a cubic-spline interpolation where x and y are vectors containing the data and x_int is a vector containing the values of the independent variable x at which we wish to estimate the dependent variable y. The result y_int is a vector the same size as x_int containing the interpolated values of y that correspond to x_int.
[breaks, coeffs, m, n] = unmkpp(spline(x,y))	Computes the coefficients of the cubic-spline polynomials for the data in x and y. The vector breaks contains the x values, and the matrix coeffs is an $m \times n$ matrix containing the polynomial coefficients. The scalars m and n give the dimensions of the matrix coeffs; m is the number of polynomials, and n is the number of coefficients for each polynomial.

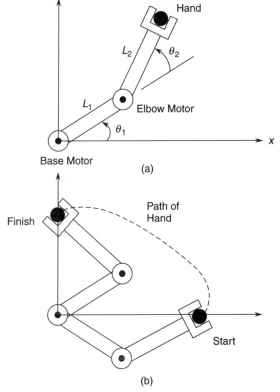

y

Hand

L_2 / θ_2

L_1 Elbow Motor

θ_1

x

Base Motor

(a)

Path of
Hand

Finish

Start

(b)

Figure 7.5–4
A robot arm having two
joints. (a) Dimensions and
arm angles. (b) The hand's
path is not a straight line,
but a complicated curve.

control each motor. In many devices the supervisory computer
uses cubic-spline interpolation to generate the angular motion
commands. The advantage of a cubic spline is that it results in
smooth robot motion. We now show how the splines are computed.

We can use trigonometry to obtain the following expressions
for the coordinates of the elbow and the hand. For the elbow,
$x_{elbow} = L_1 \cos \theta_1$ and $y_{elbow} = L_1 \sin \theta_1$. The hand's coordinates
(x, y) are given by

$$x = x_{elbow} + L_2 \cos(\theta_1 + \theta_2) = L_1 \cos \theta_1 + L_2 \cos(\theta_1 + \theta_2) \quad \textbf{(7.5–1)}$$

$$y = y_{elbow} + L_2 \sin(\theta_1 + \theta_2) = L_1 \sin \theta_1 + L_2 \sin(\theta_1 + \theta_2) \quad \textbf{(7.5–2)}$$

These two equations can be solved for θ_1 and θ_2 in terms of
x and y so that we can determine the elbow and arm angles
necessary to place the hand at a specified position given by x and
y. We omit the details of the solution and just state the results.

$$R^2 = x^2 + y^2 \quad \textbf{(7.5–3)}$$

$$\cos \theta_2 = \frac{R^2 - L_1^2 - L_2^2}{2L_1 L_2} \quad \textbf{(7.5–4)}$$

$$\cos \beta = \frac{R^2 + L_1^2 - L_2^2}{2L_1 R} \tag{7.5-5}$$

$$\alpha = \arctan \frac{y}{x} \tag{7.5-6}$$

$$\theta_1 = \begin{cases} \alpha + \beta & \text{if } \theta_2 < 0 \\ \alpha - \beta & \text{if } \theta_2 \geq 0 \end{cases} \tag{7.5-7}$$

If we use a cubic polynomial to express the joint angles as functions of time for $0 \leq t \leq T$, then we can specify four conditions for each angle. Two of these conditions should require the polynomial to pass through the starting value $\theta(0)$ and the ending value $\theta(T)$. The other two conditions require that the slope of the polynomial should be 0 at the start and finish because we want the robot to start from rest and to finish at rest. The cubic polynomial that satisfies these conditions is

$$\theta(t) = a t^3 + b t^2 + \theta(0) \tag{7.5-8}$$

where $a = 2[\theta(0) - \theta(T)]/T^3$ and $b = -3[\theta(0) - \theta(T)]/T^2$.

For example, suppose the robot arm shown in Figure 7.5–4(a) has the lengths $L_1 = 4$ and $L_2 = 3$ feet. Suppose also that in 2 seconds we want the hand to move from $x(0) = 6.5$, $y(0) = 0$ to $x(2) = 0$, $y(2) = 6.5$ feet. We obtain the following angle solutions from equations (7.5–3) through (7.5–7): $\theta_1(0) = -18.717°$, $\theta_1(2) = 71.283°$, and $\theta_2(0) = \theta_2(2) = 44.049°$. The polynomials are $\theta_1(t) = -22.5t^3 + 67.5t^2 - 18.717$ and $\theta_2(t) = 44.049$. If the robot controller uses these polynomials to generate commands to the motors, then the path of the hand looks like that shown in Figure 7.5–4b. Note that the hand's path is not a straight line between the starting and stopping points, and this motion might result in a collision with nearby objects.

In many applications we want to control the hand's path more precisely. For example, the robot might be used for welding along a specific path. Suppose we want the path to be a straight line. Then we must specify a series of intermediate locations for the hand to pass through. These locations must lie on the straight line connecting the starting and ending hand positions. These points are called *knot points*. To obtain smooth motion, we want the hand to pass through these points without stopping or changing speed, so we use cubic spline to interpolate between these points. If the hand is initially at the point (x_0, y_0) and we want it to move to (x_f, y_f) in a straight line, the line's equation is

KNOT POINT

$$y = \frac{y_f - y_0}{x_f - x_0}(x - x_0) + y_0 \tag{7.5-9}$$

Example 7.5–1 Robot path control using three knot points

Write a MATLAB program to compute the arm angle solution for three knot points. Write another program to compute the splines required to generate three knot points and to plot the path of the robot's hand. Do this problem for the case where $L_1 = 4$, $L_2 = 3$, $(x_0, y_0) = (6, 0)$, $(x_f, y_f) = (0, 4)$

Solution:

The following script file performs these calculations. It solves the specific case where $L_1 = 4, L_2 = 3, (x_0, y_0) = (6, 0), (x_f, y_f) = (0, 4)$, using three equally spaced knot points along the straight-line path.

```
% Solution for joint angles using n knot points.
% Enter the arm lengths below.
L1=4;L2=3;
% Enter the specific values of the starting point (x0,y0),
% the stopping point (xf,yf), and the number of knot points n.
x0=6;y0=0;xf=0;yf=4;n=3;
% Obtain the points on a straight line from (x0,y0) to (xf,yf).
x=linspace(x0,xf,n+1);y=((yf-y0)/(xf-x0))*(x-x0)+y0;
% Begin the angle solution. The answers will be in degrees.
R=sqrt(x.^2+y.^2);
theta2=acos((R.^2-L1^2- L2^2)/(2*L1*L2))*(180/pi);
beta=acos((R.^2+L1^2- L2^2)/(2*L1*R))*(180/pi);
alpha=atan2(y,x)*(180/pi);
if theta2 < 0
    theta1=alpha+beta;
else
    theta1=alpha-beta;
end
```

The results are theta1=[-18.7170, -17.2129, 4.8980, 35.9172, 71.2830] and theta2=[44.0486, 86.6409, 99.2916, 86.6409, 44.0486].

The second program uses these angles to compute the splines and plot the hand's path. The plot is shown in Figure 7.5–5. The hand's path is very close to a straight line, as desired.

```
% Example of robot path using splines with three knot points.
% Define the joint angles and times along the straight line path.
theta1=[-18.717, -17.2129, 4.8980, 35.9172, 71.2830];
theta2=[44.0486, 86.6409, 99.2916, 86.6409, 44.0486];
t=[0,.5, 1, 1.5, 2];
% Use 200 points for interpolation.
t_i=linspace(0,2,200);
theta1_i=spline(t,theta1,t_i);
```

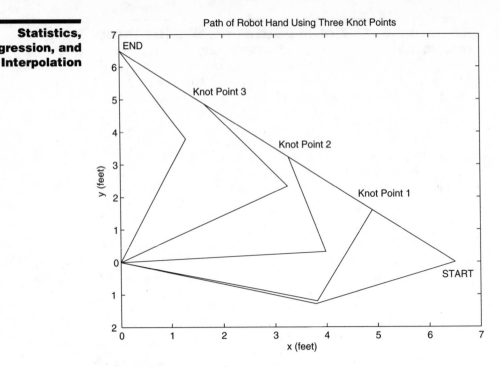

Figure 7.5–5
Path of a robot hand using three knot points.

```
theta2_i=spline(t,theta2,t_i);
% Compute the (x,y) coordinates of the hand.
x=4*cos(theta1_i*(pi/180))+3*cos((theta1_i+theta2_i)*(pi/180));
y=4*sin(theta1_i*(pi/180))+3*sin((theta1_i+theta2_i)*(pi/180));
% Compute the (x,y) coordinates of the elbow.
x_elbow=[4*cos(theta1_i*(pi/180))];
y_elbow=[4*sin(theta1_i*(pi/180))];
% Compute the coordinates to display the arm's position at 5 points.
x1=[0,x_elbow(1),x(1)];y1=[0,y_elbow(1),y(1)];
x2=[0,x_elbow(50),x(50)];y2=[0, y_elbow(50),y(50)];
x3=[0,x_elbow(100),x(100)];y3=[0,y_elbow(100),y(100)];
x4=[0,x_elbow(150),x(150)];y4=[0,y_elbow(150),y(150)];
x5=[0,x_elbow(200),x(200)];y5=[0,y_elbow(200),y(200)];
% Plot the results.
plot(x,y,x1,y1,x2,y2,x3,y3,x4,y4,x5,y5),...
axis([0 7 -2 7]),title('Path of Robot Hand'),...
xlabel('x (feet)'),ylabel('y (feet)')
```

Table 7.6–3 Guide to MATLAB commands introduced in Chapter 7

Histogram functions	See Table 7.1–1
Mean and standard deviation functions	See Table 7.2–1
Random number functions	See Table 7.3–1
Functions for polynomial regression	See Table 7.4–1
Linear interpolation commands	See Table 7.5–1
Polynomial interpolation commands	See Table 7.5–2

Miscellaneous commands	
Command	**Description**
`erf(x)`	Computes the error function *erf(x)*.

7.6
Summary

This chapter introduces MATLAB functions that have widespread and important uses in statistics and data analysis; however, their proper application requires informed judgment and experience. Section 7.1 gives an introduction to basic statistics and probability, including histograms, which are specialized plots for displaying statistical results. The normal distribution that forms the basis of many statistical methods is covered in Section 7.2. Section 7.3 covers random number generators and their use in simulation programs. Section 7.4 shows how to perform regression analysis to obtain functions that adequately describe data. Section 7.5 covers interpolation methods, including linear and spline interpolation.

Now that you have finished this chapter, you should be able to use MATLAB to

- Solve basic problems in statistics and probability.
- Create simulations incorporating random processes.
- Use regression analysis to develop functional descriptions of data.
- Apply interpolation to data.

Key Terms with Page References

Problems You can find answers to problems marked with an asterisk at the end of the text.

Section 7.1

1. The following list gives the measured gas mileage in miles per gallon for 22 cars of the same model. Plot the absolute frequency histogram and the relative frequency histogram.

   23 25 26 25 27 25 24 22 23 25 26
   26 24 24 22 25 26 24 24 24 27 23

2. Thirty pieces of structural timber of the same dimensions were subjected to an increasing lateral force until they broke. The measured force in pounds required to break them is given in the following list. Plot the absolute frequency histogram. Try bin widths of 50, 100, and 200 pounds. Which gives the most meaningful histogram? Try to find a better value for the bin width.

   243 236 389 628 143 417 205
   404 464 605 137 123 372 439
   497 500 535 577 441 231 675
   132 196 217 660 569 865 725
   457 347

3. The following list gives the measured breaking force in newtons for a sample of 60 pieces of certain type of cord. Plot the absolute frequency histogram. Try bin widths of 10, 30, and 50 newtons. Which gives the most meaningful histogram? Try to find a better value for the bin width.

   311 138 340 199 270 255 332 279 231 296 198 269
   257 236 313 281 288 225 216 250 259 323 280 205
   279 159 276 354 278 221 192 281 204 361 321 282
   254 273 334 172 240 327 261 282 208 213 299 318
   356 269 355 232 275 234 267 240 331 222 370 226

4.* If you roll a balanced pair of dice 300 times, how many times would you expect to obtain a sum of 8? A sum of either 3, 4, or 5? A sum of less than 9?

Section 7.2

5. For the data given in Problem 1,
   a. Plot the scaled frequency histogram.
   b. Compute the mean and standard deviation and use them to estimate the lower and upper limits of gas mileage corresponding to 68 percent of cars of this model. Compare these limits with those of the data.

6. For the data given in Problem 2,
   a. Plot the scaled frequency histogram.
   b. Compute the mean and standard deviation and use them to estimate the lower and upper limits of strength corresponding to 68 percent and to 96 percent of such timber pieces. Compare these limits with those of the data.

7. For the data given in Problem 3,
   a. Plot the scaled frequency histogram.
   b. Compute the mean and standard deviation, and use them to estimate the lower and upper limits of breaking force corresponding to 68 percent and 96 percent of cord pieces of this type. Compare these limits with those of the data.

8.* Data analysis of the breaking strength of a certain fabric shows that it is normally distributed with a mean of 200 pounds and a variance of 9.
   a. Estimate the percentage of fabric samples that will have a breaking strength no less than 194 pounds.
   b. Estimate the percentage of fabric samples that will have a breaking strength no less than 197 pounds and no greater than 203 pounds.

9. Data from service records shows that the time to repair a certain machine is normally distributed with a mean of 50 minutes and a standard deviation of 5 minutes. Estimate how often it will take more than 60 minutes to repair a machine.

10. Measurements of a number of fittings show that the pitch diameter of the thread is normally distributed with a mean of 5.007 millimeters and a standard deviation of 0.005 millimeters. The design specifications require that the pitch diameter must be 5 ± 0.01 millimeter. Estimate the percentage of fittings that will be within tolerance.

11. A certain product requires that a shaft be inserted into a bearing. Measurements show that the diameter d_1 of the cylindrical hole in the bearing is normally distributed with a mean of 3 centimeters with a variance of 0.0064. The diameter d_2 of the shaft is normally distributed with a mean of 2.96 centimeters and a variance of 0.0036.
   a. Compute the mean and the variance of the clearance $c = d_1 - d_2$.
   b. Find the probability that a given shaft will not fit into the bearing. (Hint: Find the probability that the clearance is negative.)

12.* A shipping pallet holds 10 boxes. Each box holds 300 parts of different types. The part weight is normally distributed with a mean of 1 pound and a standard deviation of 0.2 pound.
   a. Compute the mean and standard deviation of the pallet weight.
   b. Compute the probability that the pallet weight will exceed 3015 pounds.

13. A certain product is assembled by placing three components end to end. The components' lengths are L_1, L_2, and L_3. Each component is manufactured on a different machine, so the random variation in their lengths is independent of each other. The lengths are normally distributed with means of 1, 2, and 1.5 feet and variances of 0.00014, 0.0002, and 0.0003, respectively.
   a. Compute the mean and variance of the length of the assembled product.
   b. Estimate what percentage of assembled products will be no less than 4.48 and no more than 4.52 feet in length.

14. Use a random number generator to produce 1000 uniformly distributed numbers with a mean of 10, a minimum of 2, and a maximum of 18. Obtain the mean and the histogram of these numbers and discuss whether or not they appear uniformly distributed with the desired mean.

15. Use a random number generator to produce 1000 normally distributed numbers with a mean of 20 and a variance of 4. Obtain the mean, variance, and the histogram of these numbers and discuss whether or not they appear normally distributed with the desired mean and variance.

16. The mean of the sum (or difference) of two independent random variables equals the sum (or difference) of their means, but the variance is always the sum of the two variances. Use random number generation to verify this statement for the case where $z = x + y$, where x and y are independent and normally distributed random variables. The mean and variance of x are $\mu_x = 10$ and $\sigma_x^2 = 2$. The mean and variance of y are $\mu_y = 15$ and $\sigma_y^2 = 3$. Find the mean and variance of z by simulation and compare the results with the theoretical prediction. Do this for 100, 1000, and 5000 trials.

17. Suppose that $z = xy$, where x and y are independent and normally distributed random variables. The mean and variance of x are $\mu_x = 10$ and $\sigma_x^2 = 2$. The mean and variance of y are $\mu_{2x} = 15$ and $\sigma_{2x}^2 = 3$. Find the mean and variance of z by simulation. Does $\mu_z = \mu_x\mu_y$? Does $\sigma_z^2 = \sigma_x^2\sigma_y^2$? Do this for 100, 1000, and 5000 trials.

18. Suppose that $y = x^2$, where x is a normally distributed random variable with a mean and variance of $\mu_x = 0$ and $\sigma_x^2 = 4$. Find the mean and variance of y by simulation. Does $\mu_y = \mu_x^2$? Does $\sigma_y = \sigma_x^2$? Do this for 100, 1000, and 5000 trials.

19.* Suppose you have analyzed the price behavior of a certain stock by plotting the scaled frequency histogram of the price over a number of months. Suppose that the histogram indicates that the price is normally distributed with a mean $100 and a standard deviation of $5. Write a MATLAB program to simulate the effects of buying 50 shares of this stock whenever the price is below the $100 mean, and selling all your shares whenever the price is above $105. Analyze the outcome of this strategy over 250 days (the approximate number of business days in a year). Define the profit as the yearly income from selling stock plus the value of the stocks you own at year's end, minus the yearly cost of buying stock. Compute the mean yearly profit you would expect to make, the minimum expected yearly profit, the maximum expected yearly profit, and the standard deviation of the yearly profit. The broker charges 6 cents per share bought or sold with a minimum fee of $40 per transaction. Assume you make only one transaction per day.

20. Suppose that data shows that a certain stock price is normally distributed with a mean of $150 and a variance of 100. Create a simulation to compare the results of the following two strategies over 250 days.

You start the year with 1000 shares. With the first strategy, every day the price is below $140 you buy 100 shares, and every day the price is above $160 you sell all the shares you own. With the second strategy, every day the price is below $150 you buy 100 shares, and every day the price is above $160 you sell all the shares you own. The broker charges 5 cents per share traded with a minimum of $35 per transaction.

Section 7.4

21.* The distance a spring stretches from its "free length" is a function of how much tension force is applied to it. The following table gives the spring length y that was produced in a particular spring by the given applied force f. The spring's free length is 4.7 inches. Find a functional relation between f and x, the extension from the free length ($x = y - 4.7$).

Force f (pounds)	Spring length y (inches)
0	4.7
0.47	7.2
1.15	10.6
1.64	12.9

22. The following data gives the drying time T of a certain paint as a function of the amount of a certain additive A.
   a. Find the first-, second-, third-, and fourth-degree polynomials that fit the data and plot each polynomial with the data. Determine the quality of the curve fit for each by computing J, S, and r^2.
   b. Use the polynomial giving the best fit to estimate the amount of additive that minimizes the drying time.

A (oz)	0	1	2	3	4	5	6	7	8	9
T (min)	130	115	110	90	89	89	95	100	110	125

23.* The following data gives the stopping distance d as a function of initial speed v, for a certain car model. Find a quadratic polynomial that fits the data. Determine the quality of the curve fit by computing J, S, and r^2.

v (mph)	20	30	40	50	60	70
d (ft)	45	80	130	185	250	330

24. If the acceleration a is constant, Newton's law predicts that the distance travelled versus time is a quadratic function: $d = \frac{a}{2}t^2 + bt$. The following data was taken for a cyclist. Use the data to estimate the cyclist's acceleration a.

t (sec)	0	1	1.5	2	2.5	3	3.5	4
d (ft)	0	4	10	11	26	38	51	65

25.* The number of twists y required to break a certain rod is a function of the percentage x_1 and x_2 of each of two alloying elements present in the rod. The following table gives some pertinent data. Use linear multiple regression to obtain a model $y = a_0 + a_1 x_1 + a_2 x_2$ of the relationship between the number of twists and the alloy percentages. In addition, find the maximum percent error in the predictions.

Number of twists y	Percentage of element 1 x_1	Percentage of element 2 x_2
40	1	1
51	2	1
65	3	1
72	4	1
38	1	2
46	2	2
53	3	2
67	4	2
31	1	3
39	2	3
48	3	3
56	4	3

Section 7.5

26.* Interpolation is useful when one or more data points are missing. This situation often occurs with environmental measurements, such as temperature, because of the difficulty of making measurements around the clock. The following table of temperature versus time data is missing readings at 5 hrs and 9 hrs. Use linear interpolation with MATLAB to estimate the temperature at those times.

Time (hrs, P.M.)	1	2	3	4	5	6	7	8	9	10	11	12
Temperature (°C)	10	12	18	24	?	21	20	18	?	15	13	8

27. The following table gives temperature data in °C as a function of time of day and day of the week at a specific location. Data is missing for the

entries marked with a question mark (?). Use linear interpolation with MATLAB to estimate the temperature at the missing points.

Problems **359**

Hour	Day				
	Mon	Tues	Wed	Thurs	Fri
1	17	15	12	16	16
2	13	?	8	11	12
3	14	14	9	?	15
4	17	15	14	15	19
5	23	18	17	20	24

28. Consider the robot arm shown in Figure 7.5–4 on page 349. Suppose the arm lengths are $L_1 = 4$ and $L_2 = 3$ feet. Suppose we want the arm to start from rest at the location $x(0) = 6$, $y(0) = 0$ and stop three seconds later at the location $x(3) = 0$, $y(3) = 4$. Write a MATLAB program to compute the arm angle solution using two knot points. Write another program to compute the splines required to generate the two knot points and to plot the path of the robot's hand. Discuss whether the hand's path deviates much from a straight line.

29. Computer-controlled machines are used to cut and to form metal and other materials when manufacturing products. These machines often use cubic splines to specify the path to be cut or the contour of the part to be shaped. The following coodinates specify the shape of a certain car's front fender. Fit a series of cubic splines to the coordinates and plot the splines along with the coordinate points.

x (ft)	0	0.25	0.75	1.25	1.5	1.75	1.875	2	2.125	2.25
y (ft)	1.2	1.18	1.1	1	0.92	0.8	0.7	0.55	0.35	0

Courtesy Ford Motor Company

Engineering in the 21st Century . . .

Energy-Efficient Transportation

Western societies have become very dependent on transportation powered by gasoline and diesel fuel. There is some disagreement about how long it will take to exhaust these fuel resources, but it will certainly happen. Novel engineering developments in both personal and mass transportation will be needed to reduce our dependence on such fuels. These developments will be required in a number of areas such as engine design, electric motor and battery technology, lightweight materials, and aerodynamics.

A number of such initiatives are underway. The photo shows the Synergy 2010 concept car developed by Ford to explore new technologies for a circa 2010 family car. Designed for six passengers, the car is one-third lighter and 40 percent more aerodynamic than today's sleekest cars. It is an example of a hybrid-electric vehicle that has two power sources. Three devices—an internal combustion engine, a gas turbine, and a fuel cell—are candidates for the primary power source. The secondary power source might be a flywheel or a battery . Ford is presently investigating a small, 1.0 liter, direct-injection, compression-ignited engine to power a generator to produce electricity for motors located at each wheel. A flywheel would collect excess engine and braking energy, to be released to supplement the engine for quick acceleration or to climb hills.

The weight reduction is to be achieved with all-aluminum unibody construction and by improved design of the engine, flywheel, radiator, and brakes to make use of advanced materials such as composites and magnesium. Other manufacturers are investigating plastic bodies made from recycled materials. The fin-shaped vertical front fenders create an air extractor for the cooling system and control the airflow along the sides to reduce drag.

Further research on the design and technology concepts and the required manufacturing processes is required to make the car affordable. MATLAB can assist engineers performing such research.

8

Numerical Methods for Calculus and Differential Equations

Outline

This chapter covers numerical methods for computing integrals and derivatives and for solving ordinary differential equations. Some integrals cannot be evaluated analytically, and we need to compute them numerically with an approximate method. In addition, it is often necessary to use data to estimate rates of change, and this process requires a numerical estimate of

362

**Numerical
Methods for
Calculus and
Differential
Equations**

the derivative. Finally, many differential equations cannot be solved analytically, and so we must be able to solve them using appropriate numerical techniques.

When you have finished this chapter, you should be able to

- Use MATLAB to numerically evaluate integrals.
- Use numerical methods with MATLAB to estimate derivatives.
- Use the analytical expressions for simple integrals and derivatives to check the accuracy of numerical methods.
- Use MATLAB's numerical differential equation solvers to obtain solutions.
- Use the analytical solutions of simple differential equations to check the accuracy of numerical methods.

8.1

Review of Integration and Differentiation

We assume that you are somewhat familiar with integrals and derivatives from a prior calculus course. The integral of a function $f(x)$ for $a \leq x \leq b$ can be interpreted as the area between the $f(x)$ curve and the x-axis, bounded by the limits $x = a$ and $x = b$. Figure 8.1–1 illustrates this area. If we denote this area by A, then we can write A as

$$A = \int_a^b f(x)\,dx \qquad (8.1\text{–}1)$$

INTEGRAND

The *integrand* is $f(x)$. The *lower* and *upper limits of integration* here are a and b. The symbol x here is the *variable of integration*. Note that we can use any symbol we want for the variable of integration. Thus the area A could also be written as

$$A = \int_a^b f(t)\,dt$$

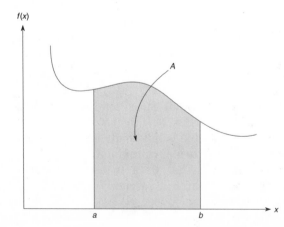

Figure 8.1–1
The area under the curve of $f(x)$ from $x = a$ to $x = b$.

Integrals are often encountered in engineering applications. Here are some examples:

Acceleration and velocity: An object's velocity $v(b)$ at time $t = b$, starting with velocity $v(0)$ at $t = 0$, is the integral of its acceleration $a(t)$:

$$v(b) = \int_0^b a(t)\, dt + v(0) \qquad \text{(8.1–2)}$$

Velocity and distance: The position of an object moving at velocity $v(t)$ from the time $t = a$ to the time $t = b$ and starting at position $x(a)$ at $t = a$ is

$$x(b) = \int_a^b v(t)\, dt + x(a) \qquad \text{(8.1–3)}$$

Capacitor voltage and current: The voltage v across a capacitor is the integral of the current i applied to the capacitor. If a capacitor initially holds a charge $Q(a)$, then if the current $i(t)$ is applied from time $t = a$ to time $t = b$, the capacitor voltage is

$$v(b) = \frac{1}{C}\left[\int_a^b i(t)\, dt + Q(a)\right] \qquad \text{(8.1–4)}$$

where C is the capacitance of the capacitor.

Work expended: The mechanical work done in pushing an object a distance d is the integral

$$W = \int_0^d f(x)\, dx \qquad \text{(8.1–5)}$$

where $f(x)$ is the force as a function of position x. For a linear spring $f(x) = kx$, where k is the *spring constant,* and the work done against the spring is

$$W = \int_0^d kx\, dx \qquad \text{(8.1–6)}$$

In many applications one or both integral limits are variables. For example, an object's velocity at time t is the integral of its acceleration. If the object is moving at time $t = 0$ with a velocity $v(0)$, its velocity is given by

$$v(t) = \int_0^t a(t)\, dt + v(0) \qquad \text{(8.1–7)}$$

Integrals have the *linearity* property. If c and d are not functions of x, then

$$\text{(8.1–8)}$$

$$\int_a^b [cf(x) + dg(x)]\, dx = c\int_a^b f(x)\, dx + d\int_a^b g(x)\, dx$$

364

**Numerical
Methods for
Calculus and
Differential
Equations**

Another useful property of integrals is the following:

$$\int_a^b f(x)\,dx = \int_a^c f(x)\,dx + \int_c^b f(x)\,dx \qquad \textbf{(8.1–9)}$$

The integrals of many functions can be evaluated analytically. We can obtain a formula for the integral, and we are said to have obtained the answer in "closed form." Here are some common examples that you have probably seen before:

$$\int_a^b x^n\,dx = \left.\frac{x^{n+1}}{n+1}\right|_{x=a}^{x=b} = \frac{b^{n+1}}{n+1} - \frac{a^{n+1}}{n+1}, \quad n \neq -1$$

$$\textbf{(8.1–10)}$$

$$\int_a^b \frac{1}{x}\,dx = \ln x \Big|_{x=a}^{x=b} = \ln b - \ln a \qquad \textbf{(8.1–11)}$$

$$\int_\pi^{2\pi} \sin x\,dx = -\cos x \big|_{x=\pi}^{x=2\pi} = -[\cos 2\pi - \cos \pi] = -2$$

$$\textbf{(8.1–12)}$$

DEFINITE INTEGRAL

INDEFINITE INTEGRAL

The integrals we have seen thus far are called *definite* integrals because they have specified limits of integration. *Indefinite* integrals do not have the limits specified. For example, the following integral is indefinite:

$$\int \cos x\,dx = \sin x \qquad \textbf{(8.1–13)}$$

Not every function can be integrated analytically. For example, the following is *Fresnel's cosine integral,* which has not been evaluated analytically:

$$\int \cos x^2\,dx \qquad \textbf{(8.1–14)}$$

In such cases we must compute the definite integral using numerical methods. These are treated in section 8.2.

Improper Integrals and Singularities

IMPROPER INTEGRAL

Some integrals have infinite values, depending on their integration limits. These are called *improper integrals.* For example, the following integral can be found in most integral tables:

$$\int \frac{1}{x-1}\,dx = \ln|x-1|$$

However, it is an improper integral if the integration limits include the point $x = 1$. To see why, consider Figure 8.1–2, which is a plot of the function $y = 1/(x - 1)$. The function becomes undefined as x approaches 1 from the left or the right. To show

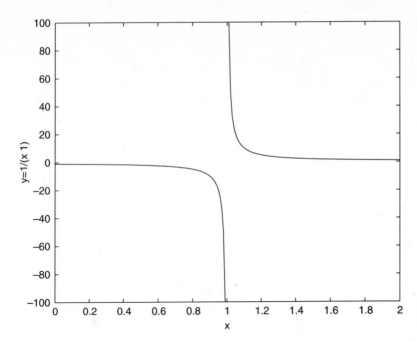

Figure 8.1–2
A function having a
singularity at $x = 1$.

that the integral is improper, take the limit of the integral as the
upper integration limit h approaches 1 from the left.

$$\lim_{h \to 1-} \int_0^h \frac{1}{x-1} \, dx = \lim_{h \to 1-} \ln|x-1| \Big|_0^h$$

$$= \lim_{h \to 1-} \left(\ln|h-1| - \ln|-1| \right) = \lim_{h \to 1-} \ln(1-h) = -\infty$$

because $\ln 0 = -\infty$. So even though an integral can be found in
an integral table, you should examine the integrand to check
for points at which the integrand is undefined. These points are
called *singularities*. If singularities lie on or within the integration   **SINGULARITY**
limits, you need to check the limit of the integral to see whether
it is improper. The same warning applies when using numerical
methods to evaluate integrals. The points at which the integrand
is undefined can cause problems for the numerical method.

Test Your Understanding

T8.1–1 Compute the area under the $\sin(x)$ curve from $x = 0$ to
$x = \pi$.

(Answer: 2)

T8.1–2 If a rocket is launched from rest with an acceleration of
5g, (a) how fast will it be going, and (b) how high will
it be 10 seconds after launch? ($1g = 9.81$ meters/second^2)

366

**Numerical
Methods for
Calculus and
Differential
Equations**

(Answer: (a) 490.5 meters/second; (b) 2452.5 meters).

Derivatives

Differentiation and integration are complementary operations. For example, if

$$g(x) = \int f(x)\,dx$$

then $f(x)$ is the derivative of $g(x)$ with respect to x. This relation is written as

$$f(x) = \frac{dg}{dx} \qquad (8.1\text{--}15)$$

The derivative of $f(x)$ can be interpreted geometrically as the slope of $f(x)$. Thus the derivative is sometimes called the "slope function."

Obtaining derivatives is much easier than obtaining integrals because a few basic rules and a short table of derivatives enable us to compute derivatives of complicated functions. The *product* rule says that if $h(x) = f(x)g(x)$, then

$$\frac{dh}{dx} = f(x)\frac{dg}{dx} + g(x)\frac{df}{dx} \qquad (8.1\text{--}16)$$

The *quotient* rule states that if $h(x) = f(x)/g(x)$, then

$$\frac{dh}{dx} = \frac{g(x)\frac{df}{dx} - f(x)\frac{dg}{dx}}{g^2} \qquad (8.1\text{--}17)$$

The following *chain rule* enables us to obtain derivatives by decomposing functions into basic functions whose derivatives are given in a table. If z is a function of y ($z = f(y)$) and if y is a function of x ($y = g(x)$), then z is indirectly a function of x, and the chain rule says that

$$\frac{dz}{dx} = \frac{dz}{dy}\frac{dy}{dx} \qquad (8.1\text{--}18)$$

Here are a few examples of derivatives:

$$\frac{dx^n}{dx} = nx^{n-1} \qquad (8.1\text{--}19)$$

$$\frac{d\ln x}{dx} = \frac{1}{x} \qquad (8.1\text{--}20)$$

$$\frac{d\sin x}{dx} = \cos x \qquad (8.1\text{--}21)$$

$$\frac{d\cos x}{dx} = -\sin x \qquad (8.1\text{--}22)$$

Using this short table of derivatives and the product rule, we can show that

$$\frac{d\,(x^2 \sin x)}{dx} = x^2 \cos x + 2x \sin x$$

Use the chain rule with $z = y^2$ and $y = \sin x$ to obtain the following derivative:

$$\frac{d\,(\sin^2 x)}{dx} = 2y\frac{dy}{dx} = 2\sin x \cos x$$

Test Your Understanding

T8.1–3 Derive the expressions for the derivatives of the following functions with respect to x:
(a) $\sin(3x)$; (b) $\cos^2 x$; (c) $x^3 \ln x$; (d) $(\sin x)/x^2$

(Answers: (a) $3 \cos(3x)$; (b) $-2 \cos x \sin x$; (c) $x^2(3 \ln x + 1)$; (d) $(x \cos x - 2 \sin x)/x^3$).

8.2
Numerical Integration

The purpose of this section is to show how to use MATLAB to calculate values of definite integrals using approximate methods. In Chapter 9 we show how to use MATLAB to obtain the closed form solution of some integrals.

Trapezoidal Integration
The simplest way to find the area under a curve is to split the area into rectangles (Figure 8.2–1a). If the widths of the rectangles are

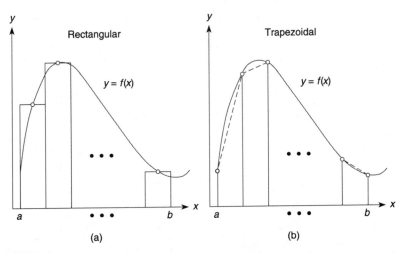

Figure 8.2–1
Illustration of (a) rectangular and (b) trapezoidal numerical integration.

small enough, the sum of their areas gives the approximate value of the integral. A more sophisticated method is to use trapezoidal elements (Figure 8.2–1b). Each trapezoid is called a *panel*. It is not necessary to use panels of the same width; to increase the method's accuracy you can use narrow panels where the function is changing rapidly. When the widths are adjusted according to the function's behavior, the method is said to be *adaptive*. MATLAB implements *trapezoidal integration* with the trapz function. Its syntax is trapz(x,y), where the array y contains the function values at the points contained in the array x. If you want the integral of a single function, then y is a vector. To integrate more than one function, place their values in a matrix y; typing trapz(x,y) will compute the integral of each column of y.

You cannot directly specify a function to integrate with the trapz function; you must first compute and store the function's values ahead of time in an array. Later we discuss two other integration functions, the quad and quad8 functions, that can accept functions directly. However, they cannot handle arrays of values. So the functions complement one another. These functions are summarized in Table 8.2–1.

As a simple example of the use of the trapz function, let us compute the integral

$$\int_0^\pi \sin x \, dx$$

Using (8.1–12), we find the exact answer to be

$$\int_0^\pi \sin x \, dx = -\cos x \Big|_0^\pi = \cos 0 - \cos \pi = 2$$

Table 8.2–1   Numerical integration functions

Command	Description
quad('function',a,b,tol,trace)	Uses an adaptive Simpson's rule to compute the integral of the function 'function' with *a* as the lower integration limit and *b* as the upper limit. The parameters tol and trace are optional. tol indicates the specified error tolerance. trace, when nonzero, generates a "point plot" that shows the integrand evaluated at the points used by the function to compute the integral.
quad8('function',a,b,tol,trace)	Uses a Newton-Cotes eight-panel rule to compute the integral of the function 'function'. The rest of the syntax is identical to quad.
trapz(x,y)	Uses trapezoidal integration to compute the integral of y with respect to x, where the array y contains the function values at the points contained in the array x.

To investigate the effect of panel width, let us first use 10 panels with equal widths of $\pi/10$. The script file is

```
x = linspace(0,pi,10);
y = sin(x);
trapz(x,y)
```

The answer is 1.9797, which gives a relative error of $100(2 - 1.9797)/2 = 1\%$. Now try 100 panels of equal width; replace the array x with x = linspace(0,pi,100). The answer is 1.9998 for a relative error of $100(2 - 1.9998)/2 = 0.01\%$. If we examine the plot of the integrand $\sin x$, we would see that the function is changing faster near $x = 0$ and $x = \pi$ than near $x = \pi/2$. Thus we could achieve the same accuracy using fewer panels if narrower panels are used near $x = 0$ and $x = \pi$.

When numerical integration was done by hand (before World War II), it was important to use as few panels as necessary to achieve the desired accuracy. However, with the speed of modern computers, it is not difficult to find a reasonable number of panels of uniform width to achieve the required accuracy for many problems. The following method usually works: Compute the integral with a reasonable number of panels (say, 100). Then double the number of panels and compare the answers. If they are close, you have the solution. If not, continue increasing the number of panels until the answers converge to a common value. This method does not always give accurate results, but it can be tried before using variable panel widths or methods more sophisticated than trapezoidal integration.

We can use numerical integration to find the velocity when either the acceleration function $a(t)$ cannot be integrated or the acceleration is given as a table of values. The following example illustrates the latter case.

Example 8.2–1   Velocity from an accelerometer

An *accelerometer* measures acceleration and is used in aircraft, rockets, and other vehicles to estimate the vehicle's velocity and displacement. The accelerometer integrates the acceleration signal to produce an estimate of the velocity, and it integrates the velocity estimate to produce an estimate of displacement. Suppose the vehicle starts from rest at time $t = 0$ and that its measured acceleration is given in the following table.

(a) Estimate the velocity after 10 seconds.
(b) Estimate the velocity at the times $t = 1, 2, \ldots, 10$ seconds.
(c) Check your program by using a case that can be solved analytically.

Time (sec)	0	1	2	3	4	5	6	7	8	9	10
Acceleration (m/s²)	0	2	4	7	11	17	24	32	41	48	51

370

**Numerical
Methods for
Calculus and
Differential
Equations**

Solution:

(a) We must use the `trapz` function here, because the acceleration is given as a table of values. We cannot use the `quad` or `quad8` functions. The relation between velocity and acceleration is

$$v(10) = \int_0^{10} a(t)\, dt + v(0) = \int_0^{10} a(t)\, dt$$

The script file follows.

```
t = [0:10];
a = [0,2,4,7,11,17,24,32,41,48,51];
vf = trapz(t,a)
```

The answer for the final velocity is given by `vf` and is 211.5 meters/second.

(b) To find the velocity at the times $t = 1, 2, \ldots, 10$, we can use the fact that $v(t_1) = 0$ and write (8.1-2) as

$$v(t_k) = \int_{t_1}^{t_k} a(t)\, dt + v(t_1) = \int_{t_1}^{t_k} a(t)\, dt \qquad (8.2\text{--}1)$$

for $k = 2, 3, \ldots, 11$. (Note that there are 11 values in the sequence $t = 0, 1, 2, \ldots, 10$. Thus t_{11} corresponds to $t = 10$.)

```
t = [0:10];
a = [0,2,4,7,11,17,24,32,41,48,51];
v(1) = 0;
for k = [2:11]
    v(k) = trapz(t(1:k),a(1:k));
end
disp([t',v'])
```

The preceding method uses more calculations than necessary because it does not take advantage of the velocity value calculated in the previous pass through the `for` loop. The following script file is thus more efficient. It is based on (8.2–1), which can be written as follows by substituting $t_1 = t_k$ and $t = t_{k+1}$.

$$v(t_{k+1}) = \int_{t_k}^{t_{k+1}} a(t)\, dt + v(t_k)$$

```
t = [0:10];
a = [0,2,4,7,11,17,24,32,41,48,51];
v(1) = 0;
for k = [1:10]
    v(k+1) = trapz(t(k:k+1),a(k:k+1))+v(k);
end
disp([t',v'])
```

In either case the answers are those given in the following table:

Time (sec)	0	1	2	3	4	5	6	7	8	9	10
Velocity (m/s)	0	1	4	9.5	18.5	32.5	53	81	117	162	211.5

(c) Because the trapezoidal rule uses straight line segments to connect the data points, it will give the exact solution for any panel width when the integrand is a linear function. So we can use the linear acceleration function $a(t) = t$ to test the program. The velocity is given by

$$v(t) = \int_0^t t\, dt = \left.\frac{t^2}{2}\right|_0^t = \frac{t^2}{2}$$

The velocity at $t = 10$ is 50. The following script file can be used to check the method used in part (b):

```
t = [0:10];
a = t;
v(1) = 0;
for k = [1:10]
    v(k+1) = trapz(t(k:k+1),a(k:k+1))+v(k);
end
disp(v(11))
```

When this file is run it produces the answer `v(11) = 50`, which is correct.

Test Your Understanding

T8.2-1 Modify the above script file to estimate the displacement at the times $t = 1, 2, \ldots, 10$ seconds.

(Partial answer: The displacement after 10 seconds is 584.25 meters.)

Quadrature Functions

As we have just seen, when the integrand is a linear function (one having a plot that is a straight line), trapezoidal integration gives the exact answer. However, if the integrand is not a linear function, then the trapezoidal representation will be inexact. We can represent the function's curve by quadratic functions to obtain more accuracy. This approach is taken with *Simpson's rule*, which divides the integration range $b - a$ into an even number of sections and uses a different quadratic for each pair of adjacent panels. A quadratic function has three parameters, and Simpson's rule

372

**Numerical
Methods for
Calculus and
Differential
Equations**

computes these parameters by requiring the quadratic to pass through the function's three points corresponding to the two adjacent panels.

To obtain more accuracy, we can use polynomials of a degree higher than two. Integration methods based on this approach are called *Newton-Cotes* methods.

MATLAB function `quad` implements an adaptive version of Simpson's rule, while the `quad8` function is based on a Newton-Cotes method using eight panels in an adaptive manner. The term *quad* is an abbreviation of *quadrature,* which is an old term for the process of measuring areas. The syntax of both functions is identical and is summarized in Table 8.2–1. In its basic form, the syntax is `quad('function',a,b)`, where `'function'` is the name of the function representing the integrand, a is the lower integration limit, and b is the upper limit. To illustrate, let us compute an integral we already know.

QUADRATURE

$$\int_0^{\pi} \sin x \, dx = 2$$

The session consists of one command:

```
≫A = quad('sin',0,pi)
```

The answer given by MATLAB is correct to four decimal places. We use `quad8` the same way; namely, `A = quad8('sin',0,pi)`. The answer given by MATLAB is correct to 12 decimal places.

Although the `quad` and `quad8` functions are more accurate than `trapz`, they are restricted to computing the integrals of functions and cannot be used when the integrand is specified by a set of points. Thus we could not have used `quad` and `quad8` in Example 8.2–1.

Slope Function Singularities

In addition to singularities of the integrand, another condition can cause problems for numerical integration methods. This occurs when the slope of the integrand becomes infinite either on or within the integration limits; that is, the *slope function has a singularity*. A simple example of this is the square root function $y = \sqrt{x}$, shown in Figure 8.2–2a. The slope of this function is its derivative, which is $dy/dx = 0.5/\sqrt{x}$. This slope is plotted in part (b) of the figure. Note that it becomes infinite at $x = 0$.

**SLOPE FUNCTION
SINGULARITY**

Let us use all three integration functions and compare their performance in computing the following integral:

$$\int_0^1 \sqrt{x} \, dx$$

To use the `trapz` function, we must evaluate the integrand at a chosen number of points. The number of points determines the

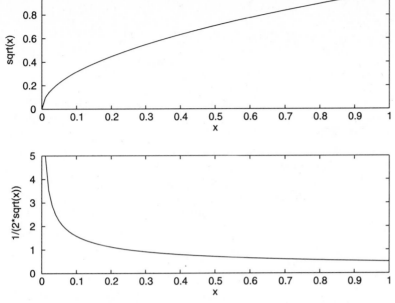

Figure 8.2–2
A function having a singularity in its slope function. The top graph shows the function $y = \sqrt{x}$. The bottom graph shows the derivative of $y = \sqrt{x}$. The slope has a singularity at $x = 0$.

panel width. Here we will use a spacing of 0.01, which requires 100 panels. The script file follows.

```
A1 = quad('sqrt',0,1)
A2 = quad8('sqrt',0,1)
x = [0:.01:1];
y = sqrt(x);
A3 = trapz(0,1)
```

The answers are $A_1 = A_2 = 0.6667$ and $A_3 = 0.6665$. The correct answer, which can be obtained analytically, is $2/3 = 0.6667$ to four decimal places. The quad function in this example produces a message warning that a singularity might be present; however, it still obtains the correct answer. The quad8 function does not produce such a message here, which indicates that this function is more capable of dealing with the singularity. The trapz is not affected by the slope singularity here, and it gives a reasonably accurate answer.

You can use quad and quad8 to integrate user-defined functions, as shown in the following example. Because the quad and quad8 functions call the integrand function using vector arguments, you must always use array operations when defining the function. The following example shows how this is done.

Example 8.2–2   Evaluation of Fresnel's cosine integral

Some simple looking integrals cannot be evaluated in closed form. An example is Fresnel's cosine integral:

$$\int_0^b \cos x^2 \, dx \qquad (8.2\text{--}2)$$

Compute the integral when the upper limit is $b = \sqrt{2\pi}$.

Solution:

Plot $\cos x^2$ and its slope versus x for $0 \le x \le \sqrt{2\pi}$ and use the plots to check for any singularities that might cause problems for the integration function. Use a small enough step size to identify such points. Using 300 plotting points, the plot shows no problems.

Use the quad function to evaluate the integral. Define the integrand with a user-defined function as shown by the following function file:

```
function c2 = cossq(x)
% cosine squared function.
c2 = cos(x.^2);
```

Note that we must use array exponentiation. The quad function is called as follows: quad('cossq',0,sqrt(2*pi)). The result is 0.6119.

The quad functions have two optional arguments. For example, the full syntax of the quad function is

```
quad('function',a,b,tol,trace)
```

where tol indicates the specified error tolerance. The function iterates until the relative error is less than tol. The default value of tol is 10^{-3}. The trace argument, when nonzero, generates a "point plot" that shows the integrand evaluated at the points used by the function to compute the integral. The spacing will be closer near singularities.

Test Your Understanding

T8.2–2 Use both the quad and quad8 functions to compute the integral

$$\int_2^5 \frac{1}{x} \, dx$$

and compare the answers with that obtained from the closed form solution.

T8.2–3 Generate the point plot for the square root function by typing quad('sqrt',0,1,.001,1). Notice where the spacing is closest. Generate the point plot using the `quad8` function and compare the two plots.

As we have seen, the derivative of a function can be interpreted graphically as the slope of the function. This interpretation leads to methods for computing the derivative numerically. Numerical differentiation must be performed when we do not have the function represented as a formula that can be differentiated using the rules presented in section 8.1. Two major types of applications require numerical differentiation. In the first type, data has been collected and must be analyzed afterward using *postprocessing* to find rates of change. In the second type, the rates must be estimated in *real time* as the measurements are made. This application occurs in control systems. For example, an aircraft autopilot needs to estimate the rate of change of pitch angle to control the aircraft properly. Numerical differentiation with postprocessing can use all of the data and need not be particularly fast. However, real-time numerical differentiation requires a fast algorithm that can use only the data measured up to the current time. These two requirements place a heavier demand on real time algorithms as compared to postprocessing algorithms.

Here we will introduce some simple algorithms for computing the derivative numerically. Consider Figure 8.3–1, which shows three data points that represent a function $y(x)$. Recall that the definition of the derivative is

$$\frac{dy}{dx} = \lim_{\Delta x \to 0} \frac{\Delta y}{\Delta x} \qquad \text{(8.3–1)}$$

The success of numerical differentiation depends heavily on two factors: the spacing of the data points and the scatter present

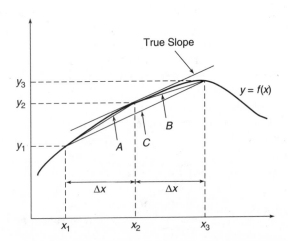

Figure 8.3–1
Illustration of methods for estimating the derivative dy/dx.

376

**Numerical
Methods for
Calculus and
Differential
Equations**

in the data due to measurement error. The greater the spacing, the more difficult it is to estimate the derivative. We assume here that the spacing between the measurements is regular; that is, $x_3 - x_2 = x_2 - x_1 = \Delta x$. Suppose we want to estimate the derivative dy/dx at the point x_2. The correct answer is the slope of the straight line passing through the point (x_2, y_2), but we do not have a second point on that line, so we cannot find its slope. Therefore, we must estimate the slope by using nearby data points. One estimate can be obtained from the straight line labeled A in the figure. Its slope is

$$m_A = \frac{y_2 - y_1}{x_2 - x_1} = \frac{y_2 - y_1}{\Delta x} \qquad (8.3\text{--}2)$$

BACKWARD DIFFERENCE
This estimate of the derivative is called the *backward difference* estimate and is actually a better estimate of the derivative at $x = x_1 + (\Delta x)/2$, rather than at $x = x_2$. Another estimate can be obtained from the straight line labeled B. Its slope is

$$m_B = \frac{y_3 - y_2}{x_3 - x_2} = \frac{y_3 - y_2}{\Delta x} \qquad (8.3\text{--}3)$$

**FORWARD
DIFFERENCE**
This estimate is called the *forward difference* estimate and is a better estimate of the derivative at $x = x_2 + (\Delta x)/2$, rather than at $x = x_2$. Examining the plot, you might think that the average of these two slopes would provide a better estimate of the derivative at $x = x_2$ because the average tends to cancel out the effects of measurement error. The average of m_A and m_B is

$$m_C = \frac{m_A + m_B}{2} = \frac{1}{2}\left(\frac{y_2 - y_1}{\Delta x} + \frac{y_3 - y_2}{\Delta x}\right) = \frac{y_3 - y_1}{2\Delta x} \qquad (8.3\text{--}4)$$

CENTRAL DIFFERENCE
This is the slope of the line labeled C, which connects the first and third data points. This estimate of the derivative is called the *central difference* estimate.

The diff Function

MATLAB provides the `diff` function to use for computing derivative estimates. Its syntax is `d = diff(x)`, where x is a vector of values, and the result is a vector d containing the differences between adjacent elements in x. That is, if x has n elements, d will have $n - 1$ elements, where $d = [x(2)-x(1), x(3)-x(2), \cdots, x(n)-x(n-1)]$. For example, if x = [5, 7, 12, -20], then diff(x) returns the vector [2, 5, -32].

Let us compare the backward difference and central difference methods by considering a sinusoidal signal that is measured 51 times during one half-period. The measurements are in error by a uniformly distributed error between -0.025 and 0.025. Figure 8.3–2 shows the data and the underlying sine curve. The following script file implements the two methods. The results are shown in Figure 8.3–3. Clearly the central difference method does better in this example.

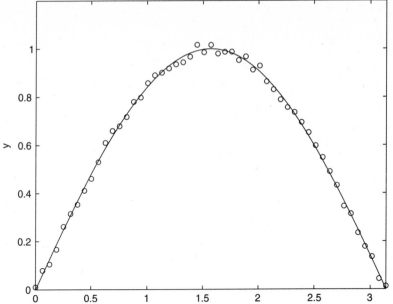

Figure 8.3–2
Measurements of a sine function containing uniformly distributed random
errors between −0.025 and 0.025.

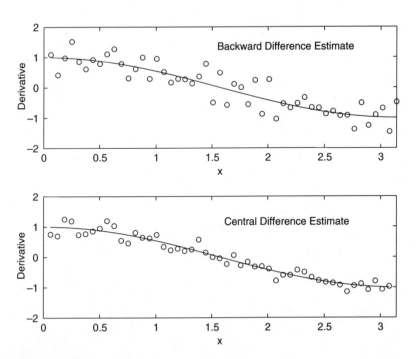

Figure 8.3–3
Comparison of backward difference and central difference methods for the
data shown in Figure 8.5–2.

```
% comparison of numerical derivative algorithms
x = [0:pi/50:pi];
n = length(x);
% true derivative
td = cos(x);
% generating function with +/-0.025 random error.
y = sin(x)+.05*(rand(1,51)-.5);
% backward difference
d1 = diff(y)./diff(x);
subplot(2,1,1)
plot(x(2:n),td(2:n),x(2:n),d1,'o'),xlabel('x'),...
ylabel('Derivative'),axis([0 pi -2 2]),...
gtext('Backward Difference Estimate')
% central difference
d2 = (y(3:n)-y(1:n-2))./(x(3:n)-x(1:n-2));
subplot(2,1,2)
plot(x(2:n-1),td(2:n-1),x(2:n-1),d2,'o'),xlabel('x'),...
ylabel('Derivative'),axis([0 pi -2 2]),...
gtext('Central Difference Estimate')
```

Many more-advanced numerical differentiation procedures have been developed; for example, a central difference method using four points instead of two is commonly used. Some algorithms are suitable only for postprocessing, whereas others have been developed specifically for real-time applications. Postprocessing algorithms are covered in advanced texts dealing with data analysis. Real-time algorithms are covered in signal-processing texts.

Test Your Understanding

T8.3-1 Modify the previous program to use the forward difference method to estimate the derivative. Plot the results and compare with the results from the backward and central difference methods.

Polynomial Derivatives

MATLAB provides the polyder function to compute the derivative of a polynomial. The derivative of

$$f(x) = a_1 x^n + a_2 x^{n-1} + a_3 x^{n-2} + \cdots + a_{n-1} x + a_n$$

is

$$\frac{df}{dx} = n a_1 x^{n-1} + (n-1)a_2 x^{n-2} + \cdots + a_{n-1}$$

$$= b_1 x^{n-1} + b_2 x^{n-2} + \cdots + b_{n-1}$$

378

Because polynomial derivatives can be obtained from the preceding formula, the polyder function is technically not a numerical differentiation operation. Its syntax has several forms. The basic form is

```
b = polyder(p)
```

where p is a vector whose elements are the coefficients of the polynomial arranged in descending powers; that is, $p = [a_1, a_2, \cdots, a_n]$. The output of polyder is the vector b containing the coefficients of the derivative; that is, $b = [b_1, b_2, \cdots, b_{n-1}]$. The second syntax form is

```
b = polyder(p1,p2)
```

This form computes the derivative of the *product* of the two polynomials p1 and p2. The third form is

```
[num, den] = polyder(p2,p1)
```

This form computes the derivative of the *quotient* $p2/p1$. The vector of coefficients of the numerator of the derivative is given by num. The denominator is given by den.

Here are some examples of the use of polyder. Let $p_1 = 5x + 2$ and $p_2 = 10x^2 + 4x - 3$. Then

$$\frac{dp_2}{dx} = 20x + 4$$

$$p_1 p_2 = 50x^3 + 40x^2 - 7x - 6$$

$$\frac{d(p_1 p_2)}{dx} = 150x^2 + 80 - 7$$

$$\frac{d(p_2/p_1)}{dx} = \frac{50x^2 + 40x + 18}{25x^2 + 20x + 4}$$

Table 8.3–1 Numerical differentiation functions

Command	Description
d = diff(x)	Returns a vector d containing the differences between adjacent elements in the vector x.
b = polyder(p)	Returns a vector b containing the coefficients of the derivative of the polynomial represented by the vector p.
b = polyder(p1,p2)	Returns a vector b containing the coefficients of the polynomial that is the derivative of the product of the polynomials represented by p1 and p2.
[num, den] = polyder(p2,p1)	Returns the vectors num and den containing the coefficients of the numerator and denominator polynomials of the derivative of the quotient p_2/p_1, where p1 and p2 are polynomials.

380

**Numerical
Methods for
Calculus and
Differential
Equations**

These results can be obtained as follows:

```
p1 = [5, 2];p2 = [10, 4, -3];
der2 = polyder(p2)
prod = polyder(p1,p2)
[num, den] = polyder(p2,p1)
```

The results are `der2 = [20, 4]`, `prod = [150, 80, -7]`, `num = [50, 40, 23]`, and `den = [25, 20, 4]`. The numerical differentiation functions are summarized in Table 8.3–1.

8.4

Analytical Solutions to Differential Equations

In this section we introduce some important concepts and terminology associated with differential equations, and we develop analytical solutions to some differential equations commonly found in engineering applications. These solutions will give us insight into the proper use of numerical methods for solving differential equations. They also give us some test cases to use to check our programs.

Solution by Direct Integration

An *ordinary differential equation (ODE)* is an equation containing ordinary derivatives of the dependent variable. An equation containing partial derivatives with respect to two or more independent variables is a partial differential equation (PDE). Solution methods for PDEs are an advanced topic, and we will not treat them in this text.

A simple example of an ODE is the equation

$$\frac{dy}{dt} = t^2 \tag{8.4–1}$$

Here the dependent variable is y, and t is the independent variable. We can solve for y by integrating both sides of the equation with respect to the independent variable t.

$$\int_0^t \frac{dy}{dt}\, dt = \int_0^t t^2\, dt = \left.\frac{t^3}{3}\right|_0^t = \frac{t^3}{3}$$

The solution is

$$y(t) = y(0) + \frac{t^3}{3} \tag{8.4–2}$$

You can always check your answer by substituting it into the differential equation and evaluating the solution at $t = 0$. Try this method for the preceding solution.

It will be convenient to use the following abbreviated "dot" notation for derivatives.

$$\dot{y}(t) = \frac{dy}{dt} \tag{8.4–3}$$

$$\ddot{y}(t) = \frac{d^2y}{dt^2} \qquad \textbf{(8.4–4)}$$

Oscillatory Forcing Function

Now consider the following equation:

$$\frac{dy}{dt} = f(t) \qquad \textbf{(8.4–5)}$$

The function $f(t)$ is sometimes called the *forcing function* **FORCING FUNCTION** because it "forces" the solution to behave with a certain pattern. Let us see what this pattern is if the forcing function is sinusoidal: $f(t) = \sin \omega t$. We can solve this case with the technique used earlier:

$$\int_0^t \frac{dy}{dt}\, dt = \int_0^t \sin \omega t\, dt = -\left.\frac{\cos \omega t}{\omega}\right|_0^t = \frac{1 - \cos \omega t}{\omega}$$

or

$$y(t)\big|_0^t = y(t) - y(0) = \frac{1 - \cos \omega t}{\omega}$$

The solution is

$$y(t) = y(0) + \frac{1 - \cos \omega t}{\omega} \qquad \textbf{(8.4–6)}$$

A Second-Order Equation

The *order* of a differential equation is the order of its highest derivative. Thus (8.4–1) is a first-order equation. The following is a second-order equation:

$$\frac{d^2y}{dt^2} = t^3 \qquad \textbf{(8.4–7)}$$

To solve it we must integrate twice. Integrating once gives

$$\int_0^t \frac{d^2y}{dt^2}\, dt = \frac{dy}{dt} - \dot{y}(0) = \int_0^t t^3\, dt = \frac{t^4}{4}$$

or

$$\frac{dy}{dt} = \frac{t^4}{4} + \dot{y}(0)$$

Integrating once more gives

$$\int_0^t \frac{dy}{dt}\, dt = y(t) - y(0) = \int_0^t \left[\frac{t^4}{4} + \dot{y}(0)\right] dt = \frac{t^5}{20} + t\dot{y}(0)$$

The solution is $y(t) = t^5/20 + t\dot{y}(0) + y(0)$. Note that because the ODE is second order, we need to specify two initial condition values

382

**Numerical
Methods for
Calculus and
Differential
Equations**

to complete the solution; one of these is the value of the derivative at $t = 0$.

Substitution Method for First-Order Equations

Consider the differential equation

$$\tau \frac{dy}{dt} + y = f(t) \tag{8.4-8}$$

where τ is a constant and $f(t)$ is a given function. This equation is often used as a model to describe time-dependent processes such as the temperature of a cooling object. We could solve this equation by direct integration, but the required algebra is a little complicated, so we will introduce another method.

Linear equations can often be solved with the trial solution form $y(t) = Ae^{st}$. Note that $dy/dt = sAe^{st}$. Substitute this form into the differential equation with $f(t) = 0$ to obtain

$$\tau \frac{dy}{dt} + y = \tau s Ae^{st} + Ae^{st} = 0$$

For the solution to be general, Ae^{st} cannot be 0 and we can cancel it out of the equation to obtain $\tau s + 1 = 0$. This equation is called the *characteristic equation*, and its root $s = -1/\tau$ is the **CHARACTERISTIC ROOT** *characteristic root*. To find A, we evaluate the solution form at $t = 0$. This evaluation gives $y(0) = Ae^0 = A$. Thus the solution is

$$y(t) = y(0)e^{-t/\tau} \tag{8.4-9}$$

FREE RESPONSE This solution is called the *free response* because it describes the behavior or response of the process when the *forcing function* $f(t)$ is 0; that is, when the process is "free" of the influence of $f(t)$. The solution $y(t)$ decays with time if $\tau > 0$. It starts at $y(0)$ when $t = 0$, equals $0.02y(0)$ at $t = 4\tau$, and equals $0.01y(0)$ at $t = 5\tau$. Thus τ gives an indication of how fast $y(t)$ decays, and τ is called **TIME CONSTANT** the *time constant*.

Now suppose that $f(t) = 0$ for $t < 0$ and suddenly increases to the constant value M at $t = 0$. Such a function is called a *step* function because its plot looks like a single stair step. The height of the step is M. The solution form for this case is $y(t) = Ae^{st} + B$. The initial condition gives $B = y(0) - A$, and thus $y(t) = Ae^{st} + y(0) - A$. Substituting this into the differential equation, we find that $\tau s + 1 = 0$ and $A = y(0) - M$. The solution for $y(t)$ is

$$y(t) = y(0)e^{-t/\tau} + M\left(1 - e^{-t/\tau}\right) \tag{8.4-10}$$

FORCED RESPONSE
TOTAL RESPONSE
The *forced response* is the term $M(1 - e^{-t/\tau})$, which is due to the forcing function. Thus we see that the *total response* for this equation is the sum of the free and the forced responses. The forced response is sometimes called the step response if the

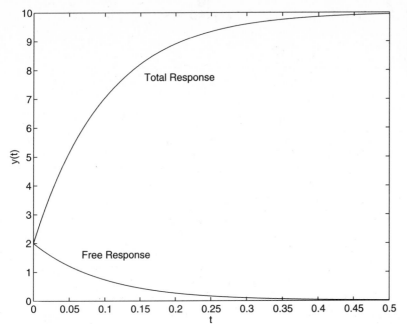

Figure 8.4–1
Free and total step response of the equation $0.1\dot{y} + y = 10$, $y(0) = 2$.

forcing function is a step function. Figure 8.4–1 shows the free
and total response for the case where $\tau = 0.1$, $y(0) = 2$, and
$M = 10$. Note that the free response is essentially 0 (1 percent of
its initial value) after $5\tau = 0.5$ seconds. Note also that the total
response is essentially constant after $5\tau = 0.5$ seconds. Thus the
time constant tells us how long it takes for the free response to
disappear and how long it takes for the total response to reach
steady state.

Nonlinear Equations

Nonlinear ODEs can be recognized by the fact that the dependent
variable or its derivatives appear raised to a power or in a
transcendental function. For example, the following equations
are nonlinear:

$$y\ddot{y} + 5\dot{y} + y = 0$$

$$\dot{y} + \sin y = 0$$

$$\dot{y} + \sqrt{y} = 0$$

Because of the great variety of possible nonlinear equation forms,
no general solution method exists for them. Each class must be
treated separately.

384

**Numerical
Methods for
Calculus and
Differential
Equations**

Substitution Method for Second-Order Equations

Consider the second-order equation

$$\ddot{y} - c^2 y = 0 \qquad \text{(8.4–11)}$$

If we substitute $y(t) = Ae^{st}$ into this equation, we obtain

$$\left(s^2 - c^2\right) Ae^{st} = 0$$

which is satisfied for all values of t only if $s^2 - c^2 = 0$. This gives two values for the unknown constant s; namely, $s = \pm c$. The general solution is

$$y(t) = A_1 e^{ct} + A_2 e^{-ct} \qquad \text{(8.4–12)}$$

Note that the solution becomes infinite as $t \to \infty$ regardless of whether c is positive or negative. If the free response becomes infinite, the equation is said to be *unstable*. If the free response "dies out" (becomes 0), the equation is said to be *stable*. We need two initial conditions to determine the coefficients A_1 and A_2. For example, suppose that $c = 2$, and we are told that $y(0) = 6$ and $\dot{y}(0) = 4$. Then from (8.4–12), $y(0) = 6 = A_1 + A_2$, and $\dot{y}(0) = 2A_1 - 2A_2 = 4$. These two equations have the solutions $A_1 = 4$, $A_2 = 2$.

UNSTABLE EQUATION

STABLE EQUATION

The following second-order equation is similar to (8.4–11) except that the coefficient of y is positive.

$$\ddot{y} + \omega^2 y = 0 \qquad \text{(8.4–13)}$$

Substituting $y(t) = Ae^{st}$ into this equation, we find that the general solution is

$$y(t) = A_1 e^{i\,\omega t} + A_2 e^{-i\,\omega t} \qquad \text{(8.4–14)}$$

This solution is difficult to interpret until we use *Euler's identities*

$$e^{\pm i\,\omega t} = \cos \omega t \pm i \sin \omega t \qquad \text{(8.4–15)}$$

If we substitute these two identities into (8.4–14) and collect terms, we would find that the solution has the form

$$y(t) = B_1 \sin \omega t + B_2 \cos \omega t$$

where B_1 and B_2 are constants that depend on the initial conditions and are $B_1 = \dot{y}(0)/\omega$ and $B_2 = y(0)$. The solution is

$$y(t) = \frac{\dot{y}(0)}{\omega} \sin \omega t + y(0) \cos \omega t \qquad \text{(8.4–16)}$$

The solution oscillates with constant amplitude and a frequency of ω radians per unit time. The *period P* of the oscillation is the time between adjacent peaks and is related to the frequency as follows:

$$P = \frac{2\pi}{\omega} \qquad \text{(8.4–17)}$$

The frequency f in cycles per unit time is given by $f = 1/P$.

The following equation is often used as a model of structural vibrations and some types of electric circuits.

$$m\ddot{y} + c\dot{y} + ky = f(t) \qquad (8.4\text{--}18)$$

Suppose for now that $f(t) = 0$. Substituting $y(t) = Ae^{st}$, we obtain

$$\left(ms^2 + cs + k\right)Ae^{st} = 0$$

which is satisfied for all values of t only if $s^2 + cs + k = 0$. The characteristic roots here can fall into one of the following three categories:

1. Real and distinct: s_1 and s_2
2. Real and equal: s_1
3. Complex conjugates: $s = a \pm i\omega$.

In the first case, the solution form is

$$y(t) = A_1 e^{s_1 t} + A_2 e^{s_2 t} \qquad (8.4\text{--}19)$$

For the second case,

$$y(t) = \left(A_1 + A_2 t\right)e^{s_1 t} \qquad (8.4\text{--}20)$$

For the third case,

$$y(t) = B_1 e^{at} \sin \omega t + B_2 e^{at} \cos \omega t \qquad (8.4\text{--}21)$$

These solutions can be obtained with the same methods used to solve the earlier equations. The values of the constants A_i and B_i depend on the initial conditions. Let us look at four specific cases.

1. **Real, distinct roots:** Suppose that $m = 1$, $c = 8$, and $k = 15$. The characteristic roots are $s = -3, -5$. The form of the free response is

$$y(t) = A_1 e^{-3t} + A_2 e^{-5t}$$

The equation has two time constants, which are the negative reciprocals of the roots. They are $\tau_1 = 1/3$ and $\tau_2 = 1/5$. Note that the term e^{-5t} disappears first and that it corresponds to the smallest time constant. The solution is essentially 0 after the term e^{-3t} disappears. This term corresponds to the largest time constant. The time constant of this term is $\tau = 1/3$, so for most practical purposes the solution will be 0 after $5\tau = 5/3$.

2. **Complex roots:** Suppose that $m = 1$, $c = 10$, and $k = 601$. The characteristic roots are $s = -5 \pm 24i$. The form of the free response is

$$y(t) = B_1 e^{-5t} \sin 24t + B_2 e^{-5t} \cos 24t \qquad (8.4\text{--}22)$$

386

**Numerical
Methods for
Calculus and
Differential
Equations**

This solution will oscillate at a frequency of 24 radians per unit time, which corresponds to a period $P = 2\pi/24 = \pi/12$. The oscillations will disappear when the term e^{-5t} disappears. The time constant of this term is $\tau = 1/5$, so for most practical purposes the oscillations will disappear after $5\tau = 5/5 = 1$. Thus we should see approximately $(5/5)/(\pi/12) \approx 4$ cycles of the oscillations before they die out.

3. **Unstable case, complex roots:** Suppose that $m = 1$, $c = -4$, and $k = 20$. The characteristic roots are $s = 2 \pm 4i$. The form of the free response is

$$y(t) = B_1 e^{2t} \sin 4t + B_2 e^{2t} \cos 4t \qquad \textbf{(8.4–23)}$$

This solution will oscillate at a frequency of 4 radians per unit time, which corresponds to a period $P = 2\pi/4 = \pi/2$. Because the term e^{2t} increases with time, the oscillation amplitude also increases. Because the free response continues to increase, this case is said to be "unstable." You can recognize an unstable linear equation by the fact that at least one of its characteristic roots will have a positive real part.

4. **Unstable case, real roots:** Suppose that $m = 1$, $c = 3$, and $k = -10$. The characteristic roots are $s = 2$ and $s = -5$. The form of the free response is

$$y(t) = A_1 e^{2t} + A_2 e^{-5t}$$

The solution will become infinite as $t \to \infty$ because of the e^{2t} term. Thus the equation is unstable.

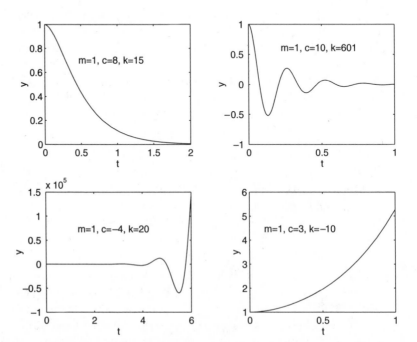

Figure 8.4–2
The free responses for the four cases discussed in the text.

Figure 8.4–2 shows the response for each case the initial conditions $y(0) = 1$, $\dot{y}(0) = 0$. In the next section we will we how to obtain these plots.

T8.4-1 Find the form of the free response of the following equations:

    a. $\ddot{y} + 11\dot{y} + 28y = 0$
    b. $\ddot{y} + 6\dot{y} + 34y = 0$
    c. $\ddot{y} - 2\dot{y} - 15y = 0$
    d. $\ddot{y} + 6\dot{y} - 40y = 0$

Summary

The solutions obtained in this section can be used to check the results of a numerical solution technique. In addition, these solutions have also pointed out the following facts that will be helpful for properly using the numerical techniques presented in the next section.

1. For certain types of differential equations, called linear equations, the characteristic polynomial can be found by making the substitution $y(t) = Ae^{st}$.
2. If any of the characteristic roots has a positive real part, the equation is unstable. If all the roots have negative real parts, the equation is stable.
3. If the equation is stable, the time constants can be found from the negative reciprocal of the real parts of the characteristic roots.
4. The equation's largest time constant indicates how long the solution takes to reach steady state.
5. The equation's smallest time constant indicates how fast the solution changes with t.
6. The frequency of oscillation of the free response can be found from the imaginary parts of the characteristic roots.
7. The rate of change of the forcing function affects the rate of change of the solution. In particular, if the forcing function oscillates, the solution of a linear equation will also oscillate and at the same frequency.
8. The number of initial conditions needed to obtain the solution equals the order of the equation.

8.5

**Numerical
Methods for
Differential
Equations**

It is not always possible to obtain the closed-form solution of a differential equation. In this section we introduce numerical methods for solving differential equations. First we treat first-order equations, and in the next section we show how to extend

388

**Numerical
Methods for
Calculus and
Differential
Equations**

the techniques to higher-order equations. The essence of a numerical method is to convert the differential equation into a difference equation that can be programmed on a calculator or digital computer. Numerical algorithms differ partly as a result of the specific procedure used to obtain the difference equations. In general, as the accuracy of the approximation is increased, so is the complexity of the programming involved. Understanding the concept of *step size* and its effects on solution accuracy is important. To provide a simple introduction to these issues, we begin with the simplest numerical method, the *Euler method*.

The Euler Method

EULER METHOD

The *Euler method* is the simplest algorithm for numerical solution of a differential equation. It usually gives the least accurate results but provides a basis for understanding more sophisticated methods. Consider the equation

$$\frac{dy}{dt} = r(t)y \tag{8.5-1}$$

where $r(t)$ is a known function. From the definition of the derivative,

$$\frac{dy}{dt} = \lim_{\Delta t \to 0} \frac{y(t + \Delta t) - y(t)}{\Delta t}$$

If the time increment Δt is small enough, the derivative can be replaced by the approximate expression

$$\frac{dy}{dt} \approx \frac{y(t + \Delta t) - y(t)}{\Delta t} \tag{8.5-2}$$

Use (8.5–2) to replace (8.5–1) by the following approximation:

$$\frac{y(t + \Delta t) - y(t)}{\Delta t} = r(t)y(t)$$

or

$$y(t + \Delta t) = y(t) + r(t)y(t)\Delta t \tag{8.5-3}$$

Assume that the right side of (8.5–1) remains constant over the time interval $(t, t + \Delta t)$. Then equation (8.5–3) can be written in more convenient form as follows:

$$y(t_{k+1}) = y(t_k) + r(t_k)y(t_k)\Delta t \tag{8.5-4}$$

where $t_{k+1} = t_k + \Delta t$. The smaller Δt is, the more accurate are our two assumptions leading to (8.5–4). This technique for replacing a differential equation with a difference equation is the Euler method. The increment Δt is called the *step size*. The Euler method for the general first-order equation $\dot{y} = f(t, y)$ is

STEP SIZE

$$y(t_{k+1}) = y(t_k) + \Delta t f[t_k, y(t_k)] \tag{8.5-5}$$

This equation can be applied successively at the times t_k by putting it in a for loop. For example, the following script file solves the differential equation $\dot{y} = ry$ and plots the solution over the range $0 \le t \le 0.5$ for the case where $r = -10$ and the initial condition is $y(0) = 2$. The time constant is $\tau = -1/r = 0.1$, and the true solution is $y(t) = 2e^{-10t}$. To illustrate the effect of the step size on the solution's accuracy, we use a step size $\Delta t = 0.02$, which is 20 percent of the time constant.

```
r = -10; delta = .02; y(1) = 2;
k = 0;
for time = [delta:delta:.5]
    k = k + 1;
    y(k+1) = y(k) + r*y(k)*delta;
end
t = [0:delta:.5];
y_true = 2*exp(-10*t);
plot(t,y,'o',t,y_true),xlabel('t'),ylabel('y')
```

Figure 8.5–1 shows the results. The numerical solution is shown by the small circles. The true solution is shown by the solid line. There is some noticeable error. If we had used a step size equal to 5 percent of the time constant, the error would not be noticeable on the plot.

Numerical methods have their greatest errors when trying to obtain solutions that are rapidly changing. Rapid changes can

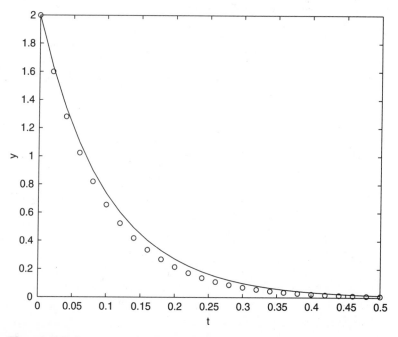

Figure 8.5–1
Euler-method solution for the free response of $\dot{y} = -10y$, $y(0) = 2$.

390

**Numerical
Methods for
Calculus and
Differential
Equations**

be due to small time constants or to oscillations. To illustrate the difficulties caused by an oscillating solution, consider the following equation

$$\dot{y} = \sin t \qquad\qquad (8.5\text{–}6)$$

for $y(0) = 0$ and $0 \le t \le 4\pi$. The true solution is $y(t) = 1 - \cos t$, and its period is 2π. To compare the results with those obtained from the ode23 function later on, we will use a step size equal to 1/13 of the period, or $\Delta t = 2\pi/13$. The script file is

```
delta = 2*pi/13; y(1) = 0;
k = 0;
for time = [delta:delta:4*pi]
    k = k + 1;
    y(k+1) = y(k) + sin(time-delta)*delta;
end
t_true = [0:delta/10:4*pi];
y_true = 1-cos(t_true);
t = [0:delta:4*pi];
plot(t,y,'o',t_true,y_true),xlabel('t'),ylabel('y')
```

The results are shown in Figure 8.5–2, where the numerical solution is shown by the small circles. There is noticeable error, especially near the peaks and valleys, where the solution is rapidly changing.

The accuracy of the Euler method can be improved by using a smaller step size. However, very small step sizes require longer

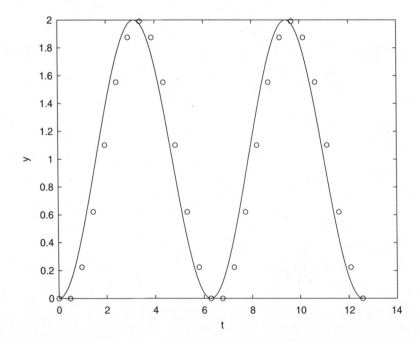

Figure 8.5–2
Euler-method solution of
$\dot{y} = \sin t$, $y(0) = 0$.

run times and can result in a large accumulated error because of round-off effects. So we seek better algorithms to use for more challenging applications.

The Predictor-Corrector Method

We now consider two methods that are more powerful than the Euler method. The first is a *predictor-corrector* method. The second method is the *Runge-Kutta* family of algorithms. In this section we apply these techniques to first-order equations. We then extend them to higher-order equations in the next section.

The Euler method can have a serious deficiency in problems where the variables are rapidly changing because the method assumes the variables are constant over the time interval Δt. One way of improving the method is to use a better approximation to the right side of the equation

$$\frac{dy}{dt} = f(t, y) \tag{8.5-7}$$

The Euler approximation is

$$y(t_{k+1}) = y(t_k) + \Delta t \, f[t_k, y(t_k)] \tag{8.5-8}$$

Suppose instead we use the average of the right side of (8.5–7) on the interval (t_k, t_{k+1}). This gives

$$y(t_{k+1}) = y(t_k) + \frac{\Delta t}{2}\left(f_k + f_{k+1}\right) \tag{8.5-9}$$

where

$$f_k = f[t_k, y(t_k)] \tag{8.5-10}$$

with a similar definition for f_{k+1}. Equation (8.5–9) is equivalent to integrating (8.5–7) with the trapezoidal rule.

The difficulty with (8.5–9) is that f_{k+1} cannot be evaluated until $y(t_{k+1})$ is known, but this is precisely the quantity being sought. A way out of this difficulty is by using the Euler formula (8.5–8) to obtain a preliminary estimate of $y(t_{k+1})$. This estimate is then used to compute f_{k+1} for use in (8.5–9) to obtain the required value of $y(t_{k+1})$.

The notation can be changed to clarify the method. Let $h = \Delta t$ and $y_k = y(t_k)$, and let x_{k+1} be the estimate of $y(t_{k+1})$ obtained from the Euler formula (8.5–8). Then, by omitting the t_k notation from the other equations, we obtain the following description of the predictor-corrector process:

$$\text{Euler predictor}: \quad x_{k+1} = y_k + h f(t_k, y_k) \tag{8.5-11}$$

$$\text{Trapezoidal corrector}: \quad y_{k+1} = y_k + \frac{h}{2}\left[f(t_k, y_k) + f(t_{k+1}, x_{k+1})\right] \tag{8.5-12}$$

This algorithm is sometimes called the *modified Euler method.* However, note that any algorithm can be tried as a predictor or a corrector. Thus many other methods can be classified as predictor-corrector. For purposes of comparison with the Runge-Kutta methods, we can express the modified Euler method as

$$g_1 = hf(t_k, y_k) \tag{8.5--13}$$

$$g_2 = hf(t_k + h, y_k + g_1) \tag{8.5--14}$$

$$y_{k+1} = y_k + \frac{1}{2}(g_1 + g_2) \tag{8.5--15}$$

For example, the following script file solves the differential equation $\dot{y} = ry$ and plots the solution over the range $0 \le t \le 0.5$ for the case where $r = -10$ and the initial condition is $y(0) = 2$. The time constant is $\tau = -1/r = 0.1$, and the true solution is $y(t) = 2e^{-10t}$. To illustrate the effect of the step size on the solution's accuracy, we use a step size $\Delta t = 0.02$, which is 20 percent of the time constant.

```
r = -10; delta = .02; y(1) = 2;
k = 0;
for time = [delta:delta:.5]
    k = k + 1;
    x(k+1) = y(k)+delta*r*y(k);
    y(k+1) = y(k)+(delta/2)*(r*y(k)+r*x(k+1));
end
t = [0:delta:.5];
y_true = 2*exp(-10*t);
plot(t,y,'o',t,y_true),xlabel('t'),ylabel('y')
```

Figure 8.5–3 shows the results, with the numerical solution shown by the small circles and the true solution by the solid line. There is less error than with the Euler method using the same step size.

To illustrate how the modified Euler method works with an oscillating solution, consider the equation $\dot{y} = \sin t$ for $y(0) = 0$ and $0 \le t \le 4\pi$. To compare the results with those obtained with the Euler method, we will use a step size $\Delta t = 2\pi/13$. Note that because the right side of the ODE is not a function of y, we do not need the Euler predictor (8.5–11). The script file is

```
delta = 2*pi/13; y(1)=0;
k = 0;
for time = [delta:delta:4*pi]
    k = k + 1;
    y(k+1) = y(k)+(delta/2)*(sin(time-delta)+sin(time));
end
t_true = [0:delta/10:4*pi];
y_true = 1-cos(t_true);
```

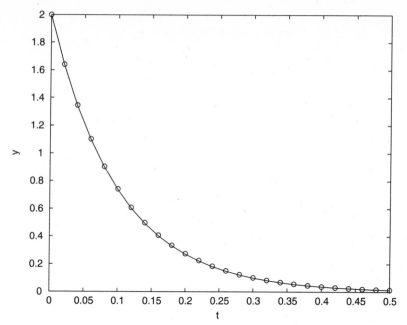

Figure 8.5–3
Modified-Euler solution of $\dot{y} = -10y$, $y(0) = 2$.

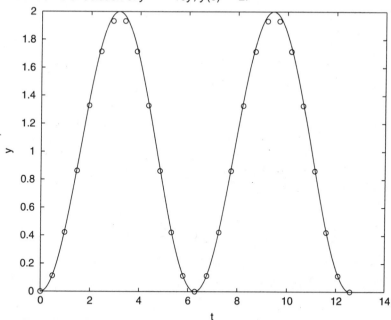

Figure 8.5–4
Modified-Euler solution of $\dot{y} = \sin t$, $y(0) = 0$.

```
t = [0:delta:4*pi];
plot(t,y,'o',t_true,y_true),xlabel('t'),ylabel('y')
```

The results are shown in Figure 8.5–4. The error is less than with
the Euler method, but there is still some noticeable error near the

394

**Numerical
Methods for
Calculus and
Differential
Equations**

peaks and valleys, where the solution is rapidly changing. This error can be decreased by decreasing the step size.

Test Your Understanding

T8.5–1 Use MATLAB to compare the solutions for $0 \leq t \leq 2$ obtained with the Euler and modified Euler methods for the following equation:

$$10\frac{dy}{dt} + y = te^{-2t} \quad y(0) = 2$$

Compare the results with the analytical solution $y(t) = (732e^{-0.1t} - 19te^{-2t} - 10e^{-2t})/361$.

Runge-Kutta Methods

The Taylor series representation forms the basis of several methods for solving differential equations, including the *Runge-Kutta methods*. The Taylor series may be used to represent the solution $y(t + h)$ in terms of $y(t)$ and its derivatives as follows.

$$y(t + h) = y(t) + h\dot{y}(t) + \frac{1}{2}h^2\ddot{y}(t) + \cdots \quad \textbf{(8.5–16)}$$

The number of terms kept in the series determines its accuracy. The required derivatives are calculated from the differential equation. If these derivatives can be found, (8.5–16) can be used to march forward in time. In practice, the high-order derivatives can be difficult to calculate, and the series (8.5–16) is truncated at some term. The Runge-Kutta methods were developed because of the difficulty in computing the derivatives. These methods use several evaluations of the function $f(t, y)$ in a way that approximates the Taylor series. The number of terms in the series that is duplicated determines the order of the Runge-Kutta method. Thus a fourth-order Runge-Kutta algorithm duplicates the Taylor series through the term involving h^4.

The second-order Runge-Kutta methods express y_{k+1} as

$$y_{k+1} = y_k + w_1g_1 + w_2g_2 \quad \textbf{(8.5–17)}$$

where w_1 and w_2 are constant weighting factors and

$$g_1 = hf(t_k, y_k) \quad \textbf{(8.5–18)}$$

$$g_2 = hf(t_k + \alpha h, y_k + \beta hf_k) \quad \textbf{(8.5–19)}$$

The family of second-order Runge-Kutta algorithms is categorized by the parameters α, β, w_1, and w_2. To duplicate the Taylor series through the h^2 term, these coefficients must satisfy the following:

$$w_1 + w_2 = 1 \quad \textbf{(8.5–20)}$$

$$w_1\alpha = \frac{1}{2} \qquad\qquad (8.5\text{--}21)$$

$$w_2\beta = \frac{1}{2} \qquad\qquad (8.5\text{--}22)$$

Thus one of the parameters can be chosen independently.

The family of fourth-order Runge-Kutta algorithms expresses y_{k+1} as

$$y_{k+1} = y_k + w_1g_1 + w_2g_2 + w_3g_3 + w_4g_4 \qquad (8.5\text{--}23)$$

$$g_1 = hf(t_k, y_k) \qquad\qquad (8.5\text{--}24)$$

$$g_2 = hf(t_k + \alpha_1 h, y_k + \alpha_1 g_1)$$

$$g_3 = hf[t_k + \alpha_2 h, y_k + \beta_2 g_2 + (\alpha_2 - \beta_2)g_1]$$

$$g_4 = hf[t_k + \alpha_3 h, y_k + \beta_3 g_2 + \gamma_3 g_3 + (\alpha_3 - \beta_3 - \gamma_3)g_1]$$

Comparison with the Taylor series yields eight equations for the 10 parameters. Thus two parameters can be chosen in light of other considerations. A number of different choices have been used. For example, the classical method, which reduces to Simpson's rule for integration if $f(t, y)$ is a function of only t, uses the following set of parameters:

$$w_1 = w_4 = 1/6 \qquad\qquad (8.5\text{--}25)$$

$$w_2 = w_3 = 1/3$$

$$\alpha_1 = \alpha_2 = 1/2$$

$$\beta_2 = 1/2$$

$$\gamma_3 = \alpha_3 = 1$$

$$\beta_3 = 0$$

MATLAB ODE Solvers ode23 and ode45

In addition to the many variations of the predictor-corrector and Runge-Kutta algorithms that have been developed, some more-advanced algorithms use a variable step-size. These algorithms use larger step sizes when the solution is changing more slowly. MATLAB 4 provides two functions, called *solvers,* that implement Runge-Kutta methods with variable step size. These are the ode23 and ode45 functions. The ode23 function uses a combination of second- and third-order Runge-Kutta methods, whereas ode45 uses a combination of fourth- and fifth-order methods. In general, ode45 is faster and more accurate, but it uses larger step

396

**Numerical
Methods for
Calculus and
Differential
Equations**

Table 8.5–1   ODE solvers

Solver name	Description
ode23	Nonstiff, low-order solver (MATLAB 4 and higher).
ode45	Nonstiff, medium-order solver (MATLAB 4 and higher).
ode113	Nonstiff, variable-order solver (MATLAB 5.0 and higher).
ode23s	Stiff, low-order solver (MATLAB 5.2 and higher).
ode23t	Moderately stiff, trapezoidal-rule solver (MATLAB 5.2 and higher).
ode23tb	Stiff, low-order solver (MATLAB 5.2 and higher).
ode15s	Stiff, variable-order solver (MATLAB 5.2 and higher).

sizes that can produce a solution plot that is not as smooth as the plot produced with ode23. These solvers, which are classified as low order and medium order, respectively, are also available in MATLAB 5. A new solver was added to MATLAB 5.0; this solver is ode113, which is based on a variable-order algorithm. In addition, the solver syntax has been changed in MATLAB 5. The examples in this section work in MATLAB 5 only. However, with a slight modification, the examples can be made to work in MATLAB 4. These modifications are indicated at the appropriate point.

MATLAB 5.2 contains four additional solvers; these are ode23t, ode15s, ode23s, and ode23tb. These and the other solvers are categorized in Table 8.5–1. Some of these solvers are classified as "stiff." A stiff solver is one that is well-suited for solving *stiff equations,* which are described in section 8.8. Note that because the current version of the Student Edition is based on MATLAB 5.0, it has only the ode23, ode45, and ode113 solvers. However, these solvers are more than sufficient to solve the problems in this text. In addition to the syntax change, new capabilities have been added to the ODE solvers in MATLAB 5. These features are covered in section 8.8.

Solver Syntax

In this section we limit our coverage to first-order equations. Solution of higher-order equations, where **y** is a vector, is covered in section 8.6. When used to solve the equation $\dot{y} = f(t, y)$, the basic syntax for MATLAB 5 is (using ode23 as the example):

```
[t,y] = ode23('ydot', tspan, y0)
```

where ydot is the name of the function file whose inputs must be t and y and whose output must be a column vector representing dy/dt; that is, $f(t, y)$. The number of rows in this column vector must equal the order of the equation. The syntax for ode23, ode45, and ode113 is identical. The vector tspan contains the starting and ending values of the independent variable t, and optionally, any intermediate values of t where the solution is desired. For example, if no intermediate values are specified, tspan is [t0, tf], where t0 and tf are the desired starting and ending values of the independent parameter t. As another

Table 8.5–2 Basic syntax of ODE solvers

Command	Description
`[t, y] = ode23('ydot', tspan, y0)`	Solves the vector differential equation $\dot{\mathbf{y}} = \mathbf{f}(t, \mathbf{y})$ specified in the function file `ydot`, whose inputs must be t and $\mathbf{y}$ and whose output must be a *column* vector representing $d\mathbf{y}/dt$; that is, $\mathbf{f}(t, \mathbf{y})$. The number of rows in this column vector must equal the order of the equation. The vector `tspan` contains the starting and ending values of the independent variable t, and optionally, any intermediate values of t where the solution is desired. The vector `y0` contains $\mathbf{y}(t_0)$. The function file must have two input arguments t and y even for equations where $\mathbf{f}(t, \mathbf{y})$ is not a function of t. The syntax is identical for the other solvers.

example, using `tspan = [0, 5, 10]` tells MATLAB to find the solution at $t = 5$ and at $t = 10$. You can solve equations backward in time by specifying `t0` to be greater than `tf`. The parameter `y0` is the value $y(t_0)$. The function file must have two input arguments t and y even for equations where $f(t, y)$ is not a function of t. You need not use array operations in the function file because the ODE solvers call the file with scalar values for the arguments.

The only change in the basic syntax from MATLAB 4 involves `tspan`. In MATLAB 4 no intermediate values of t can be specified, and the values `t0` and `tf` cannot be specified in a vector. The MATLAB 4 basic syntax is thus

```
[t, y] = ode23('ydot', t0, tf, y0)
```

The basic syntax of ODE solvers is summarized in Table 8.5–2.

As a first example of using a solver, let us solve an equation whose solution is known in closed form so that we can make sure we are using the method correctly.

Example 8.5–1 Response of an RC circuit

The model of the RC circuit shown in Figure 8.5–5 can be found from Kirchhof's voltage law and conservation of charge.

$$RC\frac{dy}{dt} + y = v(t)$$

Suppose the value of RC is 0.1 second. Use a numerical method to find the free response for the case where the applied voltage v

Figure 8.5–5
An RC circuit.

398

**Numerical
Methods for
Calculus and
Differential
Equations**

is 0 and the initial capacitor voltage is $y(0) = 2$ volts. Compare the results with the analytical solution.

Solution:

The equation for the circuit becomes

$$0.1\dot{y} + y = 0$$

First solve this for $\dot{y}$:

$$\dot{y} = -10y$$

Next define the following function file. Note that the order of the input arguments must be t and y.

```
function ydot = rccirc(t,y)
% An RC circuit model with no applied voltage.
ydot = -10*y;
```

The initial time is $t = 0$, so set t0 to be 0. The time constant is 0.1, so the response will be 2 percent of its initial value at $t = 4(0.1) = 0.4$ seconds and 1 percent at $t = 5(0.1) = 0.5$ seconds. So we can choose tf to be between 0.4 and 0.5 seconds, depending on how much of the response we wish to see. The analytical solution is $y(t) = 2e^{-10t}$. The function is called in MATLAB 5 as follows, and the solution plotted along with the analytical solution y_true.

```
[t, y] = ode45('rccirc', [0, .4], 2);
y_true = 2*exp(-10*t);
```

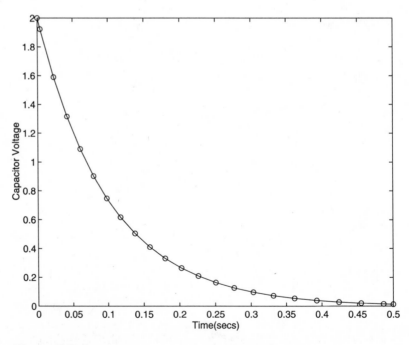

Figure 8.5–6
Free response of an RC circuit.

```
plot(t,y,'o',t,y_true), xlabel('Time(secs)'),...
ylabel('Capacitor Voltage')
```

Note that we need not generate the array t to evaluate y_true, because t is generated by the ode45 function. The plot is shown in Figure 8.5–6. The numerical solution is marked by the circles, and the analytical solution is indicated by the solid line. The numerical solution clearly gives an accurate answer. Note that the step size automatically selected by the ode45 function is 0.02, which is the same step size we used with the Euler method to obtain Figure 8.5–1. Comparing the two plots demonstrates the accuracy of the Runge-Kutta algorithm relative to the Euler method.

To solve this problem in MATLAB 4, simply replace the first line with

```
[t, y] = ode45('rccirc', 0, .4, 2);
```

Effect of Step Size

The spacing used by ode23 is smaller than that used by ode45 because ode45 has less truncation error than ode23 and thus can use a larger step size. When the solution changes rapidly, such as with an oscillatory solution, the circles representing the numerical solution do not always yields a smooth curve. Thus ode23 is sometimes more useful for plotting the solution because it often gives a smoother curve. For example, consider the equation

$$\frac{dy}{dt} = \sin t$$

whose analytical solution is $y(t) = 1 - \cos t$. To solve the differential equation numerically, define the following function file:

```
function ydot = sinefn(t,y)
ydot = sin(t);
```

Use the following script file to compute the solution for $y(0) = 0$:

```
t_true = [0:.01:4*pi];
subplot(2,1,1)
[t, y] = ode45('sinefn', [0, 4*pi], 0);
y1_true = 1 - cos(t_true);
plot(t,y,'o',t_true,y1_true), xlabel('t'), ylabel('y'),...
axis([0 4*pi -.5 2.5]),gtext('ode45')
subplot(2,1,2)
[t, y] = ode23('sinefn', [0, 4*pi], 0);
y2_true = 1 - cos(t_true);
plot(t,y,'o',t_true,y2_true), xlabel('t'),ylabel ('y'),...
axis([0 4*pi -.5 2.5]),gtext('ode23')
```

Figure 8.5–7 shows the solution generated by ode45 (the top graph) and ode23 (the bottom graph). Note the difference in step sizes.

400

**Numerical
Methods for
Calculus and
Differential
Equations**

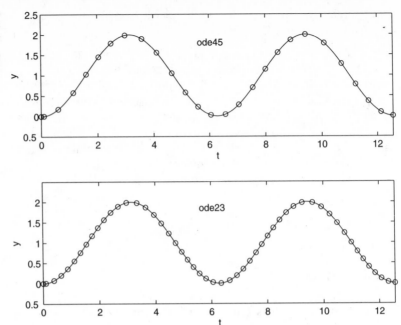

Figure 8.5–7
Numerical solutions of the equation $\dot{y} = \sin t$, $y(0) = 0$.

Numerical Methods and Linear Equations

Even though there are general methods available for finding the
analytical solutions of linear differential equations, it is nevertheless sometimes more convenient to use a numerical method
to find the solution. Examples of such situations are when the
forcing function is a complicated function or when the order of the
differential equation is higher than two. In such cases the algebra
involved in obtaining the analytical solution might not be worth
the effort, especially if the main objective is to obtain a plot of the
solution. In such cases we can still use the characteristic roots to
check the validity of the numerical results. The following example demonstrates this method for an equation with a complicated
forcing function.

Use of Global Parameters

The `global x y z` command allows all functions and files using
that command to share the values of the variables x, y, and z.
Use of the `global` command avoids the necessity of changing
the values of certain parameters in every file. Example 8.5–2
demonstrates the use of this command.

Example 8.5–2 Decaying sine voltage applied
to an RC circuit Consider the RC circuit shown in Fig-
ure 8.5–5 where $RC = 0.1$ second. Now suppose that the applied

voltage oscillates sinusoidally with a period P and a decaying amplitude. The voltage is given by

$$v(t) = 10e^{-t/\tau_1} \sin(2\pi t/P) \qquad (8.5\text{–}26)$$

Thus the voltage amplitude will be less than 2 percent of its initial value, or essentially 0 for $t \geq 4\tau_1$. Find and plot the output voltage $y(t)$ for three cases:

1. $\tau_1 = 0.3$ seconds, $P = 2$ seconds.
2. $\tau_1 = 0.05$ seconds, $P = 0.03$ seconds.
3. $\tau_1 = 0.3$ seconds, $P = 0.03$ seconds.

Interpret the results in light of the circuit's characteristic root. In all three cases, take the initial voltage $y(0)$ to be 0.

Solution:

The circuit's equation was given earlier. It is

$$RC\frac{dy}{dt} + y = v(t) \qquad (8.5\text{–}27)$$

Solving for the derivative and using $RC = 0.1$, we obtain

$$\frac{dy}{dt} = 10[v(t) - y] \qquad (8.5\text{–}28)$$

In this problem we will be examining the effects of changing the values of the parameters τ_1, P, and the final time t_f. Therefore, we will declare these parameters as global. The function file for the derivative is

```
function ydot = circuit(t,y)
% RC circuit model with a decaying sine input.
global tau_1 P
v = 10*exp(-t/tau_1)*sin((2*pi/P)*t);
ydot = 10*(v-y);
```

The ode23 solver is called with the script file circplot.m:

```
% file circplot
% Solves the circuit equation and plots the response.
global  tau_1 P tf
tau_1 = .3;
P = 2;
tf = 2;
[t, y] = ode23('circuit', [0, tf], 0);
subplot(2,1,1)
tp = [0:tf/300:tf];
v = 10*exp(-tp/tau_1).*sin((2*pi/P)*tp);
plot(tp,v),xlabel('Time (sec)'),...
ylabel('Applied Voltage (volts)')
subplot(2,1,2)
plot(t,y),xlabel('Time (sec)'),...
ylabel('Capacitor Voltage (volts)')
```

402

**Numerical
Methods for
Calculus and
Differential
Equations**

The simulation is performed by entering the desired values of τ_1, P, and t_f in the file `circplot`, saving the file, and typing `circplot` at the prompt. Note that you need not change the file `circuit`. Note also that the variable `tf` need not be declared global in the file `circuit` because that file does not use `tf`.

The circuit's time constant is $\tau = RC = 0.1$ second. Therefore, if the applied voltage v is constant, the output voltage y will reach a constant value after approximately $4\tau = 0.4$ second. So the "speed of response" of the circuit is about 0.4 second. The applied voltage will be essentially 0 after $t = 4\tau_1$. We must estimate the final time `tf` to use. This time is determined by the larger of the times $4\tau = 0.4$ and $4\tau_1$. Now let us look at each case.

Case 1: $\tau_1 = 0.3$, $P = 2$. In this case the applied voltage will be essentially 0 after $t = 4\tau_1 = 1.2$ seconds, which is longer than the response time of the circuit. So we choose a final time t_f no less than 1.2. However, because the period of the applied voltage is 2 seconds, we select $t_f = 2$ seconds to see the effects of one full period. The resulting plot is shown in Figure 8.5–8 along with a plot of the applied voltage for reference. Because the period is greater than 4τ, we do not see oscillations in the capacitor voltage; that is, the circuit's response has died out before the applied voltage can complete one cycle. The plot shows no discrepancies from the behavior predicted on the basis the circuit's time constant and the time constant and period of the applied voltage.

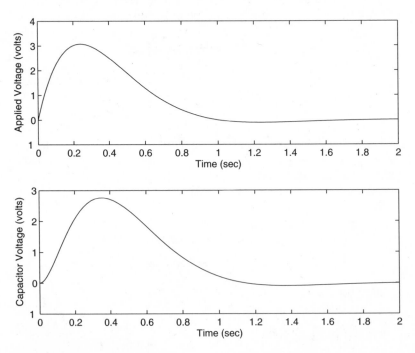

Figure 8.5–8
Plots of the applied voltage and the capacitor voltage when the applied voltage is $v(t) = 10e^{-t/0.3}\sin(\pi t)$.

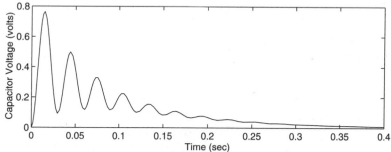

Figure 8.5–9
Plots of the applied voltage and the capacitor voltage when the applied voltage is $v(t) = 10e^{-t/0.05}\sin(2\pi t/0.03)$.

Case 2: $\tau_1 = 0.05$, $P = 0.03$. In this case the applied voltage will be essentially 0 after $t = 4\tau = 0.2$ second, and its period is 0.03, both of which are shorter than the circuit's response time (0.4 second). So the proper final time to use is determined by the response time of the circuit and thus we choose a final time of $t_f = 0.4$. The results are shown in Figure 8.5–9. Because the period is shorter than both 4τ and $4\tau_1$, we should see oscillations in the capacitor voltage, and we do. The capacitor voltage is essentially 0 after 0.4 second, as predicted.

Case 3: $\tau_1 = 0.3$, $P = 0.03$. In this case the applied voltage will be essentially 0 after $t = 4\tau_1 = 1.2$ seconds, which is longer than the period and the response time of the circuit. So we expect to see oscillations in the solution; the proper final time is determined by the decay time of the applied voltage and should be at least 1.2. The results are shown in Figure 8.5–10. Because the period is shorter than both 4τ and $4\tau_1$, we should see oscillations in the capacitor voltage, and we do.

Test Your Understanding

T8.5–2 Suppose you want to run several simulations of the equation

$$\tau\frac{dy}{dt} + y = a + b\sin ct, \quad y(0) = y_0$$

404

**Numerical
Methods for
Calculus and
Differential
Equations**

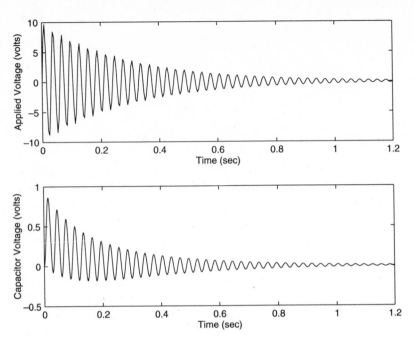

Figure 8.5–10
Plots of the applied voltage and the capacitor voltage when the applied
voltage is $v(t) = 10e^{-t/0.3}\sin(2\pi t/0.03)$.

for several values of τ, a, b, c, and y_0. Write a program to
do this using the `global` command.

Solution of Nonlinear Equations

When the differential equation is nonlinear, we often have no analytical solution to use for checking our numerical results. In such
cases we can use our physical insight to guard against grossly
incorrect results. We can also check the equation for singularities
that might affect the numerical procedure. Finally, we can sometimes use an approximation to replace the nonlinear equation
with a linear one that can be solved analytically. Although the linear approximation does not give the exact answer, its solution can
be used to see whether our numerical answer is "in the ballpark."
Example 8.5–3 illustrates this approach.

Example 8.5–3 Liquid height in a spherical
tank Figure 8.5–11 shows a spherical tank for storing water. The
tank is filled through a hole in the top and drained through a hole in
the bottom. If the tank's radius is r, you can use integration to show
that the volume of water in the tank as a function of its height h is
given by

$$V(h) = \pi r h^2 - \pi \frac{h^3}{3} \qquad (8.5\text{--}29)$$

Figure 8.5-11
Draining of a spherical tank.

Torricelli's principle (see Chapter 4) states that the liquid flow rate through the hole is proportional to the square root of the height h. Further studies in fluid mechanics have identified the relation more precisely, and the result is that the volume flow rate through the hole is given by

$$q = C_d A \sqrt{2gh} \qquad (8.5\text{–}30)$$

where A is the area of the hole, g is the acceleration due to gravity, and C_d is an experimentally determined value that depends partly on the type of liquid. For water, $C_d = 0.6$ is a common value. We can use the principle of conservation of mass to obtain a differential equation for the height h. Applied to this tank, the principle says that the rate of change of liquid volume in the tank must equal the volume flow rate out of the tank; that is

$$\frac{dV}{dt} = -q \qquad (8.5\text{–}31)$$

From (8.5-29),

$$\frac{dV}{dt} = 2\pi r h \frac{dh}{dt} - \pi h^2 \frac{dh}{dt} = \pi h (2r - \pi h) \frac{dh}{dt}$$

Substituting this and (8.5–30) into (8.5–31) gives the required equation for h.

$$\pi \left(2rh - h^2\right) \frac{dh}{dt} = -C_d A \sqrt{2gh} \qquad (8.5\text{–}32)$$

Use MATLAB to solve this equation to determine how long it will take for the tank to empty if the initial height is 9 feet. The tank has a radius of $r = 5$ feet and has a 1-inch diameter hole in the bottom. Use $g = 32.2$ feet/second^2. Discuss how to check the solution.

Solution:

With $C_d = 0.6$, $r = 5$, $g = 32.2$, and $A = \pi(1/24)^2$, (8.5–32) becomes

$$\frac{dh}{dt} = -\frac{0.0334 \sqrt{h}}{10h - h^2} \qquad (8.5\text{–}33)$$

Because this is a nonlinear equation, we have no analytical solution to use for checking our numerical results. We can use our physical insight to guard against grossly incorrect results. We can also check

406

**Numerical
Methods for
Calculus and
Differential
Equations**

the above expression for *dh/dt* for singularities. The denominator does not become 0 unless $h = 0$ or $h = 10$, which correspond to a completely empty and a completely full tank. So we will avoid singularities if $0 < h(0) < 10$. Finally, we can use the following approximation to estimate the time to empty. Replace *h* on the right side of (8.5–33) with its average value, namely, $(9 - 0)/2 = 4.5$ feet. This gives *dh/dt* = -0.00286, whose solution is $h(t) = h(0) - 0.00286t = 9 - 0.00286t$. According to this equation, if $h(0) = 9$, the tank will be empty at $t = 9/0.00286 = 3147$ seconds, or 52 minutes. We will use this value as a reality check on our answer.

The function file based on equation (8.5–33) is

```
function hdot = height(t,h)
hdot = -(.0334*sqrt(h))/(10*h-h^2);
```

The file is called as follows, using the ode45 solver.

```
[t, h] = ode45('height', [0, 2475], 9);
plot(t,h),xlabel('Time (sec)'),ylabel('Height (ft)')
```

The resulting plot is shown in Figure 8.5–12. Note how the height changes more rapidly when the tank is nearly full or nearly empty. This condition is to be expected because of the effects of the tank's curvature. The tank empties in 2475 seconds, or 41 minutes. This value is not grossly different from our rough estimate of 52 minutes, so we should feel comfortable accepting the numerical results.

The value of the final time of 2475 seconds was found by increasing the final time until the plot showed that the height became 0. You

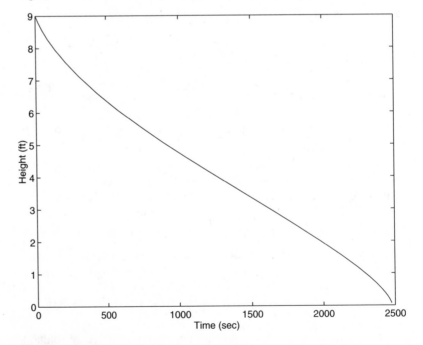

Figure 8.5–12
Plot of water height in a spherical tank.

could use a `while` loop to do this, by increasing the final time in the loop while calling `ode45` repeatedly. However, new capabilities are provided in MATLAB 5 for detecting when the height becomes 0. We will examine these capabilities in section 8.7.

Extension to Higher-Order Equations

To use the ODE solvers to solve an equation higher than order 2, you must first write the equation as a set of first-order equations. This is easily done. Consider the second-order equation

$$5\ddot{y} + 7\dot{y} + 4y = f(t) \qquad \textbf{(8.6–1)}$$

Solve it for the highest derivative:

$$\ddot{y} = \frac{1}{5}f(t) - \frac{4}{5}y - \frac{7}{5}\dot{y} \qquad \textbf{(8.6–2)}$$

Define two new variables x_1 and x_2 to be y and its derivative $\dot{y}$. That is, define

$$x_1 = y$$

$$x_2 = \dot{y}$$

These definitions imply that

$$\dot{x}_1 = x_2$$

$$\dot{x}_2 = \frac{1}{5}f(t) - \frac{4}{5}x_1 - \frac{7}{5}x_2$$

This form is sometimes called the *Cauchy form* or the *state-variable form*.

CAUCHY FORM

STATE-VARIABLE FORM

Now write a function file that computes the values of $\dot{x}_1$ and $\dot{x}_2$ and stores them in a *column* vector. To do so, we must first have a function specified for $f(t)$. Suppose that $f(t) = \sin t$. Then the required file is

```
function xdot = example1(t,x)
% Computes derivatives of two equations
xdot(1) = x(2);
xdot(2) = (1/5)*(sin(t)-4*x(1)-7*x(2));
xdot = [xdot(1); xdot(2)];
```

Note that `xdot(1)` represents $\dot{x}_1$, `xdot(2)` represents $\dot{x}_2$, `x(1)` represents x_1, and `x(2)` represents x_2. Once you become familiar with the notation for the state-variable form, you will see that the preceding code could be replaced with the following shorter form:

```
function xdot = example1(t,x)
% Computes derivatives of two equations
xdot = [x(2); (1/5)*(sin(t)-4*x(1)-7*x(2))];
```

Suppose we want to solve (8.6-1) for $0 \leq t \leq 6$ with the initial conditions $x(0) = 3$, $\dot{x}(0) = 9$. Then the initial condition for the *vector* **x** is [3, 9]. To use ode45, you type

```
[t, x] = ode45('example1', [0, 6], [3, 9]);
```

Each row in the vector x corresponds to a time returned in the column vector t. If you type plot(t,x), you will obtain a plot of both x_1 and x_2 versus t. Note that x is a matrix with two columns; the first column contains the values of x_1 at the various times generated by the solver. The second column contains the values of x_2. Thus to plot only x_1, type plot(t,x(:,1)).

Solution of Nonlinear Equations

We mentioned earlier that when solving nonlinear equations, sometimes it is possible to check the numerical results by using an approximation that reduces the equation to a linear one. The following example illustrates such an approach with a second-order equation.

Example 8.6–1   A nonlinear pendulum model

By studying the dynamics of a pendulum like that shown in Figure 8.6–1, we can better understand the dynamics of machines such as a robot arm. The pendulum shown consists of a concentrated mass m attached to a rod whose mass is small compared to m. The rod's length is L. The equation of motion for this pendulum is

$$\ddot{\theta} + \frac{g}{L} \sin \theta = 0 \qquad \text{(8.6–3)}$$

Suppose that $L = 1$ meter and $g = 9.81$ meters/second^2. Use MATLAB to solve this equation for $\theta(t)$ for two cases: $\theta(0) = 0.5$

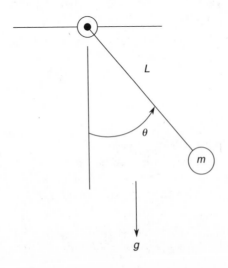

Figure 8.6–1
A pendulum.

radian and $\theta(0) = 0.8\pi$ radians. In both cases $\dot{\theta}(0) = 0$. Discuss how to check the accuracy of the results.

Solution:

If we use the small angle approximation $\sin \approx \theta$, the equation becomes

$$\ddot{\theta} + \frac{g}{L}\theta = 0 \qquad \text{(8.6–4)}$$

which is linear and has a solution given by (8.4–16):

$$\theta(t) = \theta(0)\cos\sqrt{\frac{g}{L}}t \qquad \text{(8.6–5)}$$

Thus the amplitude of oscillation is $\theta(0)$ and the period is $P = 2\pi/\sqrt{g/L} = 2$ seconds. We can use this information to select a final time and to check our numerical results.

First rewrite the pendulum equation (8.6–3) as two first-order equations. To do this, let

$$x_1 = \theta$$

$$x_2 = \dot{\theta}$$

Thus

$$\dot{x}_1 = \dot{\theta} = x_2$$

$$\dot{x}_2 = \ddot{\theta} = -\frac{g}{L}\sin x_1$$

The following function file is based on the last two equations. Remember that the output xdot must be a *column* vector.

```
function xdot = pendul(t,x)
global g L
xdot = [x(2); -(g/L)*sin(x(1))];
```

It is called as follows. The vectors ta and xa contain the results for the case where $\theta(0) = 0.5$. The vectors tb and xb contain the results for $\theta(0) = 0.8\pi$.

```
global g L
g = 9.81;L = 1;
[ta, xa] = ode45('pendul', [0, 5], [.5, 0]);
[tb, xb] = ode45('pendul', [0, 5], [.8*pi, 0]);
plot(ta,xa(:,1),tb,xb(:,1)),xlabel('Time (sec)'),...
ylabel('Angle (rad)'),gtext('Case 1'),gtext('Case 2')
```

The results are shown in Figure 8.6–2. The amplitude remains constant, as predicted by the small angle analysis, and the period for the case where $\theta(0) = 0.5$ is a little longer than 2 seconds, the value predicted by the small angle analysis. Therefore, we can

410

**Numerical
Methods for
Calculus and
Differential
Equations**

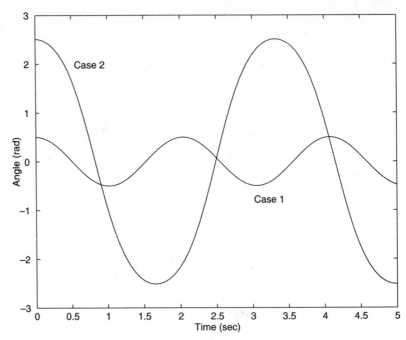

Figure 8.6–2
The pendulum angle as a function of time for two starting positions.

place some confidence in the numerical procedure. For the case where $\theta(0) = 0.8\pi$, the period of the numerical solution is about 3.3 seconds. This longer period illustrates an important property of nonlinear differential equations. The free response of a linear equation has the same period for any initial conditions; however, the form of the free response of a nonlinear equation oftens depends on the particular values of the initial conditions.

Matrix Methods

We can use matrix operations to reduce the number of lines to be typed in the derivative function file. For example, the following equation describes the motion of a mass connected to a spring with viscous friction acting between the mass and the surface. Another force $f(t)$ also acts on the mass (see Figure 8.6–3).

$$m\ddot{y} + c\dot{y} + ky = f(t) \tag{8.6–6}$$

This equation can be put into Cauchy form by letting $x_1 = y$ and $x_2 = \dot{y}$, which gives

$$\dot{x}_1 = x_2$$

$$\dot{x}_2 = \frac{1}{m}f(t) - \frac{k}{m}x_1 - \frac{c}{m}x_2$$

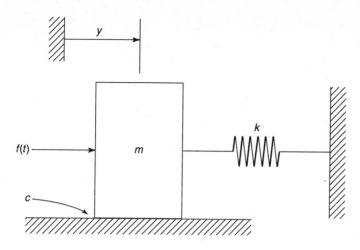

Figure 8.6–3
A mass and spring with viscous surface friction.

These two equations can be written as one matrix equation as follows:

$$\begin{bmatrix} \dot{x}_1 \\ \dot{x}_2 \end{bmatrix} = \begin{bmatrix} 0 & 1 \\ -\frac{k}{m} & -\frac{c}{m} \end{bmatrix} \begin{bmatrix} x_1 \\ x_2 \end{bmatrix} + \begin{bmatrix} 0 \\ \frac{1}{m} \end{bmatrix} f(t)$$

In compact form this is

$$\dot{\mathbf{x}} = \mathbf{A}\mathbf{x} + \mathbf{B}f(t) \qquad\qquad (8.6\text{--}7)$$

where

$$\mathbf{A} = \begin{bmatrix} 0 & 1 \\ -\frac{k}{m} & -\frac{c}{m} \end{bmatrix}$$

$$\mathbf{B} = \begin{bmatrix} 0 \\ \frac{1}{m} \end{bmatrix}$$

and

$$\mathbf{x} = \begin{bmatrix} x_1 \\ x_2 \end{bmatrix}$$

The following function file shows how to use matrix operations. In this example $m = 1$, $c = 2$, $k = 5$, and the applied force f is a constant equal to 10.

```
function xdot = msd(t,x)
% function file for mass with spring and damping.
% position is first variable, velocity is second variable.
global c f k m
A = [0, 1;-k/m, -c/m];
B = [0; 1/m];
xdot = A*x+B*f;
```

412

**Numerical
Methods for
Calculus and
Differential
Equations**

Note that the output `xdot` will be a column vector because of the definition of matrix-vector multiplication. The characteristic roots are the roots of $ms^2 + cs + k = s^2 + 2s + 5 = 0$ and are $s = -1 \pm 2i$. The time constant is 1, and the steady state response will thus be reached after $t = 4$. The period of oscillation will be π. Thus if we choose a final time of 5, we will see the entire response. Using the initial conditions $x_1(0) = 0$, $x_2(0) = 0$, the solver is called as follows:

```
global c f k m
m = 1;c = 2;k = 5;
f = 10;
[t, x] = ode23('msd', [0, 5], [0, 0]);
plot(t,x),xlabel('Time (sec)'),...
ylabel('Displacement (m) and Velocity (m/sec)'),...
gtext('Displacement'), gtext('Velocity')
```

The result is shown in Figure 8.6–4.

Test Your Understanding

T8.6–1 Plot the position and velocity of a mass with a spring and damping, having the parameter values $m = 2, c = 3$, and $k = 7$. The applied force is $f = 35$, the initial position is $y(0) = 2$, and the initial velocity is $\dot{y}(0) = -3$.

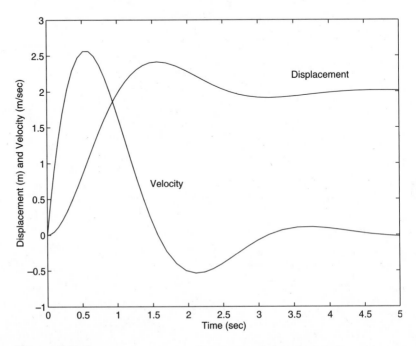

Figure 8.6–4
Displacement and velocity of the mass as a function of time.

Characteristic Roots from the `eig` Function

We saw in section 8.4 that you can obtain the characteristic polynomial and roots for a linear ODE by substituting $y(t) = Ae^{st}$ for the dependent variable $y(t)$. However, when the ODE is in state variable form, there is more than one dependent variable. In such cases you must substitute $x_1(t) = A_1e^{st}$, $x_2(t) = A_2e^{st}$, ... for the dependent variables $x_1(t)$, $x_2(t)$, ... For example, making these substitutions into the following

$$\dot{x}_1 = -3x_1 + x_2 \qquad \textbf{(8.6–8)}$$

$$\dot{x}_2 = -x_1 - 7x_2 \qquad \textbf{(8.6–9)}$$

gives

$$sA_1e^{st} = -3A_1e^{st} + A_2e^{st}$$

$$sA_2e^{st} = -A_1e^{st} - 7A_2e^{st}$$

Collect like terms and cancel the e^{st} terms to obtain

$$(s + 3)A_1 - A_2 = 0$$

$$A_1 + (s + 7)A_2 = 0$$

As we saw in Chapter 5, a nonzero solution will exist for A_1 and A_2 if and only if the determinant is zero. This requirement leads to

$$\begin{vmatrix} s + 3 & -1 \\ 1 & s + 7 \end{vmatrix} = s^2 + 10s + 22 = 0$$

This is the characteristic equation, and its roots are $s = -6.7321$ and $s = -3.2679$.

MATLAB provides the `eig` function to compute the characteristic roots when the model is given in the state-variable form (8.6–7). Its syntax is `eig(A)`, where A is the matrix that appears in (8.6–7). (The function's name is an abbreviation of *eigenvalue*, **EIGENVALUE** which is another name for characteristic root.) For example, the matrix **A** for the equations (8.6–8) and (8.6–9) is

$$\begin{bmatrix} -3 & 1 \\ -1 & -7 \end{bmatrix}$$

To find the characteristic roots, type

```
A = [-3, 1;-1, -7];
r = eig(A)
```

The answer so obtained is `r = [-6.7321, -3.2679]`, which agrees with the answer we found by hand. To find the time constants, which are the negative reciprocals of the real parts of the roots, you type `tau = -1./real(r)`. The time constants are 0.1485 and 0.3060.

414

**Numerical
Methods for
Calculus and
Differential
Equations**

Figure 8.6–5
An armature-controlled dc motor.

Programming Detailed Forcing Functions

As a final example of higher-order equations, we now show how to program detailed forcing functions within the derivative function file. We now use a dc motor as the application. The equations for an armature-controlled dc motor (such as a permanent magnet motor) shown in Figure 8.6–5 are the following. They result from Kirchhoff's voltage law and Newton's law applied to a rotating inertia. The motor's current is i, and its rotational velocity is ω.

$$L\frac{di}{dt} = -Ri - K_e\omega + v(t) \qquad \textbf{(8.6–10)}$$

$$I\frac{d\omega}{dt} = K_Ti - c\omega \qquad \textbf{(8.6–11)}$$

L, R, and I are the motor's inductance, resistance, and inertia; K_T and K_e are the torque constant and back emf constant; c is a viscous damping constant; and $v(t)$ is the applied voltage. These equations can be put into matrix form as follows, where $x_1 = i$ and $x_2 = \omega$.

$$\begin{bmatrix} \dot{x}_1 \\ \dot{x}_2 \end{bmatrix} = \begin{bmatrix} -\frac{R}{L} & -\frac{K_e}{L} \\ \frac{K_T}{I} & -\frac{c}{I} \end{bmatrix} \begin{bmatrix} x_1 \\ x_2 \end{bmatrix} + \begin{bmatrix} \frac{1}{L} \\ 0 \end{bmatrix} v(t)$$

Example 8.6–2 Trapezoidal profile for a dc motor

In many applications we want to accelerate the motor to a desired speed and allow it to run at that speed for some time before decelerating to a stop. Investigate whether an applied voltage having a trapezoidal profile will accomplish this. Use the values $R = 0.6$ ohm, $L = .002$ henry, $K_T = .04$ newton meter/ampere, $K_e = .04$ volt/radian/second, $c = 0$, and $I = 6 \times 10^{-5}$ newton meter second². The applied voltage in volts is given by

$$v(t) = \begin{cases} 100t & 0 \le t < 0.1 \\ 10 & 0.1 \le t \le 0.4 \\ -100(t - .4) + 10 & 0.4 < t \le 0.5 \\ 0 & t > 0.5 \end{cases}$$

This function is shown in the top graph in Figure 8.6–6.

Solution:

First find the time constants using the `eig` function. Use the following script file:

```
R = .6;L = .002;c = 0;
K_T = .04;K_e = .04;I = 6e-5;
A = [-R/L, -K_e/L; K_T/I, -c/I];
% compute the characteristic roots and time constants
disp('The characteristic roots are:')
eig(A)
disp('The time constants are:')
-1./real(eig(A))
```

The roots are $s = -245.7427$ and $s = -54.2573$. The time constants are $\tau_1 = 0.0041$ and $\tau_2 = 0.0184$ second. The largest time constant indicates that the motor's response time is approximately $4(0.0184) = 0.0736$ second. Because this time is less than the time needed for the applied voltage to reach 10 volts, the motor should be able to follow the desired trapezoidal profile reasonably well. To know for certain, we must solve the motor's differential equations. Use the following derivative function file:

```
function xdot = dcmotor(t,x)
% dc motor model with trapezoidal voltage profile.
% First variable is current; second is velocity.
global c I K_T K_e L R
A = [-R/L, -K_e/L; K_T/I, -c/I];
B = [1/L; 0];
if t < .1
    v = 100*t;
elseif t <=.3
    v = 10;
elseif t<=.4
    v = -100*(t-.4)+10;
else
    v = 0;
end
xdot = A*x+B*v;
```

Using the initial conditions $x_1(0) = 0$, $x_2(0) = 0$, the solver is called as follows:

```
global c I K_T K_e L R
R = .6;L = .002;c = 0;
K_T = .04;K_e = .04;I = 6e-5;
[t, x] = ode23('dcmotor', [0, .5], [0, 0]);
```

The results are plotted in Figure 8.6–6. The motor's velocity follows a trapezoidal profile as expected, although there is some slight deviation because of its electrical resistance and inductance, and its mechanical inertia.

416

**Numerical
Methods for
Calculus and
Differential
Equations**

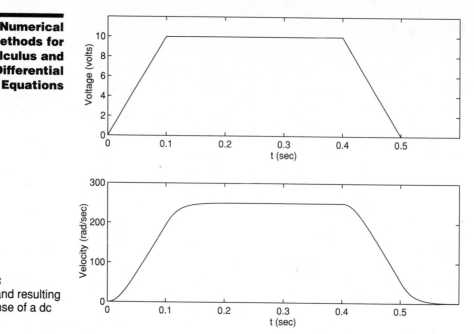

Figure 8.6–6
Voltage input and resulting
velocity response of a dc
motor.

ODE Solvers in the Control System Toolbox

Many of the functions from Version 4 of the Control System toolbox are available in Version 5 of the Student Edition of MATLAB. Some of these can be used to solve linear, time-invariant (constant-coefficient) differential equations. They are sometimes more convenient to use and more powerful than the ODE solvers discussed thus far, because general solutions can be found for linear, time invariant equations. Here we discuss several of these functions. These are summarized in Table 8.7–1. The other features of the Control System toolbox require advanced methods and will not be covered here.

Version 3 of the Control System toolbox and Version 4 of the Student Edition have some of these capabilities. However,

Table 8.7–1   LTI object functions

Command	Description
sys = ss(A, B, C, D)	Creates an LTI object in state-space form, where the matrices A, B, C, and D correspond to those in the model $\dot{x} = Ax + Bu$, $y = Cx + Du$.
[A, B, C, D] = ssdata(sys)	Extracts the matrices A, B, C, and D corresponding to those in the model $\dot{x} = Ax + Bu$, $y = Cx + Du$.
sys = tf(right,left)	Creates an LTI object in transfer-function form, where the vector right is the vector of coefficients of the right-hand side of the equation, arranged in descending derivative order, and left is the vector of coefficients of the left-hand side of the equation, also arranged in descending derivative order.
[right, left] = tfdata(sys)	Extracts the coefficients on the right and left-hand sides of the reduced-form model.

the names of the functions are different. We summarize these changes later in this section.

Model Forms

The ODE solvers in the Control System toolbox can accept various descriptions of the equations to be solved. Version 4 of the Control System toolbox (parts of which are included in Version 5 of the Student Edition) introduced the *LTI object,* which describes a linear, time-invariant equation, or sets of equations, here referred to as the *system.* An LTI object can be created from different descriptions of the system, it can be analyzed with several functions, and it can be accessed to provide alternative descriptions of the system. For example, the equation

$$2\ddot{x} + 3\dot{x} + 5x = f(t) \tag{8.7-1}$$

is one description of a particular system. This description is called the *reduced form.* The following is a state-model description of the same system:

$$\dot{\mathbf{x}} = \mathbf{A}\mathbf{x} + \mathbf{B}u \tag{8.7-2}$$

where $x_1 = x$, $x_2 = \dot{x}$, $u = f(t)$,

$$\mathbf{A} = \begin{bmatrix} 0 & 1 \\ -\frac{5}{2} & -\frac{3}{2} \end{bmatrix} \tag{8.7-3}$$

$$\mathbf{B} = \begin{bmatrix} 0 \\ \frac{1}{2} \end{bmatrix} \tag{8.7-4}$$

and

$$\mathbf{x} = \begin{bmatrix} x_1 \\ x_2 \end{bmatrix} \tag{8.7-5}$$

Both model forms contain the same information. However, each form has its own advantages, depending on the purpose of the analysis.

Because there are two or more state variables in a state model, we need to be able to specify which state variable, or combination of variables, constitutes the output of the simulation. For example, model (8.7–2) through (8.7–5) can represent the motion of a mass, with x_1 the position, and x_2 the velocity of the mass. We need to be able to specify whether we want to see a plot of the position, or the velocity, or both. This specification of the output, denoted by the vector **y**, is done in general with the matrices **C** and **D**, which are defined as follows:

$$\mathbf{y} = \mathbf{C}\mathbf{x} + \mathbf{D}u \tag{8.7-6}$$

418

**Numerical
Methods for
Calculus and
Differential
Equations**

Continuing the previous example, if we want the output to be the position $x = x_1$, then $y = x_1$; and we would select

$$\mathbf{C} = [1 \quad 0]$$

$$\mathbf{D} = 0$$

Thus, in this case, (8.7–5) reduces to $y = x_1$.

To create an LTI object from the reduced form (8.7–1), you use the `tf(right,left)` function and type

```
≫sys1 = tf(1, [2, 3, 5]);
```

where the vector `right` is the vector of coefficients of the right side of the equation, arranged in descending derivative order, and `left` is the vector of coefficients of the left side of the equation, also arranged in descending derivative order. The result `sys1` is the LTI object that describes the system in the reduced form, also called the *transfer-function form*. (The name of the function `tf` stands for *transfer function*, which is an equivalent way of describing the coefficients on the left and right side of the equation.)

Here is another example. The LTI object `sys2` in transfer-function form for the equation

$$6\frac{d^3x}{dt^3} - 4\frac{d^2x}{dt^2} + 7\frac{dx}{dt} + 5x = 3\frac{d^2f}{dt^2} + 9\frac{df}{dt} + 2f \qquad \textbf{(8.7–7)}$$

is created by typing

```
≫sys2 = tf([3, 9, 2],[6, -4, 7, 5]);
```

To create an LTI object from a state model, you use the `ss(A,B,C,D)` function, where `ss` stands for *state space*. The matrix arguments of the function are the matrices in the following standard form of a state model:

$$\dot{\mathbf{x}} = \mathbf{Ax} + \mathbf{Bu} \qquad \textbf{(8.7–8)}$$

$$\mathbf{y} = \mathbf{Cx} + \mathbf{Du} \qquad \textbf{(8.7–9)}$$

where $\mathbf{x}$ is the vector of state variables, $\mathbf{u}$ is the vector of input functions, and $\mathbf{y}$ is the vector of output variables. For example, to create an LTI object in state-model form for the system described by (8.7–2) through (8.7–5), you type

```
≫A = [0, 1; -5/2, -3/2];
≫B = [0;1/2];
≫C = [1, 0];
≫D = 0;
≫sys3 = ss(A,B,C,D);
```

An LTI object defined using the `tf` function can obtain an equivalent state-model description of the system. To create a state model for the system described by the LTI object `sys1` created previously in transfer-function form you type `ss(sys1)`. You will then see the resulting **A**, **B**, **C**, and **D** matrices on the screen. To extract and save the matrices, use the `ssdata` function as follows:

```
>>[A1, B1, C1, D1] = ssdata(sys1);
```

The results are

$$\mathbf{A1} = \begin{bmatrix} -1.5 & -1.25 \\ 2 & 0 \end{bmatrix}$$

$$\mathbf{B1} = \begin{bmatrix} 0.5 \\ 0 \end{bmatrix}$$

$$\mathbf{C1} = \begin{bmatrix} 0 & 0.5 \end{bmatrix}$$

$$\mathbf{D1} = \begin{bmatrix} 0 \end{bmatrix}$$

When using `ssdata` to convert a transfer-function form into a state model, note that the output y will be a scalar that is identical to the solution variable of the reduced form; in this case the solution variable of (8.7–1) is the variable x. To interpret the state model, we need to relate its state variables x_1 and x_2 to x. The values of the matrices **C1** and **D1** tell us that the output variable is $y = 0.5x_2$. Because the output y is the same as x, we then see that $x_2 = 2x$. The other state variable x_1 is related to x_2 by $\dot{x}_2 = 2x_1$. Thus $x_1 = \dot{x}$.

To create a transfer-function description of the system sys3, previously created from the state model, you type `tfsys3 = tf(sys3);`. To extract and save the coefficients of the reduced form, use the `tfdata` function as follows:

```
>>[right, left] = tfdata(sys3, 'v');
```

For this example, the vectors returned are `right = 1` and `left = [1, 1.5, 2.5]`. The optional parameter `'v'` tells MATLAB to return the coefficients as vectors; otherwise, they are returned as cell arrays. These functions are summarized in Table 8.7–1.

The functions `ssdata` and `tfdata` have replaced the functions `ss2tf` and `tf2ss` in Version 3 of the Control System toolbox and Version 4 of the Student Edition.

Test Your Understanding

T8.7–1 Obtain the state model for the reduced-form model

$$5\ddot{x} + 7\dot{x} + 4x = f(t)$$

Then convert the state model back to reduced form and see whether you get the original reduced-form model.

420

**Numerical
Methods for
Calculus and
Differential
Equations**

Table 8.7–2   Basic syntax of the LTI ODE solvers

Command	Description
impulse(sys)	Computes and plots the impulse response of the LTI object sys.
initial(sys,x0)	Computes and plots the free response of the LTI object sys given in state-model form, for the initial conditions specified in the vector x0.
lsim(sys,u,t)	Computes and plots the response of the LTI object sys to the input specified by the vector u, at the times specified by the vector t.
step(sys)	Computes and plots the step response of the LTI object sys.

(See the text for description of extended syntax.)

ODE Solvers

The Control System toolbox provides several solvers for linear models. These solvers are categorized by the type of input function they can accept: zero input, impulse input, step input, and a general input function. These are summarized in Table 8.7–2.

The initial **Function:** The initial function computes and plots the free response of a state model. This response is sometimes called the *initial condition response* or the *undriven response* in the MATLAB documentation. The basic syntax is initial(sys,x0), where sys is the LTI object in state-model form and x0 is the initial condition vector. The time span and number of solution points are chosen automatically. For example, to find the free response of the state model (8.7–2) through (8.7–5), for $x_1(0) = 5$ and $x_2(0) = -2$, first define it in state-model form. This was done previously to obtain the system sys3. Then use the initial function as follows:

≫initial(sys3, [5, -2])

The plot shown in Figure 8.7–1 will be displayed on the screen.

To specify the final time tf, use the syntax initial(sys,x0, tf). To specify a vector of times of the form t = [0:dt:tf], at which to obtain the solution, use the syntax initial(sys,x0,t). When called with left-hand arguments, as [y, t, x] = initial (sys,x0, ...), the function returns the output response **y**, the time vector t used for the simulation, and the state vector **x** evaluated at those times. The columns of the matrices y and x are the outputs and the states, respectively. The number of rows in y and x equals length(t). No plot is drawn. The syntax initial(sys1,sys2, ...,x0,t) plots the free response of multiple LTI systems on a single plot. The time vector t is optional. You can specify line color, line style, and marker for each system; for example, initial(sys1,'r',sys2,'y--',sys3,'gx',x0).

The impulse **Function:** The impulse function plots the unit-impulse response for each input-output pair of the system,

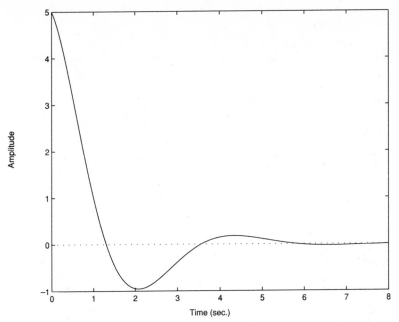

Initial Condition Results

Figure 8.7–1
Free response of the model given by (8.7–2) through (8.7–5) for $x_1(0) = 5$ and $x_2(0) = -2$.

assuming that the initial conditions are zero. (If you are unfamiliar with the impulse input, see Chapter 9, section 9.5.) The basic syntax is impulse(sys), where sys is the LTI object. Unlike the initial function, the impulse function can be used with either a state model or a transfer-function model. The time span and number of solution points are chosen automatically. For example, the impulse response of (8.7–1) is found as follows:

```
≫sys1 = tf(1,[2, 3, 5]);
≫impulse(sys1)
```

To specify the final time tf, use the syntax impulse(sys,tf). To specify a vector of times of the form t = [0:dt:tf], at which to obtain the solution, use the syntax impulse(sys,t). When called with left-hand arguments, as [y, t] = impulse(sys, ...), the function returns the output response **y** and the time vector t used for the simulation. No plot is drawn. The array y is $p \times q \times m$, where p is length(t), q is the number of outputs, and m is the number of inputs. To obtain the state vector solution, use the syntax [y, t, x] = impulse(sys, ...).

The syntax impulse(sys1,sys2, ...,t) plots the impulse response of multiple LTI systems on a single plot. The time vector t is optional. You can specify line color, line style, and marker for each system; for example, impulse(sys1,'r',sys2,'y--', sys3,'gx').

422

**Numerical
Methods for
Calculus and
Differential
Equations**

The step **Function:** The step function plots the unit-step response for each input-output pair of the system, assuming that the initial conditions are zero. (If you are unfamiliar with the step function, see Chapter 9, section 9.5.) The basic syntax is step(sys) where sys is the LTI object. The step function can be used with either a state model or a transfer-function model. The time span and number of solution points are chosen automatically. To specify the final time tf, use the syntax step(sys,tf). To specify a vector of times of the form t = [0:dt:tf], at which to obtain the solution, use the syntax step(sys,t). When called with left-hand arguments, as [y, t] = step(sys, ...), the function returns the output response **y** and the time vector t used for the simulation. No plot is drawn. The array y is $p \times q \times m$, where p is length(t), q is the number of outputs, and m is the number of inputs. To obtain the state vector solution for state-space models, use the syntax [y, t, x] = step(sys, ...).

The syntax step(sys1,sys2, ...,t) plots the step response of multiple LTI systems on a single plot. The time vector t is optional. You can specify line color, line style, and marker for each system; for example, step(sys1,'r',sys2,'y--', sys3,'gx'). To find the step response, for zero initial conditions, of the state model (8.7–2) through (8.7–5), and the reduced-form model

$$5\ddot{x} + 7\dot{x} + 5x = 5\dot{f} + f \qquad\qquad \textbf{(8.7–10)}$$

the session is (assuming sys3 is still available):

```
≫sys4 = tf([5, 1], [5, 7, 5]);
≫step(sys3,'b',sys4,'--')
```

The result is shown in Figure 8.7–2. The steady-state response is indicated by the horizontal dotted line. Note how the steady-state response and the time to reach that state are automatically determined.

The lsim **Function:** The lsim function plots the response of the system to an arbitrary input. The basic syntax for zero initial conditions is lsim(sys,u,t), where sys is the LTI object; t is a time vector having regular spacing, as t = [0:dt:tf]; and u is a matrix with as many columns as inputs and whose i th row specifies the value of the input at time t(i). To specify nonzero initial conditions for a state-space model, use the syntax lsim(sys,u,t,x0).

When called with left-hand arguments, as [y, t] = lsim (sys, u, ...), the function returns the output response **y** and the time vector t used for the simulation. The columns of the matrix y are the outputs, and the number of its rows equals length(t). No plot is drawn. To obtain the state vector solution for state-space models, use the syntax [y, t, x] = lsim(sys,u, ...). The syntax lsim(sys1,sys2,

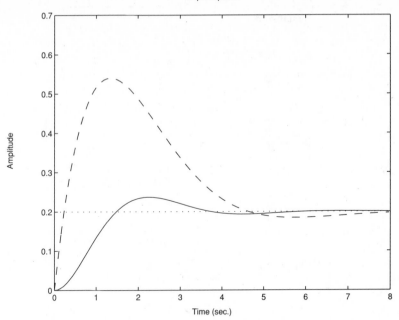

Figure 8.7–2
Step response of the model given by (8.7–2) through (8.7–5) and the model
(8.7-10), for zero initial conditions.

$\ldots,\mathtt{u,t,x0})$ plots the free response of multiple LTI systems
on a single plot. The initial condition vector $\mathtt{x0}$ is needed
only if the initial conditions are nonzero. You can specify line
color, line style, and marker for each system; for example,
$\mathtt{lsim(sys1,'r',sys2,'y--\ ',sys3,'gx',u,t)}$.
    We will see an example of the $\mathtt{lsim}$ function shortly.

LTI Viewer: Version 5 of the Student Edition and Version 4
of the Control System toolbox have the LTI Viewer to assist
in the analysis of LTI systems. It provides an interactive user
interface that allows you to switch between different types of
response plots and between the analysis of different systems. The
viewer is invoked by typing $\mathtt{ltiview}$. See MATLAB help for more
information.

Predefined Input Functions

You can always create any complicated input function to use with
the ODE solvers $\mathtt{odexxx}$ or $\mathtt{lsim}$ by defining a vector containing
the input function's values at specified times. However, MATLAB
provides several predefined functions that you might find easier
to use. These are described in the following paragraphs, and are
summarized in Table 8.7–3.
    The function $\mathtt{stepfun(t,t0)}$ returns a vector the same length
as $\mathtt{t}$ with zeros where $\mathtt{t} < \mathtt{t0}$ and ones where $\mathtt{t} \geq \mathtt{t0}$. The vector
$\mathtt{t}$ must have monotonically increasing elements.

Table 8.7–3 Predefined input functions

Command	Description
[u, t] = gensig(type,period,tf,dt)	Generates a periodic input of a specified type `type`, having a period `period`. The following types are available: sine wave (`type = 'sin'`), square wave (`type = 'square'`), and narrow-width periodic pulse(`type = 'pulse'`). The vector `t` contains the times, and the vector `u` contains the input values at those times. All generated inputs have unit amplitudes. The optional parameters `tf` and `dt` specify the time duration `tf` of the input and the spacing `dt` between the time instants.
sawtooth(t,width)	Returns a vector the same length as `t` corresponding to a sawtooth wave of period 2π. The optional parameter `width` generates a modified sawtooth wave where `width` determines the fraction between 0 and 2π at which the maximum occurs (0 ≤ `width` ≤ 1).
square(t,duty)	Returns a vector the same length as `t` corresponding to a square wave of period 2π. The optional parameter `duty` generates a square wave with a duty cycle specified by `duty`, which is the percentage of the period over which the function is positive.
stepfun(t,t0)	Returns a vector the same length as `t` with zeros where `t < t0` and ones where `t ≥ t0`.

The function `square(t)` returns a vector the same length as t corresponding to a square wave of period 2π. The function `square(t)` is similar to `sin(t)`, with extreme points at ±1, except that the wave is square. The syntax `square(t,duty)` generates a square wave with a duty cycle specified by `duty`, which is the percentage of the period over which the function is positive.

The function `sawtooth(t)` returns a vector the same length as t corresponding to a sawtooth wave of period 2π. The function `sawtooth(t)` is similar to `sin(t)`, with extreme points at ±1, except that the wave shape is a triangle. The syntax `sawtooth(t,width)` generates a modified sawtooth wave where `width` determines the fraction between 0 and 2π at which the maximum occurs (0 ≤ `width` ≤ 1).

The function `[u, t] = gensig(type,period)` generates a periodic input of a specified type `type`, having a period `period`. The following types are available: sine wave (`type = 'sin'`), square wave (`type = 'square'`), and narrow-width periodic pulse(`type = 'pulse'`). The vector `t` contains the times, and the vector `u` contains the input values at those times. All generated inputs have unit amplitudes. The syntax `[u, t] = gensig(type,period,tf,dt)` specifies the time duration `tf` of the input and the spacing `dt` between the time instants.

For example, suppose a square wave with period 5 is applied to the following reduced-form model.

$$\ddot{x} + 2\dot{x} + 4x = 4f \qquad\qquad (8.7–11)$$

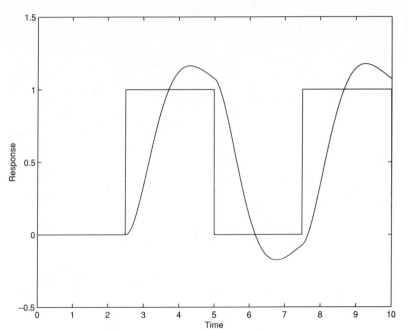

Figure 8.7–3
Square-wave response of the model $\ddot{x} + 2\dot{x} + 4x = 4f$.

To find the response for zero initial conditions, over the interval $0 \le t \le 10$ and using a step size of 0.01, the session is

```
>>sys4 = tf(4,[1,2,4]);
>>[u, t] = gensig('square',5,10,.01);
>>[y, t] = lsim(sys4,u,t);plot(t,y,t,u),axis([0 10 -.5 1.5]),...
   xlabel('Time'),ylabel('Response')
```

The result is shown in Figure 8.7–3.

8.8

In addition to incorporating four new solvers, MATLAB 5 also extends the capabilities of all the solvers. The complete syntax in MATLAB 5 is as follows and is summarized in Table 8.8–1.

New ODE Solver
Capabilities in
MATLAB 5

```
[t, y] = solver('ydot', tspan, y0, options, p1, p2, ...)
```

where the `options` argument is created with the new `odeset` function, and `p1, p2, ...` are optional parameters that can be passed to the function file `ydot` every time it is called. If these optional parameters are used, but no `options` are set, use `options = [ ]` as a placeholder.

The function file `ydot` can now take additional input arguments. It has the form `ydot(t, y, flag, p1, p2, ...)`, where `flag` is an argument that notifies the function `ydot` that

Table 8.8–1 Complete syntax of ODE solvers in MATLAB 5

Command	Description
`[t, y] = ode23('ydot', tspan, y0, options, p1, p2, ...)`	Solves the differential equation $\dot{\mathbf{y}} = \mathbf{f}(t, \mathbf{y})$ specified in the function file `ydot`, whose inputs must be t and $\mathbf{y}$ and whose output must be a *column* vector representing $d\mathbf{y}/dt$; that is, $\mathbf{f}(t, \mathbf{y})$. The number of rows in this column vector must equal the order of the equation. The vector `tspan` contains the starting and ending values of the independent variable t, and optionally, any intermediate values of t where the solution is desired. The vector `y0` contains $\mathbf{y}(t_0)$. The function file must have two input arguments t and y even for equations where $\mathbf{f}(t, \mathbf{y})$ is not a function of t. The `options` argument is created with the `odeset` function, and `p1, p2, ...` are optional parameters that can be passed to the function file `ydot` every time it is called. If these optional parameters are used, but no `options` are set, use `options = [ ]` as a placeholder. The function file `ydot` can take additional input arguments. It has the form `ydot(t, y, flag, p1, p2, ...)`, where `flag` is an argument that notifies the function `ydot` that the solver is expecting a specific kind of information. The syntax for all the solvers is identical.
`options = odeset('name1', 'value1' 'name2', 'value2',...)`	Creates an integrator options structure `options` to be used with the ODE solver, in which the named properties have the specified values, where `name` is the name of a *property* and `value` is the value to be assigned to the property. Any unspecified properties have default values. `odeset` with no input arguments displays all property names and their possible values.

the solver is expecting a specific kind of information. We will see an example of the `flag` argument shortly.

The `odeset` Function

The `odeset` function creates an options structure to be supplied to the solver. Its syntax is

```
options = odeset('name1', 'value1' 'name2', 'value2',...)
```

where `name` is the name of a *property* and `value` is the value to be assigned to the property.

A simple example will clarify things. The `Refine` property is used to increase the number of output points from the solver by an integer factor n. The default value of n is 1 for all the solvers except `ode45`, whose default value is 4 because of the solver's large step sizes. Suppose we want to solve the equation

$$\frac{dy}{dt} = \sin t$$

for $0 \leq t \leq 4\pi$ with $y(0) = 0$. Define the following function file:

```
function ydot = sinefn(t,y)
ydot = sin(t);
```

Then use the `odeset` function to set the value of `Refine` to $n = 8$, and call the `ode45` solver, as shown here:

```
options = odeset('Refine',8);
[t, y] = ode45('sinefn', [0, 4*pi], 0, options);
```

Many properties can be set with the `odeset` function. To see a list of these, type `odeset`.

Another property is the `Events` property, which has two possible values: `on` and `off`. It can be used to locate transitions to, from, or through zeros of a user-defined function. This property can be used to detect when the ODE solution reaches a certain value. To use this property, you must write the ODE file `ydot` to have three outputs, as follows:

```
[value, isterminal, direction] = ydot(t,y,flag)
```

The vector `value` should be programmed to contain the vector describing the event when the flag equals `'events'`. The vector `value` should be programmed to contain the derivatives when the flag is not set to `'events'` or is empty. `value` is evaluated at the beginning and end of each step, and if any of its elements make transitions to, from, or through zero, the solver determines the time when the transition occurred. The direction of the transition is specified in the vector `direction`. A 1 indicates positive direction, a -1 indicates negative direction, and a 0 indicates "don't care."

The `isterminal` vector is a logical vector of 1s and 0s that specifies whether a zero crossing of the corresponding element in `value` is a terminal event. A 1 corresponds to a terminal event and halts the solver; a 0 corresponds to a nonterminal event.

For example, suppose we want to simulate a dropped ball bouncing up from the floor. The equation of motion of the ball in free flight is

$$m\ddot{y} = -mg$$

or $\ddot{y} = -g$, where y is the ball's height above the floor. Put this into state-variable form by defining $y_1 = y$ and $y_2 = \dot{y}$. The equations are

$$\dot{y}_1 = y_2$$

$$\dot{y}_2 = -g$$

Define the following equation file to use with the solver. We use $g = 9.81$ meters/second^2 and an initial height of 10 meters. The `value` vector here consists of the state vector. The "event" here is a bounce, which occurs when the height is 0.

```
function [value, isterminal, direction] = ballode(t, y, flag)
if (nargin<3)|isempty(flag)
    value = [y(2); -9.81];
```

```
elseif flag == 'events'
    % Returns height and velocity
    value = y;
    %Instructs to stop when first
    %variable (height) is zero
    isterminal = [1; 0];
    % Instructs to detect an event only when the first
    % variable (height) is decreasing,
    % regardless of velocity
    direction = [-1; 0];
else
    error(['unknown flag'''flag'''.']);
end
```

We assume that the ball loses 10 percent of its speed each time its bounces. The script file to find the ball's motion up to the second bounce follows. It calls the solver before and after the bounce.

```
options = odeset('Events','on')
[t1, y1] = ode45('ballode', [0, 10], [10, 0], options);
[t2, y2] = ode45('ballode',[t1(length(t1)), 10],...
[0, -.9*y1(length(t1),2)],options);
t = [t1; t2];y=[y1; y2];
plot(t,y(:,1)),xlabel('Time (sec)'),...
ylabel('Ball Height (meters)'),axis([0 5 0 10])
```

The resulting plot of height versus time is shown in Figure 8.8–1.

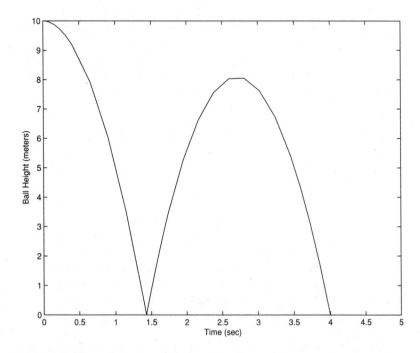

Figure 8.8–1
Height of a bouncing ball as a function of time.

A *stiff* differential equation is one whose response changes rapidly over a time scale that is short compared to the time scale over which we are interested in the solution. Stiff equations present a challenge to solve numerically. A small step size is needed to solve for the rapid changes, but many steps are needed to obtain the solution over the longer time interval, and thus a large error might accumulate. For example, the following equation might be considered "stiff":

$$\ddot{y} + 1001\dot{y} + 1000y = 0 \qquad \textbf{(8.8–1)}$$

The characteristic roots are $s = -1$ and $s = -1000$. If the initial conditions are $y(0) = 1$ and $\dot{y}(0) = 0$, the closed-form solution is

$$y(t) = \frac{1}{999}\left(1000e^{-t} - e^{-1000t}\right) \qquad \textbf{(8.8–2)}$$

That part of the response due to the term e^{-1000t} disappears after approximately $t = 4/1000 = 0.004$, but the term due to e^{-t} does not disappear until after $t = 4$. Thus it would be difficult for a plot to show the solution accurately, and a numerical solver would need a small step size to compute the rapid changes due to the e^{-1000t} term, much smaller than that required to compute the longer-term response due to the e^{-t} term. The result can be a large accumulated error because of the small step size combined with the large number of steps required to obtain the full solution.

The solvers in MATLAB 5.0 do rather well with moderately stiff equations, but if you have trouble solving an equation with one of these solvers, MATLAB 5.2 has four solvers specifically designed to handle stiff equations. These are `ode15s`, a variable-order method; `ode23s`, a low-order method; `ode23tb`, another low-order method; and `ode23t`, a trapezoidal method. Their syntax is identical to the `ode23` and `ode45` solvers.

We have not covered all of the new solver capabilities provided in MATLAB 5. For more information and additional examples, consult online help.

8.9

Summary

This chapter covered numerical methods for computing integrals and derivatives and for solving ordinary differential equations. Some integrals and many differential equations cannot be evaluated analytically, and we need to compute them numerically with an approximate method. In addition, it is often necessary to use data to estimate rates of change, and this process requires a numerical estimate of the derivative.

Now that you have finished this chapter, you should be able to the following:

Table 8.9-1 Guide to MATLAB commands introduced in Chapter 8

Numerical integration functions	See Table 8.2–1
Numerical differentiation functions	See Table 8.3-1
ODE solvers	See Table 8.5–1
Basic syntax of ODE solvers	See Table 8.5–2
LTI object functions	See Table 8.7–1
Basic syntax of the LTI ODE solvers	See Table 8.7–2
Predefined input functions	See Table 8.7–3
Complete syntax of ODE solvers in MATLAB 5	See Table 8.8–1

Miscellaneous commands	
Command	**Description**
`eig(A)`	Computes the eigenvalues of the matrix A, which are the characteristic roots of the vector-matrix differential equation $\dot{x}$ = **Ax**.
`global x y z`	Declares the variables x, y, and z to be global.

- Use the `trapz`, `quad`, and `quad8` functions to numerically evaluate integrals. Note that `trapz` must be supplied with numerical values for the integrand, whereas `quad` and `quad8` can and must use a function.

- Use numerical methods with the `diff` function to estimate derivatives.

- Use the analytical expressions for simple integrals and derivatives to check the accuracy of numerical methods.

- Use MATLAB ODE solvers to solve differential equations.

- Use the analytical solutions of simple differential equations to check the accuracy of numerical methods.

- Apply approximations to check the validity of numerical solutions of nonlinear differential equations.

Key Terms with Page References

You can find answers to problems marked with an asterisk at the end of the text.

Note: Unless otherwise directed by your instructor, for each of the following problems select the easiest method (analytical or numerical) to solve the problem. Discuss the reasons for your choice. Your instructor might require you to use a numerical method and might require you to check the numerical solution with the analytical solution if possible.

Sections 8.1, 8.2, and 8.3

1.* An object moves at a velocity $v(t) = 5 + 7t^2$ starting from the position $x(2) = 5$ at $t = 2$. Determine its position at $t = 10$.

2. The total distance D traveled by an object moving at velocity $v(t)$ from the time $t = a$ to the time $t = b$ is

$$D = \int_a^b |v(t)|\, dt$$

The absolute value $|v(t)|$ is used to account for the possibility that $v(t)$ might be negative. Suppose an object moves with a velocity of $v(t) = \cos(\pi t)$ for $0 \le t \le 1$. Find the total distance traveled and the object's location $x(1)$ at $t = 1$ if $x(0) = 2$.

3. An object starts with an initial velocity of 3 meters/second at $t = 0$ and accelerates with an acceleration of $a(t) = 5t$ meters/second^2. Plot its velocity as a function of time for $0 \le t \le 5$ and find the total distance the object travels in 5 seconds.

4. The equation for the voltage $v(t)$ across a capacitor as a function of time is

$$v(t) = \frac{1}{C}\left(\int_0^t i(t)\, dt + Q_0\right)$$

where $i(t)$ is the applied current and Q_0 is the initial charge. A certain capacitor initially holds no charge. Its capacitance is $C = 10^{-5}$ farad. If a current $i(t) = 2[1 + \sin(5t)]10^{-4}$ amperes is applied to the capacitor, plot the voltage $v(t)$ as a function of time for $0 \le t \le 1.2$ seconds.

5.* Two electrons a distance x apart repel each other with a force k/x^2, where k is a constant. Let one electron be fixed at $x = 0$. Determine the work done by the force of repulsion in moving the second charge from $x = 1$ to $x = 5$.

6. A certain object's position as a function of time is given by $x(t) = 6t \sin 5t$. Plot its velocity and acceleration as functions of time for $0 \le t \le 5$.

7.* A ball was thrown vertically with a velocity $v(0)$ meters/second. Its measured height as a function of time was determined to be $h(t) = 6t - 4.9t^2$ meters. Determine its initial velocity.

8. The volume of liquid in a spherical tank of radius r as a function of the liquid's height h above the tank bottom is given by

$$V(h) = \pi r h^2 - \pi \frac{h^3}{3}$$

432

**Numerical
Methods for
Calculus and
Differential
Equations**

a. Determine the volume rate of change dV/dh with respect to height.
b. Determine the volume rate of change dV/dt with respect to time.

9. A certain object moves with the velocity $v(t)$ given in the following table. Determine the object's position $x(t)$ at $t = 10$ seconds if $x(0) = 3$.

Time (sec)	0	1	2	3	4	5	6	7	8	9	10
Velocity (m/s)	0	2	5	7	9	12	15	18	22	20	17

10.* A tank having vertical sides and a bottom area of 100 ft² stores water. To fill the tank, water is pumped into the top at the rate given in the following table. Determine the water height $h(t)$ at $t = 10$ minutes.

Time (min)	0	1	2	3	4	5	6	7	8	9	10
Flow rate (ft³/min)	0	80	130	150	150	160	165	170	160	140	120

11. A cone-shaped paper drinking cup (the kind used at water fountains) has a radius R and a height H. If the water height in the cup is h, the water volume is given by

$$V = \frac{1}{3}\pi\left(\frac{R}{H}\right)^2 h^3$$

Suppose that the cup's dimensions are $R = 1.5$ inches and $H = 4$ inches.
a. If the flow rate from the fountain into the cup is 2 inches³/second, how long will it take to fill the cup to the brim?
b. If the flow rate from the fountain into the cup is given by $2(1 - e^{-2t})$ inches³/second, how long will it take to fill the cup to the brim?

12. A certain object has a mass of 100 kilograms and is acted on by a force $f(t) = 500[2 - e^{-t}\sin(5\pi t)]$ newtons. The mass is at rest at $t = 0$. Determine the object's velocity at $t = 5$ seconds.

13.* A rocket's mass decreases as it burns fuel. The equation of motion for a rocket in vertical flight can be obtained from Newton's law and is

$$m(t)\frac{dv}{dt} = T - m(t)g$$

where T is the rocket's thrust and its mass as a function of time is given by $m(t) = m_0(1 - rt/b)$. The rocket's initial mass is m_0, the burn time is b, and r is the fraction of the total mass accounted for by the fuel.

Use the values $T = 48,000$ newtons, $m_0 = 2200$ kilograms, $r = 0.8$, $g = 9.81$ meters/second², and $b = 40$ seconds. Determine the rocket's velocity at burnout.

14. The equation for the voltage $v(t)$ across a capacitor as a function of time is

$$v(t) = \frac{1}{C}\left(\int_0^t i(t)\, dt + Q_0\right)$$

where $i(t)$ is the applied current and Q_0 is the initial charge. Suppose that $C = 10^{-6}$ farad and that $Q_0 = 0$. Suppose the applied current is $i(t) = [0.01 + 0.3e^{-5t}\sin(25\pi t)]10^{-3}$ amperes. Plot the voltage $v(t)$ for $0 \le t \le 0.3$ seconds.

15. Plot the estimate of the derivative dy/dx from the following data. Do this using forward, backward, and central differences. Compare the results.

x	0	1	2	3	4	5	6	7	8	9	10
y	0	2	5	7	9	12	15	18	22	20	17

16. At a relative maximum of a curve $y(x)$, the slope dy/dx is 0. Use the following data to estimate the values of x and y that correspond to a maximum point.

x	0	1	2	3	4	5	6	7	8	9	10
y	0	2	5	7	9	10	8	7	6	8	10

17. Compare the performance of the forward, backward, and central difference methods for estimating the derivative of the following function: $y(x) = e^{-x}\sin(3x)$. Use 101 points from $x = 0$ to $x = 4$. Use a random additive error of ± 0.01.

Sections 8.4 and 8.5

18. Plot the free and total response of the equation

$$5\dot{y} + y = f(t)$$

if $f(t) = 0$ for $t < 0$ and $f(t) = 10$ for $t \ge 0$. The initial condition is $y(0) = 5$.

19. The equation for the voltage y across the capacitor of an RC circuit is

$$RC\frac{dy}{dt} + y = v(t)$$

where $v(t)$ is the applied voltage. Suppose that $RC = 0.2$ second and that the capacitor voltage is initially 2 volts. Suppose also that the applied voltage goes from 0 to 10 volts at $t = 0$. Plot the voltage $y(t)$ for $0 \le t \le 1$ second.

20. The following equation describes the temperature $T(t)$ of a certain object immersed in a liquid bath of constant temperature T_b.

$$10\frac{dT}{dt} + T = T_b$$

Suppose the object's temperature is initially $T(0) = 70°$ F and the bath temperature is $T_b = 170°$ C.

a. How long will it take for the object's temperature T to reach the bath temperature?

434

**Numerical
Methods for
Calculus and
Differential
Equations**

b. How long will it take for the object's temperature T to reach 168° F?

c. Plot the object's temperature $T(t)$ as a function of time.

21.* The equation of motion of a rocket-propelled sled is, from Newton's law,

$$m\dot{v} = f - cv$$

where m is the sled mass, f is the rocket thrust, and c is a air resistance coefficient. Suppose that $m = 1000$ kilograms and $c = 500$ newton seconds/meter. Suppose $v(0) = 0$ and f is constant for $t \geq 0$.

a. What is the form of the step response $v(t)$?

b. Determine the final speed the sled will reach as a function of f. How long will it take to reach that speed?

22.* The following equation describes the motion of a mass connected to a spring with viscous friction on the surface.

$$m\ddot{y} + c\dot{y} + ky = f(t)$$

where $f(t)$ is an applied force.

a. What is the form of the free response if $m = 3$, $c = 18$, and $k = 102$?

b. What is the form of the free response if $m = 3$, $c = 39$, and $k = 120$?

23. The equation for the voltage y across the capacitor of an RC circuit is

$$RC\frac{dy}{dt} + y = v(t)$$

where $v(t)$ is the applied voltage. Suppose that $RC = 0.2$ second and that the capacitor voltage is initially 2 volts. Suppose also that the applied voltage is $v(t) = 10[2 - e^{-t}\sin(5\pi t)]$. Plot the voltage $y(t)$ for $0 \leq t \leq 5$ seconds. Interpret the results in terms of the circuit's time constant and the behavior of the applied voltage.

24. The equation describing the water height h in a spherical tank with a circular drain of area A at the bottom is

$$\pi\left(2rh - h^2\right)\frac{dh}{dt} = -C_d A \sqrt{2gh}$$

Suppose the tank's radius is $r = 3$ meters and that the circular drain hole has a radius of 2 centimeters. Assume that $C_d = 0.5$ and that the initial water height is $h(0) = 5$ meters. Use $g = 9.81$ meters/second^2.

a. Use an approximation to estimate how long it takes for the tank to empty.

b. Plot the water height as a function of time until $h(t) = 0$.

25. The following equation describes a certain dilution process, where $y(t)$ is the concentration of salt in a tank of fresh water to which salt brine is being added.

$$\frac{dy}{dt} + \frac{2}{10 + 2t}y = 4$$

Suppose that $y(0) = 0$.

a. Plot $y(t)$ for $0 \leq t \leq 10$.

b. Check your results by using an approximation that converts the differential equation into one having constant coefficients.

26. The following equation describes the motion of a certain mass connected to a spring, with viscous friction on the surface

$$3\ddot{y} + 18\dot{y} + 102y = f(t)$$

where $f(t)$ is an applied force. Suppose that $f(t) = 0$ for $t < 0$ and $f(t) = 10$ for $t \geq 0$.
a. Plot $y(t)$ for $y(0) = \dot{y}(0) = 0$.
b. Plot $y(t)$ for $y(0) = 0$ and $\dot{y}(0) = 10$. Discuss the effect of the nonzero initial velocity.

27. The following equation describes the motion of a certain mass connected to a spring with viscous friction on the surface

$$3\ddot{y} + 39\dot{y} + 120y = f(t)$$

where $f(t)$ is an applied force. Suppose that $f(t) = 0$ for $t < 0$ and $f(t) = 10$ for $t \geq 0$.
a. Plot $y(t)$ for $y(0) = \dot{y}(0) = 0$.
b. Plot $y(t)$ for $y(0) = 0$ and $\dot{y}(0) = 10$. Discuss the effect of the nonzero initial velocity.

28. The following equation describes the motion of a certain mass connected to a spring with no friction

$$3\ddot{y} + 75y = f(t)$$

where $f(t)$ is an applied force. The equation's characteristic roots are $s = \pm 5i$, so the system's natural frequency of oscillation is 5 radians/second. Suppose the applied force is sinusoidal with a frequency of ω radians/second and an amplitude of 10 newtons: $f(t) = 10\sin(\omega t)$.
    Suppose that the initial conditions are $y(0) = \dot{y}(0) = 0$. Plot $y(t)$ for $0 \leq t \leq 20$ seconds. Do this for the following three cases. Compare the results of each case.
a. $\omega = 1$ radian/second.
b. $\omega = 5.1$ radians/second.
c. $\omega = 10$ radians/second.

29. Van der Pol's equation has been used to describe many oscillatory processes. It is

$$\ddot{y} - \mu(1 - y^2)\dot{y} + y = 0$$

Plot $y(t)$ for $\mu = 1$ and $0 \leq t \leq 20$, using the initial conditions $y(0) = 2$, $\dot{y}(0) = 0$.

30. The equation of motion for a pendulum whose base is accelerating horizontally with an acceleration $a(t)$ is

$$L\ddot{\theta} + g\sin\theta = a(t)\cos\theta$$

Suppose that $g = 9.81$ meters/second^2, $L = 1$ meter, and $\dot{\theta}(0) = 0$. Plot $\theta(t)$ for $0 \leq t \leq 10$ seconds for the following three cases:
a. The acceleration is constant: $a = 5$ meters/second^2 and $\theta(0) = 0.5$ radian.
b. The acceleration is constant: $a = 5$ meters/second^2 and $\theta(0) = 3$ radians.
c. The acceleration is linear with time: $a = 0.5t$ meters/second^2 and $\theta(0) = 3$ radians.

436

**Numerical
Methods for
Calculus and
Differential
Equations**

31. The equations for a armature-controlled dc motor are the following. The motor's current is i, and its rotational velocity is ω.

$$L\frac{di}{dt} = -Ri - K_e\omega + v(t) \qquad (8.6\text{–}1)$$

$$I\frac{d\omega}{dt} = K_Ti - c\omega \qquad (8.6\text{–}2)$$

where L, R, and I are the motor's inductance, resistance, and inertia; K_T and K_e are the torque constant and back emf constant; c is a viscous damping constant; and $v(t)$ is the applied voltage.

Use the values $R = 0.8$ ohm, $L = .003$ henry, $K_T = .05$ newton meter/ampere, $K_e = .05$ volt/radian/second, $c = 0$, and $I = 8 \times 10^{-5}$ newton meter second^2.

a. Find the motor's characteristic roots and time constants. If the applied voltage is constant, approximately how long will it take for the motor to reach a constant speed?

b. Suppose the applied voltage is 20 volts. Plot the motor's speed and current versus time. Choose a final time large enough to show the motor's speed becoming constant.

c. Suppose the applied voltage is trapezoidal as given here:

$$v(t) = \begin{cases} 400t & 0 \le t < 0.05 \\ 20 & 0.05 \le t \le 0.2 \\ -400(t-.2)+20 & 0.2 < t \le 0.25 \\ 0 & t > 0.25 \end{cases}$$

Plot the motor's speed versus time for $0 \le t \le 0.3$ second. Also plot the applied voltage versus time. Does the motor speed follow a trapezoidal profile?

32.* (Control System toolbox and/or Student Edition) Find the state-space form of the following model:

$$10\ddot{y} + 3\dot{y} + 7y = f(t)$$

33. (Control System toolbox and/or Student Edition) Find the state-space form of the following model:

$$10\ddot{y} + 6\dot{y} + 2y = f + 3\dot{f}$$

34.* (Control System toolbox and/or Student Edition) Find the reduced form of the following state model in terms of x_1.

$$\begin{bmatrix} \dot{x}_1 \\ \dot{x}_2 \end{bmatrix} = \begin{bmatrix} -4 & -1 \\ 2 & -3 \end{bmatrix} \begin{bmatrix} x_1 \\ x_2 \end{bmatrix} + \begin{bmatrix} 2 \\ 5 \end{bmatrix} u(t)$$

35. (Control System toolbox and/or Student Edition) The following state model describes the motion of a certain mass connected to a spring with viscous friction on the surface, where $m = 1$, $c = 2$, and $k = 5$.

$$\begin{bmatrix} \dot{x}_1 \\ \dot{x}_2 \end{bmatrix} = \begin{bmatrix} 0 & 1 \\ -5 & -2 \end{bmatrix} \begin{bmatrix} x_1 \\ x_2 \end{bmatrix} + \begin{bmatrix} 0 \\ 1 \end{bmatrix} f(t)$$

a. Use the `initial` function to plot the position x_1 of the mass if the initial position is 5 and the initial velocity is 3.

b. Use the `step` function to plot the step response of the position and velocity for zero initial conditions, where the magnitude of the step input is 10. Compare your plot with that shown in Figure 8.6–4.

36. Consider the following equation:

$$5\ddot{y} + 2\dot{y} + 10y = f(t)$$

a. Plot the free response for the initial conditions $y(0) = 10$, $\dot{y}(0) = -5$.

b. Plot the unit-step response (for zero initial conditions).

c. The *total response* to a step input is the sum of the free response and the step response. Demonstrate this fact for this equation by plotting the sum of the solutions found in parts (a) and (b) and comparing the plot with that generated by solving for the total response with $y(0) = 10$, $\dot{y}(0) = -5$.

37. (Control System toolbox and/or Student Edition) Use the `lsim` function to solve the dc motor problem given in Example 8.6–2. Compare your results with those shown in Figure 8.6–6.

38. (Control System toolbox and/or Student Edition) The model for the RC circuit shown in Figure P38 is

$$RC\frac{dv_o}{dt} + v_o = v_i$$

For $RC = 0.1$ second, plot the voltage response $v_o(t)$ for the case where the applied voltage is a single square pulse of height 10 volts and duration 0.2 second, starting at $t = 0$. The initial capacitor voltage is 0.

Figure P38

39. Van der Pol's equation is

$$\ddot{y} - \mu(1 - y^2)\dot{y} + y = 0$$

This equation is stiff for large values of the parameter μ. Compare the performance of `ode45` and `ode23s` for this equation. Use $\mu = 1000$ and $0 \le t \le 3000$ with the initial conditions $y(0) = 2$, $\dot{y}(0) = 0$. Plot $y(t)$ versus t.

40. Use MATLAB to plot the trajectory of a ball thrown at an angle of 30° to the horizontal with a speed of 30 meters/second. The ball bounces off the horizontal surface and loses 20 percent of its vertical speed with each bounce. Plot the trajectory showing three bounces.

© D & I MacDonald / The Picture Cube.

Engineering in the 21st Century . . .

Rebuilding the Infrastructure

During the Great Depression, many public works projects that improved the nation's infrastructure were undertaken to stimulate the economy and provide employment. These projects included highways, bridges, water supply systems, sewer systems, and electrical power distribution networks. Following World War II another burst of such activity culminated in the construction of the interstate highway system. As we enter the 21st century, much of the infrastructure is 30 to 70 years old and is literally crumbling or not up-to-date. One survey showed that more than 25 percent of the nation's bridges are substandard. These need to be repaired or replaced with new bridges, such as the one under construction in Savannah, Georgia, shown above.

Rebuilding the infrastructure requires engineering methods different from those in the past because labor and material costs are now higher and environmental and social issues have greater importance than before. Infrastructure engineers must take advantage of new materials, new inspection technology, new construction techniques, and new labor-saving machines.

Also, some infrastructure components, such as communications networks, need to be replaced because they are out-dated and do not have sufficient capacity or ability to take advantage of new technology. An example is the "information infrastructure," which includes physical facilities to transmit, store, process, and display voice, data, and images. Better communications and computer networking technology will be needed for such improvements. Many of the MATLAB toolboxes provide advanced support for such work, including the Financial, Communications, Image Processing, Signal Processing, PDE, and Wavelet toolboxes.

9

Symbolic Processing with MATLAB

Outline

Up to now we have used MATLAB to perform numerical operations only; that is, our answers have been numbers, not expressions. In this chapter we use MATLAB to perform *symbolic processing* to obtain answers in the form of expressions. Symbolic processing is the term used to describe how a computer performs operations on mathematical expressions in the way, for example that humans do algebra with pencil and paper. Whenever possible, we wish to obtain solutions in closed form because they give us greater insight into the problem. For example, we often can see how to improve an engineering design by modeling it with mathematical expressions that do not have specific parameter values. Then we can analyze the expressions and decide which parameter values will optimize the design.

This chapter explains how to define a *symbolic expression* such as $y = \sin x / \cos x$ in MATLAB and how to use MATLAB to simplify expressions wherever possible. For example, the previous function simplifies to $y = \sin x / \cos x = \tan x$. MATLAB can perform

SYMBOLIC EXPRESSION

439

operations such as addition and multiplication on mathematical expressions, and we can use MATLAB to obtain symbolic solutions to algebraic equations such as $x^2 + 2x + a = 0$ (the solution for x is $x = -1 \pm \sqrt{1 - a}$). MATLAB can also perform symbolic differentiation and integration and can solve ordinary differential equations in closed form.

To use the methods of this chapter, you must have either the Symbolic Math toolbox or the Student Edition of MATLAB, which contains all the functions of the Symbolic Math toolbox but has limited access to the Maple kernel. New features were introduced in the toolbox with Version 2, and there are some differences in syntax between Versions 1 and 2. This chapter is based on Version 2, on which Version 5 of the Student Edition is based.

The symbolic processing capabilities in MATLAB are based on the Maple V software package, which was developed by Waterloo Maple Software, Inc. The MathWorks has licensed the Maple "engine," that is, the core of Maple. If you have used Maple before, however, or plan to use it in the future, you should be aware that the syntax used by MATLAB differs from that used by the commercially available Maple package.

Symbolic processing is a relatively new computer application, and such software is undergoing rapid development. As a result, software upgrades might produce changes in performance and in the syntax as capabilities are improved and bugs removed. For this reason, you should check the MathWorks web site if your software does not perform as expected or gives erroneous results. The MathWorks web site is http//www.mathworks.com. Look for answers to frequently asked questions (FAQ) and technical notes. These are arranged by category (for example, one category is the Symbolic Math toolbox). You can also search for information using key words.

We cover in this chapter a subset of the capabilities of the Symbolic Math toolbox. Specifically we treat

- Symbolic algebra.
- Symbolic methods for solving algebraic and transcendental equations.
- Symbolic methods for solving ordinary differential equations.
- Symbolic calculus, including integration, differentiation, limits, and series.
- Laplace transforms.
- Selected topics in linear algebra, including symbolic methods for obtaining determinants, matrix inverses, and eigenvalues.

The topic of Laplace transforms is included because they provide one way of solving differential equations and are often covered along with differential equations.

We do not discuss the following features of the Symbolic Math toolbox: canonical forms of symbolic matrices; variable precision arithmetic that allows you to evaluate expressions to a specified numerical accuracy; and special mathematical functions such as Fourier transforms. Details on these capabilities can be found in the online help.

When you have finished this chapter, you should be able to use MATLAB to

- Create symbolic expressions and manipulate them algebraically.
- Obtain symbolic solutions to algebraic and transcendental equations.
- Perform symbolic differentiation and integration.
- Evaluate limits and series symbolically.
- Obtain symbolic solutions to ordinary differential equations.
- Obtain Laplace transforms.
- Perform symbolic linear algebra operations, including obtaining expressions for determinants, matrix inverses, and eigenvalues.

9.1

Symbolic Expressions and Algebra

The `sym` function can be used to create "symbolic objects" in MATLAB. If the input argument to `sym` is a string, the result is a symbolic number or variable. If the input argument is a numeric scalar or matrix, the result is a symbolic representation of the given numeric values. For example, typing x = sym('x') creates the symbolic variable with name x, and typing y = sym('y') creates a symbolic variable named y. Typing x = sym('x','real') tells MATLAB to assume that x is real. Typing x = sym('x','unreal') tells MATLAB to assume that x is not real.

The `syms` function, which is new in MATLAB 5, enables you to combine more than one such statement into a single statement. For example, typing syms x is equivalent to typing x = sym('x'), and typing syms x y u v creates the four symbolic variables x, y, u, and v. When used without arguments, `syms` lists the symbolic objects in the workspace. The `syms` command, however, cannot be used to create symbolic constants; you must use `sym` for this purpose.

The `syms` command enables you to specify that certain variables are real. For example,

```
>>syms x y real
```

SYMBOLIC CONSTANT

You can use the `sym` function to create *symbolic constants* by using a numerical value for the argument. For example, typing pi = sym('pi'), fraction = sym('1/3'), and sqroot2 = sym('sqrt(2)') create symbolic constants that avoid the floating-point approximations inherent in the values of π, $1/3$, and $\sqrt{2}$. If you create the symbolic constant π this way, it temporarily replaces the built-in numeric constant, and you no longer obtain a numerical value when you type its name. For example,

```
>>pi = sym('pi')
pi =
   pi
>>sqroot2 = sym('sqrt(2)')
sqroot2 =
   sqrt(2)
>>a = 3*sqrt(2)     % This gives a numeric result.
a =
   4.2426
>>b = 3*sqroot2     % This gives a symbolic result.
b =
   3*2^(1/2)
```

The advantage of using symbolic constants is that they need not be evaluated (with the accompanying round-off error) until a numeric answer is required.

Symbolic constants can look like numbers but are actually symbolic expressions. Symbolic expressions can look like character strings but are a different sort of quantity. You can use the class function to determine whether or not a quantity is symbolic, numeric, or a character string. We will give examples of the class function later.

The effect of round-off error needs to be considered when converting MATLAB floating-point values to symbolic constants in this way. You can use an optional second argument with the sym function to specify the technique for converting floating-point numbers. Refer to the online help for more information.

Symbolic Expressions

You can use symbolic variables in expressions and as arguments of functions. You use the operators + - * / ^ and the built-in functions just as you use them with numerical calculations. For example, typing

```
>>syms x y
>>s = x + y;
>>r = sqrt(x^2 + y^2);
```

creates the symbolic variables s and r. The terms s = x + y and r =sqrt(x^2 + y^2) are examples of symbolic *expressions*. The variables s and r created this way are *not* the same as user-defined function files. That is, if you later assign x and y numeric values, typing r will not cause MATLAB to evaluate the equation $r = \sqrt{x^2 + y^2}$. We will see later how to evaluate symbolic expressions numerically.

The syms function is new in Version 2 of the toolbox, and the syntax of the sym function has been expanded. In Version 1, only symbolic matrices are created with sym; symbolic expressions must be created by enclosing the expression in single quotes. We will be using the Version 2 syntax exclusively here, so users of Version 1 will need to modify many of the examples presented in this chapter, primarily by replacing the use of syms with the equivalent statements using sym. Other differences will be noted at the appropriate point. Note that Version 5 of the Student Edition is based on Version 2 of the toolbox; Version 4 of the Student Edition is based on Version 1 of the toolbox. Thus all of our examples will work with Version 5 of the Student Edition.

The syms command enables you to specify that expressions have certain characteristics. For example, in the following session MATLAB will treat the expression w as a nonnegative number:

```
>>syms x y real
>>w = x^2 + y^2;
```

To clear x of its real property, type syms x unreal. Note that typing clear x eliminates x from the workspace and does not make x a nonreal variable.

The vector and matrix notation used in MATLAB also applies to symbolic variables. For example, you can create a symbolic matrix A as follows:

```
>>n = 3;
>>syms x;
>>A = x.^((0:n)'*(0:n))
A =
    [ 1, 1, 1, 1]
    [ 1, x, x^2, x^3]
    [ 1, x^2, x^4, x^6]
    [ 1, x^3, x^6, x^9]
```

Note that it was not necessary to use sym or syms to declare A to be a symbolic variable beforehand. It is recognized as a symbolic variable because it is created with a symbolic expression.

In MATLAB the variable x is the *default* independent variable, but other variables can be specified to be the independent variable. It is important to know which variable is the independent variable in an expression. The function findsym(E) can be used to determine the symbolic variable used by MATLAB in a particular expression E. (The findsym function replaces the symvar function of Version 1.)

The function findsym(E) finds the symbolic variables in a symbolic expression or matrix, where E is a scalar or matrix symbolic expression, and returns a string containing all of the symbolic variables appearing in E. The variables are returned

DEFAULT VARIABLE

in alphabetical order and are separated by commas. If no symbolic variables are found, findsym returns the empty string.

By contrast, the function findsym(E,n) returns the n symbolic variables in E closest to x, with the tie breaker going to the variable closer to z. The following session shows some examples of its use:

```
>>syms b x1 y
>>findsym(6*b+y)
ans =
   b,y
>>findsym(6*b+y+x) %Note: x has not been declared symbolic.
???  Undefined function or variable 'x'.
>>findsym(6*b+y,1) %Find the one variable closest to x
ans =
   y
>>findsym(6*b+y+x1,1) %Find the one variable closest to x
ans =
   x1
>>findsym(6*b+y*i) %i is not symbolic
ans =
   b, y
```

Manipulating Expressions

The following functions can be used to manipulate expressions by collecting coefficients of like powers, expanding powers, and factoring expressions, for example.

The function collect(E) collects coefficients of like powers in the expression E. If there is more than one variable, you can use the optional form collect(E,v), which collects all the coefficients with the same power of v.

```
>>syms x y
>>E = (x-5)^2+(y-3)^2;
>>collect(E)
ans =
   x^2-10*x+25+(y-3)^2
>>collect(E,y)
ans =
   y^2-6*y+(x-5)^2+9
```

The function expand(E) expands the expression E by carrying out powers. For example,

```
>>syms x y
>>expand((x+y)^2) % applies algebra rules
ans =
   x^2+2*x*y+y^2
>>expand(sin(x+y)) % applies trig identities
```

```
ans =
    sin(x)*cos(y)+cos(x)*sin(y)
>>expand(6*((sin(x))^2+(cos(x))^2)) % applies another trig identity
ans =
    6
```

The function `factor(E)` factors the expression E. For example,

```
>>syms x y
>>factor(x^2-1)
ans =
    (x-1)*(x+1)
```

The function `simplify(E)` simplifies the expression E, using Maple's simplification rules. For example,

```
>>syms x y
>>simplify(x*sqrt(x^8*y^2))
ans =
    x*(x^8*y^2)^(1/2)
```

The function `simple(E)` searches for the shortest form of the expression E in terms of number of characters. When called, the function displays the results of each step of its search. When called without the argument, `simple` acts on the previous expression. The form `[r, how] = simple(E)` does not display intermediate steps, but saves those steps in the string `how`. The shortest form found is stored in `r`.

You can use the operators + − * / and ^ with symbolic expressions to obtain new expressions. The following session illustrates how this is done.

```
>>syms x y
>>E1 = x^2+5             % define two expressions
>>E2 = y^3-2
>>S1 = E1 + E2           % add the expressions
S1 =
    x^2+3+y^3
>>S2 = E1*E2             % multiply the expressions
S2 =
    (x^2+5)*(y^3-2)
>>expand(S2)             % expand the product
ans =
    x^2*y^3-2*x^2+5*y^3-10
>>E3 = x^3+2*x^2+5*x+10    % define a third expression
>>S3 = E3/E1             % divide two expressions
    S3 = (x^3+2*x^2+5*x+10)/(x^2+5)
>>simplify(S3)           % see if some terms cancel
ans =
    x+2
```

The function [num den] = numden(E) returns two symbolic expressions that represent the numerator num and denominator den for the rational representation of the expression E.

```
>>syms x
>>E1 = x^2+5;
>>E4 = 1/(x+6);
>>[num, den] = numden(E1+E4)
num =
    x^3+6*x^2+5*x+31
den =
    x+6
```

The function double(E) converts the expression E to numeric form. The expression E must not contain any symbolic variables. The term *double* stands for floating-point, *double* precision. For example,

```
>>sqroot2 = sym('sqrt(2)');
>>y = 6*sqroot2
y =
    6*2^(1/2)
z = double(y)
z =
    8.4853
```

The function poly2sym(p) converts a coefficient vector p to a symbolic polynomial. The form poly2sym(p, 'v') generates the polynomial in terms of the variable v. For example,

```
>>poly2sym([2,6,4])
ans =
    2*x^2+6*x+4
>>poly2sym([5,-3,7],'y')
ans =
    5*y^2-3*y+7
```

The function sym2poly(E) converts the expression E to a polynomial coefficient vector.

```
>>syms x
>>sym2poly(9*x^2+4*x+6)
ans =
    [9 4 6]
```

The function pretty(E) displays the expression E on the screen in a form that resembles typeset mathematics.

The function subs(E,old,new) substitutes new for old in the expression E, where old can be a symbolic variable or expression and new can be a symbolic variable, expression, or matrix, or a numeric value or matrix. For example,

```
>>syms x y
>>E = x^2+6*x+7
>>F = subs(E,x,y)
F =
   y^2+6*y+7
```

If old and new are cell arrays of the same size, each element of old is replaced by the corresponding element of new. If E and old are scalars and new is an array or cell array, the scalars are expanded to produce an array result.

In the syntax of Version 1 of the toolbox and Version 4 of the Student Edition, the order of new and old were reversed; the syntax was subs(new,old). To provide backwards compatibility, in Version 2 of the toolbox and Version 5 of the Student Edition, if subs(E,old,new) does not change E, then subs(E,new,old) is tried. This process eliminates the need to remember the order of the arguments.

If you want to tell MATLAB that f is a function of the variable t, type f = sym('f(t)'). Thereafter, f behaves like a function of t, and you can manipulate it with the toolbox commands. For example, to create a new function $g(t) = f(t + 2) - f(t)$, the session is

```
>>syms t
>>f = sym('f(t)');
>>g = subs(f,t,t+2)-f
g =
   f(t+2)-f(t)
```

Once a specific function is defined for $f(t)$, the function $g(t)$ will be available. We will use this technique with the Laplace transform in section 9.5.

MATLAB does not have a factorial function, but you can use the sym and subs functions to access the Maple factorial function to compute $n!$ as follows:

```
>>kfac = sym('k!')
>>syms k n
>>subs(kfac,k,n)
ans =
   n!
```

To compute a numeric factorial, say, 5!, use the prod function and type prod(1:5).

To perform multiple substitutions, enclose the new and old elements in braces. For example, to substitute $a = x$ and $b = 2$ into the expression $E = a \sin b$, the session is

```
>>syms a b x
>>E = a*sin(b);
>>F = subs(E,{a, b}, {x, 2})
```

```
F =
    x*sin(2)
```

Evaluating Expressions

In most applications we eventually want to obtain numerical values or a plot from the symbolic expression. Use the subs and double functions to evaluate an expression numerically. First use subs(E,old,new) to replace old with a numeric value new. Then use the double function to convert the expression E to a numeric form. For example,

```
>>syms x
>>E = x^2+6*x+7;
>>G = subs(E,x,2) % G is a symbolic constant
G =
   23
>>class(G)
ans =
   sym
>>H = double(G) % H is a numeric quantity
H =
   23
>>class(H)
ans =
   double
```

The above session is identical to that seen in Version 5 of the Student Edition. Due to a change, however, in a recent release of Version 2 of the Symbolic Math toolbox, if $f = f(x)$, then subs(f,x,n), where n is a numeric quantity, returns a value of class *double*. This change was not incorporated in the Student Edition. The examples in this chapter do not depend on this new feature; they will work with both Student Edition 5 and Version 2 of the toolbox.

Sometimes MATLAB will display all zeros as the result of evaluating an expression, whereas in fact the value can be nonzero but so small that you need to evaluate the expression with more accuracy to see that it is nonzero. You can use the digits and the vpa functions to change the number of digits MATLAB uses for calculating and evaluating expressions. The accuracy of individual arithmetic operations in MATLAB is 16 digits, whereas symbolic operations can be carried out to an arbitrary number of digits. The default is 32 digits. Type digits(d) to change the number of digits used to d. Be aware that larger values of d will require more time and computer memory to perform operations. Type vpa(E) to compute the expression E to the number of digits specified by the default value of 32 or the current setting of digits. Type vpa(E,d) to compute the expression E using d digits. (The abbreviation *vpa* stands for "variable precision arithmetic").

Plotting Expressions

The MATLAB function ezplot (E) generates a plot of a symbolic expression E, which is a function of one variable. The default range of the independent variable is the interval $[-2\pi, 2\pi]$ unless this interval contains a singularity. The optional form ezplot (E, [xmin xmax]) generates a plot over the range from xmin to xmax. Of course, you can enhance the plot generated by ezplot by using the plot format commands discussed in Chapter 4; for example, the axis, xlabel, and ylabel commands.

For example,

```
>>syms x
>>E = x^2-6*x+7
>>ezplot(E,[-2 6])
```

The plot is shown in Figure 9.1–1. Note that the expression is automatically placed at the top of the plot and that the axis label for the independent variable is automatically placed. You can use other plot-enhancement functions with ezplot to modify its appearance. For example, sometimes the automatic selection of the ordinate scale is not satisfactory. To obtain an ordinate scale

Figure 9.1–1
Plot of the function $E = x^2 - 6x + 7$ generated by the ezplot function.

from −5 to 25 and to place a label on the ordinate, you would type

```
>>ezplot(E),axis([-2 6 -5 25],ylabel('E')
```

Order of Precedence

MATLAB does not always arrange expressions in a form that we normally would use. For example, MATLAB might provide an answer in the form `-c+b`, whereas we would normally write `b-c`. The order of precedence used by MATLAB must be constantly kept in mind to avoid misinterpreting the MATLAB output (see pages 30 and 31 for the order of precedence). MATLAB frequently expresses results in the form `1/a*b`, whereas we would normally write `b/a`. MATLAB sometimes writes `x^(1/2)*y^(1/2)` instead of grouping the terms as `(x*y)^(1/2)`, and often fails to cancel negative signs where possible, as in `-a/(-b*c-d)`, instead of `a/(b*c+d)`. For example,

```
>>syms x
>>E = x^2-6*x+7
>>F = -G/3
F =
   -1/3*x^2+2*x-7/3
```

The answer is $F = -(1/3)x^2 + 2x - 7/3$, which we would normally express as $F = -(x^2 - 6x + 7)/3$.

Table 9.1–1 Functions for creating and evaluating symbolic expressions

Command	Description
class(E)	Returns the class of the expression E.
digits(d)	Sets the number of decimal digits used to do variable precision arithmetic. The default is 32 digits.
double(E)	Converts the expression E to numeric form.
ezplot(E)	Generates a plot of a symbolic expression E, which is a function of one variable. The default range of the independent variable is the interval $[-2\pi, 2\pi]$ unless this interval contains a singularity. The optional form ezplot(E, [xmin xmax]) generates a plot over the range from xmin to xmax.
findsym(E)	Finds the symbolic variables in a symbolic expression or matrix, where E is a scalar or matrix symbolic expression, and returns a string containing all the symbolic variables appearing in E. The variables are returned in alphabetical order and are separated by commas. If no symbolic variables are found, findsym returns the empty string.
findsym(E,n)	Returns the n symbolic variables in E closest to x, with the tie breaker going to the variable closer to z.
[num den] = numden(E)	Returns two symbolic expressions that represent the numerator expression num and denominator expression den for the rational representation of the expression E.
x = sym('x')	Creates the symbolic variable with name x. Typing x = sym('x','real') tells MATLAB to assume that x is real. Typing x = sym('x','unreal') tells MATLAB to assume that x is not real.
syms x y u v	Creates the symbolic variables x, y, u, and v. When used without arguments, syms lists the symbolic objects in the workspace.
vpa(E,d)	Sets the number of digits used to evaluate the expression E to d. Typing vpa(E) causes E to be evaluated to the number of digits specified by the default value of 32 or by the current setting of digits.

Table 9.1–2 Functions for manipulating symbolic expressions

Command	Description
collect(E)	Collects coefficients of like powers in the expression E.
expand(E)	Expands the expression E by carrying out powers.
factor(E)	Factors the expression E.
poly2sym(p)	Converts a polynomial coefficient vector p to a symbolic polynomial. The form poly2sym(p,'v') generates the polynomial in terms of the variable v.
pretty(E)	Displays the expression E on the screen in a form that resembles typeset mathematics.
simple(E)	Searches for the shortest form of the expression E in terms of number of characters. When called, the function displays the results of each step of its search. When called without the argument, simple acts on the previous expression. The form [r, how] = simple(E) does not display intermediate steps, but saves those steps in the string how. The shortest form found is stored in r.
simplify(E)	Simplifies the expression E using Maple's simplification rules.
subs(E,old,new)	Substitutes new for old in the expression E, where old can be a symbolic variable or expression, new can be a symbolic variable, expression, or matrix, or a numeric value or matrix.
sym2poly(E)	Converts the expression E to a polynomial coefficient vector.

Tables 9.1–1 and 9.1–2 summarize the functions for creating, evaluating, and manipulating symbolic expressions.

Test Your Understanding

T9.1–1 Given the expressions: $E_1 = x^3 - 15x^2 + 75x - 125$ and $E_2 = (x + 5)^2 - 20x$, use MATLAB to

(a) Find the product $E_1 E_2$ and express it in its simplest form.

(b) Find the quotient E_1/E_2 and express it in its simplest form.

(c) Evaluate the sum $E_1 + E_2$ at $x = 7.1$ in symbolic form and in numeric form.

(Answers: (a) $(x - 5)^5$; (b) $x - 5$; (c) $13671/1000$ in symbolic form, 13.6710 in numeric form).

Algebraic and Transcendental Equations

The Symbolic Math toolbox can solve algebraic and transcendental equations, as well as systems of such equations. A *transcendental* equation is one that contains one or more transcendental functions, such as $\sin x$, e^x, or $\log x$. The appropriate function to solve such equations is the solve function.

The function solve(E) solves a symbolic expression or equation represented by the expression E. If E represents an *equation*, the equation's expression must be enclosed in single quotes. If E represents an expression, then the solution obtained will be the roots of the expression E; that is, the solution of the equation

$E = 0$. Multiple expressions or equations can be solved by separating them with a comma, as `solve(E1,E2, ..., En)`. Note that you need not declare the symbolic variable with the `sym` or `syms` function before using `solve`.

There are three ways to use the `solve` function. For example, to solve the equation $x + 5 = 0$, one way is

```
>>eq1 = 'x+5=0';
>>solve(eq1)
ans =
    -5
```

The second way is

```
>>solve('x+5=0')
ans =
    -5
```

The third way is

```
>>syms x
>>solve(x+5)
ans =
    -5
```

You can store the result in a named variable as follows:

```
>>syms x
>>x = solve(x+5)
x =
    -5
```

To solve the equation $e^{2x} + 3e^x = 54$, the session is

```
>>solve('exp(2*x)+3*exp(x)=54')
ans =
    [ log(-9)]
    [ log(6)]
```

Note that `log(6)` is ln(6) = 1.7918, whereas `log(-9)`, which is ln(−9), is a complex number. To see this, in MATLAB type `log(-9)` to obtain $2.1972 + 3.1416i$. So we obtained two solutions, instead of one, and now we must decide whether both are meaningful. The answer depends on the application that produced the original equation. If the application requires a real number for a solution, then we should choose `log(6)` as the answer.

The following sessions provide some more examples of the use of these functions.

```
>>eq2 = 'y^2+3*y+2=0';
>>solve(eq2)
ans =
    [-2]
    [-1]
```

```
>>eq3 = 'x^2+9*y^4=0';
>>solve(eq3) %Note that x is presumed to be the unknown variable
ans =
    [ 3*i*y^2]
    [-3*i*y^2]
```

When more than one variable occurs in the expression, MATLAB
assumes that the variable closest to x in the alphabet is the
variable to be found. You can specify the solution variable using
the syntax solve(E, 'v'), where v is the solution variable. For
example,

```
>>solve('b^2+8*c+2*b=0') %solves for c because it is closer to x
ans =
    -1/8*b^2-1/4*b
>>solve('b^2+8*c+2*b=0','b') % solves for b
ans =
    [ -1+(1-8*c)^(1/2)]
    [ -1-(1-8*c)^(1/2)]
```

Thus the solution of $b^2 + 8c + 2b = 0$ for c is $c = -(b^2 + 2b)/8$.
The solution for b is $b = -1 \pm \sqrt{1 - 8c}$.

You can save the solutions as vectors by using the form [x, y]
= solve(eq1, eq2). Note the difference in the output formats
in the following example:

```
>>eq4 = '6*x+2*y=14';
>>eq5 = '3*x+7*y=31';
>>solve(eq4,eq5)
ans =
    x: [1x1 sym]
    y: [1x1 sym]
>>ans.x
x =
    1
>>ans.y =
    4
>>[x, y] = solve(eq4,eq5)
ans =
    x =
        1
    y =
        4
```

You can save the *solution in a structure* with named fields (see   **SOLUTION**
Chapter 3, section 3.7 for a discussion of structures and fields).   **STRUCTURE**
The individual solutions are saved in the fields. For example,
continue the preceding session as follows:

```
>>S = solve(eq4,eq5)
ans =
```

453

```
     x:  [1x1 sym]
     y:  [1x1 sym]
>>S.x
ans =
     1
>>S.y
ans =
     4
```

Test Your Understanding

T9.2–1 Use MATLAB to solve the equation $\sqrt{1 - x^2} = x$.

(Answer: $x = \sqrt{2}/2$).

T9.2–2 Use MATLAB to solve the equation set $x + 6y = a$, $2x - 3y = 9$ for x and y in terms of the parameter a.

(Answer: $x = (a + 18)/5, y = (2a - 9)/15$).

Example 9.2–1 Intersection of two circles

We want to find the intersection points of two circles. The first circle has a radius of 2 and is centered at $x = 3$, $y = 5$. The second circle has a radius b and is centered at $x = 5$, $y = 3$. See Figure 9.2–1.

(a) Find the (x, y) coordinates of the intersection points in terms of the parameter b.

(b) Evaluate the solution for the case where $b = \sqrt{3}$.

Solution:

(a) The intersection points are found from the solutions of the two equations for the circles. These equations are

$$(x - 3)^2 + (y - 5)^2 = 4$$

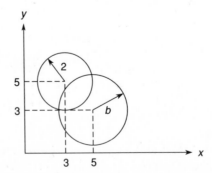

Figure 9.2–1
Intersection points of two circles.

for the first circle, and

$$(x - 5)^2 + (y - 3)^2 = b^2$$

The session to solve these equations follows. Note that the result x:
[2x1 sym] indicates that there are two solutions for x. Similarly,
there are two solutions for y.

```
>>syms x y b
>>S = solve((x-3)^2+(y-5)^2-4,(x-5)^2+(y-3)^2-b^2)
ans =
   S
   x:  [2x1 sym]
   y:  [2x1 sym]
>>S.x
ans =
   [ 9/2-1/8*b^2+1/8*(-16+24*b^2- b^4)^(1/2)]
   [ 9/2-1/8*b^2-1/8*(-16+24*b^2- b^4)^(1/2)]
```

The solution for the *x* coordinates of the intersection points is

$$x = \frac{9}{2} - \frac{1}{8}b^2 \pm \frac{1}{8}\sqrt{-16 + 24b^2 - b^4}$$

The solution for the *y* coordinates can be found in a similar way
by typing S.y.

(b) Continue the session by substituting $b = \sqrt{3}$ into the expression for *x*.

```
>>subs(S.x,b,sqrt(3))
ans =
   [33/8+1/8*47^(1/2)]
   [33/8-1/8*47^(1/2)]
>>double(ans)
ans =
   4.9820
   3.2680
```

Thus the *x* coordinates of the two intersection points are *x* = 4.982
and *x* = 3.268. The *y* coordinates can be found in a similar way.

Test Your Understanding

T9.2–3 Find the *y* coordinates of the intersection points in Example 9.2–1. Use $b = \sqrt{3}$.

(Answer: *y* = 4.7320, 3.0180.)

Equations containing periodic functions can have an infinite
number of solutions. In such cases the solve function restricts

the solution search to solutions near 0. For example, to solve the equation $\sin(2x) - \cos x = 0$, the session is

```
>>solve('sin(2*x)-cos(x)=0')
ans =
   [ 1/2*pi]
   [ -1/2*pi]
   [ 1/6*pi]
   [ 5/6*pi]
```

Example 9.2-2   Positioning a robot arm   Figure 9.2-2 shows a robot arm having two joints and two links. The angles of rotation of the motors at the joints are θ_1 and θ_2. From trigonometry we can derive the following expressions for the (x, y) coordinates of the hand:

$$x = L_1 \cos \theta_1 + L_2 \cos(\theta_1 + \theta_2)$$

$$y = L_1 \sin \theta_1 + L_2 \sin(\theta_1 + \theta_2)$$

Suppose that the link lengths are $L_1 = 4$ feet and $L_2 = 3$ feet.

(a) Compute the motor angles required to position the hand at $x = 6$ feet, $y = 2$ feet.

(b) It is desired to move the hand along the straight line where x is constant at 6 feet and y varies from $y = 0.1$ to $y = 3.6$ feet. Obtain a plot of the required motor angles as a function of y.

Solution:

(a) Substituting the given values of L_1, L_2, x, and y into the above equations gives

$$6 = 4 \cos \theta_1 + 3 \cos(\theta_1 + \theta_2)$$

$$2 = 4 \sin \theta_1 + 3 \sin(\theta_1 + \theta_2)$$

The following session solves these equations. The variables th1 and th2 represent θ_1 and θ_2.

Figure 9.2-2
A robot arm having two
joints and two links.

```
>>S = solve('4*cos(th1)+3*cos(th1+th2)=6',...
'4*sin(th1)+3*sin(th1+th2)=2')
S =
    th1:[2x1 sym]
    th2:[2x1 sym]
>>double(S.th1)*(180/pi) % convert from radians to degrees
ans =
    -3.2981
    40.1680
>>double(S.th2)*(180/pi) % convert from radians to degrees
ans =
    51.3178
    -51.3178
```

Thus there are two solutions. The first is $\theta_1 = -3.2981°$, $\theta_2 = 51.3178°$. This is called the "elbow down" solution. The second solution is $\theta_1 = 40.168°$, $\theta_2 = -51.3178°$. This is called the "elbow up" solution. When a problem can be solved numerically, as in this case, the `solve` function will not perform a symbolic solution. In part (b), however, the symbolic solution capabilities of the `solve` function are put to use.

(b) First we find the solutions for the motor angles in terms of the variable y. Then we evaluate the solution for numerical values of y and plot the results. The script file is shown below. Note that because the problem has three symbolic variables, we must tell the `solve` function that we want to solve for θ_1 and θ_2.

```
S = solve('4*cos(th1)+3*cos(th1+th2)=6',...
'4*sin(th1)+3*sin(th1+th2)=y', 'th1','th2');
yr = [1:.1:3.6];
th1r = subs(S.th1,'y',yr);
th2r = subs(S.th2,'y',yr);
th1r = (180/pi)*double(th1r);
th2r = (180/pi)*double(th2r);
subplot(2,1,1)
plot(yr,th1r,2,-3.2981,'x',2,40.168,'o'),xlabel('y (feet)'),...
ylabel('Theta1 (degrees)')
subplot(2,1,2)
plot(yr,th2r,2,-51.3178,'o',2,51.3178,'x'),xlabel('y (feet)'),...
ylabel('Theta2 (degrees)')
```

The results are shown in Figure 9.2–3, where we have marked the solutions from part (a) to check the validity of the symbolic solutions. The elbow-up solutions are marked with an o, and the elbow-down solutions are marked with an x. We could have printed the expression for the solutions for θ_1 and θ_2 as functions of y, but the expressions are cumbersome and unnecessary if all we want is the plot.

MATLAB is powerful enough to solve the robot arm equations for arbitrary values of the hand coordinates (x, y). However, the resulting expressions for θ_1 and θ_2 are complicated.

457

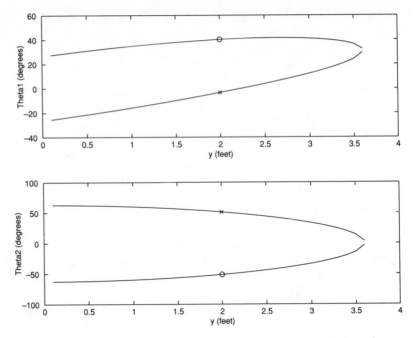

Figure 9.2–3
Plot of the motor angles for the robot hand moving along a vertical line.

Table 9.2-1 summarizes the `solve` function.

Table 9.2–1   Functions for solving algebraic and transcendental equations

Command	Description
`solve(E)`	Solves a symbolic expression or equation represented by the expression E. If E represents an *equation*, the equation's expression must be enclosed in single quotes. If E represents an expression, then the solution obtained will be the roots of the expression E; that is, the solution of the equation $E = 0$. You need not declare the symbolic variable with the `sym` or `syms` function before using `solve`.
`solve(E1,...,En)`	Solves multiple expressions or equations.
`S = solve(E)`	Saves the solution in the structure S.

9.3

Calculus

In Chapter 8 we discussed techniques for performing numerical differentiation and numerical integration; this section covers differentiation and integration of symbolic expressions to obtain closed form results for the derivatives and integrals.

Differentiation

The `diff` function is used to obtain the symbolic derivative. Although this function has the same name as the function used to compute numerical differences (see Chapter 8), MATLAB detects whether or not a symbolic expression is used in the argument and directs the calculation accordingly. The basic syntax is `diff(E)`, which returns the derivative of the expression `E` with respect to the default independent variable.

For example, the derivatives

$$\frac{dx^n}{dx} = nx^{n-1}$$

$$\frac{d\,\ln x}{dx} = \frac{1}{x}$$

$$\frac{d\,\sin^2 x}{dx} = 2\sin x \cos x$$

$$\frac{d\,\sin y}{dy} = \cos y$$

are obtained with the following session:

```
>>syms n x y
>>diff(x^n)
ans =
   x^n*n/x
>>simplify(ans)
ans =
   x^(n-1)*n
>>diff(log(x))
ans =
   1/x
>>diff((sin(x))^2)
ans =
   2*sin(x)*cos(x)
>>diff(sin(y))
ans =
   cos(y)
```

If the expression contains more than one variable, the `diff` function operates on the variable x, or the variable closest to x, unless told to do otherwise. When there is more than one variable, the `diff` function computes the *partial* derivative. For example, if

$$f(x,y) = \sin(xy)$$

then

$$\frac{\partial f}{\partial x} = y\cos(xy)$$

The corresponding session is

```
>>diff(sin(x*y))
ans =
   cos(x*y)*y
```

There are three ways to use the `diff` function, but the third way is preferred. Using the function x^2 as an example, the first way is

```
>>E = 'x^2'
>>diff(E)
ans =
    2*x
```

The second way is

```
>>diff('x^2')
ans =
    2*x
```

The third way is

```
>>syms x
>>diff(x^2)
ans =
    2*x
```

Note that the expression to be differentiated need not be placed in quotes if the variable has been declared to be symbolic. This method is preferred because the use of quoted strings bypasses the use of symbolic expressions, which is the whole point of the Symbolic Math toolbox.

There are three other forms of the `diff` function. The function `diff(E,v)` returns the derivative of the expression `E` with respect to the variable `v`. For example,

$$\frac{\partial[x\,\sin(xy)]}{\partial y} = x^2\cos(xy)$$

is given by

```
>>syms x y
>>diff(x*sin(x*y),y)
ans =
    x^2*cos(x*y)
```

The function `diff(E,n)` returns the nth derivative of the expression `E` with respect to the default independent variable. For example,

$$\frac{d^2(x^3)}{dx^2} = 6x$$

is given by

```
>>syms x
>>diff(x^3,2)
ans =
    6*x
```

Table 9.3–1 Symbolic calculus functions

Command	Description
diff(E)	Returns the derivative of the expression E with respect to the default independent variable.
diff(E,v)	Returns the derivative of the expression E with respect to the variable v.
diff(E,n)	Returns the nth derivative of the expression E with respect to the default independent variable.
diff(E,v,n)	Returns the nth derivative of the expression E with respect to the variable v.
int(E)	Returns the integral of the expression E with respect to the default independent variable.
int(E,v)	Returns the integral of the expression E with respect to the variable v.
int(E,a,b)	Returns the integral of the expression E with respect to the default independent variable over the interval $[a, b]$, where a and b are numeric quantities.
int(E,v,a,b)	Returns the integral of the expression E with respect to the variable v over the interval $[a, b]$, where a and b are numeric quantities.
int(E,m,n)	Returns the integral of the expression E with respect to the default independent variable over the interval $[m, n]$, where m and n are symbolic expressions.
limit(E)	Returns the limit of the expression E as the default independent variable goes to 0.
limit(E,a)	Returns the limit of the expression E as the default independent variable goes to a.
limit(E,v,a)	Returns the limit of the expression E as the variable v goes to a.
limit(E,v,a,'d')	Returns the limit of the expression E as the variable v goes to a from the direction specified by d, which may be right or left.
symsum(E)	Returns the symbolic summation of the expression E.
taylor(f,n,a)	Gives the first n-1 terms in the Taylor series for the function defined in the expression f, evaluated at the point $x = a$. If the parameter a is omitted, the function returns the series evaluated at $x = 0$.

The function diff(E,v,n) returns the nth derivative of the expression E with respect to the variable v. For example,

$$\frac{\partial^2[x\,\sin(xy)]}{\partial y^2} = -x^3\sin(xy)$$

is given by

```
>>syms x y
>>diff(x*sin(x*y),y,2)
ans =
    -x^3*sin(x*y)
```

Table 9.3–1 summarizes the differentiation functions.

Max-Min Problems

The derivative can be used to find the maximum or minimum of a continuous function, say, $f(x)$, over an interval $a \le x \le b$. A *local* maximum or local minimum (one that does not occur at one of the boundaries $x = a$ or $x = b$) can occur only at a *critical point*, which is a point where either $df/dx = 0$ or df/dx does not exist. If $d^2f/dx^2 > 0$, the point is a relative minimum; if $d^2f/dx^2 < 0$, the point is a relative maximum. If $d^2f/dx^2 = 0$, the point is neither a minimum or a maximum, but is an *inflection point*. If multiple candidates exist, you must evaluate the function at each point to determine the *global* maximum and global minimum.

Example 9.3–1   Topping the Green Monster

The Green Monster is a wall 37 feet high in left field at Fenway Park in Boston. The wall is 310 feet from home plate down the left-field line. Assuming that the batter hits the ball 4 feet above the ground, and neglecting air resistance, determine the *minimum* speed the batter must give to the ball to hit it over the Green Monster. In addition, find the angle at which the ball must be hit. (see Figure 9.3–1).

Solution:

The equations of motion for a projectile launched with a speed v_0 at an angle θ relative to the horizontal are

$$x(t) = (v_0 \cos \theta)t \qquad y(t) = -\frac{gt^2}{2} + (v_0 \sin \theta)t$$

where $x = 0$, $y = 0$ is the location of the ball when it is hit. Because we are not concerned with the time of flight in this problem, we can eliminate t and obtain an equation for y in terms of x. To do so, solve the x equation for t and substitute this into the y equation to obtain

$$y(t) = -\frac{g}{2} \frac{x^2(t)}{v_0^2 \cos^2 \theta} + x(t) \tan \theta$$

(You could use MATLAB to do this algebra if you wish. We will use MATLAB to do the more difficult task to follow.).

Because the ball is hit 4 feet above the ground, the ball must rise $37 - 4 = 33$ feet to clear the wall. Let h represent the relative height of the wall (33 feet). Let d represent the distance to the wall (310 feet). Use $g = 32.2$ feet/second^2. When $x = d$, $y = h$. Thus the previous equation gives

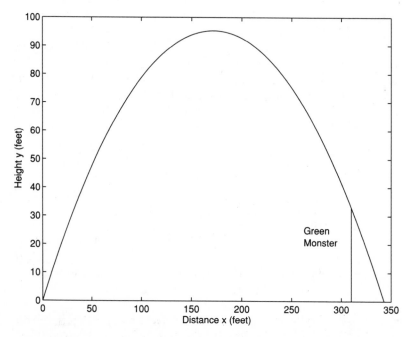

Figure 9.3–1
A baseball trajectory to clear the Green Monster.

$$h = -\frac{g}{2}\frac{d^2}{v_0^2 \cos^2 \theta} + d \tan \theta$$

which can easily be solved for v_0^2 as follows:

$$v_0^2 = \frac{g}{2}\frac{d^2}{\cos^2 \theta (d \tan \theta - h)}$$

Because $v_0 > 0$, minimizing v_0^2 is equivalent to minimizing v_0. Note also that $gd^2/2$ is a multiplicative factor in the expression for v_0^2. Thus the minimizing value of θ is independent of g and can be found by minimizing the function

$$f = \frac{1}{\cos^2 \theta (d \tan \theta - h)}$$

The session to do this is as follows. The variable `th` represents the angle θ of the ball's velocity vector relative to the horizontal. The first step is to calculate the derivative $df/d\theta$ and solve the equation $df/d\theta = 0$ for θ.

```
>>syms d g h th
>>f = (1/(((cos(th))^2)*(d*tan(th)-h)));
>>dfdth = diff(f,th);
>>thmin = solve(dfdth,th);
>>thmin = double(subs(thmin,{d,h},{310,33})))
thmin =
    0.8384
   -0.7324
```

Obviously, the negative angle is not a proper solution, so the only solution candidate is $\theta = 0.8384$ radians, or about 48°. To verify that this angle is a minimum solution, and not a maximum or an inflection point, we can check the second derivative $d^2f/d\theta^2$. If this derivative is positive, the solution represents a minimum. To check this solution and to find the speed required, continue the session as follows:

```
>>second = diff(f,2,th);    % This is the second derivative.
>>second = double(subs(second,{th,d,h},{thmin(1),310,33}))
second =
    0.0321
>>v2 = (g*d^2/2)*f;
>>v2min = subs(v2,{d,h,g},{310,33,32.2});
>>vmin = sqrt(v2min);
>>vmin = double(subs(vmin(1),{th,d,h,g},{thmin(1),310,33,32.2})))
vmin =
    105.3613
```

Because the second derivative is positive, the solution is a minimum. Thus the minimum speed required is 105.3613 feet/second, or about 72 miles per hour. A ball hit with this speed will clear the wall only if it is hit at an angle of approximately 48°.

T9.3–1 Given that $y = \sinh(3x)\cosh(5x)$, use MATLAB to find dy/dx at $x = 0.2$.

(Answer: 9.2288.)

T9.3–2 Given that $z = 5\cos(2x)\ln(4y)$, use MATLAB to find $\partial z/\partial y$.

(Answer: $5\cos(2x)/y$.)

Integration

The int(E) function is used to integrate a symbolic expression E. It attempts to find the symbolic expression I such that diff(E)=I. If the integral does not exist in closed form or MATLAB cannot find the integral even if it exists, the function will return the expression unevaluated.

As with the diff function, there are three ways to use the int function; two of the ways use quoted strings, but the following way is preferred. Using the function $2x$ as an example, the method is

```
>>syms x
>>int(2*x)
ans =
   x
```

The function int(E) returns the integral of the expression E with respect to the default independent variable. For example, you can obtain the following integrals with the next session:

$$\int x^n \, dx = \frac{x^{n+1}}{n+1}$$

$$\int \frac{1}{x} \, dx = \ln x$$

$$\int \cos x \, dx = \sin x$$

$$\int \sin y \, dy = -\cos y$$

```
>>syms n x y
>>int(x^n)
ans =
   x^(n+1)/(n+1)
>>int(1/x)
ans =
   log(x)
```

```
>>int(cos(x))
ans =
    sin(x)
>>int(sin(y))
ans =
    -cos(y)
```

Here are the other forms if the `int` function. The form `int(E,v)` returns the integral of the expression `E` with respect to the variable `v`. For example, the result

$$\int x^n\, dn = \frac{x^n}{\ln x}$$

can be obtained with the session:

```
>>syms n x
>>int(x^n,n)
ans =
    1/log(x)*x^n
```

The form `int(E,a,b)` returns the integral of the expression `E` with respect to the default independent variable evaluated over the interval $[a, b]$, where `a` and `b` are numeric expressions. For example, the result

$$\int_2^5 x^2 dx = \left.\frac{x^3}{3}\right|_2^5 = 39$$

is obtained as follows:

```
>>syms x
>>int(x^2,2,5)
ans =
    39
```

The form `int(E,v,a,b)` returns the integral of the expression `E` with respect to the variable `v` evaluated over the interval $[a, b]$, where `a` and `b` are numeric quantities. For example, the result

$$\int_0^5 xy^2\, dy = \left.x\frac{y^3}{3}\right|_0^5 = \frac{125}{3}x$$

is obtained from

```
>>syms x y
>>int(xy^2,y,0,5)
ans =
    125/3*x
```

The result

$$\int_a^b x^2\, dx = \frac{b^3}{3} - \frac{a^3}{3}$$

is obtained from

```
>>syms a b x
>>int(x^2,a,b)
ans =
1/3*b^3-1/3*a^3
```

The form int (E, m, n) returns the integral of the expression E with respect to the default independent variable evaluated over the interval [m, n], where m and n are symbolic expressions. For example,

$$\int_1^t x \, dx = \left. \frac{x^2}{2} \right|_1^t = \frac{1}{2}t^2 - \frac{1}{2}$$

$$\int_t^{e^t} \sin x \, dx = \left. -\cos x \right|_t^{e^t} = -\cos(e^t) + \cos t$$

are given by this session:

```
>>syms t x
>>int(x,1,t)
ans =
    1/2*t^2-1/2
int(sin(x),t,exp(t))
ans =
    -cos(exp(t)) + cos(t)
```

The following session gives an example for which no integral can be found. The indefinite integral exists, but the definite integral does not exist if the limits of integration include the singularity at $x = 1$. The integral is

$$\int \frac{1}{x-1} \, dx = \ln|x-1|$$

The session is

```
>>syms x
>>int(1/(x-1))
ans =
    log(x-1)
>>int(1/(x-1),0,2)
Warning: Explicit integral could not be found.
ans =
    int(1/(x-1),x = 0 .. 2)
```

Table 9.3–1 summarizes the integration functions.

Test Your Understanding

T9.3–3 Given that $y = x \sin(3x)$, use MATLAB to find $\int y \, dx$.

(Answer: $(\sin(3x) - 3x \cos(3x))/9$.)

T9.3–4 Given that $z = 6y^2 \tan(8x)$, use MATLAB to find $\int z\, dy$.

(Answer: $2y^3 \tan(8x)$.)

T9.3–5 Use MATLAB to evaluate

$$\int_{-2}^{5} x \sin(3x)\, dx$$

(Answer: 0.6672.)

Taylor Series

Taylor's theorem states that a function $f(x)$ can be represented in the vicinity of $x = a$ by the expansion

$$f(x) = f(a) + \left(\frac{df}{dx}\right)\bigg|_{x=a} (x - a) + \frac{1}{2}\left(\frac{d^2 f}{dx^2}\right)\bigg|_{x=a} (x - a)^2 + \cdots$$

$$+ \frac{1}{k!}\left(\frac{d^k f}{dx^k}\right)\bigg|_{x=a} (x - a)^k + \cdots + R_n \qquad \textbf{(9.3–1)}$$

The term R_n is the remainder and is given by

$$R_n = \frac{1}{n!}\left(\frac{d^n f}{dx^n}\right)\bigg|_{x=b} (x - a)^n \qquad \textbf{(9.3–2)}$$

where b lies between a and x.

These results hold if $f(x)$ has continuous derivatives through order n. If R_n approaches 0 for large n, the expansion is called the *Taylor* series for $f(x)$ about $x = a$. If $a = 0$, the series is sometimes called the *Maclaurin* series.

Some common examples of the Taylor series are

$$\sin x = x - \frac{x^3}{3!} + \frac{x^5}{5!} - \frac{x^7}{7!} + \cdots, \quad -\infty < x < \infty$$

$$\cos x = 1 - \frac{x^2}{2!} + \frac{x^4}{4!} - \frac{x^6}{6!} + \cdots, \quad -\infty < x < \infty$$

$$e^x = 1 + x + \frac{x^2}{2!} + \frac{x^3}{3!} + \frac{x^4}{4!} + \cdots, \quad \infty < x < \infty$$

where $a = 0$ in all three examples.

The `taylor(f,n,a)` function gives the first n-1 terms in the Taylor series for the function defined in the expression f, evaluated at the point $x = a$. If the parameter a is omitted the function returns the series evaluated at $x = 0$. Here are some examples:

```
>>syms x
>>f = exp(x);
```

```
>>taylor(f,4)
ans =
    1+x+1/2*x^2+1/6*x^3
>>taylor(f,3,2)
ans =
    exp(2)+exp(2)*(x-2)+1/2*exp(2)*(x-2)^2
```

The latter expression corresponds to

$$e^2\left[1 + (x - 2) + \frac{1}{2}(x - 2)^2\right]$$

Sums

The symsum(E) function returns the symbolic summation of the expression E; that is

$$\sum_{x=0}^{x-1} E(x) = E(0) + E(1) + E(2) + \cdots + E(x - 1)$$

The symsum(E,a,b) function returns the sum of the expression E as the default symbolic variable varies from a to b. That is, if the symbolic variable is x, then S = symsum(E,a,b) returns

$$\sum_{x=a}^{b} E(x) = E(a) + E(a + 1) + E(a + 2) + \cdots + E(b)$$

Here are some examples. The summations

$$\sum_{k=0}^{10} k = 0 + 1 + 2 + 3 + \cdots + 9 + 10 = 55$$

$$\sum_{k=0}^{n-1} k = 0 + 1 + 2 + 3 + \cdots + n - 1 = \frac{1}{2}n^2 - \frac{1}{2}n$$

$$\sum_{k=1}^{4} k^2 = 1 + 4 + 9 + 16 = 30$$

are given by

```
>>syms k n
>>symsum(k,0,10)
ans =
    55
>>symsum(k^2, 1, 4)
ans =
    30
```

```
>>symsum(k,0,n-1)
ans =
    1/2*n^2-1/2*n
>>factor(ans)
ans =
    1/2*n*(n-1)
```

The latter expression is the standard form of the result.

Limits

The function `limit(E,a)` returns the limit

$$\lim_{x \to a} E(x)$$

if x is the symbolic variable. There are several variations of this syntax. The basic form `limit(E)` finds the limit as $x \to 0$. For example

$$\lim_{x \to 0} \frac{\sin(a x)}{x} = a$$

is given by

```
>>syms a x
>>limit(sin(a*x)/x)
ans =
    a
```

The form `limit(E,v,a)` finds the limit as $v \to a$. For example,

$$\lim_{x \to 3} \frac{x - 3}{x^2 - 9} = \frac{1}{6}$$

$$\lim_{x \to 0} \frac{\sin(x + h) - \sin(x)}{h}$$

are given by

```
>>syms h x
>>limit((x-3)/(x^2-9),3)
ans =
    1/6
>>limit((sin(x+h)-sin(x))/h,h,0)
ans =
    cos(x)
```

The forms `limit(E,v,a,'right')` and `limit(E,v,a,'left')` specify the direction of the limit. For example,

$$\lim_{x \to 0-} \frac{1}{x} = -\infty$$

$$\lim_{x \to 0+} \frac{1}{x} = \infty$$

are given by

```
>>syms x
>>limit(1/x,x,0,'left')
ans =
   -inf
>>limit(1/x,x,0,'right')
ans =
   inf
```

Table 9.3–1 summarizes the series and limit functions.

Test Your Understanding

T9.3–6 Use MATLAB to find the first three nonzero terms in the Taylor series for $\cos x$.

(Answer: $1 - x^2/2 + x^4/24$.)

T9.3–7 Use MATLAB to find a formula for the sum

$$\sum_{m=0}^{m-1} m^3$$

(Answer: $m^4/4 - m^3/2 + m^2/4$.)

T9.3–8 Use MATLAB to evaluate

$$\sum_{n=0}^{7} \cos(\pi n)$$

(Answer: 0.)

T9.3–9 Use MATLAB to evaluate

$$\lim_{x \to 5} \frac{2x - 10}{x^3 - 125}$$

(Answer: 2/75.)

A first-order ordinary differential equation (ODE) can be written in the form

$$\frac{dy}{dt} = f(t, y)$$

where t is the independent variable and y is a function of t. A solution to such an equation is a function $y = g(t)$ such that $dg/dt = f(t, g)$, and the solution will contain one arbitrary constant. This constant becomes determined when we apply an additional condition of the solution by requiring that the solution have a specified value $y(t_1)$ when $t = t_1$. The chosen value t_1 is often the smallest, or starting value, of t, and if so, the condition is called the *initial condition* (quite often $t_1 = 0$). The general term for such a requirement is a *boundary condition,* and MATLAB lets us specify conditions other than initial conditions. For example, we can specify the value of the dependent variable at $t = t_2$, where $t_2 > t_1$.

INITIAL CONDITION
BOUNDARY CONDITION

Methods for obtaining a numerical solution to differential equations were covered in Chapter 8. However, we prefer to obtain an analytical solution whenever possible because it is more general and thus more useful for designing engineering devices or processes.

A second-order ODE has the following form:

$$\frac{d^2y}{dt^2} = f(t, y, \frac{dy}{dt})$$

Its solution will have two arbitrary constants that can be determined once two additional conditions are specified. These conditions are often the specified values of y and dy/dt at $t = 0$. The generalization to third-order and higher equations is straightforward.

We will occasionally use the following abbreviations for the first- and second-order derivatives:

$$\dot{y} = \frac{dy}{dt} \qquad \ddot{y} = \frac{d^2y}{dt^2}$$

MATLAB provides the `dsolve` function for solving ordinary differential equations. Its various forms differ according to whether they are used to solve single equations or sets of equations, whether or not boundary conditions are specified, and whether or not the default independent variable `t` is acceptable. Note that `t` is the default independent variable and not `x` as with the other symbolic functions. The reason is that many ODE models of engineering applications have time t as the independent variable.

Solving a Single Differential Equation

The `dsolve` function's syntax for solving a single equation is `dsolve('eqn')`. The function returns a symbolic solution of the

ODE specified by the symbolic expression eqn. Use the uppercase letter D to represent the first derivative, use D2 to represent the second derivative, and so on. Any character immediately following the differentiation operator is taken to be the dependent variable. Thus Dw represents dw/dt. Because of this syntax, you cannot use uppercase D as symbolic variable when using the dsolve function.

The arbitrary constants in the solution are denoted by C1, C2, and so on. The number of such constants is the same as the order of the ODE. For example, the equation

$$\frac{dy}{dt} + 2y = 12$$

has the solution

$$y(t) = 6 + C_1 e^{-2t}$$

The solution can be found with the following session:

```
>>dsolve('Dy+2*y=12')
ans =
   6+C1*exp(-2*t)
```

Note that you need not declare y to be symbolic prior to using dsolve.

There can be symbolic constants in the equation. For example,

$$\frac{dy}{dt} = \sin(a\,t)$$

has the solution

$$y(t) = -\frac{\cos(a\,t)}{a} + C_1$$

It can be found as follows:

```
>>dsolve('Dy=sin(a*t)')
ans =
   -cos(a*t)/a+C1
```

Here is a second-order example:

$$\frac{d^2y}{dt^2} = c^2 y$$

The solution $y(t) = C_1 e^{ct} + C_2 e^{-ct}$ can be found with the following session:

```
dsolve('D2y=c^2*y')
ans =
   C1*exp(c*t)+C2*exp(-c*t)
```

Solving Sets of Equations

Sets of equations can be solved with dsolve. The appropriate syntax is dsolve('eqn1','eqn2', ...). The function returns a symbolic solution of the set of equations specified by the symbolic expressions eqn1 and eqn2.

For example, the set

$$\frac{dx}{dt} = 3x + 4y$$

$$\frac{dy}{dt} = -4x + 3y$$

has the solution $x(t) = C_1 e^{3t} \cos 4t + C_2 e^{3t} \sin 4t$, $y(t) = -C_1 e^{3t} \sin 4t + C_2 e^{3t} \cos 4t$. The session is

```
>>[x, y] = dsolve('Dx=3*x+4*y','Dy=-4*x+3*y')
    x = C1*exp(3*t)*cos(4*t)+C2*exp(3*t)*sin(4*t)
    y = -C1*exp(3*t)*sin(4*t)+C2*exp(3*t)*cos(4*t)
```

Specifying Initial and Boundary Conditions

Conditions on the solutions at specified values of the independent variable can be handled as follows. The form dsolve('eqn', 'cond1', 'cond2', ...) returns a symbolic solution of the ODE specified by the symbolic expression eqn, subject to the conditions specified in the expressions cond1, cond2, and so on. If y is the dependent variable, these conditions are specified as follows: y(a) = b, Dy(a) = c, D2y(a) = d, and so on. These correspond to $y(a)$, $\dot{y}(a)$, $\ddot{y}(a)$, and so on. If the number of conditions is less than the order of the equation, the returned solution will contain arbitrary constants C1, C2, and so on.

For example, the problem

$$\frac{dy}{dt} = \sin(bt), \quad y(0) = 0$$

has the solution $y(t) = [1 - \cos(bt)]/b$. It can be found as follows:

```
>>dsolve('Dy=sin(b*t)','y(0)=0')
ans =
    -cos(b*t)/b+1/b
```

The problem

$$\frac{d^2 y}{dt^2} = c^2 y, \quad y(0) = 1, \quad \dot{y}(0) = 0$$

has the solution $y(t) = (e^{ct} + e^{-ct})/2$. The session is

```
>>dsolve('D2y=c^2*y','y(0)=1','Dy(0)=0')
ans =
    1/2*exp(c*t)+1/2*exp(-c*t)
```

Arbitrary boundary conditions, such as $y(0) = c$, can be used. For example, the solution of the problem

$$\frac{dy}{dt} + a y = b, \quad y(0) = c$$

is

$$y(t) = \frac{b}{a} + \left(c - \frac{b}{a}\right)e^{-at}$$

The session is

```
>>dsolve('Dy+a*y=b','y(0)=c')
ans =
    1/a*b+exp(-a*t)*(-1/a*b+c)
```

Plotting the Solution

The ezplot function can be used to plot the solution, just as with any other symbolic expression, provided no undetermined constants such as C1 are present. For example, the problem

$$\frac{dy}{dt} + 10y = 10 + 4\sin(4t), \qquad y(0) = 0$$

has the solution

$$y(t) = 1 - \frac{4}{29}\cos(4t) + \frac{10}{29}\sin(4t) - \frac{25}{29}e^{-10t}$$

The session is

```
>>y = dsolve('Dy+10*y=10+4*sin(4*t)','y(0)=0');
>>[y, how] = simple(y);
>>y
   y = 1-4/29*cos(4*t)+ 10/29*sin(4*t)-25/29*exp(-10*t)
>>ezplot(y),axis([0 5 0 2])
```

The plot is shown in Figure 9.4–1.

Sometimes the ezplot function uses too few values of the independent variable and thus does not produce a smooth plot. To overide the spacing chosen by the ezplot function, you can use the subs function to substitute an array of values for the independent variable and then use the double function to evaluate the result numerically. For example, you can continue the previous session as follows:

```
>>x = [0:.05:2];
>>P = subs(y,t,x);
>>Q = double(P);
>>plot(x,Q),axis([0 5 0 2])
```

Equation Sets with Boundary Conditions

Sets of equations with specified boundary conditions can be solved as follows. The function dsolve('eqn1','eqn2', ..., 'cond1','cond2', ...) returns a symbolic solution of a set of equations specified by the symbolic expressions eqn1, eqn2, and so on, subject to the initial conditions specified in the expressions cond1, cond2, and so on.

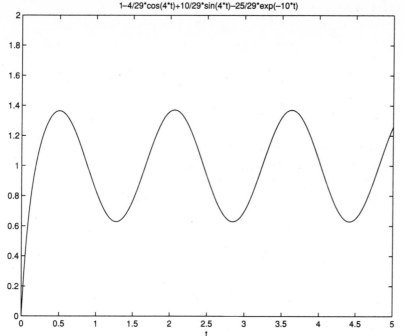

Figure 9.4–1
Plot of the solution of $\dot{y} + 10y = 10 + 4\sin(4t)$, $y(0) = 0$.

For example, the problem

$$\frac{dx}{dt} = 3x + 4y, \quad x(0) = 0$$

$$\frac{dy}{dt} = -4x + 3y, \quad y(0) = 1$$

has the solution

$$x(t) = e^{3t}\sin(4t), \quad y(t) = e^{3t}\cos(4t)$$

The session is

```
>>dsolve('Dx=3*x+4*y','Dy=-4*x+3*y','x(0)=0','y(0)=1')
ans =
    x(t) = exp(3*t)*sin(4*t), y(t) = exp(3*t)*cos(4*t)
```

It is not necessary to specify only initial conditions. The conditions can be specified at different values of t. For example, to solve the problem

$$\frac{d^2y}{dt^2} + 9y = 0, \quad y(0) = 1, \quad \dot{y}(\pi) = 2$$

the session is

```
>>dsolve('D2y+9*y=0','y(0)=1','Dy(pi)=2')
ans =
    -2/3*sin(3*t)+cos(3*t)
```

Using Other Independent Variables

Although the default independent variable is t, you can use the following syntax to specify a different independent variable. The function dsolve('eqn1', 'eqn2', ..., 'cond1', 'cond2',..., 'x') returns a symbolic solution of a set of equations where the independent variable is x.

For example, the solution of the equation

$$\frac{dv}{dx} + 2v = 12$$

is $v(x) = 6 + C_1 e^{-2x}$. The session is

```
>>dsolve('Dv+2*v=12','x')
ans =
    6+exp(-2*x)*C1
```

Test Your Understanding

T9.4–1 Use MATLAB to solve the equation

$$\frac{d^2y}{dt^2} + b^2y = 0$$

Check the answer by hand or with MATLAB.

(Answer: $y(t) = C_1 \cos(bt) + C_2 \sin(bt)$.)

T9.4–2 Use MATLAB to solve the problem

$$\frac{d^2y}{dt^2} + b^2y = 0, \qquad y(0) = 1, \quad \dot{y}(0) = 0$$

Check the answer by hand or with MATLAB.

(Answer: $y(t) = \cos(bt)$.)

Solving Nonlinear Equations

MATLAB can solve many nonlinear first-order differential equations. For example, the problem

$$\frac{dy}{dt} = 4 - y^2, \qquad y(0) = 1 \qquad \text{(9.4–1)}$$

can be solved with the following session

```
>>dsolve('Dy=4-y^2', 'y(0)=1')
ans =
2*(exp(4*t-log(-1/3))+1)/(-1+exp(4*t-log(-1/3)))
>>simple(ans)
ans =
2*(3*exp(4*t)-1)/(1+3*exp(4*t))
```

Table 9.4–1 The `dsolve` function

Command	Description
`dsolve('eqn')`	Returns a symbolic solution of the ODE specified by the symbolic expression `eqn`. Use the uppercase letter `D` to represent the first derivative; use `D2` to represent the second derivative, and so on. Any character immediately following the differentiation operator is taken to be the dependent variable.
`dsolve('eqn1','eqn2', ...)`	Returns a symbolic solution of the set of equations specified by the symbolic expressions `eqn1`, `eqn2`, and so on.
`dsolve('eqn','cond1', 'cond2', ...)`	Returns a symbolic solution of the ODE specified by the symbolic expression `eqn`, subject to the conditions specified in the expressions `cond1`, `cond2`, and so on. If `y` is the dependent variable, these conditions are specified as follows: `y(a) = b`, `Dy(a) = c`, `D2(a) = d`, and so on.
`dsolve('eqn1','eqn2', ..., 'cond1','cond2', ...)`	Returns a symbolic solution of a set of equations specified by the symbolic expressions `eqn1`, `eqn2`, and so on, subject to the initial conditions specified in the expressions `cond1`, `cond2`, and so on.

which is equivalent to

$$y(t) = 2\frac{3e^{4t} - 1}{1 + 3e^{4t}}$$

Not all nonlinear equations can be solved in closed form. For example, the following equation is the equation of motion of a specific pendulum.

$$\frac{d^2y}{dt^2} + 9\sin(y) = 0, \qquad y(0) = 1, \qquad \dot{y}(0) = 0$$

The session is

```
>>dsolve('D2y+9*sin(y)=0','y(0)=1','Dy(0)=0')
Warning: Explicit solution could not be found.
ans =
[ empty sym ]
```

Thus MATLAB was unable to find a solution. It is possible, however, that later versions of MATLAB will be able to solve this equation. Try it and see!

Table 9.4–1 summarizes the functions for solving differential equations.

This section explains how to use the *Laplace transform* with MATLAB to solve some types of differential equations that cannot be solved with `dsolve`. Application of the Laplace transform converts a linear differential equation problem into an algebraic problem. With proper algebraic manipulation of the resulting quantities, the solution of the differential equation can be recovered in an orderly fashion by inverting the transformation process to obtain a function of time. We assume that you are familiar with the fundamentals of differential equations outlined in Chapter 8, section 8.4.

The Laplace transform $\mathcal{L}[y(t)]$ of a function $y(t)$ is defined to be

$$\mathcal{L}[y(t)] = \int_0^\infty y(t)e^{-st}\, dt \qquad (9.5\text{-}1)$$

The integration removes t as a variable, and the transform is thus a function of only the Laplace variable s, which may be a complex number. The integral exists for most of the commonly encountered functions if suitable restrictions are placed on s. An alternative notation is the use of the uppercase symbol to represent the transform of the corresponding lowercase symbol; that is,

$$Y(s) = \mathcal{L}[y(t)]$$

STEP FUNCTION

We will use the *one-sided* transform, which assumes that the variable $y(t)$ is 0 for $t < 0$. For example, the *step function* is such a function. Its name comes from the fact that its graph looks like a stair step (see Figure 9.5–1).

The height of the step is M and is called the *magnitude*. The *unit-step function*, denoted $u_s(t)$, has a height of $M = 1$ and is defined as follows:

$$u_s(t) = \begin{cases} 0 & t < 0 \\ 1 & t > 0 \\ \text{indeterminate} & t = 0 \end{cases}$$

The engineering literature generally uses the term *step function*, whereas the mathematical literature uses the name *Heaviside* function. The Symbolic Math toolbox includes the `Heaviside(t)` function, which produces a unit-step function.

A step function of height M can be written as $y(t) = M u_s(t)$. Its transform is

$$\mathcal{L}[y(t)] = \int_0^\infty M u_s(t)e^{-st}\, dt = M \int_o^\infty e^{-st}\, dt = M \left. \frac{e^{-st}}{s} \right|_0^\infty = \frac{M}{s}$$

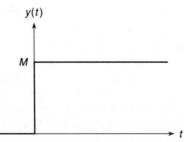

Figure 9.5–1
A step function of magnitude *M*

where we have assumed that the real part of s is greater than 0, so that the limit of e^{-st} exists as $t \to \infty$. Similar considerations of the region of convergence of the integral apply for other functions of time. However, we need not concern ourselves with this topic here, because the transforms of all the common functions have been calculated and tabulated. They can be obtained in MATLAB with the Symbolic Math toolbox by typing `laplace(function)`, where `function` is a symbolic expression representing the function $y(t)$ in (9.5–1). The default independent variable is `t`, and the default result is a function of `s`. The optional form is `laplace(function,x,y)`, where `function` is a function of `x` and `y` is the Laplace variable.

Here is a session with some examples. The functions are t^3, e^{-at}, and $\sin bt$.

```
>>syms b t
>>laplace(t^3)
ans =
    6/s^4
>>laplace(exp(-b*t))
ans =
    1/(s+b)
>>laplace(sin(b*t))
ans =
    b/(s^2+b^2)
```

Because the transform is an integral, it has the properties of integrals. In particular, it has the *linearity property*, which states that if a and b are not functions of t, then

$$\mathcal{L}[af_1(t) + bf_2(t)] = a\,\mathcal{L}[f_1(t)] + b\,\mathcal{L}[f_2(t)] \qquad \text{(9.5–2)}$$

The *inverse Laplace transform* $\mathcal{L}^{-1}[Y(s)]$ is that time function $y(t)$ whose transform is $Y(s)$; that is, $y(t) = \mathcal{L}^{-1}[Y(s)]$. The inverse operation is also linear. For example, the inverse transform of $10/s + 4/(s + 3)$ is $10 + 4e^{-3t}$. Inverse transforms can be found using the `ilaplace` function. For example,

```
>>syms b s
>>ilaplace(1/s^4)
ans =
    1/6*t^3
>>ilaplace(1/(s+b))
ans =
    exp(-b*t)
>>ilaplace(b/(s^2+b^2))
ans =
    sin(b*t)
```

The transforms of derivatives are useful for solving differential equations. Applying integration by parts to the definition of the transform, we obtain

$$\mathcal{L}\left(\frac{dy}{dt}\right) = \int_0^\infty \frac{dy}{dt} e^{-st} dt = y(t) e^{-st}\Big|_0^\infty + s\int_0^\infty y(t) e^{-st} dt$$

$$= s\,\mathcal{L}[y(t)] - y(0) = s\,Y(s) - y(0) \qquad \textbf{(9.5–3)}$$

This procedure can be extended to higher derivatives. For example, the result for the second derivative is

$$\mathcal{L}\left(\frac{d^2 y}{dt^2}\right) = s^2 Y(s) - sy(0) - \dot{y}(0) \qquad \textbf{(9.5–4)}$$

The general result for any order derivative is

$$\mathcal{L}\left(\frac{d^n y}{dt^n}\right) = s^n Y(s) - \sum_{k=1}^{n} s^{n-k} g_{k-1} \qquad \textbf{(9.5–5)}$$

where

$$g_{k-1} = \frac{d^{k-1} y}{dt^{k-1}}\bigg|_{t=0} \qquad \textbf{(9.5–6)}$$

Application to Differential Equations

The derivative and linearity properties can be used to solve the differential equation

$$a\dot{y} + y = bv(t) \qquad \textbf{(9.5–7)}$$

If we multiply both sides of the equation by e^{-st} and then integrate over time from $t = 0$ to $t = \infty$, we obtain

$$\int_0^\infty (a\dot{y} + y) e^{-st} dt = \int_0^\infty bv(t) e^{-st} dt$$

or

$$\mathcal{L}(a\dot{y} + y) = \mathcal{L}[bv(t)]$$

or, using the linearity property,

$$a\,\mathcal{L}(\dot{y}) + \mathcal{L}(y) = b\,\mathcal{L}[v(t)]$$

Using the derivative property and the alternative transform notation, the preceding equation can be written as

$$a\left[sY(s) - y(0)\right] + Y(s) = bV(s)$$

where $V(s)$ is the transform of v. This equation is an algebraic equation for $Y(s)$ in terms of $V(s)$ and $y(0)$. Its solution is

$$Y(s) = \frac{a\,y(0)}{as+1} + \frac{b}{as+1} V(s) \qquad \textbf{(9.5–8)}$$

Applying the inverse transform to (9.5–8) gives

$$y(t) = \mathcal{L}^{-1}\left[\frac{a\,y(0)}{as+1}\right] + \mathcal{L}^{-1}\left[\frac{b}{as+1} V(s)\right] \qquad \textbf{(9.5–9)}$$

From the transform given earlier, it can be seen that

$$\mathcal{L}^{-1}\left[\frac{a\,y(0)}{a\,s+1}\right] = \mathcal{L}^{-1}\left[\frac{y(0)}{s+1/a}\right] = y(0)e^{-t/a}$$

which is the free response. The forced response is given by

$$\mathcal{L}^{-1}\left[\frac{b}{a\,s+1}V(s)\right]$$ (9.5–10)

This inverse transform cannot be evaluated until $V(s)$ is specified. Suppose $v(t)$ is a unit-step function. Then $V(s) = 1/s$, and (9.5–10) becomes

$$\mathcal{L}^{-1}\left[\frac{b}{s(a\,s+1)}\right]$$

To find the inverse transform, enter

```
>>syms a b s
>>ilaplace(b/(s*(a*s+1)))
ans =
    b*(1-exp(-t/a))
```

Thus the forced response of (9.5–7) to a unit-step input is $b(1 - e^{-t/a})$.

You can use the Heaviside function with the dsolve function to find the step response, but the resulting expressions are more complicated than those obtained with the Laplace transform method.

Consider the second-order model

$$\ddot{x} + 1.4\dot{x} + x = f(t)$$ (9.5–11)

Transforming this equation gives

$$[s^2X(s) - sx(0) - \dot{x}(0)] + 1.4[sX(s) - x(0)] + X(s) = F(s)$$

Solve for $X(s)$.

$$X(s) = \frac{x(0)s + \dot{x}(0) + 1.4x(0)}{s^2 + 1.4s + 1} + \frac{F(s)}{s^2 + 1.4s + 1}$$

The free response is obtained from

$$x(t) = \mathcal{L}^{-1}\left[\frac{x(0)s + \dot{x}(0) + 1.4x(0)}{s^2 + 1.4s + 1}\right]$$

Suppose the initial conditions are $x(0) = 2$ and $\dot{x}(0) = -3$. Then the free response is obtained from

$$x(t) = \mathcal{L}^{-1}\left[\frac{2s - 0.2}{s^2 + 1.4s + 1}\right]$$ (9.5–12)

It can be found by typing

```
>>ilaplace((2*s-.2)/(s^2+1.4*s+1))
```

The free response thus found is

$$x(t) = e^{-0.7t}\left[2\cos\left(\frac{\sqrt{51}}{10}t\right) - \frac{16\sqrt{51}}{51}\sin\left(\frac{\sqrt{51}}{10}t\right)\right]$$

The forced response is obtained from

$$x(t) = \mathcal{L}^{-1}\left[\frac{F(s)}{s^2 + 1.4s + 1}\right]$$

If $f(t)$ is a unit-step function, $F(s) = 1/s$ and the forced response is

$$x(t) = \mathcal{L}^{-1}\left[\frac{1}{s(s^2 + 1.4s + 1)}\right]$$

To find the forced response, enter

```
>>ilaplace(1/(s*(s^2+1.4*s+1)))
```

The answer obtained is

$$x(t) = 1 - e^{-0.7t}\left[\cos\left(\frac{\sqrt{51}}{10}t\right) + \frac{7\sqrt{51}}{51}\sin\left(\frac{\sqrt{51}}{10}t\right)\right] \qquad \textbf{(9.5–13)}$$

Input Derivatives

Two similar mechanical systems are shown in Figure 9.5–2. In both cases the input is a displacement $y(t)$. Their equations of motion are

$$m\ddot{x} + c\dot{x} + kx = ky + c\dot{y} \qquad \textbf{(9.5–14)}$$

$$m\ddot{x} + c\dot{x} + kx = ky \qquad \textbf{(9.5–15)}$$

The only difference between these systems is that the system in Figure 9.5–2a has an equation of motion containing the derivative of the input function $y(t)$. Both systems are examples of the more general differential equation

$$m\ddot{x} + c\dot{x} + kx = dy + g\dot{y} \qquad \textbf{(9.5–16)}$$

(a)   (b)

Figure 9.5–2
Two mechanical systems. The model for (a) contains the derivative of the input $y(t)$; the model for (b) does not.

As noted earlier, you can use the `Heaviside` function with the `dsolve` function to find the step response of equations containing derivatives of the input, but the resulting expressions are more complicated than those obtained with the Laplace transform method.

We now demonstrate how to use the Laplace transform to find the step response of equations containing derivatives of the input. Suppose the initial conditions are zero. Then transforming (9.5–16) gives

$$X(s) = \frac{d + gs}{ms^2 + cs + k} Y(s) \qquad \text{(9.5–17)}$$

Let us compare the unit-step response of (9.5–16) for two cases using the values $m = 1$, $c = 1.4$, and $k = 1$, with zero initial conditions. The two cases are $g = 0$ and $g = 5$.

With $Y(s) = 1/s$, (9.5–17) gives

$$X(s) = \frac{1 + gs}{s(s^2 + 1.4s + 1)} \qquad \text{(9.5–18)}$$

The response for the case $g = 0$ was found earlier. It is given by (9.5–13). The response for $g = 5$ is found by typing

```
>>syms s
>>ilaplace((1+5*s)/(s*(s^2+1.4*s+1)))
```

The response obtained is

$$x(t) = 1 - e^{0.7t}\left[\cos\left(\frac{\sqrt{51}}{10}t\right) + \frac{43\sqrt{51}}{51}\sin\left(\frac{\sqrt{51}}{10}t\right)\right] \qquad \text{(9.5–19)}$$

Figure 9.5–3 shows the responses given by (9.5–13) and (9.5–19). The effect of differentiating the input is an increase in the response's peak value.

Impulse Response

The area A under the curve of the *pulse function* shown in Figure 9.5–4a is called the *strength* of the pulse. If we let the pulse duration T approach 0 while keeping the area A constant, we obtain the *impulse* function of strength A, represented by Figure 9.5–4b. If the strength is 1, we have a *unit* impulse. The impulse can be thought of as the derivative of the step function and is a mathematical abstraction for convenience in analyzing the response of systems subjected to an input that is applied and removed suddenly, such as the force from a hammer blow.

IMPULSE FUNCTION

The engineering literature generally uses the term *impulse function*, whereas the mathematical literature uses the name *Dirac delta* function. The Symbolic Math toolbox includes the `Dirac(t)` function, which returns a unit impulse. You can use the `Dirac` function with the `dsolve` function when the input function

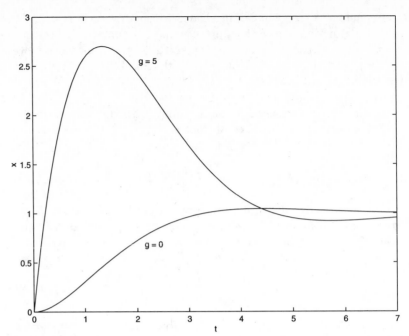

Figure 9.5–3
The unit step response of the model $\ddot{x} + 1.4\dot{x} + x = u + g\dot{u}$ for $g = 0$ and $g = 5$.

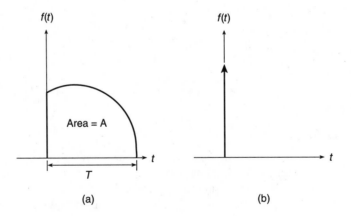

Figure 9.5–4
Pulse and impulse
functions.

is an impulse, but the resulting expressions are more complicated than those obtained with the Laplace transform.

It can be shown that the transform of an impulse of strength A is simply A. So, for example, to find the impulse response of $\ddot{x} + 1.4\dot{x} + x = f(t)$, where $f(t)$ is an impulse of strength A, for zero inital conditions, first obtain the transform.

$$X(s) = \frac{1}{s^2 + 1.4s + 1}F(s) = \frac{A}{s^2 + 1.4s + 1}$$

Then you type

```
>>syms A s
>>ilaplace(A/(s^2+1.4*s+1))
```

The response obtained is

$$x(t) = \frac{10A\sqrt{51}}{51}e^{-0.7t}\sin\left(\frac{\sqrt{51}}{10}t\right)$$

Direct Method

Instead of performing by hand the algebra required to find the response transform, we could use MATLAB to do the algebra for us. We now demonstrate the most direct way of using MATLAB to solve an equation with the Laplace transform. One advantage of this method is that we are not required to use the transform identities (9.5–3) through (9.5–6) for the derivatives. Let us solve the equation

$$a\frac{dy}{dt} + y = f(t) \qquad\qquad \textbf{(9.5–20)}$$

with $f(t) = \sin t$, in terms of an unspecified value for $y(0)$. Here is the session:

```
>>syms a L s t
>>y = sym('y(t)');
>>dydt = sym('diff(y(t),t)');
>>f = sin(t);
>>eq = a*dydt+y-f;
>>E = laplace(eq,t,s)
E =
    a*(s*laplace(y(t),t,s)-y(0)) + laplace(y(t),t,s)- 1/(s^2+1)
>>E = subs(E,'laplace(y(t),t,s)',L)
E =
a*(s*L-y(0))+L-1/(s^2+1)
>>L = solve(E,L)
L =
    (a*y(0)*s^2+a*y(0)+1)/(a*s^3+a*s+s^2+1)
>>I = simplify(ilaplace(L))
I =
(-a*cos(t)+sin(t)+exp(-t/a)*y(0)+exp(- t/a)*a^2*y(0)+
exp(-t/a)*a)/(1+a^2)
>>I = collect(I,exp(-t/a))
I =
1/(1+a^2)*(- a*cos(t)+sin(t))+(a+y(0)+y(0)*a^2)/(1+a^2)*exp(-t/a)
```

The answer is

$$y(t) = \frac{1}{1+a^2}\left\{\sin t - a\,\cos t + e^{-t/a}\left[y(0) + a^2 y(0) + a\right]\right\}$$

Table 9.5–1 Laplace transform functions

Command	Description
`ilaplace(function)`	Returns the inverse Laplace transform of `function`.
`laplace(function)`	Returns the Laplace transform of `function`.
`laplace(function,x,y)`	Returns the Laplace transform of `function`, which is a function of `x`, in terms of the Laplace variable `y`.

Note that this session consists of the following steps:

1. Define the symbolic variables, including the derivatives that appear in the equation. Note that $y(t)$ is explicitly expressed as a function of t in these definitions.
2. Move all terms to the left side of the equation and define the left side as a symbolic expression.
3. Apply the Laplace transformation to the differential equation to obtain an algebraic equation.
4. Substitute a symbolic variable, here L, for the expression `laplace(y(t),t,s)` in the algebraic equation. Then solve the equation for the variable L, which is the transform of the solution.
5. Invert L to find the solution as a function of t.

Note that this procedure can also be used to solve sets of equations.

Test Your Understanding

T9.5–1 Find the Laplace transform of the following functions: $1 - e^{-at}$ and $\cos bt$. Use the `ilaplace` function to check your answers.

T9.5–2 Use the Laplace transform to solve the problem $5\ddot{y} + 20\dot{y} + 15y = 30u - 4\dot{u}$, where $u(t)$ is a unit-step function and $y(0) = 5, \dot{y}(0) = 1$.

(Answer: $y(t) = -1.6e^{-3t} + 4.6e^{-t} + 2$.)

Table 9.5–1 summarizes the Laplace transform functions.

9.6

Symbolic Linear Algebra

You can perform operations with symbolic matrices in much the same way as with numeric matrices. Here we give examples of finding matrix products, the matrix inverse, eigenvalues, and the characteristic polynomial of a matrix.

Remember that using symbolic matrices avoids numerical imprecision in subsequent operations. You can create a symbolic

486

matrix from a numeric matrix in several ways, as shown in the following session:

```
>>A = sym([3, 5; 2, 7]);    % the most direct method
>>B = [3, 5; 2, 7];
>>C = sym(B);%B is preserved as a numeric matrix
>>sym D
>>D = subs(D,[3, 5; 2, 7]);
```

The first method is the most direct. Use the second method when you want to keep a numeric version of the matrix. Use the third method when you want to postpone assigning specific values to the matrix. The matrices A, C, and D are all symbolic and identical. The matrix B looks like the other matrices but is numeric of class double.

You can create a symbolic matrix consisting of functions. For example, the relationship between the coordinates (x_2, y_2) of a coordinate system rotated counterclockwise through an angle a relative to the (x_1, y_1) coodinate system is

$$x_2 = x_1 \cos a + y_1 \sin a$$

$$y_2 = y_1 \cos a - x_1 \sin a$$

These equations can be expressed in matrix form as

$$\begin{bmatrix} x_2 \\ y_2 \end{bmatrix} = \begin{bmatrix} \cos a & \sin a \\ -\sin a & \cos a \end{bmatrix} \begin{bmatrix} x_1 \\ y_1 \end{bmatrix} = \mathbf{R} \begin{bmatrix} x_1 \\ y_1 \end{bmatrix}$$

where the rotation matrix $\mathbf{R}(a)$ is defined as

$$\mathbf{R}(a) = \begin{bmatrix} \cos a & \sin a \\ -\sin a & \cos a \end{bmatrix} \qquad \text{(9.6–1)}$$

The symbolic matrix $\mathbf{R}$ can be defined in MATLAB as follows:

```
>>syms a
>>R = [cos(a), sin(a); -sin(a), cos(a)]
R =
    [ cos(a),    sin(a) ]
    [ -sin(a),    cos(a) ]
```

If we rotate the coordinate system twice by the same angle to produce a third coordinate system (x_3, y_3), the result is the same as a single rotation with twice the angle. Let us see if MATLAB gives that result. The vector-matrix equation is

$$\begin{bmatrix} x_3 \\ y_3 \end{bmatrix} = \mathbf{R} \begin{bmatrix} x_2 \\ y_2 \end{bmatrix} = \mathbf{RR} \begin{bmatrix} x_1 \\ y_1 \end{bmatrix}$$

Thus $\mathbf{R}(a)\mathbf{R}(a)$ should be the same as $\mathbf{R}(2a)$. Continue the previous session as follows:

```
>>Q = R*R
Q =
```

```
    [ cos(a)^2-sin(a)^2,   2*cos(a)*sin(a) ]
    [ -2*cos(a)*sin(a),  cos(a)^2-sin(a)^2 ]
>>Q = simple(Q)
Q =
    [ cos(2*a),   sin(2*a) ]
    [ -sin(2*a),  cos(2*a) ]
```

The matrix $\mathbf{Q}$ is the same as $\mathbf{R}(2a)$, as we suspected.

To evaluate a matrix numerically, use the subs and double functions. For example, for a rotation of $a = \pi/4$ radians (45°),

```
>>R = double(subs(R,a,pi/4))
```

Characteristic Polynomial and Roots

Sets of first-order differential equations can be expressed in vector-matrix notation as

$$\dot{\mathbf{x}} = \mathbf{Ax} + \mathbf{Bf}(t)$$

where $\mathbf{x}$ is the vector of dependent variables and $\mathbf{f}(t)$ is a vector containing the forcing functions. For example, the equation set

$$\dot{x}_1 = x_2$$

$$\dot{x}_2 = -kx_1 - 2x_2 + f(t)$$

comes from the equation of motion of a mass connected to a spring and sliding on a surface having viscous friction. The term $f(t)$ is the applied force acting on the mass. For this set the vector $\mathbf{x}$ and the matrices $\mathbf{A}$ and $\mathbf{B}$ are

$$\mathbf{x} = \begin{bmatrix} x_1 \\ x_2 \end{bmatrix}$$

$$\mathbf{A} = \begin{bmatrix} 0 & 1 \\ -k & -2 \end{bmatrix} \qquad \mathbf{B} = \begin{bmatrix} 0 \\ 1 \end{bmatrix}$$

The equation $|s\mathbf{I} - \mathbf{A}| = 0$ is the characteristic equation of the model, where s represents the characteristic roots of the model. Use the poly(A) function to find this polynomial, and note that MATLAB uses the default symbolic variable x to represent the roots. For example, to find the characteristic equation and solve for the roots in terms of the spring constant k, use the following session:

```
>>syms k
>>A = [0 ,1;-k, -2];
>>poly(A)
ans =
    x^2+2*x+k
>>solve(ans)
ans =
```

```
[ -1+(1-k)^(1/2) ]
[ -1-(1-k)^(1/2) ]
```

Thus the roots are $s = -1 \pm \sqrt{1-k}$.

Use the `eig(A)` function to find the roots directly without finding the characteristic equation (*eig* stands for "eigenvalue," which is another term for "characteristic root"). For example,

```
>>syms k
>>A = [0 ,1;-k, -2];
>>eig(A)
ans =
    [ -1+(1-k)^(1/2) ]
    [ -1-(1-k)^(1/2) ]
```

You can use the `inv(A)` and `det(A)` functions to invert and find the determinant of a matrix symbolically. For example, using the same matrix A from the previous session,

```
>>inv(A)
ans =
    [ -2/k,  -1/k ]
    [ 1, 0 ]
>>A*ans    % verify that the inverse is correct
ans =
    [ 1, 0 ]
    [ 0, 1 ]
>>det(A)
ans =
    k
```

Solving Linear Algebraic Equations

You can use matrix methods in MATLAB to solve linear algebraic equations symbolically. You can use the matrix inverse method, if the inverse exists, or the left-division method (see Chapter 5 for a discussion of these methods). For example, to solve the set

$$2x - 3y = 3$$

$$5x + cy = 19$$

using both methods, the session is

```
>>syms c
>>A = sym([2, -3; 5, c]);
>>b = sym([3; 19]);
>>x = inv(A)*b    % the matrix inverse method
x =
    [3*c/(2*c+15)+57/(2*c+15)]
    [23/(2*c+15)]
>>x = A\b    % the left-division method
x =
    [3*(19+c)/(2*c+15)]
    [23/(2*c+15)]
```

Table 9.6–1 Linear algebra functions

Command	Description
det(A)	Returns the determinant of the matrix A in symbolic form.
eig(A)	Returns the eigenvalues (characteristic roots) of the matrix A in symbolic form.
inv(A)	Returns the inverse of the matrix A in symbolic form.
poly(A)	Returns the characteristic polynomial of the matrix A in symbolic form.

Although the results appear to be different, they both reduce to the same solution: $x = 3(19 + c)/(2c + 15)$, $y = 23/(2c + 15)$.

Table 9.6–1 summarizes the functions used in this section. Note that their syntax is identical to the numeric versions used in earlier chapters.

Test Your Understanding

T9.6–1 Consider three successive coordinate rotations using the same angle a. Show that the product **RRR** of the rotation matrix **R**(a) given by (9.6–1) equals **R**($3a$).

T9.6–2 Find the characteristic polynomial and roots of the following matrix.

$$\mathbf{A} = \begin{bmatrix} -2 & 1 \\ -3k & -5 \end{bmatrix}$$

(Answers: $s^2 + 7s + 10 + 3k$ and $s = (-7 \pm \sqrt{9 - 12k})/2$.)

T9.6–3 Use the matrix inverse and the left-division method to solve the following set.

$$-4x + 6y = -2c$$

$$7x - 4y = 23$$

(Answer: $x = (69 - 4c)/13$, $y = (46 - 7c)/13$.)

9.7

Summary This chapter covers a subset of the capabilities of the Symbolic Math toolbox, specifically

- Symbolic algebra.
- Symbolic methods for solving algebraic and transcendental equations.
- Symbolic methods for solving ordinary differential equations.

Table 9.7–1 Guide to MATLAB commands introduced in Chapter 9

Creating and evaluating expressions	See Table 9.1–1
Manipulating symbolic expressions	See Table 9.1–2
Solving algebraic and transcendental equations	See Table 9.2–1
Symbolic calculus functions	See Table 9.3–1
The dsolve function	See Table 9.4–1
Laplace transform functions	See Table 9.5–1
Linear algebra functions	See Table 9.6–1

Miscellaneous functions	
Command	**Description**
Dirac(t)	Dirac delta function (unit-impulse function at $t = 0$).
Heavisde(t)	Heaviside function (unit-step function making a transition from 0 to 1 at $t = 0$.)

- Symbolic calculus, including integration, differentiation, limits, and series.
- Laplace transforms.
- Selected topics in linear algebra, including symbolic methods for obtaining determinants, matrix inverses, and eigenvalues.

Now that you have finished this chapter, you should be able to use MATLAB to

- Create symbolic expressions and manipulate them algebraically.
- Obtain symbolic solutions to algebraic and transcendental equations.
- Perform symbolic differentiation and integration.
- Evaluate limits and series symbolically.
- Obtain symbolic solutions to ordinary differential equations.
- Obtain Laplace transforms.
- Perform symbolic linear algebra operations, including obtaining expressions for determinants, matrix inverses, and eigenvalues.

Table 9.7–1 is a guide by category to the functions introduced in this chapter.

Key Terms with Page References

You can find the answers to problems marked with an asterisk at the end of the text.

Problems

Section 9.1

1. Use MATLAB to prove the following identities:
   a. $\sin^2 x + \cos^2 x = 1$
   b. $\sin(x + y) = \sin x \cos y + \cos x \sin y$
   c. $\sin 2x = 2 \sin x \cos x$
   d. $\cosh^2 x - \sinh^2 x = 1$

2. Use MATLAB to express $\cos 5\theta$ as a polynomial in x, where $x = \cos \theta$.

3.* Two polynomials in the variable x are represented by the coefficient vectors `p1 = [6, 2, 7, -3]` and `p2 = [10, -5, 8]`.
   a. Use MATLAB to find the product of these two polynomials; express the product in its simplest form.
   b. Use MATLAB to find the numeric value of the product if $x = 2$.

4.* The equation of circle of radius r centered at $x = 0$, $y = 0$ is

   $$x^2 + y^2 = r^2$$

   Use the `subs` and other MATLAB functions to find the equation of a circle of radius r centered at the point $x = a$, $y = b$. Rearrange the equation into the form $Ax^2 + Bx + Cxy + Dy + Ey^2 = F$ and find the expressions for the coefficients in terms of a, b, and r.

5. The equation for a curve called the "lemniscate" in polar coordinates (r,θ) is

   $$r^2 = a^2 \cos(2\theta)$$

   Use MATLAB to find the equation for the curve in terms of Cartesian coordinates (x,y), where $x = r \cos \theta$ and $y = r \sin \theta$.

Section 9.2

6.* The law of cosines for a triangle states that $a^2 = b^2 + c^2 - 2bc \cos A$, where a is the length of the side opposite the angle A, and b and c are the lengths of the other sides.
   a. Use MATLAB to solve for b.
   b. Suppose that $A = 60°$, $a = 5$ meters, and $c = 2$ meters. Determine b.

7. Use MATLAB to solve the polynomial equation $x^3 + 8x^2 + ax + 10 = 0$ for x in terms of the parameter a, and evaluate your solution for the case $a = 17$. Use MATLAB to check the answer.

8.* The equation for an ellipse centered at the origin of the Cartesian coordinates (x,y) is

   $$\frac{x^2}{a^2} + \frac{y^2}{b^2} = 1$$

   where a and b are constants that determine the shape of the ellipse.
   a. In terms of the parameter b, use MATLAB to find the points of intersection of the two ellipses described by

   $$x^2 + \frac{y^2}{b^2} = 1$$

   and

   $$\frac{x^2}{100} + 4y^2 = 1$$

   b. Evaluate the solution obtained in part (a) for the case $b = 2$.

9. The equation

$$r = \frac{p}{1 - \epsilon \cos \theta}$$

describes the polar coordinates of an orbit with the coordinate origin at the sun. If $\epsilon = 0$, the orbit is circular; if $0 < \epsilon < 1$, the orbit is elliptical. The planets have orbits that are nearly circular; comets have orbits that are highly elongated with ϵ nearer to 1. It is of obvious interest to determine whether or not a comet's or an asteroid's orbit will intersect that of a planet. For each of the following two cases, use MATLAB to determine whether or not orbits A and B intersect. If they do, determine the polar coordinates of the intersection point. The units of distance are AU, where 1 AU is the mean distance of the earth from the sun.
   a. Orbit A: $p = 1$, $\epsilon = 0.01$. Orbit B: $p = 0.1$, $\epsilon = 0.9$.
   b. Orbit A: $p = 1$, $\epsilon = 0.01$. Orbit B: $p = 1.1$, $\epsilon = 0.5$.

10. Figure 9.2–2 on page 456 shows a robot arm having two joints and two links. The angles of rotation of the motors at the joints are θ_1 and θ_2. From trigonometry we can derive the following expressions for the (x, y) coordinates of the hand.

$$x = L_1 \cos \theta_1 + L_2 \cos(\theta_1 + \theta_2)$$

$$y = L_1 \sin \theta_1 + L_2 \sin(\theta_1 + \theta_2)$$

Suppose that the link lengths are $L_1 = 3$ feet and $L_2 = 2$ feet.
   a. Compute the motor angles required to position the hand at $x = 3$ feet, $y = 1$ foot. Identify the elbow-up and elbow-down solutions.
   b. Suppose you want to move the hand along a straight, horizontal line at $y = 1$ for $2 \leq x \leq 4$. Plot the required motor angles versus x. Label the elbow-up and elbow-down solutions.

Section 9.3

11. Use MATLAB to find all the values of x where the graph of $y = 3^x - 2x$ has a horizontal tangent line.

12. Use MATLAB to determine all the local minima and local maxima and all the inflection points where $dy/dx = 0$ of the following function:

$$y = x^4 - \frac{16}{3}x^3 + 8x^2 - 4$$

13. The surface area of a sphere of radius r is $S = 4\pi r^2$. Its volume is $V = 4\pi r^3/3$.
   a. Use MATLAB to find the expression for dS/dV.
   b. A spherical balloon expands as air is pumped into it. What is the rate of increase in the balloon's surface area with volume when its volume is 30 cubic inches?

14. Use MATLAB to find the point on the line $y = 2 - x/3$ that is closest to the point $x = -3$, $y = 1$.

15. A particular circle is centered at the origin and has a radius of 5. Use MATLAB to find the equation of the line that is tangent to the circle at the point $x = 3$, $y = 4$.

16. Ship A is traveling north at 6 miles per hour, and ship B is traveling west at 12 miles per hour. When ship A was dead ahead of ship B, it

was 6 miles away. Use MATLAB to determine how close the ships come to each other.

17. Suppose you have a wire of length L. You cut a length x to make a square, and use the remaining length $L - x$ to make a circle. Use MATLAB to find the length x that maximizes the sum of the areas enclosed by the square and the circle.

18.* A certain spherical street lamp emits light in all directions. It is mounted on a pole of height h (see Figure P18). The brightness B at point P on the sidewalk is directly proportional to sin θ and inversely proportional to the square of the distance d from the light to the point. Thus

$$B = \frac{c}{d^2} \sin \theta$$

where c is a constant. Use MATLAB to determine how high h should be to maximize the brightness at point P, which is 30 feet from the base of the pole.

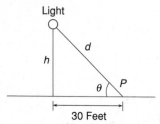

Light

d

h

θ P

30 Feet   ***Figure P18***

19.* A certain object has a mass $m = 100$ kilograms and is acted on by a force $f(t) = 500[2 - e^{-t}\sin(5\pi t)]$ newtons. The mass is at rest at $t = 0$. Use MATLAB to compute the object's velocity v at $t = 5$ seconds. The equation of motion is $m\dot{v} = f(t)$.

20. A rocket's mass decreases as it burns fuel. The equation of motion for a rocket in vertical flight can be obtained from Newton's law and is

$$m(t)\frac{dv}{dt} = T - m(t)g$$

where T is the rocket's thrust and its mass as a function of time is given by $m(t) = m_0(1 - rt/b)$. The rocket's initial mass is m_0, the burn time is b, and r is the fraction of the total mass accounted for by the fuel.

Use the values $T = 48{,}000$ newtons; $m_0 = 2200$ kilograms; $r = 0.8$; $g = 9.81$ meters/second^2; and $b = 40$ seconds.

a. Use MATLAB to compute the rocket's velocity as a function of time for $t \le b$.

b. Use MATLAB to compute the rocket's velocity at burnout.

21. The equation for the voltage $v(t)$ across a capacitor as a function of time is

$$v(t) = \frac{1}{C}\left(\int_0^t i(t)\,dt + Q_0\right)$$

where $i(t)$ is the applied current and Q_0 is the initial charge. Suppose that $C = 10^{-6}$ farad and that $Q_0 = 0$. If the applied current is $i(t) = [0.01 + 0.3e^{-5t}\sin(25\pi t)]10^{-3}$ amperes, use MATLAB to compute and plot the voltage $v(t)$ for $0 \le t \le 0.3$ seconds.

22. The power P dissipated as heat in a resistor R as a function of the current $i(t)$ passing through it is $P = i^2 R$. The energy $E(t)$ lost as a function of time is the time integral of the power. Thus

$$E(t) = \int_0^t P(t)\, dt = R \int_0^t i^2(t)\, dt$$

If the current is measured in amperes, the power is in watts and the energy is in joules (1 watt = 1 joule/second). Suppose that a current $i(t) = 0.2[1 + \sin(0.2t)]$ amperes is applied to the resistor.
a. Determine the energy $E(t)$ dissipated as a function of time.
b. Determine the energy dissipated in 1 minute if $R = 1000$ ohms.

23. The RLC circuit shown in Figure P23 can be used as a *narrow-band filter*. If the input voltage $v_i(t)$ consists of a sum of sinusoidally varying voltages with different frequencies, the narrow-band filter will allow to pass only those voltages whose frequencies lie within a narrow range. These filters are used in tuning circuits, such as those used in AM radios, to allow reception only of the carrier signal of the desired radio station. The magnification ratio M of a circuit is the ratio of the amplitude of the output voltage $v_o(t)$ to the amplitude of the input voltage $v_i(t)$. It is a function of the radian frequency ω of the input voltage. Formulas for M are derived in elementary electrical circuits courses. For this particular circuit, M is given by

$$M = \frac{RC\omega}{\sqrt{(1 - LC\omega^2)^2 + (RC\omega)^2}}$$

The frequency at which M is a maximum is the frequency of the desired carrier signal.
a. Determine this frequency as a function of R, C, and L.
b. Plot M versus ω for two cases where $C = 10^{-5}$ farads and $L = 5 \times 10^{-3}$ henrys. For the first case, $R = 1000$ ohms. For the second case, $R = 10$ ohms. Comment on the filtering capability of each case.

Figure P23

24. The shape of a cable hanging with no load other than its own weight is a *catenary* curve. A particular bridge cable is described by the catenary

$y(x) = 10\cosh((x - 20)/10)$ for $0 \le x \le 50$, where x and y are the horizontal and vertical coordinates measured in feet. (See Figure P24.) It is desired to hang plastic sheeting from the cable to protect passersby while the bridge is being repainted. Use MATLAB to determine how many square feet of sheeting are required. Assume that the bottom edge of the sheeting is located along the x-axis at $y = 0$.

Figure P24

25. The shape of a cable hanging with no load other than its own weight is a *catenary* curve. A particular bridge cable is described by the catenary $y(x) = 10\cosh((x - 20)/10)$ for $0 \le x \le 50$, where x and y are the horizontal and vertical coordinates measured in feet.

   The length L of a curve described by $y(x)$ for $a \le x \le b$ can be found from the following integral:

$$L = \int_a^b \sqrt{1 + \left(\frac{dy}{dx}\right)^2}\, dx$$

   Determine the length of the cable.

26. Use the first five nonzero terms in the Taylor series for e^{ix}, $\sin x$, and $\cos x$ about $x = 0$ to demonstrate the validity of Euler's formula $e^{ix} = \cos x + i\sin x$.

27. Find the Taylor series for $e^x \sin x$ about $x = 0$ in two ways: (*a*) by multiplying the Taylor series for e^x and that for $\sin x$, and (*b*) by using the `taylor` function directly on $e^x \sin x$.

28. Integrals that cannot be evaluated in closed form sometimes can be evaluated approximately by using a series representation for the integrand. For example, the following integral is used for some probability calculations (see Chapter 7, section 7.2):

$$I = \int_0^1 e^{-x^2}\, dx$$

   a. Obtain the Taylor series for e^{-x^2} about $x = 0$ and integrate the first six nonzero terms in the series to find I. Use the seventh term to estimate the error.

   b. Compare your answer with that obtained with the MATLAB `erf(t)` function, defined as

$$\text{erf}(t) = \frac{2}{\sqrt{\pi}}\int_0^t e^{-x^2}\, dt$$

29.* Use MATLAB to compute the following limits:

a.

$$\lim_{x \to 1} \frac{x^2 - 1}{x^2 - x}$$

b.

$$\lim_{x \to -2} \frac{x^2 - 4}{x^2 + 4}$$

c.

$$\lim_{x \to 0} \frac{x^4 + 2x^2}{x^3 + x}$$

30. Use MATLAB to compute the following limits:

a.

$$\lim_{x \to 0+} x^x$$

b.

$$\lim_{x \to 0+} (\cos x)^{1/\tan x}$$

c.

$$\lim_{x \to 0+} \left(\frac{1}{1 - x} \right)^{-1/x^2}$$

d.

$$\lim_{x \to 0-} \frac{\sin x^2}{x^3}$$

e.

$$\lim_{x \to 5-} \frac{x^2 - 25}{x^2 - 10x + 25}$$

f.

$$\lim_{x \to 1+} \frac{x^2 - 1}{\sin(x - 1)^2}$$

31. Use MATLAB to compute the following limits:

a.

$$\lim_{x \to \infty} \frac{x + 1}{x}$$

b.

$$\lim_{x \to -\infty} \frac{3x^3 - 2x}{2x^3 + 3}$$

32. Find the expression for the sum of the geometric series

$$\sum_{k=0}^{n-1} r^k$$

for $r \neq 1$.

33. A particular rubber ball rebounds to one-half its original height when dropped on a floor.

 a. If the ball is initially dropped from a height h and is allowed to continue to bounce, find the expression for the total distance traveled by the ball after the ball hits the floor for the nth time.

 b. If it is initially dropped from a height of 10 feet, how far will the ball have traveled after it hits the floor for the eighth time?

Section 9.4

34. The equation for the voltage y across the capacitor of an RC circuit is

$$RC\frac{dy}{dt} + y = v(t)$$

where $v(t)$ is the applied voltage. Suppose that $RC = 0.2$ second and that the capacitor voltage is initially 2 volts. If the applied voltage goes from 0 to 10 volts at $t = 0$, use MATLAB to determine and plot the voltage $y(t)$ for $0 \le t \le 1$ second.

35. The following equation describes the temperature $T(t)$ of a certain object immersed in a liquid bath of temperature $T_b(t)$:

$$10\frac{dT}{dt} + T = T_b$$

Suppose the object's temperature is initially $T(0) = 70°$ F and the bath temperature is $170°$ C. Use MATLAB to answer the following questions:

 a. Determine $T(t)$.

 b. How long will it take for the object's temperature T to reach $168°$ F?

 c. Plot the object's temperature $T(t)$ as a function of time.

36. This equation describes the motion of a mass connected to a spring with viscous friction on the surface

$$m\ddot{y} + c\dot{y} + ky = f(t)$$

where $f(t)$ is an applied force. The position and velocity of the mass at $t = 0$ are denoted by x_0 and v_0. Use MATLAB to answer the following questions:

 a. What is the free response in terms of x_0 and v_0 if $m = 3$, $c = 18$, and $k = 102$?

 b. What is the free response in terms of x_0 and v_0 if $m = 3$, $c = 39$, and $k = 120$?

37. The equation for the voltage y across the capacitor of an RC circuit is

$$RC\frac{dy}{dt} + y = v(t)$$

where $v(t)$ is the applied voltage. Suppose that $RC = 0.2$ second and that the capacitor voltage is initially 2 volts. If the applied voltage is $v(t) = 10[2 - e^{-t}\sin(5\pi t)]$, use MATLAB to compute and plot the voltage $y(t)$ for $0 \le t \le 5$ seconds.

38. The following equation describes a certain dilution process, where $y(t)$ is the concentration of salt in a tank of fresh water to which salt brine is being added:

$$\frac{dy}{dt} + \frac{2}{10 + 2t}y = 4$$

Suppose that $y(0) = 0$. Use MATLAB to compute and plot $y(t)$ for $0 \le t \le 10$.

39. This equation describes the motion of a certain mass connected to a spring with viscous friction on the surface

$$3\ddot{y} + 18\dot{y} + 102y = f(t)$$

where $f(t)$ is an applied force. Suppose that $f(t) = 0$ for $t < 0$ and $f(t) = 10$ for $t \ge 0$.
a. Use MATLAB to compute and plot $y(t)$ when $y(0) = \dot{y}(0) = 0$.
b. Use MATLAB to compute and plot $y(t)$ when $y(0) = 0$ and $\dot{y}(0) = 10$.

40. This equation describes the motion of a certain mass connected to a spring with viscous friction on the surface

$$3\ddot{y} + 39\dot{y} + 120y = f(t)$$

where $f(t)$ is an applied force. Suppose that $f(t) = 0$ for $t < 0$ and $f(t) = 10$ for $t \ge 0$.
a. Use MATLAB to compute and plot $y(t)$ when $y(0) = \dot{y}(0) = 0$.
b. Use MATLAB to compute and plot $y(t)$ when $y(0) = 0$ and $\dot{y}(0) = 10$.

41. The equations for an armature-controlled dc motor follow. The motor's current is i and its rotational velocity is ω.

$$L\frac{di}{dt} = -Ri - K_e\omega + v(t)$$

$$I\frac{d\omega}{dt} = K_T i - c\omega$$

L, R, and I are the motor's inductance, resistance, and inertia; K_T and K_e are the torque constant and back emf constant; c is a viscous damping constant; and $v(t)$ is the applied voltage.

Use the values $R = 0.8$ ohm, $L = 0.003$ henrys, $K_T = 0.05$ newton meter/ampere, $K_e = 0.05$ volt/radian/second, $c = 0$, and $I = 8 \times 10^{-5}$ newton meter second^2.

Suppose the applied voltage is 20 volts. Use MATLAB to compute and plot the motor's speed and current versus time for zero initial conditions. Choose a final time large enough to show the motor's speed becoming constant.

Section 9.5

42. The RLC circuit described in Problem 23 and shown in Figure P23 on page 495 has the following differential equation model:

$$LC\ddot{v}_o + RC\dot{v}_o + v_o = RC\dot{v}_i(t)$$

Use the Laplace transform method to solve for the unit-step response of $v_o(t)$ for zero initial conditions, where $C = 10^{-5}$ farads and $L = 5 \times 10^{-3}$ henrys. For the first case (a broadband filter), $R = 1000$ ohms. For the second case (a narrowband filter), $R = 10$ ohms. Compare the step responses of the two cases.

43. The differential equation model for a certain speed control system for a vehicle is

$$\ddot{v} + (1 + K_p)\dot{v} + K_I v = K_p \dot{v}_d + K_I v_d$$

where the actual speed is v, the desired speed is $v_d(t)$, and K_p and

K_I are constants called the "control gains." Use the Laplace transform method to find the unit-step response (that is, $v_d(t)$ is a unit-step function). Use zero initial conditions. Compare the response for three cases:

a. $K_p = 9$, $K_I = 50$
b. $K_p = 9$, $K_I = 25$
c. $K_p = 54$, $K_I = 250$

44. The differential equation model for a certain position control system for a metal cutting tool is

$$\frac{d^3x}{dt^3} + (6 + K_D)\frac{d^2x}{dt^2} + (11 + K_p)\frac{dx}{dt} + (6 + K_I)x$$
$$= K_D\frac{d^2x_d}{dt^2} + K_p\frac{dx_d}{dt} + K_I x_d$$

where the actual tool position is x; the desired position is $x_d(t)$; and K_p, K_I, and K_D are constants called the control gains. Use the Laplace transform method to find the unit-step response (that is, $x_d(t)$ is a unit-step function). Use zero initial conditions. Compare the response for three cases:

a. $K_p = 30$, $K_I = K_D = 0$
b. $K_p = 27$, $K_I = 17.18$, $K_D = 0$
c. $K_p = 36$, $K_I = 38.1$, $K_D = 8.52$

45.* The differential equation model for the motor torque $m(t)$ required for a certain speed control system is

$$4\ddot{m} + 4K\dot{m} + K^2 m = K^2 v_d$$

where the desired speed is $v_d(t)$, and K is a constant called the control gain.

a. Use the Laplace transform method to find the unit-step response (that is, $v_d(t)$ is a unit step function). Use zero initial conditions.
b. Use symbolic manipulation in MATLAB to find the value of the peak torque in terms of the gain K.

Section 9.6

46. Show that $\mathbf{R}^{-1}(a)\mathbf{R}(a) = \mathbf{I}$, where $\mathbf{I}$ is the identity matrix and $\mathbf{R}(a)$ is the rotation matrix given by (9.6–1). This equation shows that the inverse coordinate transformation returns you to the original coordinate system.

47. Show that $\mathbf{R}^{-1}(a) = \mathbf{R}(-a)$. This equation shows that a rotation through a negative angle is equivalent to an inverse transformation.

48.* Find the characteristic polynomial and roots of the following matrix:

$$\mathbf{A} = \begin{bmatrix} -6 & 2 \\ 3k & -7 \end{bmatrix}$$

49.* Use the matrix inverse and the left-division method to solve the following set for x and y in terms of c:

$$4cx + 5y = 43$$

$$3x - 4y = -22$$

Figure P50

50. The currents i_1, i_2, and i_3 in the circuit shown in Figure P50 are described by the following equation set if all the resistances are equal to R.

$$\begin{bmatrix} 2R & -R & 0 \\ -R & 3R & -R \\ 0 & R & -2R \end{bmatrix} \begin{bmatrix} i_1 \\ i_2 \\ i_3 \end{bmatrix} = \begin{bmatrix} v_1 \\ 0 \\ v_2 \end{bmatrix}$$

v_1 and v_2 are applied voltages; the other two currents can be found from $i_4 = i_1 - i_2$ and $i_5 = i_2 - i_3$.
a. Use both the matrix inverse method and the left-division method to solve for the currents in terms of the resistance R and the voltages v_1 and v_2.
b. Find the numerical values for the currents if $R = 1000$ ohms, $v_1 = 100$ volts, and $v_2 = 25$ volts.

51. The equations for the armature-controlled dc motor shown in Figure P51 follow. The motor's current is i, and its rotational velocity is ω.

$$L\frac{di}{dt} = -Ri - K_e\omega + v(t)$$

$$I\frac{d\omega}{dt} = K_Ti - c\omega$$

L, R, and I are the motor's inductance, resistance, and inertia; K_T and K_e are the torque constant and back emf constant; c is a viscous damping constant, and $v(t)$ is the applied voltage.

Figure P51

a. Find the characteristic polynomial and the characteristic roots.

b. Use the values $R = 0.8$ ohm, $L = 0.003$ henrys, $K_T = 0.05$ newton meter/ampere, $K_e = 0.05$ volt/radian/second, and $I = 8 \times 10^{-5}$ newton meter second^2. The damping constant c is often difficult to determine with accuracy. For these values find the expressions for the two characteristic roots in terms of c.

c. Using the parameter values in part (b), determine the roots for the following values of c (in newton meter second): $c = 0$, $c = 0.01$, $c = 0.1$ and $c = 0.2$. For each case, use the roots to estimate how long the motor's speed will take to become constant; also discuss whether or not the speed will oscillate before it becomes constant.

Appendix A

Guide to Commands and Functions in This Text

Operators and special characters

Item	Description	Pages
+	Plus; addition operator.	30, 46
–	Minus; subtraction operator.	30, 46
*	Scalar and matrix multiplication operator.	30
.*	Array multiplication operator.	46
^	Scalar and matrix exponentiation operator.	30
.^	Array exponentiation operator.	46, 49
\	Left-division operator.	30
/	Right-division operator.	30
.\	Array left-division operator.	46, 48
./	Array right-division operator.	46, 48
:	Colon; generates regularly spaced elements and represents an entire row or column.	35
( )	Parentheses; encloses function arguments and array indices; overrides precedence.	30, 38, 102
[ ]	Brackets; encloses array elements.	34
.	Decimal point.	120
. . .	Ellipsis; line-continuation operator.	29
,	Comma; separates statements and elements in a row.	28, 29
;	Semicolon; separates columns and suppresses display.	7, 34
%	Percent sign; designates a comment and specifies formatting.	29, 95
'	Quote sign and transpose operator.	34, 38
.'	Nonconjugated transpose operator.	38
=	Assignment (replacement) operator.	248

Logical and relational operators

Item	Description	Pages
==	Relational operator: equal to.	248, 249
~=	Relational operator: not equal to.	249
<	Relational operator: less than.	249
<=	Relational operator: less than or equal to.	249
>	Relational operator: greater than.	249
>=	Relational operator: greater than or equal to.	249
&	Logical operator: AND.	249, 250
|	Logical operator: OR.	250, 251
~	Logical operator: NOT.	249, 250
xor	Logical operator: EXCLUSIVE OR.	250, 251

Special variables and constants

Item	Description	Pages
ans	Most recent answer.	29
eps	Accuracy of floating-point precision.	29
i,j	The imaginary unit $\sqrt{-1}$.	29
Inf	Infinity.	29
NaN	Undefined numerical result (not a number).	29
pi	The number π.	29

Commands for managing a session

Item	Description	Pages
casesen	Turns on/off case sensitivity(MATLAB 4 only).	31, 33
clc	Clears Command window.	32, 33
clear	Removes variables from memory.	32, 33
exist	Checks for existence of file or variable.	33
global	Declares variables to be global.	430
help	Searches for a help topic.	12, 33
lookfor	Searches help entries for a keyword.	12, 33
quit	Stops MATLAB.	9, 33
who	Lists current variables.	32, 33
whos	Lists current variables (long display).	33

System and file commands

Item	Description	Pages
cd	Changes current directory.	82, 84
date	Displays current date.	84
delete	Deletes a file.	84
diary	Switches on/off diary file recording.	82, 84
dir	Lists all files in current directory.	82, 84
load	Loads workspace variables from a file.	83, 84
path	Displays search path.	81, 84
pwd	Displays current directory.	82, 84
save	Saves workspace variables in a file.	83, 84
type	Displays contents of a file.	84
what	Lists all MATLAB files.	82, 84
wk1read	Reads .wk1 spreadsheet file.	84

Input/output commands

Item	Description	Pages
disp	Displays contents of an array or string.	92
format	Controls screen-display format.	94
fprintf	Performs formatted writes to screen or file.	95
input	Displays prompts and waits for input.	92, 97
;	Suppresses screen printing.	7

Numeric display formats

Item	Description	Pages
`format short`	Four decimal digits (default).	94
`format long`	16 decimal digits.	94
`format short e`	Five digits plus exponent.	94
`format long e`	16 digits plus exponent.	94
`format bank`	Two decimal digits.	94
`format +`	Positive, negative, or zero.	94
`format rat`	Rational approximation.	94
`format compact`	Suppresses some line feeds.	94
`format loose`	Resets to less compact display mode.	94

Array commands

Item	Description	Pages
`cat`	Concatenates arrays (MATLAB 5 only).	40, 43
`find`	Finds indices of nonzero elements.	40, 41
`length`	Computes number of elements.	40, 41
`linspace`	Creates regularly spaced vector.	35, 40
`logspace`	Creates logarithmically spaced vector.	36, 40
`max`	Returns largest element.	40
`min`	Returns smallest element.	40
`size`	Computes array size.	40, 41
`sort`	Sorts each column.	40, 41
`sum`	Sums each column.	40, 41

Special matrices

Item	Description	Pages
`eye`	Creates an identity matrix.	62
`ones`	Creates an array of ones.	62
`zeros`	Creates an array of zeros.	62

Matrix commands for solving linear equations

Item	Description	Pages
`det`	Computes determinant of an array.	202, 233
`inv`	Computes inverse of a matrix.	206, 233
`pinv`	Computes pseudoinverse of a matrix.	218, 233
`rank`	Computes rank of a matrix.	215, 233
`rref`	Computes reduced row echelon form.	222, 233

Exponential and logarithmic functions

Item	Description	Pages
`exp(x)`	Exponential; e^x.	98, 99
`log(x)`	Natural logarithm; $\ln x$.	98, 99
`log10(x)`	Common (base 10) logarithm; $\log x = \log_{10} x$.	99
`sqrt(x)`	Square root; $\sqrt{x}$.	98, 99

Complex functions

Item	Description	Pages
abs(x)	Absolute value; $|x|$.	99, 100
angle(x)	Angle of a complex number x.	99, 100
conj(x)	Complex conjugate of x.	99, 100
imag(x)	Imaginary part of a complex number x.	99, 100
real(x)	Real part of a complex number x.	99, 100

Numeric functions

Item	Description	Pages
ceil	Rounds to the nearest integer toward ∞.	99, 101
fix	Rounds to the nearest integer toward zero.	99, 101
floor	Rounds to the nearest integer toward $-\infty$.	99, 102
round	Rounds toward the nearest integer.	99, 101
sign	Signum function.	99

Trigonometric functions

Item	Description	Pages
acos(x)	Inverse cosine; $\arccos x = \cos^{-1} x$.	103
acot(x)	Inverse cotangent; $\operatorname{arccot} x = \cot^{-1} x$.	103
acsc(x)	Inverse cosecant; $\operatorname{arccsc} x = \csc^{-1} x$.	103
asec(x)	Inverse secant; $\operatorname{arcsec} x = \sec^{-1} x$.	103
asin(x)	Inverse sine; $\arcsin x = \sin^{-1} x$.	103
atan(x)	Inverse tangent; $\arctan x = \tan^{-1} x$.	103
atan2(y,x)	Four-quadrant inverse tangent.	103
cos(x)	Cosine; $\cos x$.	103
cot(x)	Cotangent; $\cot x$.	103
csc(x)	Cosecant; $\csc x$.	103
sec(x)	Secant; $\sec x$.	103
sin(x)	Sine; $\sin x$.	102, 103
tan(x)	Tangent; $\tan x$.	103

Hyperbolic functions

Item	Description	Pages
acosh(x)	Inverse hyperbolic cosine; $\cosh^{-1} x$.	104
acoth(x)	Inverse hyperbolic cotangent; $\coth^{-1} x$.	104
acsch(x)	Inverse hyperbolic cosecant; $\operatorname{csch}^{-1} x$.	104
asech(x)	Inverse hyperbolic secant; $\operatorname{sech}^{-1} x$.	104
asinh(x)	Inverse hyperbolic sine; $\sinh^{-1} x$.	104
atanh(x)	Inverse hyperbolic tangent; $\tanh^{-1} x$.	104
cosh(x)	Hyperbolic cosine; $\cosh x$.	104
coth(x)	Hyperbolic cotangent; $\cosh x / \sinh x$.	104
csch(x)	Hyperbolic cosecant; $1/\sinh x$.	104
sech(x)	Hyperbolic secant; $1/\cosh x$.	104
sinh(x)	Hyperbolic sine; $\sinh x$.	104
tanh(x)	Hyperbolic tangent; $\sinh x / \cosh x$.	104

Polynomial functions

Item	Description	Pages
conv	Computes product of two polynomials.	65
deconv	Computes ratio of polynomials.	65
eig	Computes the eigenvalues of a matrix.	430
poly	Computes polynomial from roots.	65, 67
polyfit	Fits a polynomial to data.	168, 329
polyval	Evaluates polynomial.	65, 66
roots	Computes polynomial roots.	65, 66

String functions

Item	Description	Pages
findstr	Finds occurrences of a string.	266, 286
strcmp	Compares strings.	267

Logical functions

Item	Description	Pages
any	True if any elements are nonzero.	252
all	True if all elements are nonzero.	252
find	Finds indices of nonzero elements.	252
finite	True if elements are finite.	252
isnan	True if elements are undefined.	252
isinf	True if elements are infinite.	252
isempty	True if matrix is empty.	252
isreal	True if all elements are real.	252

Miscellaneous mathematical functions

Item	Description	Pages
cross	Computes cross products.	63, 64
dot	Computes dot products.	63, 64
fmin	Finds minimum of single-variable function.	108, 111
fmins	Finds minimum of multivariable function.	110, 111
function	Creates a user-defined function.	105, 111
fzero	Finds zero of single-variable function.	107, 111

Cell array functions (MATLAB 5 only)

Item	Description	Pages
cell	Creates cell array.	113
celldisp	Displays cell array.	113, 115
cellplot	Displays graphical representation of cell array.	113, 115
num2cell	Converts numeric array to cell array.	113, 116
deal	Matches input and output lists.	113, 116
iscell	Identifies cell array.	113, 116

Structure functions (MATLAB 5 only)

Item	Description	Pages
fieldnames	Returns field names in a structure array.	121
getfield	Returns field contents of a structure array.	121, 123
isfield	Identifies a structure array field.	121, 123
isstruct	Identifies a structure array.	121, 124
rmfield	Removes a field from a structure array.	121, 123
setfield	Sets contents of field.	121, 123
struct	Creates structure array.	121, 122

Basic *xy* plotting commands

Item	Description	Pages
axis	Sets axis limits.	136, 141
fplot	Intelligent plotting of functions.	138, 141
grid	Displays gridlines.	136, 141
plot	Generates *xy* plot.	134, 141
print	Prints plot or saves plot to a file.	136, 141
title	Puts text at top of plot.	134, 141
xlabel	Adds text label to *x*-axis.	134, 141
ylabel	Adds text label to *y*-axis.	134, 141

Plot-enhancement commands

Item	Description	Pages
axes	Creates axes objects.	146, 150
gtext	Enables label placement by mouse.	147, 150
hold	Freezes current plot.	149, 150
legend	Legend placement by mouse.	145, 150
refresh	Redraws current figure window.	146, 150
set	Specifies properties of objects such as axes.	150, 158
subplot	Creates plots in subwindows.	142, 150
text	Places string in figure.	147, 150

Specialized plot commands

Item	Description	Pages
bar	Creates bar chart.	160, 164
loglog	Creates log-log plot.	155, 164
polar	Creates polar plot.	160, 164
semilogx	Creates semilog plot (logarithmic abscissa).	155, 164
semilogy	Creates semilog plot (logarithmic ordinate).	155, 164
stairs	Creates stairs plot.	160, 164
stem	Creates stem plot.	160, 164

Three-dimensional plotting commands

Item	Description	Pages
contour	Creates contour plot.	179, 181
mesh	Creates three-dimensional mesh surface plot.	178, 181
meshc	Same as mesh with contour plot underneath.	180, 181
meshz	Same as mesh with vertical lines underneath.	180, 181
plot3	Creates three-dimensional plots from lines and points.	177, 181
surf	Creates shaded three-dimensional mesh surface plot.	179, 181
surfc	Same as surf with contour plot underneath.	179, 181
meshgrid	Creates rectangular grid.	178, 181
waterfall	Same as mesh with mesh lines in one direction.	180, 181
zlabel	Adds text label to z-axis.	177, 181

Program flow control

Item	Description	Pages
break	Terminates execution of a loop.	270, 286
case	Provides alternate execution paths within switch structure.	279, 286
else	Delineates alternate block of statements.	259, 286
elseif	Conditionally executes statements.	261, 286
end	Terminates for, while, and if statements.	255, 286
for	Repeats statements a specific number of times.	268, 286
if	Executes statements conditionally.	255, 286
switch	Directs program execution by comparing input with case expressions.	278, 286
while	Repeats statements an indefinite number of times.	275, 286

Histogram functions

Item	Description	Pages
bar	Creates a bar chart.	164, 308
hist	Aggregates the data into bins.	304, 308

Statistical functions

Item	Description	Pages
erf(x)	Computes the error function $erf(x)$.	317, 352
mean	Calculates the mean.	302, 316
median	Calculates the median.	302, 316
std	Calculates the standard deviation.	316

Random number functions

Item	Description	Pages
rand	Generates uniformly distributed random numbers between 0 and 1; sets and retrieves the seed value.	320, 324
randn	Generates normally distributed random numbers; sets and retrieves the seed value.	320, 324

Polynomial regression functions

Item	Description	Pages
polyfit	Fits a polynomial to data.	168, 329
polyval	Evaluates a polynomial and generates error estimates.	329

Interpolation functions

Item	Description	Pages
interp1	Linear and cubic-spline interpolation of a function of one variable.	342, 345, 348
interp2	Linear interpolation of a function of two variables.	344, 345
spline	Cubic-spline interpolation.	346, 348
unmkpp	Computes the coefficients of cubic-spine polynomials.	347, 348

Numerical integration functions

Item	Description	Pages
quad	Numerical integration with adaptive Simpson's rule.	368, 372
quad8	Numerical integration with Newton-Cotes eight-panel rule.	368, 372
trapz	Numerical integration with the trapezoidal rule.	368

Numerical differentiation functions

Item	Description	Pages
diff(x)	Computes the differences between adjacent elements in the vector x.	376, 379
polyder	Differentiates a polynomial, a polynomial product, or a polynomial quotient.	379

ODE solvers

Item	Description	Pages
ode23	Nonstiff, low-order solver.	396, 397, 426
ode45	Nonstiff, medium-order solver.	396, 397, 426
ode113	Nonstiff, variable-order solver (MATLAB 5.0 and higher).	396, 397, 426
ode23s	Stiff, low-order solver (MATLAB 5.2 and higher).	396, 397, 426
ode23t	Moderately stiff, trapezoidal rule solver (MATLAB 5.2 and higher).	396, 397, 426
ode23tb	Stiff, low-order solver (MATLAB 5.2 and higher).	396, 397, 426
ode15s	Stiff, variable-order solver (MATLAB 5.2 and higher).	396, 397, 426
odeset	Creates integrator options structure for ODE solvers.	396, 426

LTI object functions

Item	Description	Pages
ss	Creates an LTI object in state-space form.	416, 418
ssdata	Extracts state-space matrices from an LTI object.	416, 419
tf	Creates an LTI object in transfer-function form.	416, 418
tfdata	Extracts equation coefficients from an LTI object.	416, 419

LTI ODE solvers

Item	Description	Pages
impulse	Computes and plots the impulse response of an LTI object.	420
initial	Computes and plots the free response of an LTI object.	420
lsim	Computes and plots the response of an LTI object to a general input.	420, 422
step	Computes and plots the step response of an LTI object.	420, 422

Predefined input functions

Item	Description	Pages
gensig	Generates a periodic sine, square, or pulse input.	424
sawtooth	Generates a periodic sawtooth input.	424
square	Generates a square wave input.	424
stepfun	Generates a step function input.	423, 424

Functions for creating and evaluating symbolic expressions

Item	Description	Pages
class	Returns the class of an expression.	442, 450
digits	Sets the number of decimal digits used to do variable precision arithmetic.	448, 450
double	Converts an expression to numeric form.	446, 450
ezplot	Generates a plot of a symbolic expression.	449, 450
findsym	Finds the symbolic variables in a symbolic expression.	443, 450
numden	Returns the numerator and denominator of an expression.	446, 450
sym	Creates a symbolic variable.	441, 450
syms	Creates one or more symbolic variables.	441, 450
vpa	Sets the number of digits used to evaluate expressions.	448, 450

Functions for manipulating symbolic expressions

Item	Description	Pages
collect	Collects coefficients of like powers in an expression.	444, 451
expand	Expands an expression by carrying out jpowers.	444, 451
factor	Factors an expression.	445, 451
poly2sym	Converts a polynomial coefficient vector to a symbolic polynomial.	446, 451
pretty	Displays an expression in a form that resembles typeset mathematics.	446, 451
simple	Searches for the shortest form of an expression.	445, 451
simplify	Simplifies an expression using Maple's simplification rules.	445, 451
subs	Substitutes variables or expressions.	446, 451
sym2poly	Converts an expression to a polynomial coefficient vector.	446, 451

Symbolic solution of algebraic and transcendental equations

Item	Description	Pages
solve	Solves symbolic equations.	452, 458

Symbolic calculus functions

Item	Description	Pages
diff	Returns the derivative of an expression.	458, 461
Dirac	Dirac delta function (unit impulse).	483, 491
Heaviside	Heaviside function (unit step).	478, 491
int	Returns the integral of an expression.	461, 464
limit	Returns the limit of an expression.	461, 469
symsum	Returns the symbolic summation of an expression.	461, 468
taylor	Returns the Taylor series of a function.	461, 467

Symbolic solution of differential equations

Item	Description	Pages
dsolve	Returns a symbolic solution of a differential equation or set of equations.	472, 477

Laplace transform functions

Item	Description	Pages
ilaplace	Returns the inverse Laplace transform.	479, 486
laplace	Returns the Laplace transform.	479, 486

Symbolic linear algebra functions

Item	Description	Pages
det	Returns the determinant of a matrix.	489, 490
eig	Returns the eigenvalues (characteristic roots) of a matrix.	489, 490
inv	Returns the inverse of a matrix.	489, 490
poly	Returns the characteristic polynomial of a matrix.	488, 490

Appendix B

References

[Beer and Johnston, 1997] Beer, F. P. and E. R. Johnston Jr. *Vector Mechanics for Engineers: Dynamics.* 6th ed. New York: McGraw-Hill, 1997.

[Eide, 1998] Eide, A. R.; R. D. Jenison; L. H. Mashaw; and L. L. Northup. *Introduction to Engineering Problem Solving.* New York: McGraw-Hill, 1998.

[Jayaraman, 1991] Jayaraman, S. *Computer-Aided Problem Solving for Scientists and Engineers.* New York: McGraw-Hill, 1991.

[Kreyzig, 1993] Kreyzig, E. *Advanced Engineering Mathematics.* 7th ed. New York: John Wiley and Sons, 1993.

[Kutz, 1986] Kutz, M., editor. *Mechanical Engineers' Handbook.* New York: John Wiley and Sons, 1986.

[Lamport, 1994] Lamport, L. *LATEX User's Guide and Reference Manual.* 2nd ed. Reading, MA: Addison-Wesley, 1994.

[Rizzoni, 1996] Rizzoni, G. *Principles and Applications of Electrical Engineering.* 2nd ed. Homewood, IL: Irwin, 1996.

[Starfield, 1990] Starfield, A. M.; K. A. Smith; and A. L. Bleloch. *How to Model It: Problem Solving for the Computer Age.* New York: McGraw-Hill, 1990.

[The MathWorks, Inc., 1997] *Using MATLAB.* Natick, MA: The MathWorks, Inc., 1997.

Answers
to Selected
Problems

Chapter 2

1. (a) −13.3333; (b) 0.6; (c) 15; (d) 1.0323
4. (a) $x + y = -3 - 2i$; (b) $xy = -13 - 41i$;
   (c) $x/y = -1.72 + 0.04i$
7.
$$\mathbf{A} = \begin{bmatrix} 0 & 6 & 12 & 18 & 24 & 30 \\ -20 & -10 & 0 & 10 & 20 & 30 \end{bmatrix}$$

11. (a) Length = 3, absolute value =
    [2, 4, 7]; (b) Same as (a);
    (c) length = 3, absolute value = [5.831, 5, 7.2801]

15. (a)
$$\mathbf{A} + \mathbf{B} + \mathbf{C} = \begin{bmatrix} -4 & 2 \\ 22 & 15 \end{bmatrix}$$

(b)
$$\mathbf{A} - \mathbf{B} + \mathbf{C} = \begin{bmatrix} -16 & 12 \\ -2 & 19 \end{bmatrix}$$

16. (a) [1024, -128; 144, 32];
    (b) [4, -8; 4, 8]; (c) [4096, -64; 216, -8]

17. (a) Work done on each segment, in joules
    (1 joule = 1 N m) is 800, 275, 525, 750,
    1800; (b) total work done = 4150 joules.

21.
$$\mathbf{AB} = \begin{bmatrix} -47 & -78 \\ 39 & 64 \end{bmatrix}$$

$$\mathbf{BA} = \begin{bmatrix} -5 & -3 \\ 48 & 22 \end{bmatrix}$$

24. 60 tons of copper, 67 tons of magnesium,
    6 tons of manganese, 76 tons of silicon, and
    101 tons of zinc
26. M = 869 N m if **F** is in Newtons and **r** is in
    meters.
28. $2.8x - 5.12$ with a remainder of $50.04x - 11.48$
29. 0.5676
30. −15.685, 0.8425 ± 3.4008i
31. $x^5 - 42x^4 + 645x^3 - 5204x^2 + 24,960x - 57,600$

Chapter 3

10. (a) 3, 3.1623, 3.6056; (b) 1.7321i, 0.2848 +
    1.7553i, 0.5503 + 1.8174i; (c) 15 + 21i, 22 +
    16i, 29 + 11i; (d) −0.4 − 0.2i, −0.4667 −
    0.0667i, −0.5333 + 0.0667i
11. (a) $|xy|$ = 105, $\angle xy$ = −2.6 rad;
    (b) $|x/y|$ = 0.84, $\angle x/y$ = −1.67 rad

12. (a) 1.01 rad (58°); (b) 2.13 rad (122°); (c) −1.01 rad (−58°); (d) −2.13 rad (−122°)

15. Some selected values of (x, z) are $(0, 12)$, $(0.6, 11.82)$, and $(1, 11.44)$.

17. $F_1 = 198$ N if $\mu = 0.3$, $F_2 = 100$ N, and $\beta = 130°$.

20. For the test values, $t = 7.46$ and 2.73 sec.

Chapter 4

1. Production is profitable for $Q \geq 10^8$ gallons per year. The profit increases linearly with Q, so there is no upper limit on the profit.

3. To two significant digits, the two roots are $x = -5.3$ and $x = 4.5$.

5. The left end is 37.6 meters above the reference line. The right end is 100.7 meters above the reference line.

7. 0.54 rad (31°).

11. The steady state value of y is $y = 1$. $y = 0.98$ at $t = 4/b$.

15. (a) The ball will rise 1.68 m and will travel 9.58 m horizontally before striking the ground after 1.17 seconds.

22. (a) $y = 50x - 1250$; (b) $y = 3.58 \times 10^3 x^{-0.976}$; (c) $y = 2.06 \times 10^5 (10)^{-0.0067x}$

24. (a) $b = 1.2603 \times 10^{-4}$; (b) 836 years; (c) between 827 and 844 years ago

Chapter 5

3. $x = 2$, $y = -3$, $z = 5$

6. (a) $\mathbf{C} = \mathbf{B}^{-1}(\mathbf{A}^{-1}\mathbf{B} - \mathbf{A})$
   (b)
$$\mathbf{C} = \begin{bmatrix} -0.6212 & -2.3636 \\ 1.197 & 2.1576 \end{bmatrix}$$

9. $x = 3c$, $y = -2c$, $z = c$

12. $T_1 = 19.8°C$, $T_2 = -7.0°C$, $T_3 = -9.7°C$. Heat loss rate is 66.8 watts.

15. The nonunique solution is $x = 1.38z + 4.92$, $y = -0.077z - 1.38$; z can have any value.

18. The exact and unique solution is $x = 8$, $y = 2$.

19. There is no exact solution. The least squares solution is $x = 6.09$, $y = 2.26$.

516

Chapter 6

1. (a) $z = 1$; (b) $z = 0$; (c) $z = 1$; (d) $z = 1$

2. (a) $z = 0$; (b) $z = 1$; (c) $z = 0$; (d) $z = 4$; (e) $z = 1$; (f) $z = 5$; (g) $z = 1$; (h) $z = 0$

3. (a) $z = [0, 1, 0, 1, 1]$;
   (b) $z = [0, 0, 0, 1, 1]$;
   (c) $z = [0, 0, 0, 1, 0]$;
   (d) $z = [1, 1, 1, 0, 1]$

8. (a) $z = [1, 1, 1, 0, 0, 0]$;
   (b) $z = [1, 0, 0, 1, 1, 1]$;
   (c) $z = [1, 1, 0, 1, 1, 1]$;
   (d) $z = [0, 1, 0, 0, 0, 0]$

10. (a) $7300; (b) $5600; (c) 1200 shares; (d) $15,800

18. (a) $x = 9$, $y = 16$ miles

21. 33 years

23. $W = 300$ N. If $W = 300$, the wire tensions are $T_i = 429, 471, 267, 233, 200$, and 100 N, respectively.

31. Weekly inventory for cases (a) and (b):

Week	1	2	3	4	5
Inventory (a)	50	50	45	40	30
Inventory (b)	30	30	25	20	10
Week	6	7	8	9	10
Inventory (a)	30	25	20	20	10
Inventory (b)	10	5	0	0	(<0)

Chapter 7

4. (Answers rounded to integers.) You would expect to obtain a sum of 8 forty-two times; a sum of either 3, 4, or 5 seventy-five times, and a sum less than 9 two hundred and seventeen times.

8. (a) 99%; (b) 68%

12. (a) Mean pallet weight is 3000 pounds; standard deviation is 10.95 pounds. (b) 18%

19. Mean yearly profit = $64,609. Minimum expected profit = $51,340. Maximum expected profit = $79,440. Standard deviation of yearly profit = $5967.

21. If unconstrained to pass through the origin, $f = 0.1999x - 0.0147$. If constrained to pass through the origin, $f = 0.1977x$.

23. $d = 0.0509v^2 + 1.1054v + 2.3571$; $J = 10.1786$; $S = 57,540$; $r^2 = 0.9998$

25. $y = 40 + 9.6x_1 - 6.75x_2$. Maximum percent error is 7.125%.

26. The value at 5 P.M. is 22.5; the value at 9 P.M. is 16.5.

Chapter 8

1. 2360

5. Work $= 0.8k$

7. 6 meters/second

10. 13.65 feet

13. 1363.4 meters/second

21. (a) $v(t) = (f/500)(1 - e^{-t/2})$; (b) Steady-state speed is $f/500$ meters/second. The speed is within 2% of this value after $t = 8$ seconds.

22. (a) $y(t) = C_1 e^{-3t} \sin 5t + C_2 e^{-3t} \cos 5t$;
(b) $y(t) = C_1 e^{-8t} + C_2 e^{-5t}$

32. $\dot{x}_1 = -0.3x_1 - 0.7x_2 + f$; $\dot{x}_2 = x_1$, $y = 0.1x_2$

34. $\ddot{x}_1 + 7\dot{x}_1 + 14x_1 = 2\dot{u} + u$

Chapter 9

3. (a) $60x^5 - 10x^4 + 108x^3 - 49x^2 + 71x - 24$;
(b) 2546

4. $A = 1$, $B = -2a$, $C = 0$, $D = -2b$, $E = 1$, $F = r^2 - a^2 - b^2$

6. (a) $b = c \cos A \pm \sqrt{a^2 - c^2 \sin^2 A}$
(b) $b = 5.69$

8. (a) $x = \pm 10 \sqrt{(4b^2 - 1)/(400b^2 - 1)}$;
$y = \pm b \sqrt{99/(400b^2 - 1)}$
(b) $x = 0.9685$; $y = 0.4976$

12. Critical points: $x = 0$ and $x = 2$. Local minimum at $x = 0$. Inflection points at $x = 2$ and $x = 2/3$.

18. $h = 15\sqrt{2}$

19. 49.68 meters/second

29. (a) 2
(b) 0
(c) 0

36. (a) $y(t) = [0.6y(0) + 0.2v(0)]e^{-3t} \sin 5t + y(0)e^{-3t} \cos 5t$
(b) $y(t) = (1/3)[v(0) + 8y(0)]e^{-5t} - (1/3)[v(0) + 5y(0)]e^{-8t}$

45. (a) $m(t) = (K^2/4)te^{-Kt/2}$;
(b) $m_{peak} = K/5.4366$

48. $s^2 + 13s + 42 - 6k$; $s = (-13 \pm \sqrt{1 + 24k})/2$

49. $x = 62/(16c + 15)$; $y = (129 + 88c)/(16c + 15)$

Index

Symbols

+ addition 30, 46
− subtraction 30, 46
* multiplication 30
. * array multiplication 46
^ exponentiation 30
.^ array exponentiation 46, 49
\ left division 30
/ right division 30
. \ array left division 46, 48
. / array right division 46, 48
: colon
  array addressing 38
  vector generation 35
( ) parentheses
  array indices 38
  function arguments 102
  modifying precedence 30
[ ] brackets
  array elements 34
  empty matrix 62
. decimal point 120
. . . ellipsis 22, 29
, comma
  column separation 29

  statement separation 28
; semicolon
  display suppression 7
  row separation 34
% percent sign
  comment designation 29
  format specification 95
' apostrophe
  transpose 34, 38
  string designation 92
. ' nonconjugated transpose 38
= assignment or replacement
  operator 248
== equal to 248, 249
~= not equal to 249
< less than 249
<= less than or equal to 249
> greater than 249
>= greater than or equal to
  249
& and 249, 250
| or 250, 251
~ not 249, 250
>> MATLAB prompt

519

Topics